Great Engineers and Pioneers in Technology

Volume 1:

From Antiquity through the Industrial Revolution

Great Engineers and Pioneers in Technology

Volume I:

From Antiquity through the Industrial Revolution

Editors: Roland Turner and Steven L. Goulden
Assistant Editor: Barbara Sheridan

St. Martin's Press　　　　　　　　　　　　　　　　New York

Copyright 1981 by St. Martin's Press
All rights reserved. For information, write:
St. Martin's Press, Inc., 175 Fifth Ave., New York, N.Y. 10010
Manufactured in the United States of America
Illustration credits begin on page 467.

Library of Congress Cataloging in Publication Data

Main entry under title:
Great Engineers and Pioneers in Technology

  Includes index.
  CONTENTS: v. 1. From antiquity through the Industrial Revolution.
  1. Engineers—Biography. 2. Engineering—
History. I. Turner, Roland. II. Goulden, Steven L.
TA139.G7   620'.0092'2   80-28986
ISBN 0-312-34574-7 (v. 1)

Table of Contents

Editors' Preface

Since Samuel Smiles began writing in the mid-nineteenth century, the idea of the engineer as a Promethean culture hero has strongly affected the Western imagination. Yet, although there have been many studies of individual "great engineers," no recent work brings together information on many engineers in a variety of cultures and time periods. This is the aim of *Great Engineers,* a projected three-volume series that when completed will extend from the beginning of recorded history to the present. Engineers from all fields are discussed, including civil, mechanical, agricultural and chemical engineering. Special effort has been made to avoid any ethnocentric bias; non-Western cultures as well as Europe and America are given their appropriate weight in the series. Since an engineer's duties and rewards have differed from time to time and from country to country, every engineer included is placed in cultural and historical context.

Volume I of *Great Engineers* begins with the builders and craftsmen mentioned in the earliest records of civilization, and concludes with the inventors and entrepreneurs who pioneered the Industrial Revolution. Within this enormous time span, engineers are grouped into four chronological sections: Antiquity (prior to 600 A.D.), the Middle Ages (to 1400), the Renaissance and early modern period (to 1750) and the Industrial Revolution. In addition, a separate section is devoted to engineers of the Far East—China, Japan, Korea and Mongolia—to give special emphasis to this often-neglected part of the world.

This volume of *Great Engineers* includes individuals born through 1799. Those born in the new century, though often participating in the same events as their older contemporaries, will appear in the forthcoming second volume. Thus the famous civil engineer Marc Isambard Brunel (born 1769) is included in this volume, while his still more famous son, Isambard Kingdom Brunel (born 1806) will appear in Volume II. The division, though arbitrary, was necessary in order to keep both volumes within reasonable limits.

Not surprisingly, the task of selecting engineers for inclusion in Volume I proved to be an extremely difficult one. While a high percentage of the entrants are, by any standards, "great," neither the Board of Advisors nor the editors would wish to claim that these are the 350 *greatest* engineers of the period covered by this book. Nevertheless, it is our earnest hope that we have managed to include every engineer whose work has had a profound effect on the development of engineering.

Each chronological section of *Great Engineers* contains not only profiles of individual engineers, but also an introductory essay prepared by a scholar in the history of technology. These essays balance the personal focus of the individual entries by discussing broader engineering developments in the period in question. The volume opens with a general essay by the British scholar Arnold Pacey devoted to the engineer's various cultural roles throughout history.

The entries in Volume I have been selected and prepared under the supervision of an advisory board composed of American and European experts in the history of technology. The same procedure will be followed in later volumes of the series. Generally, entries deal with engineers who made some original contribution to their field—a mechanical invention, a novel or landmark structure, etc. Some individuals have been included for their importance in the transmission of technology from one culture or country to another. Since the development of engineering as a distinct profession is fairly recent, Volume I also describes the achievements of important architects and master builders through the seventeenth century.

All entries on individual engineers have two main sections: "Life and Times" and "Outstanding Engineering Achievements." The first section provides biographical information and sets the engineer in cultural context; it describes the historical circumstances that influenced his career and indicates how his work affected contemporaries and later generations. "Outstanding Engineering Achievements" gives technical details of the engineer's main projects. Both sections are intended to stand on their own. "Life and Times" should satisfy readers seeking a substantial summary of an engineer's background and activities, while "Outstanding Engineering Achievements" is designed for those who want greater depth of information. A third section, "Other Achievements," has been added in the case of engineers distinguished in some related field, such as physics or astronomy.

The main sources for each profile are listed at the end under "Further Reading." Full bibliographical citations are given for most books and articles. Only in a few instances, when a particular source recurs in many profiles, is an abbreviated author-title citation used. These sources may be found in full in the annotated bibliography at the end of the volume.

Great Engineers has been written for the general public, for students of technology and for engineers interested in the history of their profession. To help those who lack a strong technical background, a glossary of frequently used engineering terms has been included at the end of the volume. A chronology of important engineering events is also provided, both to summarize the high points of the book and to emphasize their temporal relationships. Finally, the annotated bibliography briefly describes the most important books used in preparing the entries and refers the interested reader to other, more specialized sources.

Roland Turner
Steven L. Goulden

Acknowledgments

The publisher and the editors wish to thank all members of the Advisory Board for the extreme care with which they selected the entrants and revised the entries. The advice and encouragement of the Board members have led to major improvements in the scope and quality of this first volume. Special thanks are due to Michael Deaves, Peter Desmond, Debra Reed, Michael Turk, and assistant editor Barbara Sheridan whose considerable talents have also helped to enhance the accuracy and usefulness of *Great Engineers*. Thanks are due as well to writers Tom Bulmer, Michael Levine, Tom Stuart, and Edward Tallman. The generous assistance of many libraries and institutions, in particular the New York Public Library and its Office of Special Collections as well as the Library of Congress, the Smithsonian Institution and the Science Museum in London, has enabled the editors to obtain a distinctive and varied selection of illustrations.

Advisory Board

Writers of Essays for this Volume

ARNOLD PACEY ("Engineering, the Heroic Art") is a British writer on the history of technology. One of his best-known works is *The Maze of Ingenuity: Ideal and Idealism in the Development of Technology* (1975).

DARWIN H. STAPLETON ("Engineering in the Ancient World") is assistant professor in the Department of Interdisciplinary Studies at Case Western Reserve University, Cleveland. He has most recently worked with the papers of Benjamin Henry Latrobe, on the basis of which he has written *The Engineering Drawings of Benjamin Henry Latrobe* (1980).

DONALD HILL ("Medieval Engineering: Islam and Europe") is a British writer on the history of technology. In 1978 he published his annotated translation of *The Book of Ingenious Devices,* by the Banū Mūsā Bin Shākir.

ALEX G. KELLER ("Engineering in the Renaissance") is professor in the Department of History of Science at the University of Leicester. His 1964 work, *A Theatre of Machines* is a study of books of drawings prepared by Renaissance engineers.

W. DAVID LEWIS ("The Industrial Revolution") is Hudson Professor of History and Engineering at Auburn University, Alabama. His recent books include *Delta: the History of an Airline* (1979) and *Iron and Steel in America* (1976), and he has edited (with B. Eugene Griessman) *The Southern Mystique: Technology and Human Values in a Changing Region.*

COLIN A. RONAN ("Engineering in the Far East in Historical Times") is a British writer on the history of technology. He has written extensively on the development of astronomy, most recently in a history of the Greenwich Observatory (1975). He has also been associated with Dr. Joseph Needham in the *Science and Civilization in China* project, and is currently preparing an abridged version of the massive work.

Alphabetical Index of Biographical Entries

Note: *for locating last names prefixed by* de, de', del, van, von, *etc., please ignore the prefix. For example,* Adam de Craponne *is listed under* Craponne, Adam de.

Stephenson, George
Stevens, John
Stevens, Robert Livingston
Stevin, Simon
Stringfellow, John
Sturgeon, William
Su Sung
Suyya
Symington, William

Taccola, Jacopo Mariano
Takeda Shingen
Talcott, Andrew
Tao Hsün
Taqī ad-dīn
Telford, Thomas
Than-Ston-Rgyal-Po
Theodoros of Samos
Theophilus
Thimonnier, Bartholome
Ting Huan
Tokugawa Yoshimune
Town, Ithiel
Tredgold, Thomas
Tresaguet, Pierre
Trevithick, Richard
Troughton, Edward
Tull, Jethro
Tu Mao
Turriano, Juanelo
Tu Yü

Uni

Valturio, Roberto
Vauban, Sebastian Le Prestre de
Vaucanson, Jacques de

Verantius, Faustus
Vermuyden, Cornelius
Vicat, Louis Joseph
Vignoles, Charles Blacker
Villard de Honnecourt
Vitruvius Pollio, Marcus
Volta, Alessandro

Wang Chêng
Wang Ching
Watt, James
Wedgwood, Josiah
Wei Meng-Pien
White, Canvass
Whitney, Asa
Whitney, Eli
Wilkinson, John
William of Sens
Winsor, Frederick Albert
Woolf, Arthur
Worcester, Marquis of (Edward Somerset)
Wren, Christopher
Wright, Benjamin
Wu Te-Jen

Yaita Kimbei
Yang Ch'eng Yen
Yang Su
Yang Yen
Yarranton, Andrew
Yevele, Henry
Yi Ch'on
Ying Shun-Ch'en
Yü Hsü
Yüwên K'ai

Zonca, Vittorio

Engineering, The Heroic Art

by Arnold Pacey

Engineers, Kings and Gods

The "great engineer" of a century ago was a figure who personified the way many people then felt about technology. He was a folk-hero who built railroads through the Rockies, canals through deserts, and bridges of incredible span across wild gorges. Gustave Eiffel, the French railroad engineer, caught the spirit of the age in the great tower which bears his name. As a contemporary Frenchman remarked, astonished Paris saw a "new shape of a new adventure" rising in its midst.[1] It was the adventuring spirit of engineering as well as the individualism of its practitioners which made this an age of great engineers.

Every major civilization has produced important works of engineering, often on an heroic scale. Among the best-known are the pyramids of Egypt, the aqueducts of Rome, and the Great Wall and Grand Canal of China. There were also many large-scale irrigation and water projects in India, Mesopotamia and Palestine. But though history tells us much about the emperors and warriors of those times, and a little about the writers and priests, only fragments of information have come to us about the craftsmen and designers who undertook engineering work. Engineers in ancient times did not rise to personal fame—but their achievements, even so, were appreciated, and cherished in legend. The most popular stories linked engineering and metallurgy; they described marvelous feats by mythical blacksmiths whose activities were dramatized by the flaming furnaces they mastered. One such figure was Hephaistos, the Greek artisan-god whose fire was stolen by Prometheus and given to men. The Egyptians honored Ptah, another blacksmith-god who was said to have been related to Imhotep [q.v.], the builder of the first pyramids. And the Israelites remembered Tubal-Cain, the ancient Biblical ancestor of all metalworkers and other craftsmen.[2]

The legends about these characters not only show that technical achievement was recognized and valued—they also suggest that invention was feared as well. Indeed, it may have been more congenial to celebrate craftsmen as legendary heroes rather than come to terms with real men whose genius, skill and power was very disconcerting. The Greeks of Homer's time certainly appreciated what craftsmen could do, even if they did not commemorate craftsmen's names. Thus Homer's poetry lingers lovingly over every description of craft skill and construction, and is full of "ramparts, harbors, and causeways . . . sailing ships, hawsers, oars and ropes . . . axes, adzes, augers and dowels."[3] But there was always a certain ambivalence about such things, which is clearly seen in the character of the god Hephaistos. His skill was truly fabulous and Homer never tired of praising it. But Hephaistos was represented as an ugly, lame man with a hairy chest—a figure of fun among the other

Two of the five flights of the grand staircase in the Palace of Minos, whose vast number of rooms and hallways were the foundation for the legend of the labyrinth built by the engineer Daedalus; Knossos, Crete, 1800 B.C.

Underfloor terracotta channels that drained wastes from the Minoan bathrooms. Fresh water was piped to the palace by the hydraulic system of the legendary Daedalus, but was brought upstairs by servants. Knossos, 1800 B.C.

gods. The engineer, then, was a man to be valued for his skill, but not as a member of polite society.

One other deity the Greeks linked with craft skill was the goddess Pallas Athena. Homer wrote of an expert carpenter who was "well versed in all his craft's subtlety" through Athena's inspiration, and he mentioned a goldsmith who was taught his trade jointly by Athena and Hephaistos. This reflects a respect for the practicality of women, whose craft skills were admired more wholeheartedly than those of men, and who could teach the craftsman about the utility of what he made.[4]

In most early civilizations, then, the achievements of engineers and craftsmen were regarded with wonder and even awe, and were celebrated in verse and legend. But if it was the names of gods rather than of men which express this heroic view of engineering most clearly in Homer's Greece, in other civilizations it was kings, emperors and even civil servants whose names became most strongly connected with daring feats of construction. Among the people of Old Testament Israel, for example, engineering works brought fame to the kings who commissioned them, not to artisans who designed them. King Uzziah was remembered for the catapults and other engines of war he had installed for the defense of Jerusalem, and Hezekiah for an improved water supply with a tunnel cut through rock.[5] Solomon, the great predecessor of these two kings, employed a craftsman from Tyre to

work on the Temple. This man's achievements are described at length, perhaps because he was closely connected with the king of Tyre. He was a skilled metal-worker who was also an inventor, able "to find out every device."[6]

In Israel, as in Greece, it is only very occasionally that a technician is identified by name. Hezekiah's water supply tunnel of about 700 B.C. still exists, with an inscription describing how its builders started at both ends and met at the midpoint, but there is no account of its designer's career. It is all the more unusual, then, that Eupalinos [q.v.] is recorded as the engineer of a similar tunnel, also for water supply, which was made on the island of Samos about 530 B.C. ■

Engineers and Bureaucrats

The great engineer does not become a folk-hero to the bureaucrat, no matter how much his services are appreciated, and this twentieth-century commonplace was also true of the Roman Empire and of dynastic China. In these two very different empires, the majority of big engineering projects were government undertakings, and engineers worked for large organizations and not as individual consultants. They thus remained almost as anonymous as the constructors of earlier times.

For example, the book on Rome's aqueducts written by Sextus Julius Frontinus [q.v.] is the work of a professional administrator, not an engineer, and reflects an official point of view. When Frontinus names the man responsible for building an aqueduct, this was often the commissioner under whom the aqueduct was planned. The commissioner's office employed several hundred people—plumbers and surveyors, ma-

Roman soldiers crossing a pontoon bridge, or bridge of boats; from Trajan's Column, Rome, 113 A.D.

sons and engineers—and no effort is made to say which members of this staff designed any given aqueduct. Thus even an imaginative planner of new works, such as Appius Claudius Crassus [q.v.], was an administrator and politician, not an engineer. And while Frontinus himself had an excellent technical knowledge of aqueducts, his job was primarily that of a manager.[7] By contrast, Marcus Vitruvius Pollio [q.v.] had worked as a military engineer before he wrote his "ten books" on subjects connected with architecture and engineering. Another man with a strong practical bent was Gaius Sergius Orata, who is credited with the invention of the Roman system for heating houses. But he was a businessman, not an engineer. He lived near Naples around 80 B.C., and made a good income from buying up houses and installing heated bathrooms before reselling them. Pliny thought him unscrupulous, but his enterprise caused him to be remembered when the engineers who worked for the imperial bureaucracy were not.

In China, too, many of the best-known names associated with engineering achievements are officials who planned and managed them. One such is Sung-li, the government minister who supervised construction of the summit level of the Ming Grand Canal in 1411. This had an elaborate water supply, and boats ascended to it through locks of a distinctly modern type.[8] Other officials became known through their connection with Chinese government policies for distributing technical books. The policy was based on the wood-block printing process introduced around 870 A.D. Many books were produced in editions of a thousand or more copies to inform provincial officials of improved techniques in agriculture, medicine or construction. In the eleventh century, one civil servant who became well-known as an author[9] was Su Sung [q.v.], who wrote one book about medicinal herbs and another about an elaborate water clock he designed. Contemporary with these developments, the publication of books on civil engineering marks "a very rich period" of achievement in China,[10] extending from about a century after the introduction of printing up to about 1270. Bridge-building gives one indication of this, with the erection of several iron-chain suspension bridges and the building of some daringly flat masonry arches. These times of heroic construction and technical advance are reflected in the present volume by a cluster of Chinese names from the three centuries between 1000 and 1300.

The frustration we may feel at the anonymity of most early engineers is eased somewhat when we turn from the great empires of China and Rome to the small kingdoms of medieval Europe. Here the records of municipalities, abbeys and royal households mention many names of craftsmen involved in engineering construction. One comprehensive analysis of such documents in England identifies no less than twenty-six men who, prior to 1550, described themselves as "engineers."[11] Most of them were designers of siege engines or carpenters who constructed military works, but many undertook civil projects also: one built a wharf by the River Thames, another erected a windmill. Indeed, from about 1200 onwards, the records of a tiny, nascent bureaucracy, the Office of the King's Works in England, give us the kind of information which is so singularly lacking for the aqueducts of Rome; almost for the first time, it is possible to distinguish clearly between administrators, designers and craftsmen. One example is Geoffrey Chaucer, the poet, who was at one time an administrator in the Office of Works. Henry Yevele [q.v.] stands out as one of its greatest architects; he extended the work done by William of Sens [q.v.] at Canterbury Cathedral and designed part of Westminster Abbey. Another outstanding figure in the history of the Office was the military designer James St. George [q.v.], who worked on the construction of a castle in Switzerland[12] before building the major castles of North Wales for the English King.

More typical, though, than any of these was an individual who took the word "engineer" into his surname, Richard L'enginour (fl. 1277–1315). He worked as an assistant to James St. George, building bridges and pontoons for river crossings in North Wales. He also constructed a siege engine known as a "springald," and supervised building work on the Conway town walls. Later, he managed a group of water-mills at Chester, where he eventually became mayor. He was so well thought of in the Office of Works that he was given a pension of 12d per day for life (over £18 per year). James St. George himself got three times as much, with separate provision for his wife Ambrosia should she be widowed. But then, James was an engineer of unique standing; there was no other craftsman in medieval England who was given such important assignments.[13]

Although military engineering and the construction of castles had reached a high level of sophistication by the thirteenth century, it was the great cathedrals of that time which showed the most daring and adventurous structural design, and particularly the cathedrals of northern France. With vaulted ceilings 130 or more feet

Amiens Cathedral, constructed 1220–1228, soaring to a height of 478 feet (145 m).

(40 meters) above the ground and steep roofs rising considerably higher, they required flying buttresses of remarkable complexity to support the vaults and take up wind pressures. Soaring to still greater heights were towers and spires, many of which proved too ambitious and were left unfinished. The culmination of this development is to be seen in the cathedrals at Chartres (begun in 1194), Amiens (1220) and Beauvais (1247).

Of course, cathedral-building was more than engineering. It was an art form, expressing religious beliefs through symbolism, and religious emotion through mass and space and soaring verticals. It expressed other things as well, not least the competitive spirit of the prosperous commercial cities in which many of the cathedrals were built. It was an art in which aesthetic and technical innovation was continuously pursued, as if the builders, always unsatisfied with their handiwork, were constantly driven to explore and experiment, and to attempt the untried.

The Artist-Engineer

The engineering structure of a cathedral was not just a framework on which works of art could hang, but an integral part of the medium with which the artist worked. Indeed, the artist who designed the cathedral was also the engineer responsible for its structure—and often also designed any special hoists or other equipment needed while building was under way. William of Sens was not untypical in these respects. But there is a deeper point to appreciate here: all works of engineering—mechanical or structural—have some of the same qualities as a work of art, whether their designers think of them that way or not. As one civil engineer has put it, "every manmade structure, no matter how mundane, has a little bit of cathedral in it, since man cannot help but transcend himself as soon as he begins to design and construct."[14] This is true of railroad structures in the nineteenth century as well as buildings in the Middle Ages; all were products of the culture of their time and expressive of human striving and aspiration. And in their daring as well as in scale, engineering structures were often the most heroic of all artistic creations.

But did the heroic quality of a work demand that its designer be celebrated as a great artist or even a "great engineer"? With the cathedrals, there was probably a strong feeling that the greatness of the work far surpassed the greatness of any man, whether designer or craftsman. Thus it was left for later generations possessing the humanistic values of the Renaissance to focus on the creativity of individuals—which meant creativity in both engineering and art. So marked was this combination, indeed, that a number of historians have spoken of the Renaissance as an age of "artist-engineers"; Leonardo da Vinci [q.v.] illustrates what is meant by this very clearly.

There was also at this time great curiosity about the process of invention, and three especially notable inventions widely discussed were printing, the magnetic compass and firearms. In due course, Johannes Gutenberg [q.v.] became known as the inventor of printing by moveable type. This emphasis on a single, creative individual was, of course, misleading in that it overlooked other pioneers, not to mention the earlier Chinese printing technique. But it supported the contemporary idea that certain individuals had a special creative genius. These were men with access to divine inspiration, among whom the deeply spiritual and profoundly gifted Michelangelo [q.v.] was taken as the outstanding example. Another much-discussed inventor was the artist-engineer Filippo Brunelleschi [q.v.], one of the pioneers of Renaissance architecture. He invented hoists for lifting stones on building sites and devised special techniques for constructing the dome of Florence Cathedral. His inventions were rewarded by prizes, and in one case by a patent.

But the manifold heritage of the Renaissance came not only from this stress on invention and on the individuality of engineers. There was also a more general acceptance that some practical arts were fitting occupations for men of learning or noble birth. This applied particularly to the artist-engineers previously mentioned and also to military engineers. Among such men, a select few had something approaching professional status, and were no longer regarded simply as rather accomplished craftsmen. There was also an injection of book-learning into their work, with a growing interest in scholarly aspects of engineering, including its mathematical basis and its literary background in the writings of ancient authors.

The mathematical emphasis, already evident in Leonardo's work, came to fruition with Galileo [q.v.], who had himself learned much through the study of ancient authors, particularly Archimedes [q.v.]. Technical problems that came Galileo's way included land drainage, pumps and some aspects of military engineering. Books he wrote covered the elements of three major technological subjects: ballistics, machines and the use of scale models in structural design. His writings provided a wide range of new ideas which were taken up most strongly a generation later in France, particularly by a succession of teachers of surveying, architecture and military engineering.[15] Edmé Mariotte (1620–84) is perhaps the best known of them. Recent historical studies have shown that these teachers—many working as private tutors—contributed much to the early development of engineering education in France; it is even suggested that they helped bring about a "Galilean revolution" in the conceptual framework of engineering. More specifically, they applied Galileo's ideas to a wide range of problems, particularly related to hydraulics. Mariotte, for example, made calculations and tests to help the designers of elaborate machines which pumped water to the Palace of Versailles, and one of his pupils (Sébastien Truchet, 1657–1729) became consulting engineer for the Orleans Canal. Other studies were made of the efficiency of water wheels and the flow of water in pipes. Daniel Bernoulli [q.v.], remembered for the Bernoulli

theorem in hydraulics (1738), had a loose affinity with this group.

Among the small number of mathematics teachers and elite engineers who did this work, something of the heritage of the Renaissance artist-engineer lingered on. In many practical projects architectural work was also involved, and fountains for the gardens at Versailles or other big mansions presented problems in hydraulic design. Thus the type of engineering in which the work of Galileo and Mariotte was most actively developed became known in France as *architecture hydraulique*.[16] These words, indeed, formed the title of the most important general book on engineering to be produced in the first half of the eighteenth century. Its author was Bernard Forest de Belidor [q.v.], and in its extensive illustrations it shows the artistry of engineering as well as the technical achievements of the period. It is also noteworthy for its extended account of Thomas Newcomen's [q.v.] steam-powered pumping engine.

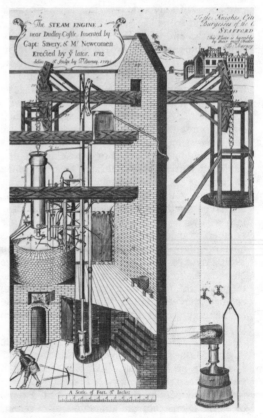

Steam-powered pumping engine built by Thomas Newcomen.

Engineering Archetypes

Recognition of the engineer as a species of artist is a Renaissance idea which seems a long way removed from twentieth-century attitudes. Yet there have always been a few engineers whose work has an obvious affinity with artistic creation. Robert Maillart, pioneer designer of reinforced concrete bridges, has been hailed as an "artist-engineer" of the present century, and detailed studies have been made to identify "the connection between the utilitarian and the artistic features" of his work.[17] One of the best British writers on nineteenth century engineers also suggests that an appreciation of the engineer as artist is essential for understanding two of the greatest figures of that time, Marc Brunel [q.v.] and his more famous son, Isambard Kingdom Brunel.[18] Designs made by Isambard Brunel for important parts of the London-Bristol railroad include "exquisite sketches . . . of tunnel mouth, bridge, pediment or balustrade" which reveal "not Brunel the engineer, but Brunel the artist."[19] His sketchbooks remind one "of the notebooks of Leonardo da Vinci" in their imagination and scope.

Near the end of his life, during two visits to Rome, Isambard Brunel spent hours alone in St. Peter's. He was not a religious man, and these contemplations provoked comment from his travelling companions. His biographer suggests that Brunel felt rather particularly "at one" with that building. A great deal of the spirit in which Brunel himself worked was expressed there; and he felt a strong resonance with his own aims under the dome conceived by Michelangelo and modelled partly on Brunelleschi's earlier dome at Florence.

To suggest that Brunel saw St. Peter's as an archetype for the artistic impulse that had gone into his own work is to suggest no more than a number of modern scientists and technologists have openly said about their own attitudes. In 1961, Alvin Weinberg, Director of Oak Ridge National Laboratory, commented that when historians of the future look back at the twentieth century, they will find in "the huge rockets, the high-energy accelerators, the high-flux research reactors, symbols of our time just as surely as . . . Notre Dame [is] a symbol of the Middle Ages."[20] Other writers have taken up the image of a space probe, which "like a cathedral is a symbol of aspiration to higher things."

For many people, though, it is not St. Peter's or Notre Dame, nor the aqueducts or pyramids which best demonstrate the cultural significance of engineering. Rather, it is the attitudes and achievements of individual engineers. That is why the image of the "great engineer" is so important. From the time when Andrea Palladio [q.v.] and his contemporaries sought to explain their work in terms of the writings of Vitruvius, the great engineer of the past has been regularly used as an archetype of what modern engineering should be about. Galileo saw his work in terms of what Archimedes had achieved; many British engineers today seem haunted by the near-mythic, Promethean figure of Isambard Brunel.

For an engineer from the past to be appreciated in this way, it is not sufficient only that he should be identified with major constructional achievements. Many engineers well-known to historians remain in obscurity, among them two previously mentioned: Richard L'enginour and Edmé Mariotte. An even better example is Joseph Karl Hell (1718–85), a contemporary of John Smeaton [q.v.] who built and improved Newcomen-type steam engines at mines in the Austrian Empire, and who was a brilliant inventor of water-pressure engines and pneumatic devices. In terms of technical achievement, he was as great an engineer as Smeaton, but the industry in which he worked was declining, and he had few successors with whom to leave his heritage. Men such as Joseph Hell remain unrecognized because circumstances did not allow them to enhance the significance of engineering or extend its cultural meaning.

Another reason why some engineers of high achievement remain unknown is that the whole significance of what they did was expressed in what they designed, not in their lives. For this reason, the builders of medieval cathedrals known to historians by name are very rarely revered as "great engineers" or even great architects.[21] It is only occasionally that one of them is a significant cultural figure as an individual—as, for example, William of Sens because of his personal heroism and ingenuity. For much the same reasons, engineers in the twentieth century also tend to remain anonymous; it is their achievements that have meaning, and the organizations for which they work, not their own individuality. So in recent years we have celebrated the Apollo moon rockets, the CERN nuclear accelerator and the Concorde airliner without ever hearing the names of those who led design teams or dreamed up key ideas.

Myths and Responsibilities

It should by now be clear that the "great engineer" is, in one sense, part of the mythology of technology. His archetypal image serves us rather as the image of Hephaistos and other gods served the Greeks—as a symbol of what engineering is all about. We use his memory in the same way as we use the image of the pyramid or the cathedral—as an archetype for the cultural meaning of technology.

Biographers and other writers bear an important responsibility here, because it is very often their interpretations of technology which canonize men as great engineers. Brunelleschi's reputation was greatly enhanced for later generations by the way Giorgio Vasari wrote about him in a collection of biographies published in 1550. In a similar way, many British engineers were first immortalized by Samuel Smiles in books which commented on the "dramatic interest," the heroism, and the "noble efforts" of these men. The element of myth-making in all this becomes even clearer when we notice that the study of great engineers or inventors as isolated individuals flies in the face of modern trends in historical scholarship. As one eminent historian of the Industrial Revolution has remarked, it is misleading to present invention "as the achievement of individual genius, and not as a social process." [22] Similarly, to concentrate on "great engineers" may mean ignoring modern research on more representative engineers and on the social history of technology.

When historians do make comments of this kind, one answer they can be given is that the use of symbols and archetypes for understanding many human endeavors is persistent and inevitable; biographers of the great engineers can serve the community by ensuring that the symbols we use are clearly understood. And this present volume does much to enlarge such understanding, for although it accepts the canon we have inherited from the Renaissance and the nineteenth century, it also adds enormously to that canon in the international dimension and in relation to the scientific background of engineering.

But there is another, more serious bias in our accepted appreciation of the "great engineer." The men who are most often celebrated in this way are those whose careers express a daring inventiveness or a quasi-artistic creativity. Only rarely do "great engineers" stand out as men whose lives were dedicated to humanitarian ends, and some great engineers, placed on pedestals in their own lifetimes, became arrogant and careless even of their technical responsibilities. In England, where engineering training was almost nonexistent for much of the nineteenth century, engineers would not always ad-

The first cast-iron bridge in the West, built across the Severn at Coalbrookdale, 1779.

mit to the limitations imposed by their ignorance of theory. Thus ships they built were unseaworthy, sewers caved in, and bridges collapsed due to miscalculation (as did Robert Stephenson's Dee Bridge at Chester in 1847). Even the great Brunel made serious mistakes about the locomotives on his railroad, and regularly saddled his financial backers with projects that were too grandiose and expensive. And when reformers did at length do careful scientific tests on the design of sewers and began to install improved drainage in London, the "great engineers" refused to accept that improvements had been made, and even resorted to sabotage, digging up streets at night in order to tamper with the new drains. [23] The historian who describes these episodes notes that the great railroad engineers of the time were "the folk-heroes of mid-Victorian England," but that they "showed a swashbuckling disdain for the social evils around them."

So at the same time as we recognize the cultural significance of the engineer's endeavors and of the monuments he erects, we should also note that the vocation of the engineer is not simply that of an artist on an heroic scale, building cathedrals, railroads and space vehicles to demonstrate the adventuring spirit of man. Engineering is also a social and humanitarian vocation. Thus the great figures we remember in the history of engineering should also include men who dedicated themselves to reform of the profession, or to humanitarian service. Such men include Georgius Agricola [q.v.], much-loved physician and sympathetic observer of mine engineering; John Smeaton [q.v.], who emphasized "civil" engineering as opposed to the military branch; William Strutt who attempted to create a technology of social welfare[24] applicable in hospitals and homes; John Roe, whose careful, detailed experiments in the 1830s and '40s created improved designs of sewers; and Edwin Chadwick, a reformer prepared to challenge the professional arrogance of many nineteenth century engineers in his efforts to create effective forms of public health engineering.[25]

These men are all great figures in the history of engineering, though not all are recognized as such. For it is a strange thing that while so many engineers are remembered for their creativity and daring, few indeed are known primarily as benefactors of mankind. That, rather than any objection from the academic historian, seems the greatest limitation in the popular concept of the "great engineer." ∎

Notes

1. Samuel C. Florman, *The Existential Pleasures of Engineering,* St. Martin's Press, New York, 1976, p. 124.
2. Genesis, *4,* 22.
3. Florman, *op. cit.,* p. 105.
4. M. I. Finley, *The World of Odysseus,* Chatto & Windus, London, 1964.
5. 2 Chronicles, *26,* 15 and 2 Kings *20,* 20.
6. 2 Chronicles, *2,* 14.
7. L. Sprague de Camp, *The Ancient Engineers,* Doubleday, New York, 1960.
8. Mark Elvin, *The Pattern of the Chinese Past,* Eyre Methuen, London, 1973, p. 104.
9. *Ibid,* pp. 180, 184.
10. Joseph Needham, *Science and Civilization in China,* Cambridge University Press, Cambridge, England, 1954–71, Vol. 4 (3), p. 325.
11. John Harvey, *English Medieval Architects: a Biographical Dictionary,* Batsford, London, 1954.
12. This is the castle at Yverdon, on Lake Neuchâtel, which was then in Savoy; James took his name from St. Georges d'Espéranche, also in Savoy.
13. R. A. Brown, H. M. Colvin and A. J. Taylor, *The History of the King's Works,* Her Majesty's Stationery Office, London, 1963, Vol. 1, pp. 204–6.
14. Florman, *op. cit.,* page 126.
15. Arnold Pacey, *The Maze of Ingenuity,* MIT Press, Cambridge, Mass., pp. 107–115 (on Galileo) and pp. 123–5 (on his French successors).
16. Jacques Grinevald, "Révolution industrielle . . . et Révolutions scientifiques," in *La Fin des Outils: Technologie et Domination,* Cahiers de l'IUED Genève, No. 5, Presses Universitaire de France, Paris, pp. 164 and 182–3.
17. David P. Billington, *Robert Maillart's Bridges: the Art of Engineering,* Princeton University Press, 1979.
18. L. T. C. Rolt, *Isambard Kingdom Brunel,* Longman, London, 1957, pp. 5–6.
19. *Ibid,* pp. 141, 325.
20. Alvin M. Weinberg, "The Impact of Large-scale Science on the United States," *Science, 134* (1961), p. 161 (21 July 1961).
21. See, for example, the biographical dictionary by Harvey, *op. cit.*
22. T. S. Ashton, *The Industrial Revolution 1760–1830,* revised edition, Oxford University Press, 1968, p. 11.
23. S. E. Finer, *The Life and Times of Sir Edwin Chadwick,* Methuen, London, 1952, reprinted 1970, pp. 439 and 448–9.
24. Pacey, *op. cit.,* pp. 250, 255–7.
25. Finer, *op. cit.,* see pp. 220–2 on John Roe.

Engineering in the Ancient World

by Darwin H. Stapleton

In both prehistoric times (from the dawn of man until about 3000 B.C.) and ancient times (about 3000 B.C. to 600 A.D.), men and women altered the world by creating new materials and new structures. In those instances where the alterations required the planning and coordinated work of several people, we describe the activity as "engineering." Existing structures and remains, archeological excavation and written records provide ample evidence that the engineering achievements of prehistoric and ancient people rank with the greatest achievements of modern engineering. Certainly these prehistoric and ancient engineers were less sophisticated in their knowledge of materials and stresses, used far simpler mathematics, and were essentially ignorant of electricity and petrochemicals; but their goals and values were the same as today's engineers. They attempted to provide ample supplies of water for agricultural and urban areas; they built public buildings and monuments for religious and state purposes; they struggled to ensure military security; and they hoped that what they did would endure to serve future generations. By and large they were successful.

The prehistoric period encompasses the history of man prior to the beginning of writing (c. 3500 B.C.). During most of that period little engineering took place. However, the groundwork for the future was being laid by the development of a range of tools, the continual experimentation with new materials, the initiation of settled agriculture and the rise of more complex social organizations.

It was in prehistoric times, for instance, that metallurgy and mining became established skills. Nearly pure copper, gold and silver can be found on or near the earth's surface, and these native metals were hand worked into jewelry as long ago as 9000 B.C. The development of the pottery kiln about the same time provided sufficient heat to melt and cast native copper, and sometime in the next three or four thousand years (probably in central Asia) copper was successfully smelted from ores. The spread of this skill meant the denuding of forests for fuel and poisoning the air with fumes and soot. Later (c. 4500 B.C.) these prehistoric forerunners of metallurgical engineers discovered that tin ore could be mixed with copper ore and smelted to make bronze, a harder metal than copper. By this later period gold, silver, copper and tin were being dug below the surface, with miners often excavating galleries into productive veins. Miners' tools were made of hard stone and wood, and included the familiar picks, chisels and hammers of modern mining.

Most historians agree that the provision of adequate water supplies was a foundation for the rise of civilization in Egypt, Mesopotamia, the Indus Valley and China. By about 5000 B.C. farmers had found that they could greatly increase crop yields by watering their fields them-

Surveyors, mathematicians, and draftsmen measuring the land in Egypt, about 1400 B.C.

1

Two-man, two-horse armored chariots from a mosaic at Ur of the Chaldees, about 3000 B.C.

selves rather than depending entirely on rain. In hilly regions this may have simply meant diverting a brook, but in the fertile plains and river valleys water was below the fields and varied greatly in availability according to the season. At first individual farmers dug wells or short irrigation ditches, but soon they recognized the value of cooperative efforts in building dams, weirs, canals and reservoirs.

Perhaps the best example of the rise of water supply engineering comes from Iran and Armenia, where tunnels called quanats have served agriculture for thousands of years. Normally quanats were begun in water-bearing rock deep in a hillside and excavated at a gradual slope out onto the neighboring plains. At the quanat's mouth, water was channeled into fields of grain. The successful quanat engineer had some knowledge of his area's geology, the ability to maintain a continuous slope in the tunnel, and the skill to control a gang of workers. In order to speed the work (as well as to provide access for repairs and drinking water when the tunnel was completed), numerous shafts were dug along the line of the quanat and headings were then excavated in either direction. By such means these early engineers constructed quanats up to 20 miles (32 km) long; many of them are still in use today.

Such cooperative activities were a prerequisite to civilization; and, indeed, some historians have argued that organized irrigation was the immediate precursor of government, law, religion and urban society. Certainly the first residents of Mesopotamia to leave written records, the Sumerians (c. 3500 B.C. to 2000 B.C.), were known for their engineering skill.

Sumerian engineers were usually government officials educated in mathematics, astronomy and law, and then given a practical training in surveying and construction. Their skills were useful in war, so they may have held military rank. They were responsible for the construction and repair of the irrigation system, a task which included accurate mapping (clay tablet maps are preserved), and demanded a thorough knowledge of wood, stone and brick materials. Sumerian engineers also designed and built important elements of their cities, such as temples, palaces, city walls and gates, and sewer systems. In spite of the importance of engineers in Sumeria, not one is mentioned by name in surviving texts, perhaps due in part to their role as government servants rather than independent practitioners.

The same anonymity holds for Egypt with a few exceptions, notably the architect-engineer-physician Imhotep [q.v.]. When Egypt was united into one kingdom about 3000 B.C., Egyptian builders had already done a considerable amount of stone construction, but they had not ventured beyond the forms of which wood and brick were capable. Imhotep took this great leap forward while building a tomb for his pharaoh, Zoser (c. 2650 B.C.). Generations of previous rulers had chosen to be buried under a slope-walled rectangular block of bricks or stones (called a mastaba), but Imhotep built a tomb of six graduated stone mastabas, with an overall height of 200 feet (60 meters). This became known as the "Step Pyramid," and it is the first of the true pyramids.

Later the "Great Pyramid" was built about 2500 B.C. for the pharaoh Khufu, reaching a height of 480 feet (146 meters). It required the quarrying of about 2.3 million blocks of stone weighing about 2½ tons each. Most were quarried near the building site, but the covering layer was brought from the other side of the Nile River. There has been an unresolved debate concerning what sorts of tools may have been used to move and raise the blocks, but it seems likely that they were the simplest of levers, wedges and sledges. From an engineering standpoint, the pyramids represent the meticulous organization of a large work force (perhaps 10,000 men and 1,000 animals) over a long period of time (perhaps 20 years), rather than the application of a novel theory or sophisticated devices.

Compared to the pyramids the megaliths of Stonehenge in England are puny, yet they were a significant engineering feat for a contemporary but "uncivilized" area of the world. The social, religious or calendrical purposes of Stonehenge are still a matter of speculation, but it is clearly an engineering work of great skill. Studies suggest that the ancient Britons constructed Stonehenge in at least three distinct periods from

Fallen granite statue of Rameses II at Thebes; carved from a single block, it weighed 1000 tons and was brought down the Nile from Aswan.

about 2750 B.C. to 1500 B.C. In the final phase, earlier circles of stones were removed and new ones erected which make up the present monument. The outer circle consisted of 80 stones, each weighing about 30 tons. They were brought to the site from 20 miles (32 kms) away, probably on sledges. All of the stones of the inner circle (originally about 90 weighing up to five tons apiece) were brought from quarries about 125 miles (200 km) away at the mouth of the Bristol Channel. It seems likely that the builders used water transport as much as possible to get these stones to their destination.

The erection of both circles was simple but time-consuming, requiring careful preparation of setting holes and building up earth under the stones to raise them to nearly vertical before they slid into their holes. The location of each stone had been predetermined by measurement and astronomical sighting. As with the pyramid engineers, the Britons organized their work carefully and executed it well.

Also contemporary with the Egyptian and Sumerian civilizations were those of the Indus Valley (in modern Pakistan) and China. Currently we know less about their engineering than we might like, largely because the Indus writing has yet to be deciphered and insufficient archeological excavation has taken place in both regions. But what has been found at the Harappan and Mohenjo-Daro sites in the Indus Valley suggests that the engineers there were the most precise and thorough city planners of antiquity. Streets were laid out in straight lines, a copious amount of water was brought into the city center, and buildings were regular and solidly built.

The early Chinese showed a genius for river

control and improvement, an engineering field in which they continued to lead the world until the last few hundred years. They developed the navigable canal and about 200 B.C. the engineer Shih Lu laid out the first canal to cross from one watershed to another. At about the same time the emperor Ch'in Shih Huang-ti undertook the construction of what has come to be known as the Great Wall of China. Beginning with some existing fortifications, Shih Huang-ti had his engineers create a barrier to keep out the Hun raiders which meandered some 2,500 miles (4,000 km) across China's northern border. As completed it ranks as the largest single military work in world history.

The Chinese also became the world leaders in metallurgy during the ancient period. Bronze technology appeared in China after 2000 B.C., probably as a result of diffusion from central Asia. Bronze could be worked by hammering and heating, but it was easier to cast into shapes of swords, spearheads, and simple utensils. Of such products China produced little that was different from other bronze-working areas. But Chinese metallurgists also mastered the art of casting very complex statuettes and ceremonial .

The sunrise trilithon of Stonehenge built in 1500 B.C. of 5-ton stones brought 215 miles (345 km) by sea and 25 miles (40 km) overland.

vessels which today occupy honored places in art museums. The methods used in these castings are imperfectly known today.

The metallurgical achievements of China which have left the greatest legacy, and those which fall within the realm of engineering, were the smelting and casting of iron. Knowledge of how to smelt iron ore certainly came to China by 700 B.C., about 500 years after it originated in Asia Minor. By 300 B.C. the Chinese had developed iron manufacturing on an industrial scale, and were probably already using the blast furnace to produce cast iron. The typical blast furnace of the time was an upended rectangular solid about 10 feet (3 meters) high, hollowed out so that ore, charcoal, and limestone could be poured into the top. After combustion, which was aided by air forced into the combustion chamber by bellows, liquid iron could be drawn out from the bottom of the furnace. It was over a thousand years before blast furnaces of this type were known in Europe, where iron was available only in small amounts from combining the ore, limestone and charcoal in a bloomery fire.

The Chinese produced large enough quantities of iron to innovate in civil engineering technology. Suspension bridges with cast iron chains were common in Western China from about the sixth century A.D., providing the Chinese highway builders with a cheap and effective way of crossing mountain gorges. Somewhat later the Chinese began using iron in small buildings as structural members, roofing and siding, examples of which survive in medieval pagodas. Enormous cast iron statues of men and beasts were also made, some of which served as supporting elements of buildings.

Discussion of Chinese engineering achievements requires some consideration of the exchange of Chinese techniques with other cultures, particularly those of the Mediterranean region and Asia Minor. The transfer of technology between cultures has been a regular occurrence in every era, but it has not always been followed by the diffusion or spread of a technology. The initial establishment of a transferred technology may not succeed or may remain an isolated instance; in such cases the transfer is of no significance in the recipient culture. But the situations which are of more interest are those in which the technique spreads and becomes common in the recipient culture.

There was constant communication between China and western cultures from the beginning of the historic era. Trade routes through the Indian Ocean and the China Sea, and overland through central Asia carried precious metals and gems, expensive textiles (especially silk from China), spices and novelties. To some extent these products of foreign manufacturing processes stimulated thinking about innovations. Sometimes military expeditions captured foreign technicians. One of the most bizarre cases occurred about 50–30 B.C., when a group of Roman officers (some of whom may have been engineers) were captured by the Parthians, who took them to central Asia; they were then taken prisoner by a Chinese army. They were apparently settled as a colony in Kansu province. In the eighth century A.D. an Islamic army operating on the Chinese frontier captured some Chinese technicians, who proceeded to introduce the art of papermaking to the West.

More significant for the transfer of technology were the occasional technically-informed travelers who made the long transcontinental or transoceanic trip, and those engineers who emigrated in the hopes of finding a market for their skills. The number of these contacts grew as the ancient period progressed, particularly when the Roman Empire and the Han Empire in China regularized travel and communication over wide areas, and later when Islam spread from Asia to the Atlantic. Under these conditions the waterwheel was brought to China in the first century A.D., and the crank came to Europe about the ninth century A.D. In general there was enough interchange between China and the west that the direction of engineering development was parallel, but transfers of technology were infrequent enough that specific devices took centuries to take root elsewhere.

Some knowledge of the Indus and Chinese achievements was carried westward by the Persian culture, which rose on the Iranian plateau after 1000 B.C. and was consolidated and extended by Cyrus the Great (550–530 B.C.). With borders extending from the Indus to Turkey and Egypt, communications were a serious concern of the Persian emperors. Their engineers responded by building a network of the best roads in the civilized world. Since the emperors decreed that the roads could be used only by the army and government officials, the royal mail could travel 90 miles (145 km) a day, a rate not regularly attained again until the Napoleonic highways were laid out in Europe. The Persians also overhauled the decaying irrigation systems of Mesopotamia and Egypt, and dug navigational canals between the Nile and the Red Sea and across the Athos Peninsula in Greece [see Artachaies, q.v.]. Their capital, Persepolis, was a collection of magnificent buildings, including a huge audience hall with a roof 65 feet (20 meters) above the floor and supported by seven-foot (2 meters) thick columns.

The Persian Empire was overthrown by Alexander the Great, whose new empire united Greece with the Persian domains and created the fertile mix of cultures which has come to be known as Hellenism. The Greek people had settled their mountainous peninsula sometime after 1000 B.C., and over the next several hundred years established colonies throughout the Mediterranean. Greek culture produced an outstanding group of thinkers and writers, or at least a group well-known to us, since many of their writings have been preserved. Some of these Greeks helped to lay the foundation of the mathematical and physical sciences which in modern times have become an integral part of engineering. Euclid and Pythagoras in geometry, Philon [q.v.] and Archimedes [q.v.] in physics, and Aristotle in logic and science are names recognized by everyone with a scientific education. It was rare, however, for Greek philosophers to undertake actual engineering work. Engineers were regarded as craftsmen and belonged to a lower social class, even though they may have been quite well educated.

Greek and Hellenistic engineers engaged in a variety of activities, including architecture and city planning. The Greeks brought the temple form to perfection, providing the model which the Romans and all Western Civilization have copied. The prime example is the Parthenon at Athens, built in the fifth century B.C. on a rocky hill called the Acropolis and dedicated to the goddess Athena. The engineer-architects Iktinos [q.v.] and Kallikrates [q.v.] used marble lavishly, while the sculptor Pheidias created beautiful decorative friezes as well as an impressive statue of Athena. The Greeks believed in consistent architectural proportions, and in this case the ratio 9:4 is repeated in many elements, beginning with the Parthenon's length and width. Generally the Parthenon and other Greek temples are admired for their combination of building skill with aesthetic grace.

While temples were often the focal point of Greek cities, water supply was also an important feature. The Greeks believed that impure water was the major cause of epidemic disease, and went to considerable trouble to find supplies of fresh water. The demands of the Greek cities supported the rise of what appears to have been a group of professional water supply engineers. As a result, many Greek cities, particularly the colonies, show similarities in the style and workmanship of their water supply systems. An example is the city of Syracuse on the southern tip of Italy, founded about 734 B.C. A network of tunnels and above-ground channels up to 15 miles (24 km) long bring water from a range of hills to the city center. A substantial portion of the system still provides water for drinking and irrigation.

The Greeks developed Mediterranean shipbuilding to the most sophisticated level it was to know for centuries. They were the heirs of the maritime traditions of the Egyptians and Mesopotamians. Both cultures had probably used a variety of floatable materials for boats in prehistoric times, including skin bladders, pottery jars, hollowed out logs, bark canoes and bundles of reeds. It was this last and seemingly unlikely material which was the basis for the earliest vessels to attain the scale which required engineering skills. Long bundles of reeds were lashed together to make a crescent-shaped craft up to 50 feet (15 meters) long which could carry 10 tons of crew and cargo. The earliest versions may have been poled or rowed, but the sail soon made its first appearance on these reed ships. Thor Hyerdahl's modern recreations of reed boats have shown that they are quite serviceable even on the open ocean.

About the beginning of the historic era shipwrights created the planked boat by literally sewing wooden planks together along their ends with leather or fiber cords, just as is done today in northwestern Africa. At first these boats were built without internal stays, and stiffening had to be provided by a trussing cord running from stem to stern, but gradually a system of framing was instituted. The ancients never followed the modern practice of framing a hull first, but always built up the planking before adding internal members.

The Greeks (and their contemporaries the Phoenicians) took the planked boat, which was still in the steeply curved form established by the reed boat, and after about 1000 B.C. created the galley. This vessel had a relatively horizontal profile, bringing more of the keel in contact with the water, and was propelled by 20 to 50 oars or a sail, depending upon weather conditions. The Greeks developed galleys with two and three banks of oars on each side, which brought much more muscle-power into propulsion. The three-banked galley, called the trireme, was the dominant war vessel in the Mediterranean until the end of the pre-Christian period.

The Greeks must also be recognized as innovators in metallurgy and machinery. The seven metals of antiquity (gold, silver, lead, tin, copper, iron and mercury) were fully available to the Greeks, either on the peninsula or in the

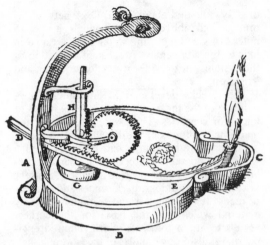

Rack and gear used by Heron to raise or lower the wick of an oil-lamp.

colonies. The Greek colony of Cyprus, for example, discovered such a rich lode of copper ore that its name is a cognate of the word copper. The Greek genius explored the capabilities of these metals, with an intent (but not the method) parallel to modern metallurgical engineering. Early inventions (about 600–500 B.C.) were the screw, the lathe, the pulley, and bronze and iron armor for soldiers. Somewhat later the Greeks introduced the toothed gear wheel, the crossbow and the force pump, all of which used metal to some degree.

Two leading mechanical engineers of the Hellenistic era who used these devices were Ktesibios [q.v.] and Heron [q.v.], both active in Alexandria, Egypt. Ktesibios' father was a barber, a profession which required instruments of careful fitting in manufacture and accuracy in use. Ktesibios transferred those requirements to the design of precision bronze devices, including a water pump and a water organ. Heron wrote several treatises on mechanics, including the *Pneumatica,* which describes devices such as temple doors which open automatically when a fire is started on the altar.

We do not know the name of the Greek mechanical engineer or group of engineers who made a bronze calendrical computer about 80 B.C. which was lost in a shipwreck off the Aegean island of Antikythera. Its discovery in 1901 and the recent careful analysis by Derek Price indicates that there was at least one colony of sophisticated Greek bronze workers who manufactured geared calendrical computers. The Antikythera mechanism was a rectangular wooden box about two feet by one foot by one-half foot (about 60 cm by 30 cm by 15 cm), with three sets of circular dials on the outside and a gear train within. The gears had equilateral triangular teeth and were made of bronze. The dials were marked with Greek letters to indicate the positions of the sun, moon and the zodiac. It seems probable that the mechanism was reset daily to show the progress of those heavenly bodies, and it may have anticipated lunar eclipses. There is evidence that the gear train was actuated by a crank, probably turned daily to advance the sun dial one day and in consequence the other dials to their proper positions.

While the Antikythera mechanism was probably made to be displayed in a public location (such as a temple or government hall), much the same as a large decorative clock today, it did not tell the time of day but rather gave astronomical information which an astrologically-minded culture thought valuable. The Greek mechanical engineers who designed it achieved a level of complexity for mechanical computers which was not significantly improved upon for hundreds of years.

By the era of the Antikythera mechanism the Greeks had become a part of the rising Roman empire. Traditionally established in 753 B.C., the city of Rome gradually expanded its territory until in the third century B.C. it mushroomed beyond the Italian peninsula into Greece, Spain and Africa. At the empire's height about 100 A.D. it controlled all the lands on the rim of the Mediterranean. Learning from the Greeks and Persians, Roman engineers became the greatest creators of public works in history. Pre-eminent in civil and military engineering, much of their work survives to this day, with many of their roads, bridges, waterworks and buildings still in service.

Roman engineers seem to have enjoyed a higher status in their society than Greek engineers in theirs. There are numerous examples of Roman public officials who were trained or skilled in engineering, the most famous of whom was the Emperor Hadrian (75–138 A.D.). Promising young men were trained in engineering in the military and public works bureaucracies, and they often became wealthy in their profession. Relatively few did so by extravagant expenditures or corrupt practices, however, because Roman engineers consistently demonstrated that their supreme values were orderliness, efficiency and economy, even when building some of the largest structures in human history.

The city of Rome itself contained many major examples of Roman engineering. The water

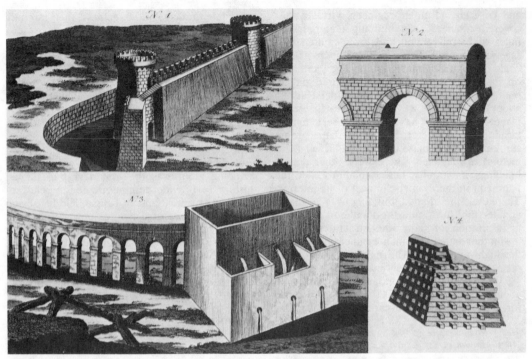

Roman civil engineering: 1, a fortified wall; 2 and 3, arched aqueducts; 4, cross-section of a wall.

system, partly utilized today, was a work of several centuries. The first aqueduct, a tunnel 10½ miles (17 km) long (similar to the quanats of Armenia and Iran), was a project of Appius Claudius Crassus [q.v.] in the late fourth century B.C. Over the next 400 years Rome acquired eight more aqueducts, the last a 35-mile (56 km) tunnel completed in 109 A.D. Contrary to the popular impression, only about 15 percent of the city's aqueducts were carried on the magnificent arcades which we associate with Roman water technology.

This extensive water system was rationalized by the water commissioner Sextus Julius Frontius [q.v.], who wrote a book about his work. His estimates indicate that the aqueducts brought to Rome about 265 million gallons (1 million cubic meters) per day, or, if modern estimates of Rome's population in his era are accurate, about 300 gallons (1100 liters) per person. The bulk of this water was for public purposes, including baths, fountains and toilets, although some was diverted to homes, industries and water mills.

An axiom of water supply engineering is that more pure water supplied means more waste water to discharge. Rome had an adequate system of underground sewers, including the Cloaca Maxima begun in the third century B.C.

All the sewers emptied into the Tiber River, which has since then been unfit for drinking or swimming.

Massive public buildings were another engineering contribution to Rome. The Colosseum, completed in 80 A.D., was constructed of stone

Cross-section of sewers in ancient Rome. To help the flow, sewers downstream had a greater sectional area than those upstream.

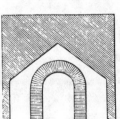

and concrete. (Roman engineers virtually discovered concrete as a building material.) Its miles of barrel-vaulted and groin-vaulted passageways insured that crowds of up to 60,000 could move in and out smoothly. The Pantheon, originally built in 27 B.C., was repaired and rebuilt several times, most notably under Hadrian about 120 A.D. It was a temple to the seven planetary gods and has a typical Greek temple facade, but its interior is a drum-shaped room surmounted by a masonry dome 143 feet (43.5 meters) in diameter. There were other domed buildings in antiquity, but none approached the Pantheon in the dramatic impact of its interior. Thereafter the domed building was a major architectural form, and the Pantheon served as an inspiration for many other structures.

Another famous Roman engineering work is the highway system. The empire's network of main paved roads extended for 54,000 miles (85,000 km), while secondary roads stretched about 120,000 miles (195,000 km) more. Routes for main highways were carefully surveyed for

Heavy Roman crane worked by a treadmill; from the Aterii Monument, 1st. Century B.C.

adequate drainage and directness, then carefully layered with sand, stone and concrete up to a thickness of four or five feet (1–1.5 meters). This rigid roadbed normally held up for thirty to forty years under the wear of weather, animal traffic and wheeled carts. Even without repairs during the later Roman and early medieval period, many Roman roads remained in use.

In mechanical engineering the Romans made extensive use of a new device, the water wheel. Apparently originating in the hills of eastern Europe or Asia Minor, the water wheel for grinding grain was the first device in human history to provide continuous non-muscle mechanical power. (Sails, of course, had harnessed the wind for non-mechanical power since prehistoric times.) Two versions of the water wheel appeared almost simultaneously: the vertical mill, in which the shaft of a simple turbine-like wheel drives directly the upper of a pair of millstones; and the horizontal mill with the familiar upright wheel connected by a pair of gears to the millstones. This latter type was capable of greater power variation, and Roman engineers seized upon it to create large grist mills capable of producing several times more meal or flour in a given time than hand or donkey mills. About the beginning of the fourth century A.D. in France near Arles the Romans erected a virtual flour factory with eight water wheels which could produce 28 tons of flour per day. By the end of the Roman Empire in the later fifth century, water-powered grist mills had spread throughout Europe and the Middle East; but the adaptation of water wheels to other sorts of tasks did not occur until the medieval period.

Roman military engineers were the best the world had ever known. Field armies normally had an engineering corps to erect fortifications, build siege machinery and catapults, and to make bridges. One of their outstanding achievements was construction of a bridge across the mouth of the Danube River about 105 A.D. Apollodoros [q.v.], the engineer, contended with a deep, swift-running river with a muddy bottom, but succeeded in erecting 20 stone piers 60 feet (18 meters) apart and 150 feet (46 meters) high, and in connecting them with a trussed wooden superstructure. In the middle and later days of the Roman empire military engineers also built great fortifications, ranging from Hadrian's wall in northern England to the fortress of Constantinople, which made that city virtually impregnable.

The successor to the Roman empire in the eastern Mediterranean was the Byzantine empire, consolidated under Justinian (527–565

Hadrian's Wall, built 125 A.D.; 73½ miles (118 km) long, it separated Roman-occupied England (left) from Scotland (right).

A.D.). Here the Greco-Roman heritage of engineering was first preserved and then transmitted to Islamic culture, and much later to a revived Western Europe. The great monument of the early Byzantine era was the cathedral of Hagia Sophia (St. Sophia) at Constantinople (532–537 A.D.). The architects Isidoros [q.v.] and Anthemios [q.v.] drew upon the Pantheon; but they surpassed the earlier structure by putting a dome above two half-domes, creating an enormous interior space and a ceiling 184 feet (56 meters) above the floor.

If in a few instances like the Hagia Sophia Byzantine engineers matched the vigor of their Roman predecessors, they were more like the Greeks in being fascinated by mechanical toys and philosophical considerations. Byzantine emperors in particular had a predilection for toys and hidden devices which entertained or awed their guests. They copied and studied Greco-Roman writings on physics, mechanics, pneumatics and mathematics, and they patronized the descendants of the craftsmen who had built calendrical computers and clever automata. For centuries visitors from Western Europe marvelled at the sophistication of Byzantine engineering.

The Byzantines preserved their empire partly by extending Roman military engineering technique. They developed masonry fortifications to a high art, so that their relatively small forces withstood the attacks of Huns, Bulgars, Arabs and others. They also utilized the incendiary liquid which came to be known as "Greek fire" and so successfully protected the knowledge of its composition that its precise formula is unknown today. Presumably pitch, bitumen or raw petroleum formed a base to which sulfur and quicklime were added. This mixture was squirted through pump nozzles at the enemy, most dramatically through pipes in the bow of a ship during naval battles. It was also put into containers and thrown by catapults in land battles.

From prehistory to the Byzantine era, engineers and their forerunners engaged in a wide range of activities which established the general outlines of engineering skills, knowledge and goals. In ancient times the profession of engineering was not as well defined as medicine, law or the priesthood, and it was to be centuries more before engineers became a self-conscious professional group. Yet in spite of its lack of definition, engineering contributed to the rise of civilized life and was responsible for much of the beauty and inspiration of the ancient world which we still draw upon. Engineering also facilitated the development of organized warfare, and helped make air and water pollution constant companions of mankind. Modern engineering not only builds upon, but also reflects, ancient engineering. ∎

IMHOTEP
fl. ca. 2650 B.C., Memphis, Egypt
Egyptian Architect, Physician, and Astronomer

Life and Times:

The royal architect during the reign of Pharaoh Zoser, Imhotep is generally credited with inventing the pyramid, since that structure developed from Imhotep's step pyramid. His was also the first known building completely constructed of stone. He was also a powerful figure in the Egyptian court, known as "Royal Chancellor under Pharaoh Zoser, Administrator of the Great Mansion, Hereditary Noble and Heliopolitan High Priest." Imhotep was worshiped after his death as the son of Ptah, god of property and crafts, and became the patron deity of Memphis. He left a son, Rahotep, from whom according to legend a long line of architects descended.

Outstanding Engineering Achievements:

In 2980 B.C. Imhotep built for Pharaoh Zoser the Step Pyramid of Sakkara, the oldest pyramid in Egypt. It had a rectangular base of 358 by 411 feet (109 by 125 meters) and was 200 feet (61

Figure of Imhotep holding a scroll; 3⅝ inches (9 cm) high.

The Step-Pyramid of Sakkara, the oldest pyramidal structure in Egypt, built by Imhotep nearly 5000 years ago.

engineer, Imhotep acquired enough knowledge of hydraulics to help establish the irrigation system of ancient Egypt.

Imhotep was known not only as an architect and engineer, but also as a skilled astronomer and physician. His tomb at Sakarra became a shrine for miracle cures. ∎

meters) high, the equivalent of an 18-story building. To build this enormous structure, Imhotep placed six "mastaba tombs"—flat-topped, masonry-walled rectangular masses with sloping sides—on top of one another. The components were 30 to 40 feet (9 to 12 meters) high, decreasing in size towards the top. The limestone used in the pyramid was transported by boat or sled and moved into place on temporary earth inclines. Like other Egyptian architects, Imhotep probably used only the simplest construction aids and methods, such as a sighting square to determine right angles. Distances were usually measured off with ropes.

The Step Pyramid of Sakkara was set within an enclosure about one mile (1.6 km) long, surrounded by a recessed stone wall. On one side of the enclosure ran a series of temples and colonnades, built at the same time as the pyramid. The earliest known examples of stone architecture, these structures provided the prototypes for a number of popular Egyptian designs, including the reed-pillar and the fluted column. In addition to his work as a construction

Further Reading:

James H. Breasted, *A History of Egypt.* London, 1951.

L. Sprague de Camp, *The Ancient Engineers.* London, 1963.

I.E.S. Edwards, *The Pyramids of Egypt.* 1947.

Ahmed, Fakhry, *The Pyramids.* Chicago, 1961.

KHUFU (CHEOPS)
fl. ca. 2500 B.C.
Egyptian pharaoh

Life and Times:

The Old Kingdom, the age of the pyramids represents the high point in ancient Egyptian history. The power wielded by Zoser, the first great pharaoh of the period, found fitting expression in the Step Pyramid built by his architect Imhotep [q.v.]. Only a century later the autocratic pharaohs of the Fourth Dynasty ordered the construction of monuments which surpassed even Imhotep's achievements. The most famous are the pyramids at Giza, near the ancient capital of Memphis and modern Cairo. The first and largest of these was built for Khufu.

Khufu's mother was Hetepheres, daughter and heiress of Huni, the last pharaoh of the Third Dynasty. His father, Snefru, married her and inaugurated the Fourth Dynasty; the date of Khufu's accession to the throne is uncertain. It seems clear that Khufu continued Snefru's policies of exploiting the mineral wealth of Nubia and Sinai, keeping the nobility in check, and sponsoring construction projects throughout Egypt. None were as massive as the great pyramid, which took most of Khufu's 23-year reign to build. Khufu's name was revered long after his death; it was only in classical times that he acquired his legendary reputation as a cruel oppressor.

The remains at Giza reveal that Khufu had an unusually large family. In the shadow of his great pyramid, Khufu built a crypt for his mother, three small pyramids for his three wives, eight large tombs for his favorite children, and 64 tombs for older family members and for high court officials. Among the latter was buried the vizier Hemiunu, "overseer of all the king's works." He must have been responsible for housing, feeding, and organizing the scores of thousands of workers who built the pyramid. Unfortunately, his tomb contains no inscriptions detailing his activities. Nevertheless, it is possible that in Hemiunu we have the engineer who designed and built the Great Pyramid of Giza.

The Great Pyramid of Khufu, composed of 2.3 million stone blocks of 2½ tons each.

Major Engineering Achievements:

The great pyramid is the largest masonry structure ever built. The square base originally measured 756 feet (230 meters) on a side. The pyramid tapered upward at an angle of 51°50' through 206 progressively smaller courses of masonry; the capping stone (now missing) brought it to a height of 480 feet (146 meters). The pyramid is composed of some 2.3 million limestone blocks, averaging 2½ tons each in weight. To this core were attached casing blocks of fine limestone, some weighing 15 tons, which provided a smooth facing for the four sides. Practically all these blocks were later removed for use elsewhere, exposing the core's stairway-shaped surfaces.

Buried within the pyramid are passageways leading to a number of funeral chambers, only one of which was actually used to house Khufu's remains. The granite-lined King's Chamber, measuring 17 by 34 feet (5 by 11 meters), is roofed with nine slabs of granite which weigh 50 tons each. To relieve the weight on this roof, located 300 feet (91 meters) below the apex of the pyramid, the builder stacked five hollow chambers at short intervals above it. Four of the "relieving chambers" are roofed with granite lintels, while the topmost has a corbelled roof. Although somewhat rough and ready in design and execution, the system effectively distributes the massive overlying weight to the sturdy walls of the King's Chamber.

Sheer precision marks every other aspect of the pyramid's construction. The four sides of the base are practically identical in length—the error is a matter of inches—and the angles are equally accurate. Direct measurement from corner to corner must have been difficult, since the pyramid was built on the site of a rocky knoll (now completely enclosed in the structure). Moreover, it is an open question how the builder managed to align the pyramid almost exactly north-south. Still, many of the techniques used for raising the pyramid can be deduced.

After the base and every successive course was in place, it was leveled by flooding the surface with Nile water, no doubt retained by mud banks, and then marking reference points of equal depth to guide the final dressing. Complications were caused by the use of blocks of different heights in the same course. The rising joints—those between the adjacent blocks of a given course—were adjusted before the blocks were put in place on the pyramid. Though perfectly fitted, the joints were usually askew, neither vertical to the line of the bed nor at right angles to the line of the facade. Since the Egyptians had no pulleys, the blocks then had to be hauled up an earth ramp to the wall. A thin layer of viscid mortar was spread on the bed to reduce friction, after which each block was slipped snugly into place. The result has been termed "optician's work . . . on a scale of acres"; some joints are as narrow as one-fiftieth of an inch (0.5 mm).

In comparison with the work of Imhotep a century before, the Great Pyramid shows a considerable advance in technique: the blocks are much bigger and the joints much better. In fact, Egyptian masonry had reached its apex, and no improvements would be made during the next two thousand years. ■

Further Reading:

Ahmed Fakhry, *The Pyramids*. Chicago, 1961.
G. A. Reisner, *A History of the Giza Necropolis*. Cambridge, 1942-55.
W. Stevenson Smith, *The Art and Architecture of Ancient Egypt*. 1958.

UNI
fl. ca. 2350 B.C.
Egyptian Official and Engineer

Life and Times:

Egyptian history begins with the country's unification under a strong monarchy. Unopposed by external enemies, the pharaohs of the Old Kingdom kept the local nobles in check and drained the country's wealth in order to construct pyramids. Over the centuries power slipped from the grasp of these god-kings, but an occasional pharaoh displayed vigor and arrested the decline of the monarchy. Such a leader was Pepi I, who reasserted his power over local authorities, repelled invasions, and projected Egyptian power beyond the traditional frontiers. Pepi was one of three pharaohs loyally served by the official Uni, a man who rose from humble beginnings to join the inner circle at court.

Under the obscure Teti II, Uni held a minor position at the royal capital of Memphis, near modern Cairo. When Pepi I came to the throne he made Uni a judge and as the years passed granted him various signs of favor. Having gained the confidence of his master, Uni was chosen to preside at the conspiracy trial of one of the king's wives. Uni must have conducted himself well, for Pepi later assigned him to organize an army against Bedouin tribes harassing Egyptian mining operations in the Sinai desert. Uni proved to be a capable general. He conducted six campaigns, one sea-borne, striking deep into Bedouin country and bringing back captives by the thousands.

When Pepi died after a reign of twenty years, his son Mernere, still a youth, appointed Uni governor of the south. The position was one of great responsibility, for the southern nobles were far removed from the royal capital at Memphis. Yet Pepi had reimposed central authority so firmly that Uni never had to resort to arms. Instead, he spent his final years carrying out various missions for Mernere, during which he displayed considerable engineering skill.

Outstanding Engineering Achievements:

Mernere sent Uni to the alabaster quarry at Hatnub, some 150 miles (240 km) south of Memphis, to bring back a table of stone. While the stone was being cut at the quarry, Uni supervised the construction of a boat (possibly a raft) of acacia wood, 103 feet (31 meters) long and 51½ feet (15.6 meters) wide. In only seventeen days the table and boat were ready, and Uni returned to Memphis.

Uni next received a more difficult assignment that took him to the first cataract of the Nile, the site of the modern Aswan Dam, about 500 miles (800 km) south of Memphis. The rapids interfered with river traffic. Mernere, who wished to tighten his grip on Nubia to the south, ordered Uni to bypass the cataract by cutting canals around it. The task took one year, but Uni succeeded in digging five canals through the granite, the first canals ever made at that spot. The uninterrupted route south permitted later pharaohs to annex Nubia to their domains. So well, in fact, did Uni do his work that no improvements were needed until the reign of Sesostris III, some six centuries later. ■

Further Reading:

James H. Breasted, *Ancient Records of Egypt*, Vol. I. Chicago, 1906–07.
———, *A History of Egypt*. London, 1951.
R.J. Forbes, *Studies in Ancient Technology*, Vol. II. Leiden, 1955–64.

INENI (ANENA)
b. ca. 1550 B.C., Egypt
d. ca. 1485 B.C., Thebes, Egypt
Egyptian Architect

Life and Times:

In 1567 B.C., when the king of Thebes expelled the foreign Hyksos from Egypt, he inaugurated the 500-year period of Egyptian history known as the New Kingdom. The Theban kings soon began a building program to enlarge the temple at Karnak, near their capital city, about halfway between the Nile delta and the southern border of modern Egypt. With each succeeding reign, more and larger additions were made; today the temple is the largest columnar structure in the world, measuring 338 feet by 1,220 feet (103 meters by 372 meters).

Ineni is the first of the temple's architects whose name has survived. He served four kings: Amenhotep I, Thutmose I, Thutmose II and Thutmose III, who reigned with his aunt, Hatshepsut. Ineni was a foreman under Amenhotep I, but with the accession of Thutmose I he was promoted to superintendent of all building projects. Ineni carried out a number of tasks during that king's 30-year reign. Although he remained in favor under the successors of Thutmose I, no further work is mentioned in his tomb inscription; presumably he had by that time retired and was a pensioner at court.

Outstanding Engineering Achievements:

Ineni's only known project for Amenhotep, a 35-foot-tall (10.6 meters) gate on the south of the Karnak temple, has not survived. For Thutmose I Ineni built two pylons, or wide, narrow towers with sloping walls bisected by gateways. The first, 175 feet (53 meters) wide, was intended to be the main western entrance to the temple. Thutmose later expanded his plan, instructing Ineni to build a 250-foot (76 meters) wide pylon further to the west. Thutmose ordered the area left between the two pylons, some 225 feet (68.5 meters) wide and 40 feet (12 meters) deep, converted into a court with cedar columns. In front of the new entrance to the temple Ineni was to erect two granite obelisks.

The obelisks were hewn at Aswan, the site of the modern high dam, 150 miles (240 km) south of Thebes. To transport them Ineni constructed a boat measuring 207 feet by 69 feet (63 meters by 21 meters). It carried the shafts safely from the quarry to the temple.

Obelisk at Aswan, abandoned c. 1500 B.C., when a crack developed; 120 feet (37 m) long, it would have weighed 1200 tons.

Time did not treat Ineni's work well. By the end of Thutmose's reign two of the cedar columns were rotting and had to be replaced with stone ones; Thutmose III replaced the rest. The larger pylon is now in ruins, and one of the two obelisks in front of it has disappeared. The other, 64 feet (19.5 meters) high and weighing 143 tons, shows a decided list—Ineni did not provide a sufficiently long-lasting foundation for it.

Ineni may, however, have been responsible for a lasting innovation in Egyptian tomb architecture. The pyramids built early in Egypt's history had not proved to be safe from graverobbers, and the smaller above-ground tombs that replaced them were even more vulnerable. Ineni built the first known rock-cut tomb and inaugurated a tradition that lasted down to King Tutankhamen's day and beyond. ∎

Further Reading:

James Baikie, *Egyptian Antiquities in the Nile Valley*. London, 1932.

James H. Breasted, *Ancient Records of Egypt*. Vol. II. Chicago, 1906–07.

SENMUT (SENEMUT or SENENMUT)
fl. 1495–1475 B.C.
Egyptian Architect and State Official

Life and Times:

The nobleman Senmut was a court favorite of the celebrated Queen Hatshepsut, the older and dominant personality in a co-regency with Thothmes (Thutmose) III during Egypt's eighteenth dynasty (New Kingdom). Hatshepsut entrusted Senmut with the education of her daughter Nefru-rā, and he was put in charge of a commercial expedition to Punt, the land of incense to the south of the Red Sea.

One of Senmut's major tasks was to design for Hatshepsut a mortuary temple at Dayr al-Bahrī in the style of the temple of Neb-hepet-Rē Mentuhotep. The grand terraced monument was built next to the now ruined older temple. The queen, whose status was somewhat ambiguous (she may never officially have been accorded the title "pharaoh"), had the walls decorated with scenes to emphasize her fame and supposedly divine antecedents. Likewise, Senmut took care to record his own exalted position; his inscriptions refer to him as "overseer of overseers," the "one to whom all occurrences in Egypt are reported."

On the death of Hatshepsut in 1482 B.C., Senmut's enormous influence was probably curtailed. It is possible that Thothmes III, now sole ruler, had Senmut liquidated. However, recent scholarship casts some doubt on Thothmes' fabled hatred of Hatshepsut and her entourage. In excavations of the queen's temple, a stone image of Senmut was found in a small inner room. It is unlikely that this would have been allowed to remain had Senmut fallen into great disfavor.

Outstanding Engineering Achievement:

Senmut erected two obelisks at Karnak to commemorate the feast of Myriads of Years, probably Hatshepsut's coronation festival. These obelisks, the tallest built up to that time, were each 97½ feet (30 meters) long; the one that remains is the oldest obelisk in modern Egypt.

All operations were directed by Senmut. He supervised the quarrying of the red granite at Aswan—each shaft was cut from a single piece of stone—and organized the transportation of the columns down the Nile to Karnak. The shafts, weighing 646 tons between them, were set end to end with bases touching, in a massive barge. This was propelled down the river by 27 tugboats, each with about 32 oarsmen.

There are no ancient diagrams to explain how an obelisk was erected, but it is widely believed that the column was towed base-first up an earth ramp; the earth under the base was moved away, allowing the shaft, secured by ropes, to slide at an angle of 45° on to a grooved pedestal. The obelisk was then pulled upright with hauling tackle.

Senmut's talents as an overseer may not have been as great as he claimed. His crew missed the groove cut along one side of the pedestal of the surviving obelisk, and as a result, the monolith is slightly off-center. ∎

Further Reading:

L. Sprague de Camp, *The Ancient Engineers*. London, 1963.

James Kip Finch, *The Story of Engineering*. New York, 1960.

Senmut the engineer, holding the baby daughter of his employer, Queen Hatshetsut.

BEKHENCHONS (BEKNEKHONSU)
b. ca. 1306 B.C.
d. ca. 1220 B.C.
Egyptian Priest and Architect

Life and Times:

The city of Thebes (el-Karnak) overlooks the Nile about halfway between the river delta and the southern border of modern Egypt. When the king of Thebes expelled the foreign Hyksos from Egypt in 1567 B.C., he inaugurated Egypt's 500-year age of empire, the New Kingdom. During this period Amon, the god of the city, gained great prestige, and impressive temples were built in his honor. But work on the temple of Amon at Luxor near Thebes, begun by Amenophis III, was interrupted by his successor, Ikhnaton, who worshipped only the sun. Ikhnaton may have been a prophet of monotheism, but he allowed many of Egypt's territories to slip from his hands. His successors, notably Rameses II, returned to the worship of Amon and restored the Egyptian empire. Moreover, Rameses II was a great builder. Wishing to enlarge and complete the temple at Luxor, he chose the priest Bekhenchons as architect.

Bekhenchons began to work before he was 16, serving as chief of a stable for Rameses' predecessor, Seti I. He then became a priest of Amon, a career that lasted seventy years. As he rose through the ranks of the priesthood, his duties came to include conducting religious rituals as well as supervising and training serfs who worked for the temple. For the last 27 years of his life Bekhenchons served as high priest of Amon; he also acted as a judge. At some point he married Mersagret, who eventually rose to be chief of the harem of Amon, a position of some distinction. It is not known what training Bekhenchons had as an architect; but Rameses' choice proved a good one.

Outstanding Engineering Achievement:

Bekhenchons gave the Luxor temple its final form, adding two obelisks, six colossi, a pylon and a forecourt to the existing structure. Of the two obelisks, one was removed to Paris in 1836, where it stands in the Place de la Concorde. The sensation caused even in the nineteenth century by transporting the granite monolith, which is 74 feet (22.5 meters) tall and weighs 254 tons, points out the engineering skill possessed by the ancient Egyptians.

The other obelisk, 82 feet (25 meters) tall,

Statues of Rameses II and the obelisk by Bekhensons at the Temple of Luxor.

looms high above the colossi and the pylon, a wide tower with sloping walls bisected by a gateway. The colossi are all statues of Rameses, standing or seated. The walls of the pylon, which provides a backdrop to the statues, are decorated with sunken reliefs depicting the foreign wars of Rameses, while the obelisks commemorate these same events in hieroglyphics. Though far from modest, Rameses did acknowledge his debt to Amon, who made his victories possible.

The forecourt behind the pylon is of some technical interest: its columns bulge in the middle. Seven centuries after Bekhenchons, Greek architects gave their columns a slight convex curve *(entasis)* to achieve a harmonious effect. (It has previously been thought that the purpose of the curve was to make the columns appear straight when viewed from a distance, but this theory now appears unlikely.) Bekhenchons' columns, albeit somewhat crudely, thus anticipate one of the subtlest achievements of Greek architecture. ∎

Further Reading:

James Baikie, *Egyptian Antiquities in the Nile Valley.* London, 1932.
James H. Breasted, *Ancient Records of Egypt,* Vol. III. Chicago, 1906–07.
George Sarton, *A History of Science,* Vol. I. Cambridge, 1952–59.

THEODOROS OF SAMOS
fl. 575 B.C.
Greek Architect and Inventor

Life and Times:

The island of Samos, located in the Aegean Sea near the coast of Asia Minor, had its golden age in the sixth century B.C. Trade and industry flourished, and Samian fleets carried the island's metalwork and woollen products throughout the Greek-speaking world. The islanders used their wealth to good effect, bringing to their shores such literary giants as the story-teller Aesop and the poet Anacreon. But Samos did not neglect its native sons: by sponsoring ambitious public works, the island's rulers nurtured the genius of such engineers as Eupalinos [q.v.], Mandrokles [q.v.] and Theodoros.

Theodoros and his brother Telekles appear to have been trained by their father, the architect Rhoekos. Theodoros worked with both of them in Samos. It is possible that Theodoros also traveled to Egypt, and probable that he visited Sparta in Greece and Ephesus in Asia Minor. No details survive of his personal life. Yet so great was his fame in antiquity—as an architect, sculptor, gem-engraver and inventor—that some recent scholars believe two or three members of the family may have been named Theodoros.

Outstanding Engineering Achievements:

Theodoros is said to have invented ways of polishing gems. If this is true, his was the last technical improvement in the art for two thousand years. It is certain that gems engraved by Theodoros were much admired in antiquity. He is also credited with bringing to Greece an Egyptian technique for founding bronze statues in two or more parts. Theodoros and Telekles are said to have each sculpted half of a bronze statue of Apollo for a temple in Samos. When the two pieces were joined, the fit was perfect.

Among the many inventions attributed to Theodoros is the key, as well as such stonecutters' tools as the level, square and rule. The latter claims are dubious, since all were previously known in Egypt. No doubt Theodoros was credited with these devices because of his fame as an architect. At least three buildings are attributed to him: a meeting-hall in Sparta, the temple of Hera in Samos, and (in part) the temple of Artemis at Ephesus.

The temple of Hera, built sometime between 575 and 560 B.C., was for a time the largest building in the Greek world. Theodoros collaborated with his father in its construction. The temple was notable not only for its size—its platform measured 171 feet by 311 feet (52 meters by 95 meters)—but also for its innovative design. The body of the temple was surrounded by a double row of 132 columns. Made of soft limestone, they varied in diameter depending on their location in the temple. Modern archeologists have discovered that they were all turned on a lathe, giving some support to the ancient claim that Theodoros invented the lathe. Unfortunately, the temple's wooden roof caught fire about 530 B.C., and the building was destroyed.

Theodoros was soon called in to work on a still larger temple, this time in Ephesus. The site, though sacred, was swampy, a problem which Theodoros had faced in Samos. His solution was to spread a bedding of clay on the site, over which he laid down a platform of limestone, 180 feet (55 meters) wide and 377 feet (115 meters) long. Theodoros is not known to have done any further work on the temple of Artemis (which is mentioned in the New Testament); perhaps he died. But the foundation he built was solid enough to support both the sixth-century temple built by Chersiphron [q.v.] and Metagenes [q.v.] and the still more massive fourth-century temple of Deinokrates [q.v.] which replaced it. Modern archeologists have detected very little settling.

One other accomplishment should be cited: Theodoros wrote a book about the temple of Hera, the first architectural treatise whose title we know. Like most of his work, the treatise has not survived. ■

Further Reading:

J.J. Coulton, *Ancient Greek Architects at Work.* 1977.
William Dinsmoor, *The Architecture of Ancient Greece.* London, 1950.
George Sarton, *A History of Science,* Vol. I. Cambridge, 1952–59.

CHERSIPHRON OF KNOSSOS
METAGENES OF KNOSSOS
fl. 550 B.C.
Greek Engineers

Life and Times:

Some time around 900 B.C. a group of Greeks crossed the Aegean Sea to settle at Ephesus, on the coast of Asia Minor. At Ephesus was a site sacred to a local goddess, whom the Greeks identified with their own Artemis. As the cult of Artemis of Ephesus grew in popularity, one shrine succeeded another on the site. Finally, in the middle of the sixth century B.C. the Ephesians decided to honor their goddess with a large temple. The engineer Theodoros of Samos [q.v.] was called in to build a foundation on the swampy ground, but the bulk of the work was carried out under the supervision of Chersiphron and his son Metagenes. With generous financial assistance from the wealthy Croesus, whose kingdom of Lydia dominated central Asia Minor, Chersiphron and Metagenes were able to build on a scale unprecedented in the Greek world. Their solutions to the technical problems they encountered became part of engineering history, and the temple of Artemis was later counted among the seven wonders of the ancient world.

Both Chersiphron and Metagenes were born in the Cretan capital of Knossos. That once thriving island had become a backwater by the sixth century, so it is not surprising that Cretan engineers should cross the seas to find work. But little is known of the lives of either father or son.

Outstanding Engineering Achievement:

Whether Chersiphron or Theodoros drew up the design for the temple is uncertain. In any case, the temple was to be surrounded on three sides by a double row of columns, and in front would be three rows of columns with sculptured bases. Except for the latter, the temple's 127 columns, measuring 41 feet (12 meters) in height and up to six feet (1.8 meters) in diameter, were to be carved from single blocks of marble. Given the softness of the ground, wagons could not be used to transport the column shafts—they would founder from the weight.

Chersiphron's solution to this problem was ingenious. He had the columns roughly hewn into shape at the quarry, some seven miles (11 km) from the construction site. At each end of the column he inserted an iron pivot, sealed with lead. He then constructed an open wooden framework as long as the column, with shafts in front and behind linked by a crosspiece at each end. Each crosspiece had a socket in which the pivot at the end of the column could turn freely. When the column was fitted into this framework, the entire arrangement worked like a giant garden-roller. Chersiphron simply hitched oxen to the front shaft, and they pulled the column to the site.

Once the columns were set up, construction of the roof presented its own problems. The columns were widely spaced, but Chersiphron wished to span the gaps between them with stone instead of the more usual wooden architraves, or lintels. At this point Metagenes made his own contribution to the project, devising a means of bringing the architraves from the quarry to the construction site. Probably inspired by his father's garden-roller device for hauling columns, Metagenes constructed two wooden wheels, 12 feet (3.6 meters) in diameter, with broad felloes. On the inside of each wheel was a central socket large enough to receive the square end of the architrave; the latter thus served as an axle for this large set of wheels. On the outside of each wheel Metagenes installed a pivot. He then constructed a wooden framework long enough to enclose the wheel-and-axle assembly. The sidepieces of this framework had sockets into which were fitted the pivots on the outside of the wheels. As oxen pulled on the framework, the wheel-and-axle assembly rolled along freely to the construction site.

Once the architraves reached the construction site, ramps were built to haul them up into position. Chersiphron then introduced yet another innovation: at the top of the ramp, between the columns to be spanned, he laid a bed of sandbags to receive the architraves. He then let the sand out of the sandbags below so that the architraves could settle slowly into place without breaking.

Chersiphron and Metagenes subsequently described their techniques in a treatise on temple construction which was still in use five centuries later. But their masterpiece lasted only two centuries; in 356 B.C. a madman burned it down in an attempt to gain immortality. ∎

Further Reading:

J.J. Coulton, *Ancient Greek Architects at Work*. 1977.

Aage Drachmann, *The Mechanical Technology of Greek and Roman Antiquity*. Wisconsin, 1963.

Pliny, *Natural History,* Book 36. Cambridge, 1938–63.

Vitruvius, *On Architecture,* Book 10. Cambridge, 1914.

EUPALINOS
fl. 530 B.C.
Greek Architect

Life and Times:

A native of Megara, Eupalinos spent most of his career working for Polycrates, tyrant of Samos. He became one of the island's most famous builders, and is viewed by some historians as the first true civil engineer. In any event, he is one of the few ancient engineers whose accomplishments we know in some detail. The historian Herodotos mentions Eupalinos as the first *architekton,* or master of building arts, and describes the tunnel as the greatest engineering triumph of the Greeks.

Outstanding Engineering Achievement:

A specialist in water systems, Eupalinos is best known for constructing a water tunnel over half a mile (0.8 km) long through Mount Castro on Samos. Especially impressive, considering the technology of the time, was his ability to tunnel into opposite sides of the mountain with such precision that the two excavations were only 15 feet (4.5 m) apart in the middle. The tunnel, which took 10 years to complete, was 3,600 to 4,200 feet (1,100 to 1,280 meters) long and measured about eight feet (2.4 meters) high and eight feet (2.4 meters) wide. The conduit itself was about three feet (0.9 meters) deep, allowing for proper ventilation of the incoming water. The tunnel was part of an extensive system of aqueducts supplying a town on the site of the present-day village of Tigani. ■

Further Reading:

Isaac Asimov, *A Biographical Encyclopedia of Science and Technology.* Garden City, New York, 1964.

James Kip Finch, *The Story of Engineering.* Garden City, New York, 1960.

MANDROKLES OF SAMOS
fl. 512 B.C.
Greek Bridge Builder

Life and Times:

After Cyrus the Great of Persia defeated King Croesus of Lydia in 546 B.C., his generals quickly subdued the Greek cities on the coast of Asia Minor. The existing city governments were abolished, and Greek rulers friendly to Persia were installed. Although yearly tribute and military service in time of war were required by the Persian king, his yoke cannot have been too galling. After an initial wave of emigration, no revolts occurred for a generation. When King Darius invaded Europe in 512 in an attempt to add Thrace to his dominions, it is not surprising that Greeks served him loyally. Among them was the engineer Mandrokles.

Mandrokles came from the Aegean island of Samos, a center of engineering activity throughout the sixth century B.C. He must have known the work of such skilled engineers as Theodoros and Eupalinos [q.v.]. Mandrokles may well have studied under them; but nothing is known of his background or why Darius chose him as bridge builder in his European campaign. Mandrokles' work was evidently satisfactory, for Darius rewarded him with a crown and "ten of each thing"—that is, gifts in abundance.

Outstanding Engineering Achievement:

Mandrokles is known for successfully bridging the Bosporos, enabling Darius' army to march quickly from Asia into Europe instead of being ferried across the half-mile (0.8 meters) wide strait. As far as is known, no precedent existed for this task. Mandrokles solved the problem by anchoring boats in a line from shore to shore and covering them with wooden planks. This was the first boat-bridge in history, built some three centuries before the earliest comparable structure in China.

Mandrokles' bridge was intended to stay in place until the end of the Thracian campaign. But a rebellion in the nearby cities of Byzantium and Chalkedon caused the bridge to be destroyed. After his conquest of Thrace, Darius was forced to return to Asia by ship through the Dardanelles. ■

Further Reading:

J.B. Bury, *History of Greece.* London, 1967.

Herodotus, *Histories,* Book 4. London, 1880.

ARTACHAIES (ARTAHAYA)
fl. 500 B.C.
Persian Engineer

Life and Times:

It has been argued that, because of their nomadic origin, the ancient Persians lacked technical skills and depended entirely upon Phoenician or Greek hirelings to carry out their engineering projects. There is no doubt that the Persian kings Darius and Xerxes were well served by Phoenician and Greek engineers, notably Mandrokles [q.v.] and Harpalos [q.v.]. However, the claim of Persian incompetence or indifference in matters of engineering does not hold up under scrutiny.

In the hundred years from the accession of Cyrus to the death of Xerxes (mid-sixth to mid-fifth century B.C.) Persian rulers sponsored numerous major public works. Cyrus authorized a large-scale water diversion project near Babylon. Darius dug a canal from the Nile to the Red Sea and constructed a network of roads to link his vast empire, including the 1,500-mile (2,414 km) Royal Road from Sardis to Susa. And Xerxes, when his attempt to conquer Greece had failed, devoted his energies to vast building projects at Persepolis and Ecbatana. It is unreasonable to suppose that a people who could envision such a variety of engineering projects lacked all skill to carry them out. But chance has left us the names of only two Persian engineers, Artachaies and Boubares, who served under Xerxes.

Because Darius' sea-borne attack on Athens had come to grief, his son Xerxes decided to march into Greece. Much of the land route north of the Aegean Sea had been in Persian hands since 492 B.C. It was to this occupied area that Xerxes, in about 482 B.C., sent two officers—Artachaies, son of Artaios, and Boubares, son of Megabazos—to prepare the way for the invasion. Artachaies, of whom slightly more is known, belonged to the royal Achaemenid family and probably was in charge of the operation. If the Greek historian Herodotus can be trusted, Artachaies was the tallest man in Persia and had the loudest voice in the world.

His mission was comprehensive. He was to lay down roads and establish supply dumps along the route, bridge the Strymon river, and cut a canal across the peninsula dominated by Mt. Athos. Ten years before a storm had driven the Persian fleet onto the rocks of Mt. Athos; the canal would bypass this dangerous area, permitting the navy to hug the shore alongside the advancing army. Artachaies successfully carried out all these tasks. In 480, after the huge Persian invasion force had crossed the Hellespont, it progressed without difficulty along Artachaies' route. Artachaies, however, fell sick and died while the Persians were bivouacked at Abydos, near the canal. Xerxes deeply mourned his death and buried him with great pomp.

Outstanding Engineering Achievement:

At its narrowest, the Athos peninsula was a mile and a half (2.4 km) wide. Artachaies chose a favorable location, where the ground was level except for a few hills no more than fifty feet (15 meters) high. The canal was to be wide enough for two warships to be rowed abreast, perhaps 100 feet (30 meters). So that the mouths of the canal would not silt up, breakwaters were to be built at either end.

Having laid out the line of the canal, Artachaies assigned sectors to army units of several nationalities; the local inhabitants also furnished forced labor. Some details of the methods used have survived. The laborers formed bucket brigades: the earth turned up at the bottom of the trench was passed up from level to level and disposed of on either side of the canal route. The Phoenicians are said to have worked efficiently, opening a cut twice the width required and gradually narrowing it as they dug deeper. The other army units dug straight down at first, until the banks inevitably caved in.

Later generations of Greeks came to doubt that such elaborate preparations were actually made for Xerxes' invasion. They need only have visited the Athos peninsula, where a line of ponds still marks the course of the canal. The kinsmen of the Greeks, who dwelt in the northern Aegean sea, knew better. Half a century later the Thracians, through whose territory Xerxes had marched, held his road sacred and never sowed crops on it. The people of Akanthos, where Artachaies was buried, considered him a demi-god and invoked his name in prayer. ∎

Further Reading:

Herodotus, *Histories,* Book 7. London, 1880.
Richard S. Kirby, et al., *Engineering in History.* New York, 1956.

HIPPODAMOS OF MILETOS
fl. 480 B.C.
Greek City Planner and Philosopher

Life and Times:

The orderly planning of cities was practically unknown to the ancient world before the fifth century B.C. Sheer conservatism may have kept the older Greek cities a hodgepodge of crooked streets; but even the colonists sent out from the Greek mainland built their overseas settlements along the same chaotic lines. The desire for order appeared first among the Greeks of the eastern Aegean, particularly at Miletos. One of that city's colonies was laid out on a rectangular plan late in the sixth century B.C. There is no reason to believe that the Milesian philosopher Hippodamos was associated with that effort. Nevertheless, he became the Greek world's first advocate of regular city planning.

The date of Hippodamos' birth is uncertain. His native city of Miletos was known as the cradle of Greek philosophy, and he studied natural phenomena there. Hippodamos may have been a Pythagorean, for his political theories reveal a characteristic interest in harmony, number and proportion. Miletos revolted against Persian domination in 499 B.C.; Hippodamos fled to Athens sometime before 494 B.C., when the Persians utterly destroyed his birthplace.

With his long hair and foppish clothes, Hippodamos caused a sensation among the more austere Athenians. His theories of social justice and legal reform may have seemed equally outlandish, but his concern with civic organization proved of some interest to Themistokles, the Athenian statesman. Themistokles believed that

Athens' safety depended on its naval power. Elected to office in 493 B.C., he was able to begin construction of a port at Piraeus, five miles (8 km) from Athens. Themistokles appointed Hippodamos to lay out the lines of the city.

Hippodamos probably worked intermittently on Piraeus over the next few decades, a period punctuated by the Persian invasions of 490 B.C. and 480 B.C. At some point after the final defeat of Xerxes in 479 B.C., he spent several years at Miletos, participating in the rebuilding of that city. The Athenian government granted him a house in Piraeus, where he lived until 443 B.C. In that year he went to Thurii in southern Italy to plan a new model colony, his last known activity.

Outstanding Engineering Achievements:

The 200-foot-high (60 meters) p.omontory of Akte is joined to the Greek mainland southwest of Athens by a low-lying peninsula. On this site, which shelters the large harbor of Kantharos to the west and the smaller harbors of Zea and Munichia to the east, Hippodamos planned the port of Piraeus. Zea was planned as the principal naval station, leaving Kantharos to be devoted mainly to commerce. Alongside Kantharos, as surviving boundary markers show, Hippodamos laid out the emporium, where merchants could store their goods and do business with each other. The emporium was bounded on the side opposite Kantharos by the first of three main thoroughfares that ran the length of the peninsula. These were intersected by streets at right angles. At one of these intersections, conveniently near the emporium, was to be the agora—the combined marketplace and administrative center of Piraeus.

Although the marketplace was later known as the Hippodamian agora, there is no evidence that Hippodamos participated in its actual construction. Hippodamos' contribution was that of a city planner, not an architect. He designated areas for future commercial, military, religious and public use—apparently the first instance of zoning. Hippodamos also laid out the streets of Piraeus in a grid pattern, despite variations in terrain. The orientation of the grids varied in the different neighborhoods whose boundaries he established.

Hippodamos' hand can be seen in the still more ambitious plan for the reconstruction of Miletos. Again, the site was a peninsula; one set of streets ran its length while another set crossed at right angles, forming a total of 400 blocks. Midway down the peninsula an extensive central

Conjectural map of the Pireaus as Hippodamus planned it; A, agora; M, munitions dump.

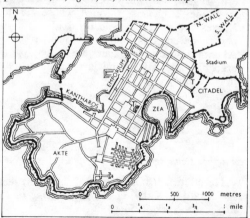

area was set aside for later development as public buildings. Beyond the central area the peninsula was wider, permitting larger blocks and wider streets. Thus, in the narrower part of the peninsula the blocks, measuring 76 feet by 96 feet (23 meters by 29 meters), were separated by streets 12 feet (3.6 meters) wide. Beyond the central area the blocks measured 112 feet by 140 feet (34 meters by 43 meters), and the streets were 14 feet (4 meters) wide. Two larger avenues, some 25 feet (7.6 meters) wide, led to the public area. This was eventually the site of an agora, a council house, theaters, gymnasia, a stadium and other buildings. Hippodamos' visionary city plan proved adequate for centuries of growth.

Nothing is known of Hippodamos' plan for Thurii, except that there were three streets running in one direction and four in the other. ■

Further Reading:

Aristotle, *Politics,* Book 2. London, 1932.

A.W. Lawrence, *Greek Architecture.* New York, 1957.

R.E. Wycherley, *How the Greeks Built Cities.* London, 1949.

HARPALOS
fl. 480 B.C.
Greek Bridge Builder

Life and Times:

When the Greek cities of Asia Minor and the eastern Aegean revolted against Persian rule in 499 B.C., Athens contributed some aid. The revolt was a failure; but an attempt by Persia's King Darius to retaliate against Athens also failed when his fleet was wrecked in a storm off Mt. Athos. Learning from his predecessor's experience, Darius' son Xerxes decided to invade Greece by land. His expedition gave the Greek engineer Harpalos the opportunity to accomplish one of the most famous engineering feats of antiquity.

Harpalos was one of the many Greeks from the eastern Aegean who served the Persian king. Nothing is known of his life or his training as an engineer. He was not with the team of Phoenician and Egyptian engineers assigned to throw two boat-bridges across the Hellespont, the strait between Asia Minor and Europe. In the winter of 480, soon after the bridges were completed, a fierce storm arose and destroyed them. Hearing of this disaster at his headquarters in Lydia, the enraged Xerxes ordered the Hellespont to be fettered, branded, and given 300 lashes. His subordinates carried out these orders as well as possible, berating the Hellespont for its ingratitude. At Xerxes' command, those responsible for building the bridges were beheaded. Harpalos was then assigned to rebuild the bridges, a task he successfully accomplished. So impressed was the ancient world by the bridging of the Hellespont that Harpalos became known as one of the seven greatest engineers of antiquity.

Outstanding Engineering Achievement:

Near ancient Abydos, at the probable site of the bridge, the Hellespont is more than a mile wide. Harpalos had at his disposal stores of timber and brushwood, huge ropes ordered the previous year from Egypt and Phoenicia, and the Persian navy. Two lines of warships, 360 and 316 in number, were anchored in position across the channel, facing upstream. Harpalos left three gaps in each line for small ships to pass from the Aegean to the Sea of Marmara. He then stretched six cables, two of flax and four of papyrus, the length of each line of ships; the cables were kept taut for at least part of this distance by means of wooden windlasses on either shore. The flax ropes, at 110 pounds per yard (55 kg per meter), were somewhat heavier than the papyrus ropes.

Harpalos next made the roadway across which the Persian army would march. He laid planks across the cables, fastening them in place, and above the planks placed a layer of brushwood. Earth was then heaped on the roadway and stamped flat. So that horses and pack animals would not be frightened by the sight of the water, Harpalos built a palisade on either side of the roadway. The Persian army, some 180,000 strong, spent two days crossing the strait.

Harpalos' bridges were still in place two years later, when they were disassembled by the retreating Persians who had survived the unsuccessful campaign. The pursuing Greeks captured and carried home some of the ropes, which were long displayed in the temples of Athens as a thanks-offering to the gods for victory. ■

Further Reading:

J.B. Bury, *History of Greece.* London, 1927.

Herodotus, *Histories,* Book 7. London, 1880.

KALLIKRATES (CALLICRATES)
fl. 460 B.C.–432 B.C.
Greek Engineer

Life and Times:

Xerxes' invasion of Greece in 480 B.C., though ultimately defeated, left Athens a pile of rubble. Despite Spartan objections, the Athenians soon fortified Athens as well as its port, Piraeus, some five miles (8 km) distant. In the following decades Athens' economic and political power increased. Pericles, who came to power in 460 B.C., presided over the city during its thirty most glorious years. A friend to philosophers and a patron of the arts, he adorned the Acropolis with the Parthenon and other temples. But Pericles was a practical man as well. Aware of the city's vulnerability to siege, he moved quickly to protect the approaches to Piraeus. With all the talent of Athens to draw on, Pericles chose the otherwise unknown Kallikrates to work both on the city's defense and on its beautification.

Outstanding Engineering Achievements:

One of Pericles' first acts in office was to order construction of the "Long Walls" connecting Piraeus and Athens. Kallikrates was put in charge of this work, done largely between 460 and 458 and finally completed in 445. The two walls ran parallel to one another and 550 feet (167 meters) apart for most of their course, diverging to meet the walls of Athens and Piraeus at strategic points. Kallikrates used large blocks of tufa rock to construct the walls, which were up to thirteen feet (4 meters) thick and perhaps twenty feet (6 meters) high. Their total length was 10 miles (16 km).

As Pericles had hoped, these defenses were indeed invulnerable to direct attack. After the Peloponnesian war broke out in 431, the Spartans made repeated raids on Athenian territory, devastating its farmland. But the farmers found shelter behind the Long Walls, and imported grain flowed uninterrupted from Piraeus to Athens. When Athens was finally defeated in 404 B.C., one of the first acts of the jubilant Spartans was to destroy the walls to the accompaniment of flutes.

Kallikrates also worked on the Parthenon with Iktinos [q.v.], under the supervision of the artist Pheidias. Construction lasted from 447 B.C. until 432 B.C. Although Kallikrates is generally viewed as a subordinate in this project, he may have co-authored with Iktinos a treatise on the temple's construction.

The temple of Athena Nike on the Acropolis was formerly thought to be the work of Kallikrates, along with up to seven other temples. These attributions are speculative, however. ■

Further Reading:

Ernest A. Gardner, *Ancient Athens.* New York, 1907.

James McCredie, "The Architects of the Parthenon," in Guenter Kopcke and Mary R. Moore (eds.), *Studies in Classical Art and Archeology.* Locust Valley, N. J., 1979.

IKTINOS
fl. 447–429 B.C.
Greek Architect

Life and Times:

Devastated by Persian invaders in 480 B.C., Athens recovered rapidly during the next several decades. It became the center of an empire, fostered a remarkable cultural flowering and competed with Sparta for leadership of the Greek world. By mid-century the Athenian leader Pericles had decided to transform the city's Acropolis, still strewn with rubble from the days of the Persian occupation, into the showplace of Greece. Pericles lived to see the completion of the Parthenon, the first of the temples that would grace the rocky site. The outbreak of the Peloponnesian War with Sparta in 431 B.C.

The Parthenon, or Temple of Athena Polias, erected by Iktinos in 438 B.C. and destroyed in an explosion in 1687.

and a plague in Athens delayed further work; as a result, Pericles' beautification program was completed only a few years before his city's crushing defeat at the hands of Sparta.

Pericles had appointed Pheidias, the greatest sculptor of the day, as overall superintendent of work on the Acropolis. The architect directly responsible for the Parthenon was Iktinos; Kallikrates [q.v.], his assistant, played only a subordinate role. We have no biographical information concerning Iktinos, nor has the treatise on the Parthenon which he wrote with Kallikrates survived. Nevertheless, that temple and the still better preserved one at Bassai give ample evidence of Iktinos' skill as an architect and engineer.

Outstanding Engineering Achievement:

Iktinos worked under a number of constraints in building the Parthenon. The temple was to be constructed on the site of an earlier one destroyed by the Persians, using as much as possible of the material salvaged from that building. In addition, Pheidias planned to carve a large cult statue of Athena, forty feet (12 meters) tall, which the Parthenon was to house. Iktinos' temple had to be large enough so that the statue would not appear cramped. But money was no object—Athens could draw on the wealth of her entire empire. Over the centuries, the Parthenon was used as a house of worship by a variety of

nationalities and religions. In 1687, it was being occupied by Turks who were using it to store munitions. An explosion occurred that destroyed the Parthenon. Restoration was begun in 1834; attempt is also being made to protect the monument from contemporary atmospheric pollution.

Structural work on the Parthenon began in 447 B.C. and was completed by 438 B.C. Iktinos enlarged the existing limestone platform of the old temple to a width of 160 feet (49 meters) and a length of 360 feet (110 meters). The building itself, constructed entirely of marble, measured 101½ feet by 228 feet (31 meters by 69 meters); it was the largest such temple on the Greek mainland. Around the body of the building he built a colonnade, customary in Greek temple architecture. The bases of the columns were 6¼ feet (2 meters) in diameter and were spaced 14 feet (4 meters) apart. Subtle harmonies were thus established, for these distances were all in the ratio of 4:9. Moreover, the combined height of the columns and entablatures (lintels) bore the same ratio to the width of the building.

Iktinos strengthened the Parthenon's almost subliminal aesthetic impact by designing the building with hardly a straight line. The tapered shafts of the columns had a slight convex curve, as if bulging from the weight of the entablatures. These, in turn, curved slightly upward in the middle of each side of the building, a distortion matched by a corresponding curve in the platform below. The walls of the building and the columns surrounding it leaned inward, while the cornice of the roof leaned outward. Some of these features were functional: the tilted columns acted as buttresses, while the curved platform allowed water to run off. But the main purpose was aesthetic, to temper the severe geometric regularity of the Greek temple. Though Iktinos did not invent any of these refinements, no other temple combined them all so effectively. Considerable credit, of course, must go to the masons involved.

Iktinos may, however, have been the first architect to use iron cantilever beams. These served to support the heavy statues located in the pediments above the front and rear entrances to the Parthenon. Five beams were placed in each pediment; they were from 4½ to 11 inches (11 to 28 cm) wide, 2½ to 5 inches (6 to 12 cm) tall, and 3 feet 9 inches to 4 feet (1.1 to 1.3 meters) long. In back the beams ran a foot (0.3 meters) or more into the stone structure of the building; in front, they received the weight of the statues whose bases were notched to fit over them. The stress on the cornice below was thus reduced.

Iktinos used structural iron to a much greater extent in his next assignment: construction of a small temple to Apollo at Bassai, in the rural southern Greek state of Phigalia. Funds were limited; hence Iktinos used more limestone than marble, introduced few of the refinements found in the Parthenon, and built on a small scale—47½ by 125½ feet (14 by 38 meters). Iktinos roofed the temple in stone, using an experimental approach. He hollowed out the tops of the 15-foot (4.5 meters) marble ceiling beams, removing more than half the section, and in the casings that remained he fitted rectangular iron beams. These must have measured 15 feet (4.5 meters) in length, with a section 9½ by 18 inches (24 by 46 cm). At least 18 of these beams would have been required for the temple. The iron, however, has long since rusted away.

Part of Iktinos' plan for a third project, never carried out, have survived. Commissioned to build a large auditorium for the celebration of religious rites at Eleusis, near Athens, Iktinos proposed a hall 170 feet (52 meters) square, topped by a lantern with open sides. The roof was to be supported by 20 columns, an arrangement which would require spans of more than 33 feet (10 meters). No doubt Iktinos again intended to use iron reinforcements for his roof beams, but the daring plan was never accepted. ∎

Further Reading:

William B. Dinsmoor, "Structural Iron in Greek Architecture," *American Journal of Archeology.* Vol. XXVI, 1922.

A.W. Lawrence, *Greek Architecture.* New York, 1957.

James McCredie, "The Architects of the Parthenon," in Guenter Kopcke and Mary R. Moore (eds.), *Studies in Classical Art and Archaeology.* Locust Valley, N. J., 1979.

ARCHYTAS
fl. 375 B.C., Taras (Taranto), Italy
Greek Statesman, Philosopher and Mathematician

Life and Times:

Greek colonization of Sicily and southern Italy began in the eighth century B.C. At first dependent on their mother cities on the Greek mainland, the colonies prospered through trade and farming in the centuries that followed. To Greater Greece, as the Italian frontier was known, came such enterprising individuals as the philosopher Pythagoras. About 530 B.C. he established a quasi-religious society which for a time exercised great influence in a number of cities. But by the end of the fifth century, expulsions and massacres had eliminated the Pythagoreans from every city except Taras. There Pythagoreanism found a refuge under the government of Archytas.

Archytas was probably from a well-to-do family, like most Pythagoreans; the study of mathematics and astronomy required leisure time. Although Pythagorean governments in other Italian cities had been oligarchies, Taras was a democracy. When elected prime minister of the city, Archytas served well and loyally, never attempting a coup. In return, the citizens voted to suspend the constitutional provision barring reelection to the post; in all, Archytas served seven terms. A good deal of his popularity must have been due to his repeated military successes against the native Italians, who often threatened the Greek colonies.

Archytas found time to conduct scientific and philosophical investigations and to instruct a number of disciples. His fame soon spread to mainland Greece; in about 388 Plato, who believed philosophers should be kings, visited Taras to meet Archytas. Their friendship lasted almost 30 years. Plato had one complaint: Archytas used mechanical equipment to solve geometrical problems, and Plato felt that so grossly material an approach was beneath the dignity of a true philosopher. It was Plato who had more influence than Archytas on the subsequent course of Greek science.

Outstanding Engineering Achievement:

Archytas was known in later antiquity as the founder of theoretical mechanics, though his treatise on the subject has not survived. He may also have developed the screw, which was certainly known before Archimedes' time. Archytas has been credited with discovering the use of the pulley, but it was probably in existence long before him. Several sources describe his invention of an aerodynamic toy, a wooden dove that flew by compressed air. We learn that once the dove landed it could fly no farther, a seemingly realistic detail. Some 500 years later a similar device made its appearance in China, the work of the astronomer Chang Heng [q.v.]. Finally, Archytas developed a kind of baby's rattle, either to divert children so that they would not break household objects or to teach them music at an early age.

Other Achievements:

A noted astronomer, Archytas argued that the universe was infinite in extent. His most famous geometrical proof was the doubling of the cube, a solution which for the first time in history used a curve of double curvature. Archytas also studied the theory of numbers, distinguishing three kinds of means: arithmetic, geometric and harmonic. He applied number theory to the study of musical intervals and scales, going much further than earlier investigators (notably Pythagoras) in this respect. It is likely that Archytas sought to establish a mathematical basis for all the sciences of the day, an enterprise which clearly reveals his Pythagoreanism. ■

Further Reading:

Pierre Brunet and Aldo Mieli, *Histoire des Sciences: Antiquité.* Paris, 1935.

H. Diels and W. Kranz, *Fragmente der Vorsokratiker.* Berlin, 1903.

G.C. Field, *Plato and His Contemporaries.* London, 1930.

George Sarton, *A History of Science,* Vol. I. Cambridge, 1952–59.

KRATES (CRATES) OF CHALKIS
fl. 335–325 B.C.
Greek Hydraulic and Civil Engineer

Life and Times:

The military exploits of Alexander the Great are well known. After his accession to the Macedonian throne in 336 B.C., it took years to conquer the Persian empire. The task of consolidating these vast possessions would have been difficult even if he had not spent the next six years on further campaigns. Nevertheless, he did not neglect to found dozens of cities, improve a half-dozen harbors, and sponsor important hydraulic engineering projects. Assisting him in these works of conquest and consolidation were a number of engineers, notably Deinokrates [q.v.], Diades [q.v.] and Krates.

Krates was from Chalkis, the leading city of Euboia in Greece. Since Euboia had come under Macedonian control in 338 B.C., Krates probably accompanied Alexander even before the invasion of Persia in 334. Krates served as a sapper and miner in several military campaigns before turning to tasks of civilian construction. Following the conquest of Egypt, Alexander decided to build a new port city in the Nile delta. Krates and other engineers began work on Alexandria even before Alexander left Egypt in 331.

Krates presumably remained at Alexandria, working under the supervision of Deinokrates, until some time before 324. Alexander then ordered him to go to Boiotia, an agricultural region between Athens and his native Chalkis, in order to drain the marshes near Lake Kopais. Krates obediently began the task, but his work was interrupted by party strife among the Boiotians. No further information on his life is known.

Outstanding Engineering Achievements:

The site chosen by Alexander for the city of Alexandria was on a neck of land a few miles wide between the Mediterranean and Lake Mareotis. The harbor was spacious, but the nearest branch of the Nile, the Canopic mouth, lay ten miles (16 km) to the east. Krates was probably charged with digging a canal from the city to the Nile. In addition to linking the isolated site with Memphis and other leading cities of Egypt, the canal served to bring fresh water to Alexandria. A side branch of the canal joined the harbor with the lake, easing communication with nearby villages. Krates may also have begun work on the system of underground canals and cisterns that distributed drinking water throughout Alexandria until modern times. It is uncertain how far the work had progressed when Krates was reassigned to Greece.

The nature of Krates' work at Kopais is unclear. This lake—actually a reed swamp covering 100 square miles (260 square km)—was fed by two rivers, the Kephissus and the Herkyna. The only natural drainage of this land-locked area was provided by dozens of underground fissures in the limestone cliffs to the north and east. When earthquakes occurred, the fissures were often blocked by rubble. Attempts to clear the fissures and control the flow of the rivers had actually begun in prehistoric Late Helladic times. To that period, 1,100 years before Krates, must be assigned the two canals whose stone-lined earthen banks, up to 50 yards (46 meters) wide, diverted the waters of the rivers from the center of the swamp.

Krates may have dug a crude earthen canal whose traces have been detected near the Herkyna, or he may simply have cleared some of the fissures. But he probably attempted a more ambitious task—driving two drainage tunnels, each more than a mile (1.6 km) long, through the hills to the northeast and east. The northeast tunnel followed the winding trace of a pass over the hill. Sixteen shafts were sunk along this route to depths of up to 200 feet (61 meters). Although a straight line would have been appreciably shorter than the curving course actually followed, the builder no doubt felt that the tunnel would be completed sooner, with fewer ventilation problems, if there were 32 working faces along the route. Two thousand feet (610 meters) of each tunnel were completed before the work was abandoned.

This type of irrigation, known as quanat irrigation, had been practised for centuries. Whether these tunnels were the work of Krates or of his Late Helladic predecessors, one at least was sound in conception. When Lake Kopais was finally drained in the late nineteenth century, a tunnel was drilled straight through the hill to the northeast, not far from the ancient tunnel. ■

Further Reading:

E. Breccia, *Alexandria ad Aegyptum.* Bergamo, 1930.

James Kip Finch, *The Story of Engineering.* Garden City, New York, 1960.

M.L. Kambanis, "The Drainage of Lake Copais," *Bulletin de Correspondence Hellénique.* Vols. XVI and XVII (1892 and 1893).

E.J.A. Kenny, "The Ancient Drainage of the Copais," *Annals of Archaeology and Anthropology.* Vol. XXII (1935).

DEINOKRATES (DINOCRATES)
fl. 331 B.C.
Greek or Macedonian Architect

Life and Times:

In 356 B.C. the magnificent temple of Artemis at Ephesus, built by Chersiphron [q.v.], Metagenes [q.v.] and Theodoros of Samos [q.v.], was burned down by a madman seeking to accomplish an immortal act. That same year Alexander the Great of Macedonia, who would begin his career of conquest only two decades later, was born. Both events profoundly affected the life of Deinokrates. By reconstructing the temple he gave final shape to one of the seven wonders of the ancient world. After entering the service of Alexander, Deinokrates was charged with the construction of Alexandria, a city that became the intellectual and mercantile capital of the eastern Mediterranean during the Hellenistic era.

Little is known of the man who ranked as the leading architect of his day. Deinokrates may have been a Macedonian, although other sources assert that he was from Rhodes, the prosperous Greek island in the eastern Aegean. The reconstruction of the temple of Artemis, for which Deinokrates was probably responsible, cannot be precisely dated, although it was probably complete by the time Deinokrates sought employment with Alexander. Deinokrates approached Alexander with a proposal to carve Mt. Athos, a prominent landmark on the Greek coast, in his likeness. No doubt flattered, Alexander declined the offer but hired Deinokrates.

After his conquest of Egypt late in 332, Alexander decided to found a city with adequate port facilities. Choosing a natural harbor on the Mediterranean coast, Alexander himself traced out the lines of the city and appointed Deinokrates to supervise its construction. Alexander marched to Persia in 331 to continue his conquests, leaving an associate, Kleomenes, in charge of Egypt's finances. In Alexander's absence—he never returned to Egypt—Kleomenes grew corrupt; his machinations caused constant delays in the construction work. A year after Alexander's death in 323, one of his generals, Ptolemy, gained control of Egypt and had Kleomenes killed. Thereafter the work of building Alexandria went quickly, although it is not known how long Deinokrates served as architect.

Outstanding Engineering Achievements:

The sixth-century temple of Artemis had been built on a grand scale. Deinokrates replaced it with one even grander. First he razed the ruins down to the bases of the pillars. The old platform, constructed by Theodoros, was 377 feet (115 meters) long and 180 feet (55 meters) wide; Deinokrates incorporated it in a still larger platform, 417 feet by 239 feet (127 meters by 73 meters). He built new foundations on the pavement of the old temple, thus raising the floor by 7½ feet (2 meters) over the previous level. The area of the body of the temple was to be no larger than that laid out by Chersiphron, Deinokrates' predecessor. In a display of virtuosity, Deinokrates built new walls and columns directly above the bases of the old ones buried below. Like Chersiphron's temple, Deinokrates' had 127 columns, many of them with sculptured bases. But Deinokrates' columns soared 65 feet (20 meters) into the sky; the distance from the platform to the ridge of the roof was an unprecedented 108 feet (33 meters).

Deinokrates' later accomplishments at Alexandria dwarfed his achievements at Ephesos. To him can be attributed the impregnable walls of the city, ten miles (16 km) in circuit and studded with towers. The two main streets were also Deinokrates' work. Each one hundred feet (30 meters) wide, they intersected in the heart of the city; one, the Canopic Street, ran four miles (6 km) from the eastern to the western end of Alexandria. Deinokrates laid out the city's streets in a checkerboard pattern originated by Hippodamos. It is uncertain whether Alexander, Deinokrates or one of their successors was responsible for the policy of land use that made Alexandria unique in its time: fully one-fourth of the city's area was occupied by public buildings, with another fourth devoted to parks and open spaces.

Deinokrates must have begun the harborworks needed to accommodate the warships and trading fleets that plied the Mediterranean. He may also have built the mole, three-quarters of a mile (1 km) long, that connected the city with

The ancient port of Alexandria, laid out by Deinokrates; the map was published, 1740, by Belidor; south is at the top.

the offshore island of Pharos. Krates [q.v.] has been named as the builder of the canal from Alexandria to the Nile; but he probably worked under Deinokrates' supervision.

Active construction continued in Alexandria until the middle of the third century B.C. But despite the achievements of his successors—the lighthouse on Pharos, the museum, the library—Deinokrates deserves the credit for planning one of the world's great cities. It is regrettable that 2,300 years of continuous occupation have obliterated all but a fraction of his handiwork. ∎

Further Reading:

E. Breccia, *Alexandria ad Aegyptum.* Bergamo, 1930.

J. Henderson, "The Temple of Artemis at Ephesus," *Journal of the Royal Institute of British Architects.* Vol. XL (1932–33).

Strabo, *Geography,* Book 17. London, 1932.

DIADES
fl. 330 B.C.
Thessalian Military Engineer

Life and Times:

Two years after Alexander the Great succeeded to the throne of Macedonia in 336 B.C., he fulfilled his father's dream of invading Asia. Philip II had left Alexander a highly trained army and a corps of siege engineers. The latter proved useful when a city offered resistance, as at Halikarnassos (334 B.C.) and Tyre and Gaza in Phoenicia (332 B.C.). The most formidable of

Alexander's engineers was Diades, whose siege equipment played a decisive part in the conquest of Tyre.

Diades studied siegecraft under his countryman, Polyeidos of Thessaly, who served Philip II. Diades may have seen action during Philip's unsuccessful attempts to take the Greek cities of Perinthos and Byzantion in 340 B.C. He was much more prominent, however, in Alexander's campaigns. Diades also wrote a treatise on siegecraft, summaries of which have been preserved.

Outstanding Engineering Achievements:

One of the most effective siege weapons of the day was a tall wooden tower, which was rolled up against the city under attack. From the tower fire could be directed at the defenders on the battlements below, or bridges could be lowered onto the city wall, permitting the attackers to cross over. Naturally, such towers were extremely heavy and hard to move. But Diades developed techniques for taking them apart, transporting them in his siege train, and reassembling them quickly at the next city to be attacked. Twenty stories (almost 200 feet; 61 meters) tall, they were covered with animal skins to ward off blazing arrows. Nevertheless, they could be destroyed by a determined enemy. The defenders of the island city of Tyre managed to burn down two of them with fireships.

Tyre held out for seven months against the Macedonian forces. Unable to storm the city from the landward side, Alexander ordered Diades to equip nonessential ships with military engines. Diades installed rams and the recently-developed, torsion-powered catapults on transports and slow warships lashed together in pairs. With these he pounded the walls of the city at several weak points until they gave way. In the final assault, specially fitted troop transports lowered their drawbridges onto the breaches in the walls, and Alexander's troops burst into the city. Never before had catapults been powerful enough to weaken city walls, nor had a naval bombardment ever been attempted.

Diades perfected several kinds of siege engines, if he did not, as he claimed in his treatise, invent them. The tortoise was a wheeled wooden framework from which a ram was suspended. Under cover of the thick wooden roof, soldiers could swing the ram like a pendulum against the walls and gates of a city. Tortoises could be up to 50 feet (15 meters) wide, 60 feet (18 meters) long and more than 20 feet (6 meters) tall. Diades surmounted one of his tortoises with a three-

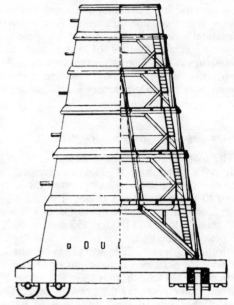

Movable siege tower such as the Romans used for assaulting fortifications.

story tower containing catapults and a water supply for fighting fires. He also developed a large drill for boring holes in city walls, as well as the crow, a grappling device projected onto a city wall to permit scaling. ■

Further Reading:

Eric W. Marsden, *Greek and Roman Artillery: Historical Development*. Oxford, 1969.

W.W. Tarn, *Alexander the Great*. Cambridge, 1948.

W. Sodel and V. Foley, "Ancient Catapults," *Scientific American*, March, 1979.

APPIUS CLAUDIUS CRASSUS (CAECUS)
fl. 312 B.C.
Roman Official and Administrator

Life and Times:

As Rome gradually expanded in central Italy during the fourth century B.C., it found its sources of supply increasingly inadequate. Frequent conflicts with rival tribes and cities meant that troops from Rome had to move quickly across the surrounding Campagna. The fear of a siege, never far from Roman minds since the

Gallic conquest of the city in 390, also prompted concern for secure water supplies. Appius Claudius Crassus, a prominent official of the late fourth century, helped satisfy both needs by supervising two engineering projects of cardinal importance: the first paved Roman road, the Appian Way, and the first Roman aqueduct, the Aqua Appia.

Generally known by the surname Caecus, Appius Claudius Crassus was by many standards a key figure in early Roman history. Born into a patrician family, he was an expert in legal matters who served twice as consul, once as dictator and once as censor. In the latter office he maintained the roll of citizens *(census),* but also had wide supervisory powers over the city administration. Appius Claudius lived at a time of acute tension between the ruling patrician oligarchy and the plebeians, who sought to increase their eligibility for office and their influence in the government of the Republic. Though himself a patrician, Appius Claudius favored compromise with the plebeians and sponsored policies aimed at satisfying their most important demands; as censor he made sons of freedmen eligible for membership in the Senate. But subsequent officials partly undid Appius Claudius' reforms, and resolution of the conflict had to wait a generation. More enduring were Appius Claudius' engineering projects, both apparently completed while he served as censor.

Outstanding Engineering Achievements:

The Appian Way originally ran from Rome to the city of Capua, a distance of 162 miles (261 km). In later years it was extended farther south to the tip of Italy and became an important route for travel to Africa. The original pavement was apparently gravel, though later Roman engineers repaved the road with basaltic lava atop a multi-layered rock foundation.

The Aqua Appia brought water to Rome from the Anio River valley, 10½ miles (17 km) south of the city. Unlike later aqueducts, it was primarily an underground structure, entering Rome more than 50 feet (15 m) below the surface. Some remains of the Aqua Appia have been found on the Aventine Hill, and at the bottom of some of the stone quarries near the Anio River. Most of its course outside Rome, however, has not been traced. ■

Further Reading:

Thomas Ashby, *The Aqueducts of Ancient Rome.* Oxford, 1935.

The old Appian Way, named for its builder, Appius Claudius.

William H. Burr, *Ancient and Modern Engineering and the Isthmian Canal.* New York, 1902.

L. Sprague de Camp, *The Ancient Engineers.* London, 1963.

E. B. van Deman, *The Building of Roman Aqueducts.* Washington, 1943.

Neal FitzSimons, ed., *Engineering Classics of James Kip Finch.* Kensington, Maryland, 1978.

Norman Smith, "Roman Hydraulic Technology," *Scientific American,* May, 1978.

KAUTILYA
fl. 300 B.C.
Indian Statesman and Technologist

Life and Times:

The classical civilization of the Mediterranean produced important treatises on certain branches of engineering—Sextus Julius Frontinus [q.v.] on water works, Philo of Byzantium [q.v.] on applied mechanics, Marcus Vitruvius Pollio [q.v.] on architecture. But the West had to wait until the late Middle Ages and Renaissance for broad technological surveys of the kind written by Lazarus Ercker [q.v.] and Georgius Agricola [q.v.]. In India, on the other hand, such works were already known in the pre-Christian era. The most famous and comprehensive of these is the *Arthashastra,* or Treatise on Polity, written in the fourth century B.C. by Kautilya.

Kautilya lived at a time of political uncertainty and cultural efflorescence in India known as the Ayurvedic period. The Mauryan empire was established in the southern part of the subcontinent, while Sanskrit texts were written on a wide range of topics. Kautilya had a part in both developments. An important politician as well as a scholar, he served as adviser and prime minister to Chandragupta, first ruler of the Mauryan state. Indeed, part of the *Arthashastra* is devoted to political matters; its justification of absolute power for the ruler and subterfuge in the interest of state have prompted some scholars to view Kautilya as an Indian Machiavelli. Yet he was also an Indian Agricola, for he believed that the ruler should have a firm understanding of scientific and technical matters important to the well-being of his subjects. The *Arthashastra* is thus a vital source of information on the scientific knowledge and engineering practices of its time.

Outstanding Engineering Achievements:

Kautilya's interests included astronomy, medicine and chemical and metallurgical technology. His observations in all these fields are especially important because the *Arthashastra* is one of the first Sanskrit texts that can be precisely dated. A reference in the work to glass beads, for instance, indicates that Indian artisans had developed the technique of glass blowing by the third century B.C.

Among the most thorough sections of Kautilya's work are those describing the extraction and purification of metals. Indian metallurgists of the time evidently produced a number of metals in quantity, including gold, silver, iron, copper, tin, lead, mercury and a number of alloys. The *Arthashastra* describes the alloys of each of these metals, stressing the importance of treating them with alkali prepared from plant ash to remove impurities. Charcoal, a by-product of food preparation, is identified as useful for smelting iron and for treating lime in kilns. Kautilya also describes an early version of cupellation, a means of purifying gold or silver by heating the precious metal in the presence of lead; impurities would combine with the lead while the precious metal separated out. This method was used by both jewelers and assayers interested in determining the metal content of ores. Interestingly, Kautilya advises that goldsmiths should be penalized for adulterating gold with base metals, an indication that alchemy was not favored in his time. Finally, the *Arthashastra* contains a thorough description of metal-working techniques, including compact work, hollow-ing, soldering, combining (or amalgamation), enclosing and gilding.

The sections of the *Arthashastra* dealing with astronomy provide information on both the theoretical views and instrument-making techniques of the time. Kautilya presents a set of equations describing the apparent motions of the sun and moon, sightings of which were made with a 12-digit gnomon or sun-dial, the standard instrument of astronomical measurement in India. ■

Further Reading:

Sir Prafalla Chandra Ray, *A History of Hindu Chemistry from the Earliest Times to the Middle of the Sixteenth Century*. London, 1902–1909.

KHARES (CHARES) OF LINDOS
fl. 300 B.C., Rhodes
Greek Sculptor and Monument Builder

Life and Times:

By the third century B.C., the beginning of the Hellenistic era, the grain-trading center of Rhodes had become one of the wealthiest independent communities in the Greek world. The island attracted a colony of artists and writers, including the sculptor Lysippus, who founded a school of sculpture there. Several of his pupils became famous for executing monumental sculptures that required the skills both of an artist and of an engineer. Some of these have been preserved, but the most massive example of the genre is now lost: the Colossus of Rhodes, designed and executed by Khares of Lindos.

Little is known of Khares' life or the details of his work. Known to the ancients as one of the seven wonders of the world, the Colossus was built to celebrate the defeat of the warlord Demetrios, who attempted to conquer Rhodes in 305–304 B.C. The work was apparently dedicated to Helios, the sun-god protector of the island. Khares began the Colossus shortly after the defeat of Demetrios and completed the project around 280 B.C.

Outstanding Engineering Achievement:

The Colossus of Rhodes stood about 105 feet (32 meters) high (60 or 70 cubits in the classical allusions to it). The monument was cast in bronze, the main source of which was the supply of bronze weapons abandoned by Demetrios' army when they retreated from the island. It is apparently not true that the Colossus "bestrode" the harbor. The monument was shaken several times by earthquakes, the most damaging of which occurred in 224 B.C. Pieces of the monument were picked away over the course of centuries. The last fragments were scrapped in 656 A.D. ■

Further Reading:

Marshall Clagett, *Greek Science in Antiquity*. New York, 1955.

ARCHIMEDES
b. 287 B.C., Syracuse, Sicily
d. 212 B.C., Syracuse
Greek Mathematician and Mechanical Engineer

Life and Times:

Known as one of the most colorful—certainly one of the most eccentric—geniuses in the history of science, Archimedes was the son of a Greek astronomer, Pheidias. He was born in the Greek settlement of Syracuse, Sicily, a distant relative of the Syracusan King Hieron II. Being well connected in the Syracusan court, he was able to devote himself to scientific inquiry without concern for earning a living. He was indifferent for the most part to the practical applications of his inventions.

Archimedes studied in Alexandria at the famous academy established by the Ptolemaic dynasty, where he associated with future mathematicians such as Conon, Dositheus and Eratosthenes. Some scholars view Archimedes as a contemporary of Euclid, perhaps for a time a student of the great mathematician. Quickly establishing a reputation for extraordinary mathematical and inventive ability, he returned to Syracuse and a life of leisured study.

Some sources report that Archimedes was married. Far more certain is his reputation for eccentricity, the subject of many colorful stories. His absent-mindedness has been compared to that of Isaac Newton: both easily forgot meals, sleep and other bodily functions while immersed in consideration of a mathematical problem. Perhaps the best-known story about Archimedes concerns his discovery of the principle of hydrostatics, or displacement of water by a submerged

Archimedes, the genius who discovered the law of the lever and the displacement principle, was employed as a military engineer.

body. Upon conceiving the notion in his bath, he jumped up and ran naked through the streets to the palace of his patron, King Hieron, shouting "Eureka" (I've found it).

Unlike the *Elements* of Euclid, Archimedes' numerous writings were not read widely in antiquity. Present-day knowledge of them comes from Byzantine interest in his theories during the sixth through tenth centuries. Though specific Archimedian treatises were studied earlier at Alexandria, it was not until the end of the fifth century, with Eutacius of Ascalon, that the systematic study of Archimedes' collected work begins.

During the second Punic War (218–202 B.C.), a Roman fleet attacked Syracuse for allying itself with Rome's rival, Carthage. Despite his distaste for practical affairs, Archimedes turned military engineer and applied many of his discoveries to the defense of his native city. Indeed, the Greek historian Plutarch maintains that the vastly outmanned Syracusans were able to resist the Roman siege for some three years only because of the ingenious mechanical devices designed by Archimedes. The city's fall in 212 B.C. provides a last sad anecdote about the great mathematician. According to Plutarch, the Roman commander, Marcellus, sent a soldier to fetch Archimedes to headquarters. Archimedes, absorbed as usual with a mathematical problem impatiently waved the soldier away; whereupon he was killed.

The remorseful Marcellus, who had never intended Archimedes' death, carried out his last wish by erecting a monument with a cylinder circumscribing a sphere, together with the Archimedean formula stating the ratio by which an including solid exceeds an included solid. With the death of Archimedes, the line of great Hellenic engineers comes to an end.

Outstanding Engineering Achievements:

Archimedes is credited with discovering the law of the lever, the basic principle of the compound pulley. His treatise on Place Equilibrium begins with the hypothesis that "equal weights at equal distance balance." On this basis, Archimedes formulated his theorum that "two weights balance at distances reciprocally proportional to their magnitudes," the so-called theory of mechanical advantage. With this he founded the science of statics, and began the development of the notion of a center of gravity based on quantitative measurement of weights and distances. Two thousand years ahead of their time, Archimedes' ideas in this area went unnoticed until a translation of his writings into Latin in 1544 brought renewed interest among such scientists as Galileo [q.v.].

The experiments conducted by Archimedes to demonstrate the law of the lever and the concomitant notion of center of gravity consisted in putting a long stock or strong branch on a stone or into a wide cut of wood, so that the arm moving the weight would be short while the remaining side was long. He found that there was less need for operating force the longer the arm not lifting the stone. Archimedes proceeded from here to discover the centers of gravity of the simpler planes and solid figures.

Plutarch tells that Archimedes demonstrated his law of the lever to King Hieron by single-handedly beaching a fully-loaded merchant ship by means of a system of compound pulleys. This was the occasion of the famous remark attributed to him: "Give me a place to stand on and I will move the earth."

Archimedes first proposed the theory of equilibrium of liquid bodies, the basis of the science of hydrostatics, in his treatise on Floating Bodies. This principle maintains that a solid body when immersed in a liquid displaces a portion of the liquid equal to its own volume. Archimedes was brought to his discovery by a request from King Hieron to verify that a recently completed crown consisted of pure gold, as claimed by the goldsmith who made it. Forbidden to damage the crown or alter it physically, Archimedes was stymied until he noticed in his bath that his body displaced water in proportion to its own volume (see above). Armed with this knowledge, he was able to determine that the crown displaced more water than an equal weight of gold. He therefore concluded that the crown was adulterated with a bulkier metal such as silver. Archimedes became famous, but the goldsmith was executed.

Archimedes' screw, also called a cochlea, was a pipe twisted into a corkscrew shape, divided inside by a partition running the length of the pipe. Held at an angle while one end dipped below the surface of the water, it was rotated on its axis, drawing water higher with each successive turn until the liquid came spilling out from the top. The screw could be used as a pump to raise the level of water, or to remove water from a ship; it was also used frequently as a cogwheel to launch ships. Said to have been invented while Archimedes was in Egypt, the screw is still found in irrigation systems there.

During the Roman siege of Syracuse, Archimedes designed catapults and grapnels to help fight off the invader. So fearful were his devices, according to Plutarch, that the Romans fled at the mere sight of a rope protruding above the city walls. Among Archimedes' military inventions were cranes with iron hooks that seized Roman ships running close to shore, capsizing them or dropping them onto rocks. Some sources also claim that he experimented with mirrors capable of reflecting a beam of light powerful enough to set ships on fire; but the size of the equipment required and the difficulty of focusing on a moving target make it unlikely that he perfected such a device.

Archimedes is also said to have built a large version of a weapon called "the dolphin," used to arm merchant ships. This was a leaden weight slung by rope and pulleys from the end of the yardarm. In case of an attack, the dolphin could be swung onto the enemy ship, smashing through the deck.

The formidable fortress of Euryalos, built to insure the strategic height above Syracuse, was the work of Archimedes. Considered a masterpiece of ancient military architecture, it was designed to maximize opportunities for both defense and counterattack. The multiple-towered wall of the citadel was protected by three large trenches cut into the rocky crust that formed the only approach. Subterranean chambers in the mountain itself housed the garrison. Tunnels six to ten feet (2 to 3 meters) wide were excavated to create an underground highway for mounted troops and infantry moving between the citadel and the screening trenches. Sally ports were camouflaged with weeds and large rocks enabling the defenders to emerge from any part of an underground network of tunnels extending about 1600 feet (500 meters). The system also ran some 350 feet (100 meters) to a northern fortress, also provided with underground passageways.

Invention of the capstan, a rotating vertical shaft used for hoisting heavy weights, is also attributed to Archimedes, on the occasion of the launching of Hieron's giant ship, the *Alexandreia*. And he may have invented the first gear trains.

Other Outstanding Achievements:

In addition to his engineering works, Archimedes is credited with a number of discoveries in pure and applied mathematics. Scholars, indeed, consider him one of the greatest mathematicians in history. He developed methods for finding the areas of curvilinear plane figures and volumes bounded by curved surfaces. Another formula, known as Archimedes' Problem, is used to calculate the volume of a sphere and other volumes created by the rotation on their axes of such shapes as rectangles, triangles, hyperbolas, parabolas, and ellipses.

Archimedes is perhaps best known among mathematicians for developing a means of calculating the value of pi, the ratio of the circumference of a circle to its diameter, which he set at between $3\frac{1}{7}$ and $3\frac{10}{71}$. His method consisted of calculating the diameters and perimeters of polygons within and outside the circle. The addition of sides to the polygons resulted in their assuming a more and more circular shape. Archimedes discovered that as the perimeter of the inner polygon became longer, that of the outer polygon became shorter, while the circumference of the circle was caught in between.

In his youth, Archimedes constructed a planetarium which demonstrated the movements of the planets and other heavenly bodies, and contained what some speculate was a closed star globe of the constellations. This device was remarkable for representing in a single mechanism the different paths and velocities of the various celestial spheres which were then thought to contain the planets and stars. His

treatise *On Spheremaking* describes the art of constructing mechanical astronomical devices.

The known works of Archimedes include *Equilibrium of Planes; Quadrature of the Parabola; On the Sphere and The Cylinder; Circle Measurement; On the Spirals; Conoids and Spheroids; The Sand-Reckoner;* two books on *Floating Bodies; Choices; On Mechanical Theorems; Method; The Cattle-Problem*; and the fragmentary *Stomachion*. ∎

Further Reading:

L. Sprague de Camp, *The Ancient Engineers*. London, 1963.
Dictionary of Scientific Biography, s.v. "Archimedes."
James Kip Finch, *The Story of Engineering*. Garden City, New York, 1960.
T. L. Heath, *The Works of Archimedes*. New York, 1958.

KTESIBIOS (CTESIBIUS)
fl. 270 B.C., Alexandria, Egypt
Greek Mechanical Engineer

Life and Times:

Although his accomplishments were to some extent overshadowed by those of Archimedes [q.v.], Ktesibios has nevertheless been called the "king of classical engineers." The son of a barber, he is thought to have served the Ptolemaic dynasty as a paid retainer. The one book that Ktesibios wrote has been lost, and little else is known of his personal life. It has been noted, however, that despite the prevailing disdain for mechanical pursuits, he approached his work with greater seriousness than many of his colleagues.

Outstanding Engineering Achievements:

Ktesibios is credited with beginning the study of pneumatics, which deals with devices operated by compressed air. One of his early experiments, conducted in his father's barber shop, consisted of a mirror connected via two pulleys and a cord to a lead ball fitted into a hollow tube. The ball could be used to adjust the position of the mirror; when descending it forced air from the tube, producing a musical tone. From this device, viewed as the first in history to

make use of the piston and cylinder, came
Ktesibios' notion of pneumatic machinery.

The first practical application of this invention
was a two-cylinder water pump designed by
Ktesibios. The device consisted of two bronze
cylinders fitted with pistons, which were attached to a hand-operated beam in such a way
that one piston rose while the other fell. The
vacuum created by the rising piston forced water
into the cylinder, where it entered a discharge
pipe. This mechanism was used as late as the
nineteenth century, when it was applied to the
design of fire engines.

Ktesibios put his pump to a different use when
he designed the so-called hydraulic pipe, or
water, organ. This consisted mainly of a two-
cylinder pump that forced water into a series of
tubes, separated by valves from air pipes of
varying lengths. A keyboard regulated the flow
of water by controlling the opening and closing
of the valves, producing musical tones as water
forced air from the pipes.

Ktesibios' experience in pneumatics also interested him in hydraulic devices, operated by
changes in fluid pressure. One of his famous
inventions in this area was his improvement of
an ancient Egyptian water clock called the clepsydra. The earlier version of the clepsydra functioned irregularly due to clogging from dirt and
narrowing of the orifices; the rate of flow also
decreased as water drained from the vessel,
creating undesired variations in water pressure.
Ktesibios solved this problem by constructing his
improved version from gold or precious stones,
materials that would neither rust nor become
layered with dirt and could easily be cleaned
without wearing away in the process. In order to
ensure a constant flow of water, Ktesibios re-

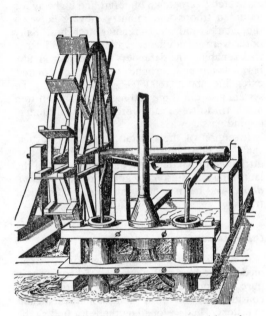

*Two-cylinder water-pump by Ktesibios. Powered by a
waterwheel, one piston was raised while the other
lowered, providing a more constant flow.*

placed the traditional single vessel with a three-
vessel system, designed to allow a certain
amount of water to pass through in a given time.
The second vessel was provided with an overflow
duct that maintained a steady level of water in
the chamber. The passage of time could be read
by means of a pointer, moved by a rising piece of
cork borne up on the water in the third vessel.

Ktesibios later devised a more efficient time
piece, called the parastatic clock. This too made
use of a pointer rising from the middle of a drum
at a constant rate, propelled by water to mark
hours in a series of lines drawn on a vertical
cylinder. The flow of water could be controlled,
either by an adjustable, cone-shaped valve or by
changes in the mounting of the cylinder itself. In
this way, the mechanism could allow for seasonal
variations in the length of the day.

Ktesibios also invented the bent siphon to
draw off liquids by means of atmospheric pressure, as well as several kinds of war machines.
Among the latter were two catapults, one operated by compressed air. The catapults of
Ktesibios apparently never saw military action.
Many historians atrribute this to the inadequacy
of metal-working techniques in his time, which
could not provide materials strong enough to
withstand the stresses caused by Ktesibios' machines. ■

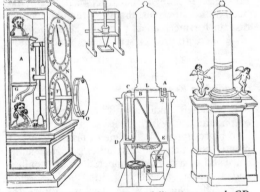

*Clepsydra of Ktesibios. Water falling into vessel, CD,
raises a float carrying a figure that points to the hours;
each day, the filled vessel siphons onto the wheel
below, geared to turn the pillar on its axis once every
366 days.*

Further Reading:

L. Sprague de Camp, *The Ancient Engineers.* London, 1963.

A. G. Drachman, *Ktesibios, Philon, and Heron.* Copenhagen, 1948.

Dictionary of Scientific Biography, s.v. "Ktesibios."

SOSTRATOS (or SOSTRATUS)
fl. 260 B.C.
Greek Architect

Life and Times:

Some sources maintain that Sostratos was the son of Deinokrates [q.v.], court architect of Alexander the Great. He lived in Egypt during the reign of Ptolemy Philadelphos, one of Alexander's successors. Sostratos is best known for designing one of the Seven Wonders of the Ancient World, a lighthouse called the Pharos of Alexandria.

Outstanding Engineering Achievement:

At the northeastern tip of the island of Pharos, near Alexandria, Sostratos built what

Terracotta incense burner in the shape of the Pharos Lighthouse by Sostratos, and contemporary with it.

the ancients called the father of lighthouses. It remains unclear as to whether the island or the lighthouse first bore the name Pharos. A stone engraving attributes the work to Sostratos.

Estimated at 380 to 600 feet (115 to 180 meters) high, the lighthouse was constructed of white marble in the Babylonian style of ascending stories decreasing in size. The upper towers were circular, the lower ones square and adorned with broad balconies. To ensure stability, the marble blocks were cemented with molten lead. The foundation was built of glass, the most water-resistant material available to Sostratos.

The lighthouse originally contained 300 rooms and housed a garrison. Attendants at the summit kept a coal fire burning constantly. To supply the fuel, Sostratos built an inclined ramp broad enough for pack animals across the bottom half of the structure; the coal was then hoisted to the top by windlass. To concentrate the light of the fire, Sostratos placed at the top a large mirror made of glass or polished stone. The result was to make the light visible for about 35 miles (56 km).

Sostratos' creation survived the ravages of nature, but not of man. During the ninth century A.D., after Egypt had fallen into Moslem hands, the lighthouse was partly destroyed by Byzantine raiders. It was at this time that the famous mirror fell, never to be replaced. The lower section served for a time as a mosque, but was abandoned at the end of the tenth century when Cairo replaced Alexandria as capital of Egypt. The remaining ruins of the lighthouse fell into the sea in the fourteenth century during an earthquake. Some say that the foundations can still be seen on a clear day in the waters near the modern Fort Kait Bay. ■

Further Reading:

L. Sprague de Camp, *The Ancient Engineers.* London, 1963.

KLEON (CLEON)
fl. 258–252 B.C.
Greek Hydraulic Engineer

Life and Times:

After Alexander the Great died, his general Ptolemy took control of the Egyptian portion of the empire. Although the rulers were now Greek, the great mass of people spoke their own language and lived according to their native customs. Ptolemy and his son, Ptolemy II, began the ambitious task of hellenizing Egypt in order to make their rule more secure. As part of this policy, Ptolemy II ordered a vast land reclamation project in the Fayum, an area west of the Nile where retired Greek mercenaries could be granted farms. Here Pharaohs of the Twelfth Dynasty had also built dams and dug canals nearly two millenia before. And although Kleon, the project's engineer, was Greek, he used time-tested Egyptian construction techniques.

The details of Kleon's early life and training are unknown. But chance has preserved his personal and business correspondence from the years 258 to 252 B.C. in the sands of the Fayum 60 miles (97 km) north of Cairo. Kleon had been appointed chief engineer of the Fayum project some time before 258. He reported to Apollonios, Ptolemy's finance minister and the second most powerful man in Egypt. The government held Kleon in high esteem, authorizing a canal to be named after him. In addition to supervising government work, Kleon also contracted with private businessmen to carry out projects.

Kleon's career ended abruptly in 252, when Ptolemy II visited the Fayum to inspect the irrigation and drainage works. Perhaps Apollonios suspected Kleon of dishonesty; at any rate, Ptolemy asked to see Kleon's books, and the royal accountants discovered certain irregularities. Ptolemy reproached Kleon with having accepted kickbacks from contractors and demoted him. Kleon's assistant, Theodoros, became chief engineer. Kleon protested in vain and soon retired, supported in disgrace by his wife and two sons.

Outstanding Engineering Achievements:

Kleon's technical abilities were never called into question. To permit boatloads of stone and other supplies to be brought from a tributary of the Nile to the area under reclamation, he supervised construction of the 30-mile (48 km) Canal of Kleon. Practically every year saw the opening up of new areas for agriculture, work which required the digging of canals and the hauling of dirt. Since Kleon's regular staff was fully occupied with the upkeep of existing canals and dams, new work had to be contracted out. For large projects, such as moving 300,000 cubic

meters (400,000 cubic yards) of earth, as many as eight contractors were required.

Kleon's largest private assignment was for Apollonios, who wished to enlarge his own Fayum estate. Kleon supervised the drainage of 6,000 acres (2,500 hectares) of marshland, a task requiring the construction of 50 miles (80 km) of ditches and dykes. A map of this project, giving dimensions and volumes to be removed, is the earliest surviving engineering plan.

Much of the work was done in the traditional manner. Egyptian peasants were required to do seven to ten days' worth of labor a year, though under the Ptolemies this could be commuted to cash payments. Working conditions were not ideal; as in Pharaonic times, some of Kleon's laborers went on strike. Techniques, too, were age old. The banks of the canals were lined with brush to reduce erosion. The mattresses of brush or reeds were kept in place by networks of ropes, and these in turn were tied to pegs sunk into the banks. But the use of iron tools, unknown to the ancient Egyptians, did permit certain improvements. Since stone could be cut more easily, some of Kleon's canal banks and all of his dams were reinforced with masonry. ∎

Further Reading:

A. Bouché-Leclercq, "L'Ingénieur Cleon." *Revue des Etudes Grecques.* Vol. XXI (1908).

R. J. Forbes, *Studies in Ancient Technology,* Vol. II. Leiden, 1955–64.

W.W. Tarn, *Hellenistic Civilization.* London, 1966.

PHILON (PHILO)
fl. 250–230 B.C., Byzantium
Greek Military Engineer and Philosopher
Life and Times:

What little is known of Philon's life comes from occasional references to him in ancient sources. Marcus Vitruvius Pollio [q.v.] includes him in a list of inventors along with Archimedes [q.v.] and Ktesibios [q.v.]. Eutocius notes Philon's work on the duplication of the cube. Whatever else is known of him has been inferred from the remaining fragments of his nine-volume work on mechanics. It is only through his reference to the bronze-spring catapult invented by Ktesibios that any dates regarding Philon's career have been determined. The fact that he could travel to Rhodes and Alexandria to study catapults has prompted some historians to suggest Philon was either a wealthy man or the recipient of handsome patronage. Some sources consider him to have been less an engineer than an artisan.

Outstanding Engineering Achievements:

Philon is best remembered for having written the first comprehensive treatment of applied mechanics and military engineering. His text was written in the common Greek vernacular of that time to insure its accessibility to architects, contractors and generals. Scholars surmise that the work consisted of nine books, including volumes on the lever, the construction of seaports, catapults, pneumatics, fortresses and the besieging and defense of towns. Four complete volumes and part of another remain to us.

Philon's volume on catapults sets down rules for building a catapult based on the length or weight of the projectiles used. Philon seems to have learned this method of construction during his travels to Alexandria and Rhodes. He also described ways to improve catapults through the tightening of sinews with wedges. Modern scholars find Philon especially useful for describing catapults designed by other engineers, including two inventions of Ktesibios and an automatic model attributed to Dionysios of Alexandria [q.v.].

The crossbow, the euthytonon, ascribed to Philon; plan (top) and elevation.

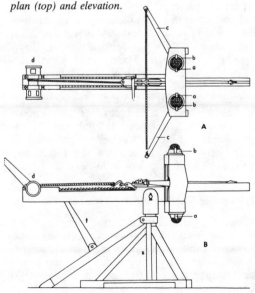

The book on pneumatics contains a number of chapters describing the experiments of the founder of that science, Ktesibios [q.v.]. Fragmentary portions of the text also describe pneumatic toys, such as trick jars and inexhaustible bowls. What survives of the two volumes on fortresses and siege warfare describes defense techniques such as the construction of walls and towers, the digging of moats, erection of palisades and the placement of catapults. Philon also wrote fifty-two short chapters on how to provision a town against siege. The proper construction of storerooms is described, along with what food to have on hand, storage methods, rationing arrangements and how to poison food supplies at the point of enemy conquest. Other sections of the book deal with communications, discussing techniques of cryptography and an optical telegraph for transmitting messages to allies. Philon did not neglect the psychological side of war in his treatment of bribery and starvation as means of reducing a town.

Philon is said to have made a crossbow which automatically brought arrows into firing position, based on the design of Dionysios of Alexandria. He was also the first to observe the contraction of air in a globe holding a lit candle over water. ∎

Further Reading:

Dictionary of Scientific Biography, s.v. "Philon."

A. G. Drachmann, *Ktesibios, Philon, and Heron*. Copenhagen, 1948.

John G. Landels, *Engineering in the Ancient World*. Berkeley, 1978.

E. W. Marsden, *Greek and Roman Artillery*. Oxford, 1969.

HERMODOROS OF SALAMIS
fl. 148 B.C.–132 B.C.
Greco-Roman Architect

Life and Times:

After its final victory over Carthage in the western Mediterranean, Rome turned its attention east, where the smaller states that had replaced Alexander's empire were constantly battling one another. During the second century B.C. Rome intervened repeatedly in Greek affairs, and the growing Roman interest in Greek culture was stimulated by the booty Roman generals brought back after each campaign. The unruly kingdom of Macedonia proved a rich source of art objects. Defeated and looted by Roman generals in 194 B.C. and 168 B.C., it rebelled unsuccessfully in 149 B.C. The Roman victor in that war, Quintus Caecilius Metellus, returned to Rome with boatloads of statues and hundreds of captives. Among them was the architect Hermodoros.

Hermodoros came from Salamis, once the principal city of Cyprus but by the second century B.C. a place of secondary importance. No doubt the search for work had drawn Hermodoros to Macedonia. Captured during Metellus' rapid campaign, Hermodoros and a number of other artists soon found themselves working in Rome. It is not known whether Hermodoros was enslaved or remained free. In any case, he became one of Rome's most distinguished builders and did much to popularize Greek architecture.

Outstanding Engineering Achievement:

Soon after Metellus' triumphal return to Rome, he commissioned Hermodoros to build a temple to Jupiter Stator. Hermodoros constructed the building in the Greek style, surrounding the body of the temple with a row of columns that supported the roof. Even more remarkable to Romans than the design was the material employed: Hermodoros' temple was the first in Rome to be built entirely of marble. Hermodoros may also have designed the temple to Juno that stood alongside. Both temples were enclosed by a marble portico constructed by a family of Macedonian sculptors in Metellus' employ. In the portico Metellus displayed the many statues he had seized in Greece. Little now remains of the temples beyond their foundations.

Hermodoros carried out two other commissions in Rome. In 132 B.C. he built a temple of Mars in the Flaminian Circus for Decimus Junius Brutus, conqueror of the Callaici in Spain. He also built drydocks in the Campus Martius. Although no trace has been found of either of these works, they are described in contemporary documents. ■

Further Reading:

Fabricius, "Hermodoros," in August Pauly and Georg Wissowa, eds., *Realenzyklopaedie der klassischen Altertumswissenschaft*. Stuttgart, 1894.

Samuel B. Platner, *Topography and Monuments of Ancient Rome*. Boston, 1911.

QUINTUS MARCIUS REX
fl. 145 B.C.
Roman Administrator

Life and Times:

The second century B.C. was a time of rapid growth for Rome as the city extended its rule in the western and eastern Mediterranean. Economic and military expansion also meant physical expansion for the city, as new wealth and residents poured in. In addition to commissioning new public buildings, the Roman Senate found it necessary to undertake the repair and expansion of the city's water supply. This it entrusted in the middle of the century to Quintus Marcius Rex.

Little is known of Marcius' personal life. As praetor he supervised the administration of civil law, issued general legal ordinances and served as assistant to the consuls. It is unlikely that Marcius was a trained builder, and he probably left the details of the waterworks project to subordinates. Nevertheless, his name has remained associated with the first major expansion of Rome's water system since the days of Appius Claudius Crassus [q.v.].

Part of Marcius' project involved restoring and protecting the city's older aqueducts, including Crassus' Aqua Appia. A more significant task, however, was the construction of a new aqueduct named after Marcius, the Aqua Marcia. This was the first high-level aqueduct, a structure for which Roman engineers became famous. Completed in 145 B.C., the Aqua Marcia was the largest aqueduct of its time, known to subsequent generations as "the pride of ancient Rome." Later city aqueducts followed its route fairly closely; indeed two, the Tepula and Julia, were built atop Marcia in tiers.

Outstanding Engineering Achievement:

Since they lacked the means of pumping water over long distances, Roman engineers relied on gravity to move water along a gradual gradient. The Aqua Marcia carried water to Rome across the Campagna from the springs of the Anio River, located in hills southeast of the city. It followed the shortest and highest route across the Campagna, a distance of 58 miles (93 km) (including six miles (9.6 km) on arch supports), and entered Rome 195 feet (59 meters) above the level of the Tiber River. The aqueduct was made of stone. To prevent leakage, the interior of the water course was lined with a mortar called *opus signinum,* a hydraulic cement that hardened under water. ■

Further Reading:

Neal FitzSimons, ed., *Engineering Classics of James Kip Finch.* Kensington, Maryland, 1978.

ATHENAIOS (ATHENAEUS)
fl. ca. 100 B.C.
Greek Writer on Military Engineering

Life and Times:

Warfare in the classical world was not all a matter of Macedonian phalanxes and Roman legions. Long spears and short swords alike were of little use when the enemy chose to remain behind the walls of his city. But the ancients were equal to the occasion, displaying more engineering genius in siegecraft than they often did in the arts of peace. Alexander the Great's capture of Tyre in 332 B.C. and Demetrios the Besieger's attempt on Rhodes in 305–304 B.C. were among the first sieges notable for the use of sophisticated military engines. Centuries later the devices used against these cities were still being described by writers on military engineering, including Athenaios.

Athenaios' place and date of birth are uncertain. The Greek dialect he used points to the kingdom of Pergamon in Asia Minor; he may have been associated with the important library there. Conjectures as to his dates are based on the contents of his treatise, *On Siege Engines (Peri Mechanematon).* He must have lived after Ktesibios (fl. 270), whom Athenaios mentions. The book's dedication to a certain Marcellus suggests some time in the first century B.C., when the Roman presence in the eastern Mediterranean was firmly established. Although other books on siegecraft survive—notably that of Vitruvius, who apparently used some of the same sources as Athenaios—*On Siege Engines* is an important work. It is our only source of some

information on the achievements of such engineers as Diades [q.v.], Ktesibios [q.v.] and Apollonios. The surviving manuscript's illustrations are unique, since they appear to have been faithfully copied from a late classical original. Until some archeologist turns up an ordnance dump, we will have no clearer picture of Greek military engines.

Outstanding Engineering Achievement:

Athenaios describes catapults, towers, tortoises and miscellaneous devices. The catapults were of two kinds, throwing either bolts or rocks. One of the best catapults known to Athenaios launched bolts .6 meters (2 ft) long that weighed 320 grams (11 ounces). It could throw the bolts a distance of 650 meters (2100 feet), some 25% farther than the standard catapults of the time.

Towers had been a standard weapon since Diades conducted the siege of Tyre for Alexander. The smallest in use in Athenaios' time was 8 meters (26 ft) wide at the base, although the upper stories were narrower. This tower rose 28 meters (92 feet) in six stories, a height sufficient to overlook the walls of most cities. The largest tower known to Athenaios was 11 meters (36 ft) wide at the bottom and 55 meters (180 feet; 20 stories) high. He describes the platforms from which the assailants launched missiles into the city, as well as the racks for hanging fresh skins over the woodwork; these offered at least some protection from incendiary devices used by the city's defenders. The difficulty of rolling so large a tower against a city wall can be imagined.

Less cumbersome than towers were the various kinds of tortoises. Tortoises were originally

Tortoise, a Roman version of a tank, attacking a tower; fanciful sketch was published by Valturio in 1460.

small wheeled vehicles equipped with a roof to protect soldiers operating a ram. As the walls and gates of cities became thicker and rams correspondingly heavier, tortoises increased in size. The largest described by Athenaios was 14 meters (45 ft) wide, 18 meters (60 ft) long, and 13 meters (43 ft) tall. Two kinds of rams were concealed beneath all this wooden armor. A thick horizontal beam, suspended from the framework, could be pulled back by the soldiers operating it and released to swing against the wall. A second kind used a metal-tipped beam around which a rope was wrapped to drill a hole in the wall, an adaptation of the ancient hand drill turned by a bow string.

Tortoises were also used to protect soldiers assigned to fill in ditches and level the approach to a city. Over the path thus cleared a tower could be brought against the city walls. With short Corinthian columns supporting their roofs, tortoises must have been beautiful as well as terrible to behold.

Athenaios briefly describes a variety of other military engines: boats equipped with towers and catapults; scaling ladders topped with grappling hooks, which could be swung into position by large cranes; and devices like caltrops. These were spiked balls that were set out five or six rows deep around tortoises or towers as a protective measure. They served to reduce the momentum of large rolling stones dropped from the city walls. ■

Further Reading:

E. W. Marsden, *Greek and Roman Artillery*. Oxford, 1969.

Marcus Vipsanius Agrippa, Rome's first water commissioner and architect of the original Pantheon.

haps best known for defeating Marcus Antonius, Octavius' chief rival for power, in the decisive naval battle of Actium (31 B.C.). He also hunted down the pirate Sextus Pompeius, whose ships were disrupting Roman commerce in the Mediterranean.

With Octavius installed in power, Agrippa became his most important adviser and took responsibility for the preparedness and disposition of the empire's military forces. He served three times as consul, twice as governor of Syria and once as aedile and tribune. Agrippa also devoted himself to extensive public works, serving in 34 B.C. as Rome's first Water Commissioner (Curator Aquarum). It was largely Agrippa's work which gave rise to the saying, "Augustus found Rome in mud and left it in marble."

Agrippa is said to have been a modest man, hard-working with sound technical judgment. In his own interest he scrupulously maintained a subordinate role to Augustus. He eventually married the emperor's daughter, Julia; his two sons, Gaius and Lucius, died in military service.

MARCUS VIPSANIUS AGRIPPA

b. 63 B.C., Rome
d. 12 B.C., Campania, Italy
Roman Engineer and Statesman

Life and Times:

Born into an obscure family, Marcus Vipsanius Agrippa struck up a lifelong friendship with the young Gaius Octavius, later Caesar Augustus, while studying in the Greek city of Apollonia. He helped command the forces of Octavius during the civil wars that followed the assassination of Julius Caesar. Agrippa is per-

Outstanding Engineering Achievements:

Agrippa was the builder of the original Pantheon, or Temple of All the Gods. Constructed in 27 B.C., it is the only ancient building with its dome still intact today. It consisted in its original form of a rectangular portico opening onto a large rotunda. Just how much of the present building is Agrippa's work is difficult to determine, as is the resemblance of the original work to the Pantheon as it looks today. Damaged by fire during the reign of Titus, the Pantheon was repaired by the architect Domitian, damaged by another fire under Trajan and reconstructed again by Hadrian. All of the temple's interior decorations were looted during the Middle Ages and Renaissance. Some scholars view only the portico, which bears the inscription "Marcus Agrippa, son of Lucius, made this in his third consulship," as part of the original structure.

Agrippa was also builder of the renowned aqueduct near Nîmes, the Pont du Gard (18 B.C.). About 155 feet (47 meters) in height, the structure was part of a 24-mile (38 km) system carrying water from a source near Uzès to Nîmes. Three levels, decreasing in width as they increased in height, supported a water conduit about four feet (1.2 meters) wide and five feet (1.5 meters) high. With its massive piers and arches, Agrippa's Pont du Gard is one of the best preserved of all Roman engineering works.

With his military background, Agrippa knew the importance of roads to the integrity of the empire. Augustus thus appointed him to plan and supervise construction of a road system in Gaul and other recently-acquired territories. The network developed by Agrippa not only facilitated the movement of troops but also integrated large areas into the empire, encouraging trade and permitting the imposition of Roman taxes.

Among his other public works, Agrippa is known for the aqueducts Julia, built in 33 B.C., and Virgo, built in 20 B.C. Julia drew water from large cold springs near Salone, about eight miles from Rome. It followed the same line as the city's other aqueducts until half a mile from the present-day Porta Maggiore, where it veered north, entering Rome near the Pincian Hill. Virgo was a low-level aqueduct, and still supplies the ship fountain in the Piazza de Spagna. Agrippa supervised the repair of older aqueducts as well, and further improved the Roman waterworks by constructing 130 water distributing stations, 300 large cisterns and 500 fountains. He is said to have taken a boat ride through Rome's main sewer, the Cloaca Maxima, to direct its renovation.

Agrippa also converted the shallow Lake Lucrinus near present-day Naples into a military training area, draining the lake by joining it with the deeper Lake Avernus, half a mile (0.8 km)

The Pont du Gard near Nîmes, an aqueduct built by Agrippa in 18 B.C. and still standing.

inland in the crater of an extinct volcano. He then joined Avernus with the Bay of Naples and turned it into a storm-proof anchorage. Known as "Portus Julius," the complex was destroyed by an earthquake and volcanic eruption in 1538.

Wealthy from the confiscated property of his political enemies, Agrippa spent his own money as well as the state's on public works. He financed and built the first public bath in Rome, a forerunner of the immense bath halls erected under later emperors. He also built a bridge across the Tiber river, a series of temples and porticos and a hall for counting votes as well as a number of large apartment blocks for the city's populace.

Though not primarily a military engineer, Agrippa developed two new naval weapons while campaigning in the civil wars. One was a collapsible tower for missile-hurling troops, designed to be set up on the deck of a ship while approaching an enemy vessel. The other was a grappling hook shot from a catapult, strong enough to catch another ship and pull it close for boarding. ■

Further Reading:

L. Sprague de Camp, *The Ancient Engineers*. London, 1963.

James Kip Finch, *The Story of Engineering*. Garden City, New York, 1960.

A. P. Guest, *Engineering: Our Debt to Greece and Rome*. London, 1930.

Norman Smith, *Man and Water*. London, 1976.

ANDRONIKOS OF KYRRHOS
fl. 50 B.C., Athens, Greece
Greek Architect and Horological Engineer

Life and Times:

Long after it had lost its political independence, Athens was respected as the cultural center of the Mediterranean world. Successive rulers, whether Macedonian, Greek or Roman, endowed the city with temples, monuments, theaters and other public buildings. Yet one of the best preserved—and most unusual—structures of this period was the gift of an obscure individual. The building is the Tower of the Winds, contemporary with and located near the agora (marketplace) of Julius Caesar, just northwest of the Acropolis. The donor was Andronikos, who came from Kyrrhos in Syria.

Andronikos seems to have been an exceptionally original architect; no prototypes for his tower are known to us. Equally impressive is his skill as a maker of sundials. Unfortunately, little is known of his life.

Outstanding Engineering Achievement:

The Tower of the Winds is octagonal in shape, measuring 9½ feet (2.9 meters) on a side and 25½ feet (7.7 meters) in diameter. The entire structure, including the roof tiles, is made of marble. Two porches with doorways lead into the building; a small cylindrical tower adjoins it on the south side. At the top of each side is a relief representing the wind blowing from that direction. At the summit of the building, 47 feet (14.3 meters) above the ground, stands a bronze statue of Triton, a demi-god of the sea, holding a rod in one hand. The statue, mounted on a pivot, acts as a weathervane, pointing the rod to the carving of the wind then blowing.

On each face of the tower is a sundial. Though the gnomons that cast shadows are now missing, the incised lines representing the hours of the day can still be seen. The lines on the north side were not labeled, since the sun seldom struck there. A ninth sundial was located on the side of the small cylindrical tower. Each of the sundials was accurate to within three or four minutes.

Inside the main tower was a water clock. The clock's storage tank, located in the adjoining cylindrical tower, received its water from a fountain in the nearby Acropolis. Grooves and holes in the floor of the tower have permitted scholars to make a hypothetical reconstruction of the clock's operation.

The Tower of the Winds is the only clock-tower surviving from antiquity. To Andronikos'

The octagonal Tower of the Winds, a weather station in Athens by Andronikos.

remarkable building can be traced the custom of putting weathervanes on top of steeples.

The elegance of the tower's design is matched by that of a multiple sundial, signed by Andronikos, discovered in the sanctuary of Poseidon on the island of Tenos. ■

Further Reading:

A.W. Lawrence, *Greek Architecture.* New York, 1957.

Joseph V. Noble and Derek J. de Solla Price, "The Water Clock in the Tower of the Winds," *American Journal of Archeology,* Vol. LXXII (1968).

MARCUS VITRUVIUS POLLIO
fl. 25 B.C.
Roman Writer on Architecture

Life and Times:

Vitruvius is our main source on the history of engineering in ancient Rome. A native of northern Italy, he considered himself a coordinator of craftsmen in his field. Vitruvius grew up and began his career at the time of Julius Caesar. He wrote his chief work, *De Architectura,* early in the reign of Caesar Augustus, a time of extensive public reconstruction and improvement in Rome. Little is known of his personal life other than what has been inferred from *De Architectura.* Some attempt has been made to identify

Vitruvius with Lucius Vitruvius Mamurra, chief engineer of Julius Caesar. Most sources agree, however, with the third century writer Faventius that his family name was Pollio.

Vitruvius is believed to have been a military engineer for Julius Caesar in Africa, responsible for weapons maintenance, bridge building and transportation. In this capacity he became familiar with surveying and with the construction of catapults and ballistae. It is said that on retirement from his military post Vitruvius became a protegé of the emperor's sister, Octavia. Parts of *De Architectura* dealing with hydraulic engineering may have been drawn from Vitruvius' experience working for Marcus Agrippa [q.v.] in the construction and repair of aqueducts.

Outstanding Engineering Achievement:

Vitruvius achieved fame as author of the engineering classic *De Architectura,* a comprehensive manual on the state of architecture in his time. The work includes discussion of both building and machine construction, civil and military. Acknowledging the ancient Greeks as the primary source and inspiration of his writing, Vitruvius sought constantly to balance the demands of science and art. Historians date the work between 31 and 27 B.C., noting that it was dedicated to Octavius before he assumed the title Augustus at the latter date.

Vitruvius saw his work as "a complete encyclopedia for the architect." Following the practice of his time, he made no systematic distinction between architectural and mechanical engineering. The work consists of ten volumes, falling into three general areas: machine construction, clock making and building. Book I defines the nature of the architect and his field, and discusses town planning. Book II deals with construction methods and materials. Books III and IV describe religious architecture, particularly Tuscan temples and classical Greek designs. Book V deals with civil engineering and public architecture in general, with emphasis on the theatre; analysis of acoustics leads to a discussion of music and the nature of sound in general.

Book VI discusses how to plan a private house, while Book VII deals with interior design questions. Book VIII turns to the topic of transportation and waterworks and Book IX, after a lengthy discourse on optics and astronomy, describes time-measuring devices, including water clocks and sundials. The last of the ten books covers mechanics, particularly in regard to

military engineering and water engines. Vitruvius paid particular attention to waterwheels; the undershot waterwheel has been called "Vitruvian" because of his description of it.

Used widely in antiquity as a textbook on engineering, *De Architectura* fell into obscurity during the Middle Ages. Copies were nevertheless preserved in monasteries. With the revival of interest in classical architecture during the Renaissance, Vitruvius' work was re-discovered. Manuscripts began to circulate among scholars, artists and architects, and a printed version appeared in 1484. The Italian architect Alberti, who wrote his own *Ten Books of Architecture,* cited Vitruvius as his model. Most Renaissance scholars, however, believed that architectural pursuits had declined continuously since the golden age of Greece. Only during this century has the significance of Roman architecture been appreciated, bringing a reevaluation of Vitruvius and his work. ■

Further Reading:

Dictionary of Scientific Biography (Suppl.), s.v. "Vitruvius."

James Kip Finch, *The Story of Engineering.* Garden City, New York, 1960.

A. P. Guest, *Engineering: Our Debt to Greece and Rome.* London, 1930.

John Q. Landels, *Engineering in the Ancient World,* Berkeley, 1978.

John Miller, *Master Builders of Sixty Centuries.* New York, 1938.

PLINY THE ELDER (CAIUS PLINIUS SECUNDUS)
b. 23 A.D. Comum (modern Como), Italy
d. August 24, 79, Stabiae (modern Castellamare), Italy
Roman public servant and scholar

Life and Times:

The classical Greeks placed a high value on general education, but it was the practical Romans who actually compiled the first encyclopedias. Through these works the Roman world learned the results of Greek research in all domains of knowledge. One of the earliest and best works in this genre was the vast *Natural*

History of Caius Plinius Secundus (Pliny the Elder).

Pliny's family was of the equestrian order, Rome's upper middle class. Thus Pliny received a good education, first in his native Comum and then at Rome itself. He began a military career at the age of 23, serving in Germany and making the acquaintance of the future emperor Titus. After his return to Italy in 58, Pliny abandoned public service for some time, perhaps out of distaste for the emperor Nero. However, after Titus' father Vespasian had ascended to the throne, Pliny spent his last ten years serving with distinction as procurator in a number of provinces. He also completed the *Natural History*, which he dedicated to Titus in 77. His last assignment was the command of the important fleet at Misenum, in the Bay of Naples. When Vesuvius erupted, Pliny landed at Stabiae to make observations and rescue survivors; there he was overcome by fumes and died.

Major Engineering Achievement:

The fields covered in the *Natural History* include astronomy, geography, zoology, botany, medicine, mineralogy, and metallurgy, and the techniques, processes, and materials used in a wide range of trades and industries. In describing farm implements, Pliny notes that the Gauls used a reaping machine mounted in front of a cart pushed by an ox. Horizontal blades lopped off the tops of standing stems of grain, which then fell into the cart. (A carving of this machine was discovered in 1958.) Pliny's description of mills and presses used in food processing reveals that, though several kinds of beam presses were still used to squeeze the juice from grapes or olives, screw presses had been introduced for oil seeds. The discussion of timber includes their places of origin, qualities, techniques for seasoning, and best uses, mentioning that the Romans prized furniture veneered with precious woods and other materials. Pliny also covers such topics as rope-making, the manufacture of papyrus and parchment, the tanning of hides, glass-making, and the preparation of fabrics. We learn that mining techniques were primitive, although fire or water was sometimes used to break up rocks. In contrast, the Romans showed some sophistication in their treatment of ores. Gold was refined by amalgamation, a technique unknown to previous civilizations. Pliny details methods for refining copper, roasting and smelting lead-containing ores, making solder, tin-plating, assaying silver, and making gold leaf.

Despite the collapse of the Roman Empire and the near extinction of classical culture, manuscripts of the *Natural History* were preserved in many of the important European monasteries. Pliny's air of authority, as well as his naive blending of the fantastic and the practical, enhanced the book's appeal during the Middle Ages. Though long since discredited as a scientific textbook, the *Natural History* remains our best single source on classical technology.

Further reading:

K. C. Bailey, *The Elder Pliny's Chapters on Chemical Subjects*.

Robert J. Forbes, *Studies in Ancient Technology*. Leiden, Netherlands, 1955–64.

Singer et al., *A History of Technology*, Vol. 2.

SEXTUS JULIUS FRONTINUS
b. 30–35 A.D., Rome
d. 103–104 A.D., Rome
Roman Engineer and Water Commissioner

Life and Times:

Sextus Julius Frontinus is said to have been a member of an obscure branch of the prominent aristocratic family of Julii. His career was marked by many professional achievements. Coming into his first major political office in 70 A.D., he became consul in 73 A.D. He was subsequently appointed Roman governor of Britain and is believed to have been responsible for the founding of a military post at Isca (modern Caerleon). At this time he apparently wrote *Strategemata*, a field officer's manual offering tactical advice drawn from the history of both Rome and ancient Greece.

Frontinus was appointed Water Commissioner by the Emperor Nerva in 97 A.D., and continued in that capacity during Trajan's reign. It is uncertain exactly how long Frontinus held the office for which he has become famous, but he was again honored with the consulship by Trajan in 98 and 100 A.D.

Frontinus' choice of offices puzzles many historians. As a patrician of at least partly noble heritage, he owned property and followed the pattern of the Roman aristocracy by assuming military and political positions. On the other hand, he chose later in life a less prestigious social function than he had fulfilled until then, that of Water Commissioner. He may have been motivated by his conviction that a well-managed water supply was essential to Rome's well-being, as well as by a conviction that the post had been held by "some of the most outstanding men of state."

The preface of his classic work on the Roman aqueducts, *De Aquis,* presents the conflicted self-image of a rebellious aristocrat with a deep sense of duty who, while assuming a lesser position, also refused to involve himself in what he termed the most technical, or common, aspects of his field. Yet he was a thorough and responsible administrator of the Roman waterworks. Upon taking office, he personally inspected the system of aqueducts in Rome and subsequently wrote a detailed treatise on what he discovered, both for his own benefit and for those who would follow him.

Outstanding Engineering Achievements:

When Frontinus assumed the post of Cura Aquarum, or Water Commissioner, he had no technical training to speak of. It is believed that his knowledge of hydraulics came from Greek writers whose works he had previously read.

Frontinus' experience as a military engineer served him well as the head of a staff of seven hundred and a water system spreading over two hundred and fifty miles (400 km), much of it underground. He made a point of periodically inspecting the system in person, in order to keep the waterways well-maintained. The work force which Frontinus commanded was comprised of two units of slaves, some of whom were maintained from public funds and water rates, though the majority were Trajan's personal property. The work force also consisted of overseers, reservoir-keepers, plasterers, stonemakers and other such craftsmen.

Frontinus is famous for his treatise on the state of the Roman aqueducts upon his assuming office. The comprehensive, two-volume report of *De Aquis* delineates the output, capacity and dimensions of each aqueduct, all of which Frontinus had inspected. He measured the volume of water at various points to determine possible leakage and calculated that 17% of the city's water was being used for commercial purposes, 39% for private purposes and 44% for public purposes, including 19 barracks, 95 public buildings, 39 public baths and 591 fountains. He also recorded that water came into houses through lead pipes and that the quality of the water was tested in bronze or copper vessels, either through a sedimentation test or a test measuring the color and taste of cooked vegetables.

In 1429, a lost manuscript of this invaluable source of knowledge on ancient engineering was found in the library of Monte Cassino, and has been used during the restoration and reconstruction of Rome since that time. It remains our most comprehensive source on Roman civil engineering to date.

Also undertaken by Frontinus was the first ancient water-waste survey, prompted by his discovery that public water was being diverted for numerous unauthorized purposes. As Water Commissioner, he uncovered some 10,000 special pipes that had been conveniently taking in overflow from fountains, as well as old ducts illegally drawing water once a new duct had been installed. He found a number of pipes illegally bringing water to shops, irrigated fields and places of entertainment.

Frontinus also initiated a series of repairs among the standing aqueducts in Rome. The doubling of the city's water supply as a result of his work was estimated to have been comparable in value to the discovery of new water sources. ■

Further Reading:

Thomas Ashby, *The Aqueducts of Ancient Rome.* Oxford, 1935.

L. Sprague de Camp, *The Ancient Engineers.* London, 1963.

A. P. Guest, *Engineering: Our Debt to Greece and Rome.* London, 1930.

Norman Smith, *Man and Water.* London, 1976.

———, "Roman Hydraulic Technology," *Scientific American,* May, 1978.

HERON (HERO)
fl. 62 A.D., Alexandria, Egypt
Greek Mechanical Engineer, Inventor and Mathematician

Life and Times:

Little is known of Heron's life. The one secure date is that of an eclipse which he mentioned and which is known to have occurred in 62 A.D. One of our best sources on ancient technology, Heron lived in the waning days of Greek culture, but earned a place among the great engineers as both an ingenious inventor and a mathematician. Some historians maintain that he was also a physician.

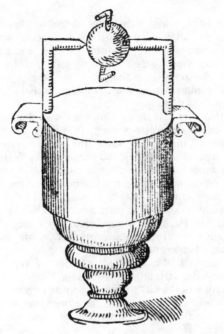

Heron's aeolipyle, a hollow sphere which would be set spinning as it released jets of steam.

Heron has been referred to as "the machine man." He is believed to have been well-educated, and particularly well-read in the works of such great engineers as Ktesibios and prominent mathematicians of his time. Unlike Ktesibios, who enjoyed the patronage of the Ptolemaic dynasty in Egypt, Heron worked in Alexandria after the Roman conquest. It was a time of great demand for improvements in military machines and engines, and compressed air had begun to be used as a means of power, further establishing the study of pneumatics begun by Ktesibios.

Like Marcus Vitruvius Pollio [q.v.], Heron both experimented and described the scientific work that took place in his time. His work has played a great part in our understanding of ancient scientific and technological innovations.

Some historians maintain that Heron reflected a decline in Greek science, and that his practical approach was the work of a technician rather than of a sophisticated theoretician. Others point out, however, that his period's rediscovery of Babylonian mathematics, which was incorporated into Greek science, produced theories and innovations which cannot be discounted. Recent historians view Heron as a cultured man and a vital link between the mathematics of his era and what was eventually passed down to Europe during the Renaissance. His writings reflect his preference for the practical application of science, and he is said to have viewed weapons as a higher form of knowledge than any quiet philosophic pursuit. As might be expected, Heron was an experienced military engineer.

Outstanding Engineering Achievements:

Heron was famous as the inventor of highly innovative instruments and machines. His experiments with levelling led to his invention of the first theodolite, a portable surveying instrument, and the dioptra, an instrument for levelling and alignment. The dioptra, which borrowed a technique of refined screw-cutting, was made of a hollow brass cylinder approximately three feet (.9 meter) in height, which rested on three projecting points from the base. A column, made vertical by means of a plumb line, was connected to a horizontal plate supporting a spindle. Another cylinder approximately a foot (30 cm) in diameter turned about the spindle. Attached to the second cylinder was a toothed wheel by means of which the cylinder could either rotate in azimuth or be held in place with a tangent screw. This second cylinder, which was held on a straight-edged axis approximately six feet (1.8 meters) in length, could be moved in height by a vertical plate attached to the axis on which the cylinder stood. A water-

Fire engine operated by rocking the beam between the two cylinders; derived by Heron from Ktesibios.

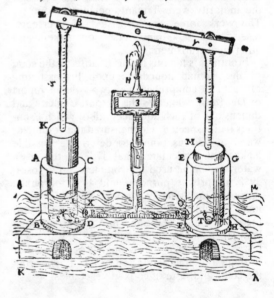

level was provided for the axis, which at each end held a plate serving as a sight. The instrument could be adjusted to the correct alignment by worm-gears.

This primitive forerunner of modern surveyors' transit instruments yielded inaccurate centering figures due to its absence of a means of adjustment. No attempt seems to have been made to divide the horizontal and vertical circles into degrees allowing for precise measurements. Right angles were noted in azimuth, and all other angles were determined by either measuring the chords or by off-sets. Heron wrote that his work was useful "for geographical or surveying purposes, and for the determination of the relative positions of islands and seas and generally for the estimation of distances between inaccessible points."

Perhaps the most famous of Heron's inventions was the aeolipyle. Known as the first reaction steam engine, this device functioned by means of escaping jets of steam, which caused it to rotate. The invention consisted of a hollow metal sphere, pivoting around a vertical axis. Two tubes bent at right angles were attached at opposite ends to the sphere. Water would then be boiled in the sphere, and steam would rush out through the tubes, to turn the ball in reaction. This was one of the first demonstrations of what we call today the law of action and reaction, not explicitly stated until Newton. The aeolipyle is the basis for the rotating lawn sprinklers commonly seen in suburban homes, in which jets of water, as opposed to steam, provide power. In Heron's time, however, the device was only a curiosity, used by priests and magicians to fool the gullible. Similar devices invented by Heron were used in opening temple doors or moving statues automatically.

A more useful invention was Heron's two-cylinder, hand-operated water pump, used to put out fires as late as the nineteenth century. The device consisted of two pistons whose rods were joined by a beam pivoted at the center. The pistons were inserted into two open-ended cylinders, each with an opening in its side. These openings were joined by a tube, which in turn was joined to a second tube ending in a rotating nozzle. When the cylinders were inserted into water, each piston alternately drew in and expelled water from its cylinder. The pistons were operated reciprocally by working the beam that joined them. This motion sent a stream of water, constantly reversing in direction, through the tube joining the two cylinders; from here it was forced into the second tube and out the nozzle. Heon derived this fire engine from Ktesibios.

Heron also invented the hodometer, or road measurer, an instrument for determining the distance travelled by a wheeled vehicle. His original device used gears which converted each turn of the wheel into rotations on a pointer. The hodometer is the ancestor to our modern taximeter and pedometer.

Along with Vitruvius, Heron is our best source for understanding ancient technology. His writings survey many fields and provide a lucid summary of the period's scientific knowledge. The most widely known of his books are *Pneumatica, On the Dioptra, Mechanica, Metrica* and *Stereometrica*.

Pneumatica, meaning compressed air, or, more accurately, pressure-mechanisms, is largely derived from the previous works of Ktesibios of Alexandria [q.v.] and Philon of Byzantium [q.v.]. Consisting of two books, *Pneumatica* opens with the discussion of theories on the properties of air, problems in a continuous vacuum and what liquids do when acted upon by gravity. Heron successfully drew on two distinct schools of learning—represented by Aristotle and Archimedes—to discuss his ideas here. In the first part of the work he describes without mathematical qualification, using only Aristotelian empirical arguments to explain his theories. The second part of the discussion unfolds more in the Archimedean vein of idea demonstration, deducing from unproved assumptions on a strictly quantitative basis. Heron discusses seventy-five devices of his own invention, including a trick wine dispenser with hidden air pockets from which wine, water or a mixture of both could be poured; an organ powered by air pressure; a fountain operated by compressed air; and an engine propelled by a jet of water. He also describes devices used in connection with religious rituals.

On the Dioptra is both a treatise on the surveying instrument invented by Heron and a practical engineering manual on surveying and general field work. The art of levelling is explained, as well as how to determine distances on difficult terrain. Heron discusses a number of methods for ascertaining the distance between two points invisible to each other, and how by means of a primitive triangulation to measure range and spot adequate starting points for a tunnel from opposite sides of a hill. *On the Dioptra* also contains information on positioning the vertical air shafts which are required in such subterranean tunnels, and discusses astronomical measurements that can be used to determine distances over large areas or over bodies of water.

The original text of *Mechanica,* perhaps the most famous of Heron's writings, has survived only in fragments. An Arabic edition, retranslated into Greek in the ninth century A.D., provides us with most of our knowledge of the work. Although a less coherent work than the original must have been, the translated edition of *Mechanica* contains drawings which represented some of the earliest attempts at mechanical draughtsmanship, depicting gears, levers and pulleys in two dimensions. *Mechanica* consists of three books; the first discusses theories of mechanical engineering, the second describes a number of mechanical devices including the windlass, lever, pulley, wedge and screw, and the third provides information on their practical application. As a manual of practical mechanics in antiquity, this is an unparalleled source of information for historians of technology.

Also composed of three books, *Metrica* is a geometrical treatise on measurement. Rediscovered by modern scholars only in 1896, it reveals the extent of Heron's mathematical knowledge. His aim in *Metrica* is to provide a survey of the mathematics of his time, seen from the standpoint of practical measurement as opposed to the classical Greek tradition of rigorous, abstract geometric theory. The first book of the work discusses plane figures and the surfaces of common solids, the second deals with solid figures, and the last book explains methods of dividing plane and spherical areas into segments bearing fixed ratios to each other. *Metrica* contains the famous "Heronic formula" for determining the areas of triangles, quadrilaterals and regular polygons. Measurement of circles, ellipses, parabolas, sphere segments and many other figures is also discussed.

Essentially an extension of *Metrica, Stereometrica* is a work on solid geometry. Beginning with pure theory on the measurement of spheres, cones and pyramids, the book proceeds to a discussion of practical applications. Among other useful points, Heron shows how to calculate a given theater's seating capacity from the lowest to highest row, the number of jars which could be stacked in the hold of a ship, and how many tiles are needed to roof a particular house.

Heron's other books include *Belopoeica,* a treatise on catapult construction; *Cheiroballistra,* on hand projectile weapons; *Geodaesia* and *Mensurae,* lost works on water clocks and time measurements; a commentary on Euclid's *Elements;* and the *Definitions,* a dictionary of geometric terms which provide valuable information on theories of geometry taught in the schools of antiquity. *Catoptrics* is Heron's treatise on the reflection of light from mirrors, in which he states that the angle of incidence and the angle of reflection are equal. *Automatopoietike* is an account of the numerous mechanisms used by Heron in construction in miniature theaters.

Heron was also famous for inventing ingenious mechanical toys which operated on water, heated air or steam. Some of his puppet theaters were powered by weights in the form of pistons dropping into cylinders. In his two miniature theaters, tables and statues moved seemingly by themselves, and doors opened and closed automatically. Heron also developed the first water atomizer, a flexible container that could be used to squeeze water out of a nozzle. He is said to have proposed a correct geometrical theory for the construction and planning of tunnels and to have built a windmill adapted as the source of power for an organ. ∎

Further Reading:

A. G. Drachmann, *Ktesibios, Philon, and Heron.* Copenhagen, 1948.

———, *The Mechanical Technology of Greek and Roman Antiquity.* Madison, 1963.

A. P. Guest, *Engineering: Our Debt to Greece and Rome.* London, 1930.

John G. Landels, *Engineering in the Ancient World.* Berkeley, 1978.

APOLLODORUS
fl. 98-117 A.D.
Roman Architect and Engineer

Life and Times:

During the early years of the second century A.D., the Roman Emperor Trajan fought two campaigns against the Dacians, a people of Thracian stock living in the area of present-day Rumania. The war was successful but hard-fought, the Romans being handicapped by an exposed line of commuinication along the Danube River. To help his troops overcome the geographical obstacles they faced, Trajan took with him the Syrian engineer Apollodorus.

Apparently the emperor's favorite architect-engineer, Apollodorus was involved in a number of official projects, including a new forum and gymnasium in Rome. He is best known, however, for building a large bridge across the Danube at the start of the second Dacian campaign. Considering the size and speed of the river and the time constraints which Apollodorus

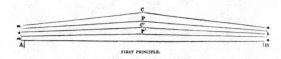

FIRST PRINCIPLE.

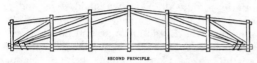

SECOND PRINCIPLE.

Timber-truss and stone-pier bridge across the Danube built by Apollodorus for the emperor Trajan.

faced, the bridge was one of the most impressive feats of ancient military engineering. Constructed of wood and stone in less than two years, it stood at present-day Turnu Severin (Drobetae) below a section of the Danube valley known as the Iron Gates. Unfortunately, the bridge did not long survive Trajan's reign. It was partly dismantled by the succeeding emperor, Hadrian, who planned—temporarily—to abandon the Dacian territory. Though the bridge was restored by the Emperor Constantine in 328 A.D., today only a few of the piers remain.

Apollodorus took advantage of his experience in the Dacian campaign to build a more enduring monument upon his return to Rome. This was Trajan's column, a carved stone pillar on which important incidents of the campaigns were depicted in an ascending spiral. Most of the column survives, providing important insights into Roman military equipment and organization.

Outstanding Engineering Achievement:

Apollodorus' bridge across the Danube consisted of a wooden deck and 20 wooden arches resting on stone piers. The bridge was about 3,400 feet (1036 meters) long and rose 150 feet (46 meters) over the river. Though only the deck was removed by Hadrian, the wooden arches apparently decayed rapidly once maintenance stopped. ■

Further Reading:

L. Sprague de Camp, *The Ancient Engineers.* London, 1963.

Singer et al., *A History of Technology,* Vol. II.

Hans Straub, *A History of Civil Engineering.* London, 1952.

GAIUS JULIUS LACER
fl. 100 A.D.
Roman Architect

Life and Times:

The early second century A.D. was a time of internal peace and economic prosperity in the Roman empire. As trade expanded, the famous Roman road system was extended. Growing cities also found it necessary to build new public facilities. One product of these trends was the Roman bridge over the Tagus River at Alcantara in northern Spain. Though conventionally attributed to the Emperor Trajan, the bridge was actually built by the architect Gaius Julius Lacer.

Lacer is known to us only through his association with the bridge, which contains at one end a small chapel dedicated to him. Built in a rich tin- and gold-mining area, the bridge was jointly financed by 12 nearby towns. It is one of the best-preserved of Roman engineering works, still in use with its original pavement intact.

Outstanding Engineering Achievement:

Built of large, unmortared blocks, the bridge at Alcantara is often viewed as an engineering feat equal to the Colosseum and the Pont du Gard. It is some 600 feet (183 meters) long and 150 feet (46 meters) above the river level. Six unequal semi-circular arches support the bridge, the central two each spanning 100 feet (30 meters). ■

Further Reading:

M. Cary and H.H. Scullard, *A History of Rome.* New York, 1975.

Singer et al., *A History of Technology,* Vol. II.

ANTHEMIOS OF TRALLES
fl. 530 A.D., Constantinople
ISIDOROS OF MILETOS
fl. 530 A.D., Constantinople
Greek Architects and Mathematicians

Life and Times:

During the reign of the Emperor Justinian (527–565 A.D.), the Eastern Roman Empire

Hagia Sophia, Santa Sophia, or the Church of the Holy Wisdom, designed by Anthemios and Isidoros.

drawing of isosceles triangles which found their way into Book 15 of Euclid's *Elements*.

Yet whatever their other accomplishments, design and construction of the Hagia Sophia was by far both men's greatest task. The project stretched the finances of the entire empire; contemporary accounts, though probably exaggerated, put its cost at 320,000 pounds (144,000 kg.) of gold. Complete with gold sheeting on the interior of the dome, ivory-inlaid steps and a silver-lined pulpit, the Hagia Sophia came to symbolize the Byzantine state and people. Emperors were crowned there, and the beleaguered inhabitants of Constantinople held a solemn Mass in the church on the eve of the city's capture by the Turks. The fate of the church and city were indeed closely intertwined. Crusaders from Western Europe, who sacked Constantinople in 1203, vandalized the Hagia Sophia. Though partially restored, the structure never regained its former magnificence. Following the Turkish conquest of 1451, the Hagia Sophia became a mosque, which it remains today.

reached its peak in size and power. German tribes in North Africa, Italy and parts of Spain were subdued, and Roman naval supremacy in the Mediterranean was restored. Administrative and legal reform resulted in the famous Code of Justinian, which standardized Roman law and influenced European government for the next thousand years. To demonstrate his prestige and authority, Justinian undertook an extensive building program in his capital city of Constantinople. The greatest ornament of this program—numbered ever since among the world's most famous architectural monuments—was the Hagia Sophia, or Church of the Holy Wisdom. The enormous place of worship, built between 532 and 537, was the work of Anthemios of Tralles and Isidoros of Miletos.

Though little is known of the backgrounds of Anthemios and Isidoros, they were evidently architects of some prominence in Constantinople. Together they established a mathematical academy and participated in the construction of public works on the strategic Persian frontier. Anthemios experimented with engines powered by steam and hot air, evidently on the model of Heron's [q.v.] machines; to him is attributed the treatise *On Remarkable Mechanical Devices*, a collection of curiosities for the amusement of imperial courtiers. Isidoros, more interested in pure mathematics, formulated rules for the

Outstanding Engineering Achievement:

The Hagia Sophia is most famous architecturally for combining the long, cruciform interior of the Christian basilica with the square exterior favored by Greek churches. The dome, a common feature of Roman architecture, required modification in order to rest securely on the square base. Anthemios and Isidoros sought to achieve stability by designing the dome's framework with pendentives, arched triangular structures that extended from each of the building's corners to the center of the dome. This was not entirely successful; the dome collapsed twice in earthquakes, the first 21 years after its construction. Rebuilt in 989 with heavier material, however, the dome has withstood all subsequent natural disasters. Its diameter of 107 feet (32.6 meters) made it, for centuries, the largest roof span in the world. ■

Further Reading:

Dictionary of Scientific Biography, ss. vv. "Anthemios" and "Isidoros."

Steven Runciman, *Byzantine Civilization*. London, 1933.

Medieval Engineering: Islam and Europe

by Donald Hill

No essay could do justice to the history of engineering in the Middle Ages, from A.D. 750 to 1400, in the whole of the Old World. Some selection is necessary, and it seems most sensible to deal mainly with western Europe and southwest Asia, namely Latin Christendom and Islam. In the first place, this juxtaposition will permit a discussion of the Islamic achievement in mechanical engineering, a subject that is relatively little known, even to specialists. Secondly, both Europe and Islam were heirs to the Greek and Roman traditions of engineering, traditions which they continued and developed from their own resources and in their own ways, with enrichments from other areas such as India and East Asia. The relationships between the communities were not always hostile, and exchanges of ideas between them occurred at many places and at many times. Likely areas for such transmissions were Sicily, the Iberian peninsula during the long centuries of the Reconquista and Syria at the time of the Crusades. Commerce also played a part in the dissemination of information. Scandinavia and Islam were in contact with each other through Byzantium, and in the tenth century there were close commercial ties between Fatimid Egypt and the south Italian community of Amalfi.

For many branches of knowledge we can see fairly clearly how information passed from one area to another. In ninth-century Baghdad, many Greek and Indian works on science, mathematics, astronomy and medicine were translated into Arabic. With these works as a foundation, Islamic scholars composed many original works, so that by the end of the ninth century an integrated, recognizably Islamic science had come into being. Similar activity took place during the twelfth and early thirteenth centuries in Toledo, where many Arabic man-

uscripts—original works and translations—were rendered into Latin. These works exerted a powerful influence on European scientific thought in the ensuing centuries.

We know of no similar written transmissions for engineering techniques, and we must infer how ideas passed between the two communities. Even within the confines of Islam and Europe, information on the development of engineering has to be gathered from scattered sources: some

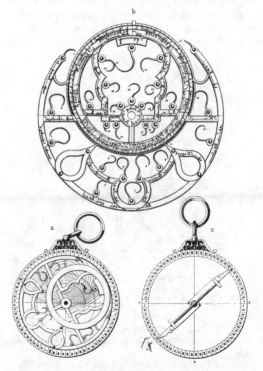

Arabic astrolabe of 1208, a device for taking sightings and calculating the location of the stars.

archaeological finds; pictures of machines that happen to appear in larger illustrations; passing references in the works of historians, geographers, and travellers; and a few very valuable treatises on machines. Among the latter are the *Book of Ingenious Devices* by the Banu Musa [q.v.] (three brothers, sons of Musa ibn Shakir), written in Baghdad about 850; a treatise on water clocks by a certain al-Muradi, written in Andalusia in the eleventh century; a book on the construction of a monumental water clock in Damascus, written by Ridwan in 1203; and the masterly book on machines, *The Book of Knowledge of Ingenious Mechanical Devices*, completed by al-Jazari [q.v.] in Mesopotamia in 1206. The eighth section of al-Khazini's [q.v.] great work on physics, *The Book of the Balance of Wisdom,* is devoted to a description of steel-yard clepsydras; this treatise was written in Khurasan in 1121.

European developments are described in *De diversis artibus* by the monk Theophilus [q.v.], written in 1122–23, the notebook of Villard de Honnecourt [q.v.] written about 1235, the *Texaurus* of Guido da Vigevano [q.v.] written in 1335, and a book composed by an anonymous engineer during the Hussite wars of the fourteenth century. From the fifteenth century onwards, European works on engineering become more and more numerous. It is worth mentioning, however, that a work on machines by the

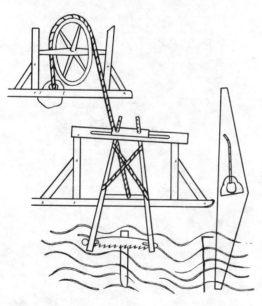

Thirteenth-century machine for sawing underwater piles, with a weight to hold the saw at a set height (from Villard de Honnecourt).

Turkish horologist Taqi al-Din [q.v.], including descriptions of a steam-driven spit and six cylinder 'Monobloc' pump powered by a water-wheel, antedates the justly famous books of Georgius Agricola [q.v.] and Agostino Ramelli [q.v.]. Taqi al-Din's book appeared in 1552, Agricola's in 1556 and Ramelli's in 1588.

Although European and Islamic engineering both had their roots in the classical world and show many points of similarity, there are significant differences in the application of techniques by the two cultures. These differences were caused by a complex mixture of historical, social and economic factors, and we can do no more here than refer briefly to some possible reasons for the divergencies between Europe and Islam.

The Arab conquests began in 634, and in a short time Syria, Egypt and Iraq had been subjugated. The conquests proceeded, rather more slowly, through North Africa into Spain, and eastwards into Iran and Central Asia. At its greatest extent, about 750, the Arab Empire stretched from the Pyrenees to the Oxus. The term "Arab" rather than "Muslim" is used for this period because the Empire was ruled by Arab Caliphs and an Arab aristocracy. From 660 until 750 the Umayyad dynasty ruled from Damascus; they were overthrown by the Abbasids, who ruled from Baghdad until about 900, although a branch of the Umayyads assumed power in Spain, which became one of the most prosperous and cultured provinces of Islam. Towards the end of the ninth century a progressive disintegration of the Empire began as local dynasties set themselves up in Iran, Central Asia and in Iraq itself. The Caliphs in Baghdad, although they retained nominal authority, were mere figureheads. In the tenth century a North African dynasty, the Fatimids, were the rulers of Egypt. From the twelfth century onwards eastern Islam was subjected to attack, first by the Seljuk Turks, then by the Mongols. Dynasties, of whatever race, tended to be short-lived, and only with the triumph of the Ottoman Turks in the late fourteenth century was Islam again united under a single dynasty.

Nevertheless, it would be wrong to lay too much stress on political disunity, at least before the middle of the thirteenth century. After the first century of Islam, the Arabs quickly assimilated the cultures of the conquered peoples and gave in return a new religion and in much of the Empire the unifying influence of the Arabic language. A new Islamic culture arose out of the older civilizations, with Arabic as the vehicle of expression for literature and science. New Islamic cities were founded—the founding of cities is enjoined as a meritorious act by Islam. Some of these cities came to nothing, but others—Baghdad, Cairo, Basra, Qayrawan—became, together with some of the older cities, centers of Islamic cultures and learning. Even some of the small, obscure dynasties were notable patrons of scholars. Despite political fragmentation, Islam retained its cultural and economic cohesion throughout the Middle Ages and beyond. Communications were not severed, travel was relatively easy, and trade flourished.

The great city, set in the center of a thriving agricultural area based upon irrigation, was characteristic of Islam. The population of Baghdad in the ninth century is estimated at 1.5 million. Only a small proportion of the urban population was engaged in the production of foodstuffs and raw materials. Among the inhabitants were the courtly circles, the military, administrators, merchants, artisans, writers, scientists and theologians. There were many slaves, but a large number of these were also nonproductive. Slaves were employed as domestic servants, palace guards, mercenary soldiers, eunuchs, concubines, scribes and administrators. It was not unusual for gifted slaves to rise to positions of power and influence. In some areas, for instance in Iraq and Egypt, soldiers of slave origin became so powerful that they were able to take control of the state.

The types of crops grown in a particular area depended, of course, upon local climatic and hydraulic conditions. Taking Islam as a whole, produce included a range of cereals, nearly all the fruits and vegetables known today (with the exception of the potato and the tomato), sugarcane, spices and herbs, flax, cotton and hemp. Irrigation was the most productive form of agriculture. Production by rainfall was possible only in certain areas, for instance in Mesopotamia (the area between the upper reaches of the Tigris and the Euphrates), parts of the Levant, and some coastal regions of North Africa. In the steppe-lands and semi-deserts that formed a large part of the Islamic world, the main agricultural activity was, and still is, the pasturing of animals for meat, dairy products, skins and textiles. Trade in agricultural produce—both raw and processed—was widespread, both inside provinces and over longer distances. The needs of large cities such as Baghdad and Bokhara could not be satisfied completely by the produce of the agricultural lands surrounding them, and the population of the Holy Cities had to feed largely by imports. The granary for Baghdad was Mesopotamia, which shipped large quantities of flour down the Tigris to the capital. The town of Bilbays in Lower Egypt, in addition to supplying local needs, sent 3,000 donkey loads of flour annually to Mecca and Medina. There was also a flourishing trade in textiles, minerals, manufactured goods and luxuries. Transport was by river, sea, and by organized caravans of donkeys or camels.

Europe presented a sharply different picture in the early Middle Ages. Politically, the area was divided into a number of small states carved out of the Roman Empire by barbarian invaders. Towards the end of the eighth century there was a brief re-awakening of the imperial concept under Charlemagne, who temporarily united large parts of northern Europe under his rule. But the Age of Migrations was not yet over. The pagan Vikings began their damaging incursions into France, Britain and Ireland late in the eighth century. The Magyars, also pagans, attacked eastern Europe early in the tenth century. Only in the late tenth century, when these groups settled and became converted to Christianity, did central and northern Europe become fairly stable. A large area of southern Europe—most of the Iberian peninsula, the Mediterranean islands, and parts of southern Italy—were still under Muslim control. Byzantium was a bulwark of Christianity from its foundation until the end of the eleventh century. Then the pattern gradually changed. Sicily was conquered by the Normans in the second half of the eleventh century. In 1085 Toledo was occupied by the Christians, who continued their slow but relentless reconquest of the Iberian peninsula. On the other hand, a Byzantine army suffered a disastrous defeat by the Turks at the battle of Manzikert in 1071. Thereafter the gradual occupation of Anatolia by the Turks became inevitable.

A feature of the European scene after 1000 was the gradual concentration of power in royal hands. In France and England particularly, this led to the emergence of nation states, much in their modern form. The self-governing city was characteristic of Italy. But in northern Europe, the feudal system became established. This constituted a hierarchy with the king at its head, beneath him the higher nobility, beneath them the landed gentry, and so on down to the peasantry. The nobility and the gentry usually lived on their lands and drew their living partly from farming their own domains and partly by taxing the peasants. In theory, though not always in practice, the peasants received protection in return for their dues. The introduction of fully armored cavalry increased the demands on the land, which was the main source of wealth.

The great monastic institutions were another important feature of life in medieval Europe. Clerical landlords could be every bit as exacting as their lay counterparts, but on balance the influence of the monasteries was beneficial. They were islands of peace and learning in an otherwise barbarous environment, and some of the orders, notably the Cistercians, were great promoters of agricultural improvements and the industrial applications of water power.

Feudalism began to decline with the gradual strengthening of central government. As life became more secure the need for protection lessened, and peasants saw that they were receiving little in return for their taxes and labor. Another potent factor in weakening the hold of feudalism was the growth of towns. Royal charters were granted to towns and cities, which had been small and few in number in the early Middle Ages. Urban communities proliferated and their populations grew. A new class of merchants and entrepreneurs came into being, owing no allegiance to the landed nobility, and there was a drift of serfs and landless peasants from the countryside to the towns. The urban communities could not have been supported without the marked improvements in agriculture that took place from about 1000 onwards. These improvements included the perfecting of the heavy wheeled plough, the introduction of the three-field rotational system for crops, and the replacement of oxen by horses for agriculture and transport. Productivity increased considerably, although the main crops were still the same—cereals, pulses and animal produce.

Although the foregoing summary contains over-simplifications, it provides some background against which the technologies of Islam and Europe can be assessed. In medieval times utilitarian technology was closely involved with agriculture, providing water to the fields and processing agricultural produce to provide food and clothing. The level of technology was therefore determined by the efficiency of agriculture and by the size of the non-productive population. There are indications that the feudal system, combined with monasticism, was not inimical to the progress of agriculture, because lay and clerical landlords lived on their estates and had a direct interest in their productivity. In Islam the system of land tenure was quite different. The land was owned by the state, which could award fiefs to military leaders or other notables. The fiefs were not usually heritable, as they were in Europe, and the fiefholders lived in the cities, simply drawing a monetary stipend from the produce of the land. There is some

evidence that this system led to a deterioration in agriculture in some regions, but any suggestion of a general decline throughout Islam is not tenable. The Muslims were great agriculturalists, and there are a number of Arabic works on agronomy that display a wide knowledge of agricultural techniques and an awareness of how to treat various crops to obtain the best results. The Muslims introduced irrigation to Spain, together with several varieties of fruit and vegetables that were new to Europe. It is certain that the people of Islam enjoyed a higher standard of living than most parts of Europe.

To make any valid comparison between the two areas we have to distinguish the early and later Middle Ages, divided at about 1000. In the first period the Islamic world was an established civilization, with large populations to feed and clothe, and adequate means for doing so. Muslims also found means for making life pleasant for many people, and for providing diversions and amusements for the upper stratum of society. This situation did not change radically in the later period. The early period in Europe was characterized by small populations living in scattered communities, partially isolated from one another by poor communications. Each community processed the products of its local agriculture to provide for its own needs.

In the later period, with the growth of population, the emergence of urban life and improvements in agriculture and transport, the applications of power became increasingly important in Europe. More power was used for the processing of foodstuffs, but there was also a marked increase in the industrial use of water power. Mills for fulling cloth, forging metals and sawing timber became commonplace. This activity was promoted by a new class of entrepreneurs, whose main motive was profit. Muslims also used water power for sawing timber, crushing sugarcane and driving paper mills, but in the absence of adequate research we do not know the extent of the industrial use of power in Islam. If indeed Islam lagged behind Europe in this field, then the reasons must be sought in a variety of factors, which are beyond the scope of this paper to discuss.

Questions of space dictate that some aspects of engineering are omitted in the following survey. Attention will be confined to several areas: power (water and wind), water supply, siege artillery, clocks and automata.

Power: Water and Wind

There are three basic types of water-wheel:

Remains of a Moorish undershot waterwheel, probably the tenth-century, power for a mill; Cordoba, Spain. (Background, a Roman bridge.)

the undershot wheel, the overshot wheel, and the horizontal wheel. The undershot wheel was described in the first century B.C. and was in use in Europe and Asia from the classical period up to modern times. It was a paddle-wheel set upon a horizontal axle and turned by the impact of the flowing water on the blades. The overshot wheel had buckets set along its rim, onto which water was directed through a channel leading from the water supply to the top of the wheel. The wheel was turned by the weight of the water, not by its velocity. There is no evidence for this type of wheel earlier than the fifth century A.D., but it was certainly used in the Middle Ages both in Europe and Islam.

In a water-mill the transmission of power from both types of wheel to the millstones was similar. The wheel's axle led to a vertical toothed wheel inside the millhouse, which meshed with a horizontal toothed wheel upon the axle of which the millstones were mounted. Additional gearing permitted the use of a second pair of stones in some cases and a secondary gear-train could be used to power a hoist for lifting sacks of grain into the mill. The undershot wheel was the less efficient of the two types, since it required a rapidly flowing stream to operate. Its output varied with seasonal changes in the depth and velocity of the stream. The overshot wheel, on the other hand, could provide satisfactory power with a relatively small flow of water; seasonal variations were allowed for by the use of sluices. Maximum efficiency has been estimated at 30% for the undershot wheel and 66% for the overshot wheel.

The horizontal wheel consisted of a number of vanes radiating from a central hub, often with a cowling around the perimeter to give added strength. Water was directed onto the vanes from a jet leading from the bottom of a water tower, into the top of which the water was channelled from a stream or pond. In an eighth-century Saxon mill at Tamworth, water was conducted from a millpond across a sloping wooden platform and into a narrow channel, which served the same purpose as the piped jet. The horizontal wheel was turned by both axial and tangential components of flow. In the seventeenth century the so-called "tub wheel" appeared in northern Europe. In this design the wheel was mounted inside a vertical cylinder, into which water pours through the top. Although this axial flow machine was not known in the Middle Ages, the Banu Musa describe a wheel in which axial flow was used by placing a ring of nozzles below a vaned wheel. Opinions vary widely about the efficiency of the jet-driven horizontal wheel, but it seems to have been of the same order as that of the undershot wheel.

A fourth type of wheel was the scoop-wheel, in which scoops were attached to the ends of spokes radiating from a central hub. Like the overshot wheel, it was driven mainly by the weight of the water. This is found only in al-Jazari's book, but we do not know whether it was his own invention or was derived from earlier models. The scoop-wheel certainly existed beyond the Islamic-European sphere, however, for it was used by Chinese engineers before al-Jazari's time.

Any statement about the power output of the three main types of wheel, in general terms, would be misleading, because output varied with the size and construction of the wheel and the local hydraulic conditions. Under average conditions an undershot wheel would produce three to five horsepower (2.2 to 3.7 kw), an overshot wheel ten horsepower (7 kw) and a horizontal wheel one to two horsepower (.7 to 1.5 kw). If, however, a large undershot wheel were placed in a deep, fast-flowing stream its output could be much higher. This was sometimes achieved by using ship-mills, moored to the banks of rivers, or by fixing the wheels to the piers of bridges to take advantage of the increased velocity of flow at these points. There is abundant evidence for both arrangements in Europe and Islam. In some places large dams were built to increase the head of water above the mills and so provide greater power. In the tenth century there was one such dam at Shiraz that supplied power to 10 mills, and another of similar size at Ahwaz in southwestern Iran. In both cases the artificial lakes produced by the dams were used to supply irrigation water. Late in the twelfth century three large dams were constructed on the River Garonne near Toulouse; the water from the dams powered 43 mills. Tidal mills were used near Basra in the tenth century and first appeared in Europe in the twelfth century.

The type of mill used depended on local hydraulic conditions, the availability of building materials and the needs of the population. The horizontal wheel was best suited to highland terrain where mountain streams flowed. A brick or masonry water tower was built near the stream, with the inlet channel at the top and the millhouse at the bottom. Many examples of this kind of construction in this type of terrain are known from archaeology and from written records. Large urban centers located on great rivers were supplied by more powerful mills, with undershot or overshot wheels.

Only certain types of stone are suitable for the manufacture of millstones, and these special stones usually had to be transported over long distances. Stones for the mill at Tamworth were imported from the Rhineland. The mountains near Herat in Khurasan were quarried for millstones, which were transported all over the province. In Tunisia, an area near Qayrawan produced stones that were exported to all parts of North Africa.

Until about the end of the tenth century, water-wheels in both Europe and Islam were used mainly for driving grist-mills, i.e. mills for grinding corn and other seeds. The Domesday survey in England recorded 5,624 mills in 1086, and there is no reason to suppose that other parts of Europe were more backward in the use of power at this time. This figure for the number of mills in England has sometimes been quoted as evidence that labor-saving devices were more prevalent in Europe than in Islam, with the suggestion that Christian disapproval of slavery contributed to this attitude. The conjecture does not bear close examination. Slavery existed in both communities. The proportion of slaves in the total population was probably higher in Islam, but many were non-productive and had to be fed. Taking the population of England at the time of Domesday at 1.1 million, there was on average one mill to about 200 persons. Most of

the mills must therefore have been small and low-powered, serving local communities. That there were so many was probably due to the isolation of many communities, together with the desire of landlords, lay and clerical, to collect milling dues from their peasants, rather than to altruistic or progressive motives. Indeed, as late as 1321 the people of St. Albans preferred to grind their corn at home rather than pay dues to the Abbey mills. The Abbot had all the hand-querns confiscated and, as a humiliation to the peasants, paved the courtyard of the Abbey with them.

A far different pattern prevailed in the Islamic world. The population of Baghdad at the height of its prosperity has been estimated at 1.5 million, greater than the population of contemporary England. Corn for the city was grown in Iraq and Mesopotamia, the latter being regarded as the main granary for the city. The tenth-century geographer Ibn Hawqal tells us that powerful ship-mills operated on the Tigris all the way from Mosul to Baghdad. The mills were moored to the banks with iron chains and were made of wood and iron. Each mill had two pairs of stones, each pair grinding five tons of corn daily. In the writings of Ibn Hawqal, al-Mugaddasi and others, there is abundant evidence that mills were erected wherever there was an adequate supply of water. In the twelfth century the traveller Ibn Jubayr reported that the banks of the Khabur river in Mesopotamia were lined with mills. Many other examples of large-scale milling could be cited from other parts of Islam. Large Muslim populations were thus fed by the production of numerous powerful Zrist mills, while in Europe smaller, less powerful mills served the needs of smaller communities. In the course of the Middle Ages the situation gradually changed, as populations in Europe grew while those in parts of Islam remained static or declined. Nevertheless, the comparison is probably valid for most of the period.

The industrial use of water power presents a different picture. Europe from the eleventh century onwards was undoubtedly affected by an entrepreneurial spirit that saw water power as a means of increasing productivity and hence profits. The usual method for transferring power from vertical wheels to machinery was by attaching cams to the horizontal axles of the wheels. The cams activated a number of trip-hammers in succession, and these hammers operated machinery for fulling cloth, forging iron, sawing timber and a variety of other tasks. There can be no doubt that, in the High Middle Ages, the use of water power for industrial purposes was an integral and ever-expanding part of European life.

The situation in Islam is not so clear, partly because much of the original material has yet to be studied by historians of technology. Mills were indeed used for industrial purposes: sawing timber, crushing sugarcane and paper manufacture were some applications. Several of al-Jazari's devices have cams on the axles of miniature water-wheels, usually for the purpose of activating automata. He may have borrowed this idea from industrial mills that he had seen in Mesopotamia. It seems likely, however, that the industrial use of water power in Islam did not parallel that of Europe, though we cannot be sure of this until extensive research has been carried out.

The windmill is suitable only for water raising and for grist-milling, the latter in agricultural areas that do not have ready access to water or to the produce of water-mill. No one with any sense builds a windmill where water power is available. This is borne out, for example, by a recent survey of mills and mill sites in Hampshire, an agricultural county with an abundance of chalk streams: there were 192 water-mills and eight windmills. Windmills with vertical axles are described by the tenth century Arab geographers in southern Afghanistan. These were low-powered grist mills, and their use did not spread to other parts of Islam or into Europe. The European windmill with vertical sails on a horizontal axle seems to have been an independent invention, inspired perhaps by the Vitruvian water-mill. It appeared in the twelfth century and soon became a common feature of the landscape in northern Europe. The windmill found its greatest use in low lying areas requiring drainage, such as the Low Countries, the fenlands of England and Venice. The typical medieval windmill was the post mill, in which the millhouse rests on a strong bearing on top of a heavy wooden post. The mill can be turned into the wind by a bar attached to the floor supports of the millhouse. The tower mill, in which only the cap rotates, was a fifteenth century innovation.

Surprise has been expressed by some historians that Islam never made use of the windmill with vertical sails. Certainly these would have been useful in some areas, but there are a number of cogent reasons for their non-appearance. In the first place, the windmill only makes sense for grist-milling where there is rainfall cultivation of cereals. Irrigation needs water, and where there is water there is water power. Secondly, if communications are good and transport of flour is a normal activity—the situation in many parts of Islam—then there is no need for windmills. Finally, reliable winds and a large supply of massive hardwood timbers for the post, transverse members, and framing are necessary. Only in a few areas of Islam did all of these conditions come together. More typically in the Muslim world, irrigated lands provided grain which was milled and transported to cities along rivers. Overland transport with baggage animals was also relatively cheap and easy, compared with the movement of materials over the wet lands of Europe.

Water supply

The supply of water for drinking, bathing and irrigation was a flourishing activity in medieval Islam. In Europe the Roman water supply systems fell into disuse and disrepair, leaving most communities to rely upon wells, springs and

Chain-of-pots systems for raising water by manpower, top, and by horsepower, bottom.

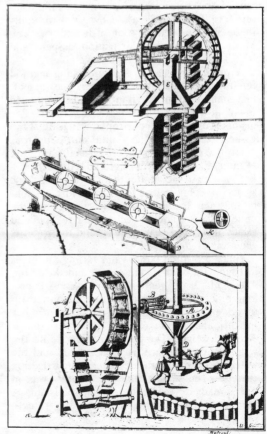

rivers. The lack of proper drainage or sewage removal, combined with wet climate, muddy roads and the movement of livestock produced widespread pollution of water sources. Irrigation, of course, was not important in northern Europe.

In most of the Islamic world the supply of water for irrigation and drinking was, and remains, literally a matter of life or death. Arab geographers pay a great deal of attention to the subject. In the works of Ibn Hawqal and Muqqadasi the sources of water for cities such as Bokhara with its surrounding countryside, or the great oasis of Khuwarizm, are given in great detail. The course of each river, stream and canal is described, together with the number and location of water-raising machines and mills. For outlying villages we are told whether their water came from wells, springs or streams. At Samarkand water was led into the city through a raised, lead-lined aqueduct, because the level of the ground around the city had been lowered by the excavation of clay for building. In these areas, and indeed in all parts of the Muslim world, engineers constantly maintained and extended ancient irrigation systems. In ninth-century Iraq, for example, a canal was dug to supply the newly-founded city of al-Jaafariyya. The Muslims also introduced irrigation to Spain, and with it a number of fruits and vegetables.

A particularly useful and interesting method for utilizing underground water is the quanat, first mentioned in Assyrian times and still used today in Iran and southeastern Arabia. The quanat is essentially a horizontal well, one of the earliest examples of the skillful and dangerous enterprise of tunnelling. Vertical shafts are sunk at intervals of about 50 meters (150 feet) on a line leading to the aquifer. The bottoms of these shafts are connected to form an almost horizontal passage leading from the aquifer to the outlet. A good aquifer will yield a reliable and steady flow from year to year, and the water is generally of good quality.

There are three basic water-raising machines in Islam: the *shaduf,* the *saqiya* and the noria. The *shaduf* is of great antiquity. It consists of a long pole balanced on a fulcrum supported on a wooden post. At the end of its longer arm is a bucket, and at the end of the other arm is a counterweight. The bucket is dipped into the water source, the arm is then rotated and the water discharged into a cistern or irrigation channel. The *saqiya,* like the *shaduf,* was in widespread use before the advent of Islam. A horizontal axle is mounted over the source,

Chinese version (1637) of the Islamic saqiya or cahin of pots for moving or raising water.

usually a well. A wheel with wooden cogs is fixed to this axle. On the other side of the wheel from the cogs a chain-of-pots is suspended over wooden pegs. The chain-of-pots consists of a series of earthenware vessels suspended by two ropes or chains. A horizontal cogwheel meshes with the first. To its axle a draw-bar is fixed and the animal, usually a donkey but in Arabia often a camel, is tethered to the end of this bar. As the animal walks in a circular path, the cogwheels turn and the chain-of-pots is in constant motion. The pots dip into the water, rise vertically, and at the top of their travel they tilt and discharge their contents into a tank to which the supply channel is connected. Both *shaduf* and *saqiya* are still in use today. They can be maintained by the local carpenter and do not depend, as a pump does, upon fuel supplies or the availability of spare parts. When crops require a constant supply of water, any interruption of that supply can be disastrous.

The third water-raising machine, the noria, is now largely out of use, although fine examples can still be seen, notably on the Orontes river at

Hama in Syria. The machine consisted of a large wheel—up to 30 meters (100 feet) in diameter—mounted on a horizontal axle over a running stream. The wheel was constructed of open timberwork, sometimes reinforced with iron. Paddles were attached to the perimeter of the wheel, and inside its rim was a series of buckets. The water turned the wheel as it struck the paddles, the buckets filled and were raised to the top of the wheel, where they discharged into the supply system.

Some interesting developments of these basic machines are described by al-Jazari in Category V of his book on mechanical devices. In the first of these, a flume-beam swape was erected on a horizontal axle close to the edge of the water source. This swape was an elaboration of the *shaduf;* instead of a solid pole the bucket was connected to a channel, so that as the swape rose above the horizontal the water ran through the channel into the supply system. A lantern gear was fixed to the swape's axle. A gear wheel with teeth on one quarter of its perimeter meshed with the lantern gear. To the horizontal axle of this gear wheel another vertical gear was fixed, inside the "engine house," and a horizontal gear wheel meshed with this one. An animal was tethered to the draw-bar attached to the vertical axle of the last gear wheel. The animal walked in a circular path, as in the *saqiya.* The segmental gear wheel engaged the lantern gear, causing the swape to rise and discharge its contents; when the gears disengaged the swape fell back into the water.

The second machine was a quadrupled version of the first. Not only did this increase the output but, as the author states, it produced a more even, less jerky, operation. Another machine embodying a flume-beam swape had a slot-rod running lengthwise under the channel. A spigot attached to the arm of a crank entered the slot-rod. The crank was turned, through a system of gears, by an animal walking in a circular path. As the spigot oscillated in the slot-rod the swape rose and fell.

The fourth machine was an adaptation of the *saqiya.* Below the structure containing the chain-of-pots was a concealed pool over which a scoop-wheel was mounted. Water from an ornamental lake was led through a pipe on to the scoops of the wheel. As the wheel rotated it turned the wheel of the chain-of-pots through two pairs of gear wheels. As an additional attraction, the wooden model of an animal was mounted on a platform attached to the axle by a miniature draw-bar. This device, though ornamental, was

simply an elegant variation of a utilitarian machine. A water-raising device in Damascus that supplied water to a hospital and a mosque was essentially a large-scale version of the machine described by al-Jazari, except that it had a paddle-wheel instead of a scoop-wheel and there was no model animal. In operation for many centuries before it fell into disuse about 1960, it was recently restored to working order by the staff and students of Aleppo University.

The last of al-Jazari's water-raising machines, a pump for raising water to a height of about 10 meters (30 feet), is a complete departure from the traditional designs. A paddle-wheel was erected over a stream, and on the other end of its axle was a vertical gear wheel. This wheel meshed with a horizontal wheel mounted in a triangular box. The box was erected over a sump that was connected to the stream. On the surface of the horizontal wheel, near its rim, was a peg entering a slot-rod that was pivoted at one corner of the box. A ring at each side of the slot-rod was attached to a connecting rod, on the other end of which was a piston consisting of two copper discs, the space between them packed with hemp. These pistons entered smooth copper cylinders, at the ends of which were suction pipes descending into the sump, and delivering pipes that were joined together above the machine to form a single outlet that discharged into the irrigation system. Both suction and delivery pipes were provided with non-return clack valves. As the slot-rod oscillated, one piston was on the suction stroke while the other was on the delivery stroke. This machine was probably intended to provide a more efficient means of raising water than the noria. It was particularly suitable to an area such as Mesopotamia, al-Jazari's homeland, where the fast flowing streams are generally well below the level of the fields.

Clocks

The two most significant features of timekeeping in the Middle Ages are the monumental water-clocks of Islam and the invention and spread of the mechanical clock in Europe.

The water-clock is of ancient origin. In its simplest form, the outflow clepsydra, it was known in Egypt by about 1500 B.C. and was in widespread use in the Old World in the first millennium B.C. It consisted of a vessel, shaped like the frustrum of a cone, with a small hole in its side near the base, from which water discharged. The descent of water in the vessel gave a measure of time, but it was not a satisfactory timepiece because the rate of outflow decreased as the water level sank. It was therefore necessary to draw a line on the inside and mark the space for each hour on this line by experiment.

The inflow clepsydra was a great improvement over the simple water-clock. It consisted of an upper vessel with a constant water supply, an overflow pipe, and an orifice discharging into a lower vessel of constant cross-section. Since the outflow from the reservoir was constant, the water in the receiving vessel rose at a steady rate. A float was placed in the receiver with a long rod soldered to its upper surface; the tip of the rod rose over a vertical scale, recording the passage of the hours. Vitruvius [q.v.] describes a number of developments in the construction of water-clocks, most of which he ascribes to the Greek engineer Ktesibios [q.v.], who flourished about 250 B.C. These innovations included the addition of automata and celestial analogues.

Monumental water-clocks were built in Syria in Byzantine times, and the tradition continued to flourish under Islam. Most water-clocks recorded the passage of the temporal hours, i.e. the hours of daylight divided by 12 to produce "hours" that varied in length from day to day throughout the year. Clockmakers therefore had to solve the problem of varying the rate of flow from day to day.

The ancestor of Islamic water-clocks is described in a treatise ascribed to Archimedes [q.v.]. The treatise exists only in Arabic and certainly contains Islamic additions, but the basic idea may indeed have originated with Archimedes. Arab engineers such as Ridwan and al-Jazari acknowledge their indebtedness to this treatise and accept the authorship of Archimedes for the basic water machinery. This consisted of a reservoir of constant cross-section, from the bottom of which an outflow pipe led out. Its end was bent down and formed into the seat of a conical valve. The plug of the valve, which seems to have been somewhat cruder than those used later by Islamic engineers, was on the top of a float in a float-chamber that was positioned below the outlet from the reservoir. When water discharged, the float rose and closed the valve momentarily; water then discharged from the outlet at the bottom of the float-chamber and the valve opened momentarily. An almost constant head was therefore maintained in the float-chamber. This was therefore a closed-loop system operated by feed-back control, indeed a brilliant conception.

The flow regulator of Archimedes' clock, which varied the length of the temporal hours from day to day, was connected to the outlet

from the float-chamber. This was less impressive, consisting of a rotable pipe with the orifice at its outer end. At the end of the pipe was a pointer that travelled over a scale inscribed around the outer rim of a semicircular plate. The scale was divided into equal sections for the 12 signs of the zodiac, and each sign was subdivided into degrees. The pointer was moved one degree every day. This was very inaccurate. The use of a semicircle meant that the flow was often the same for days of different length. There were also two other errors, since the construction assumed that the variations in daylight throughout the year follow a sine curve and that the discharge from an orifice varies directly as the head falls. Both assumptions are incorrect. The drive for the time-recording devices was provided by a heavy float in the reservoir; a chain attached to the top of the float activated various signalling mechanisms.

The earliest descriptions we have of water-clocks in Islam occur in a treatise by a certain al-Muradi, written in Andalusia in the eleventh century. The only surviving manuscript is badly defaced, but it seems that the water machinery was fairly crude—consisting of simple outflow clepsydras—whereas the transmissions were quite sophisticated and included segmental and epicyclic gears. In 1121 al-Khazini completed his great work on physics, the *Book of the Balance of Wisdom,* the eighth Treatise of which deals with steelyard clepsydras. The basic structure of this device consisted of an outflow clepsydra suspended from the short arm of a beam balanced on a fulcrum. There were two movable weights, a small one and a large one, which were moved along a scale inscribed on the beam as the clepsydra emptied. The small one recorded the minutes, the large one the hours.

In 1203 Ridwan wrote a treatise describing the clock constructed by his father over the Jayrun Gate in Damascus about 40 years earlier. This had fallen into disrepair, and the restoration was undertaken by Ridwan. The water machinery was similar to that described in the Archimedes clock, but the flow regulator was a full circle divided into equal sections. This was more accurate than its semicircular predecessor, but the two major errors persisted. The float in the reservoir activated various automata through a series of pulley systems.

In the first Category of his book on mechanical devices, al-Jazari describes six water-clocks and four candle-clocks. The first water-clock resembled Ridwan's, except that the flow regulator was accurately calibrated by empirical methods. The pull from the float in the reservoir was

Mechanical clock from south Germany, ca. 1450, with chime and a single hand.

transmitted through a pulley system to operate the time-recording devices; these included doors, one of which opened every hour, the discharge of balls from the beaks of two falcons every hour, and a circle that carried representations of the zodiacal signs, the sun and the moon, and rotated at constant speed throughout the day. In the second clock, otherwise very similar to the first, al-Jazari introduces the tipping-bucket, a device that he often used in clocks and other machines. It consisted of a vessel mounted on two stub axles, into which water discharged from an orifice. At the end of each hour it tilted and discharged its contents, then swung back to its horizontal position. The water itself, or a cam on the bucket, could be used to activate other mechanisms.

In all his descriptions al-Jazari displays a mastery of constructional skills. He describes how vessels are made of uniform cross-section by the use of templates, recommends the use of paper models as a constructional aid, uses laminated timber in pulley wheels to minimize warping, checks wheels for static balance on a mandrel, calibrates orifices accurately, and so on. His descriptions are so detailed and accurate that a modern craftsman can reproduce the machines by studying his text and illustrations. A full-scale reconstruction of the first clock was made for the World of Islam Festival in London in 1976. It was faithful to al-Jazari's instructions in every detail, and worked perfectly.

The mechanical clock, which was to exert a powerful influence on the development of mechanical engineering, appeared towards the close of the thirteenth century in northern Europe. Chinese engineers had developed true mechanical clocks at least three centuries earlier, but their work lies beyond the scope of this essay. In any case, Western clocks differed so completely from their Chinese counterparts that they seem to have been invented independently.

A weight-driven clock depends for its successful operation on the escapement, a device that slows the driving mechanism—in the case of European clocks a descending weight—so that its cycle takes at least 12 hours. We do not know who invented the first effective escapement in the West, although a number of Europeans were working on the problem during the second half of the thirteenth century. The earliest satisfactory mechanism was the verge escapement, which remained the only form of escapement in European clocks until about 1670. It consisted of three parts: the crown-wheel, a wheel with an uneven number of teeth standing at an angle of 90 degrees to the plane of the wheel; a shaft (or "verge") bearing two rectangular projections known as "flags" or "pallets"; and, at the top of the shaft, either a horizontal bar called a "foliot" or a large wheel called a "balance."

The action of the escapement was as follows: as the weight was applied to the clock's gear train, the crown-wheel turned. The top pallet was thereby pushed aside by a tooth on the moving crown-wheel, turning the shaft and the foliot on top of the shaft. During this turn the tooth of the crown-wheel "escaped" from contact with the top pallet and, at the same moment, the lower pallet was caught by a tooth on the lower part of the crown-wheel, whose movement of course was opposite that of the top of the wheel. Because there were an uneven number of teeth on the crown-wheel, the lower pallet was engaged by a tooth, when the upper coincided with a space between two teeth. The shaft was impelled to move in one direction by the force of the crown-wheel tooth on the pallet until it escaped; at this point the other pallet was engaged by a tooth on the other side of the crown-wheel, impelling the shaft to rotate in the opposite direction.

The speed of the clock could be varied either by applying a different weight to the gear train or by moving tiny weights along the arm at the foliot to slow or speed up its motion. Striking trains, driven from the main gear train, were added soon after the invention of the escapement. The striking train, for sounding a bell every hour, may have been derived from European water-clocks. Although these never reached the sophistication of their Islamic counterparts, a manuscript of the tenth or eleventh century describes a European water-clock with a striking train.

Use of the mechanical clock spread rapidly over Europe after the invention of the escapement. In the second half of the fourteenth century, no European city considered its civic pride satisfied until it had a clock of great intricacy and elaboration. These clocks had a variety of automata: planets wheeling in cycles and epicycles, angels trumpeting, cocks crowing, kings, apostles and prophets marching and countermarching—all this activity being set in motion when the bell struck the hour. In 1364, Giovanni de' Dondi [q.v.], a distinguished physician and astronomer, wrote a description of a clock that he had constructed over the previous 16 years. This was only incidentally a timepiece. It included the celestial motions of the sun, moon and five planets, and provided a perpetual calendar of all religious feasts, both fixed and movable. To obtain these effects very elaborate mechanisms were necessary, including elliptical and segmental gearing. So accurate were Giovanni's instructions and drawings that several modern reconstructions of the clock have been made from them. There is no doubt that this type of elaborate clock marks an epoch in the history of machine design.

Siege Artillery

In classical times artillery used ropes or animal fibers to provide thrust. The throwing arm was inserted in a skein of fibers, which were twisted tightly to span the weapon. Upon release of the torsion, the arm (or arms) flew forward, and the missile was discharged. Effective against troop formations or light fortifications, these machines were not of much use against heavy masonry walls because the missiles, though travelling fast, were fairly light. Another disadvantage was the variation in the elasticity of the spanning fibers as the humidity of the air varied.

In the Middle Ages, as the art of fortification improved, two new machines appeared, both of which were more effective against masonry walls than the classical types. Both are called trebuchets, although the nomenclature varies and they have other names in some European languages. In Arabic the words *manjaniq* and *arrada* are used for all siege artillery. The *arrada* seems to have been smaller than the *manjaniq,* but one usually has to infer which type of machine is being referred to by the description in the text. Both machines had a beam supported on an axle that rested in bearings fixed to the top

of vertical supports, with a sling and a pouch at the tip of the longer end of the beam. Thereafter the similarity, both in construction and dynamics, ends.

One type of trebuchet, the traction trebuchet, had a special fitting at the short end of the beam, to which a number of ropes were fixed. At the other end was a short sling carrying a pouch, in which the missile rested. A team of men pulled on the ropes while the artilleryman (called in Arabic the *rami,* or slinger) held down the other end. At a signal from the artilleryman, the pulling team tugged sharply on the ropes and the artilleryman released the sling. The beam flew up and the missile was discharged by the impulsive torque, added velocity being imparted by the "whip" of the beam. An Arabic writer assigns an important role to the *rami:* he had to hold the sling at the correct angle and time its release to a split second. Only by his skills could maximum distance and the correct trajectory be achieved. Clearly, some drilling was also necessary for the men on the ropes, so that they exerted their force in unison.

Trebuchets seem to have originated in China, where they were known in ancient times. Some details of Chinese traction trebuchets are available. The beam could be a single spar, or several spars bound together. The number of spars was usually from 1 to 10, but machines with 15 spars were known. The spars were from 5.6 to 8.4 meters (18.4 to 27.6 ft) long, with diameters varying from seven to 12.5 centimeters (2.8 to 4.9 inches). The missile, weighing from two to 130 pounds (.9 to 59 kg), was placed in the copper "nest" at the end of the sling. At the other end of the beam from 40 to 125 ropes were fixed to the attachment. These were between 12.4 and 15.5 meters (40.9 and 50.9 ft) in length and 16 millimeters (.6 inches) thick. The beam was divided by the fulcrum into a long and short arm in the ratio 5:1 or 6:1 for the light machines and 2:1 or 3:1 for the heavy ones. The range of the missiles was from 85 to 133 yards (78 122 meters). Information from Arabic sources does not differ in essentials from these data. Single spars were more common than composite ones, presumably because the Chinese used bamboo which was lighter and stronger than wood. In a treatise written for Saladin, Murda ibn Ali says that the best wood was cherry and that the best effects were obtained if the wood was flexible rather than rigid.

Use of the traction trebuchet apparently began to move westward in the seventh century A.D., passing to the Turks of Central Asia and reaching Islam late in the century by way of

Khurasani or Soghdian artificers. This suggestion fits in well with the reports of Arabic historians. In the early Arabic conquests fortified towns presented a problem to the besiegers, and many sieges were only ended by ruses or treachery. Only in Umayyad times in the second half of the seventh century was regular artillery introduced. The first unequivocal description of an artillery piece occurs in an account of the siege of Mecca in 683. Thereafter there are mentions of the traction trebuchet in 708, 710 and 865. It probably remained in widespread use in Islam until the late medieval period. In Europe references to the traction trebuchet are rare. It is first mentioned at the beginning of the twelfth century, and in 1147 a battery of these machines was used by northern Crusaders to capture Muslim Lisbon. It is also referred to by Aegidio Colonna (d. 1316), but it was probably never as widely used in Europe as farther east.

The counterweight trebuchet was a larger, more powerful machine. It had a heavy beam, supported on an axle that was carried in bearings on large towers made of framed timbers. To the short arm a large wooden box was suspended, loaded with stones or lead to a weight of between 10 and 30 tons. At the other end was a very long sling at the end of which was the missile pouch. The sling was laid in a wooden channel fixed to the bottom of the machine in the plane of the trajectory. The trebuchet was spanned by a winch; the rope from the drum of the winch was attached to a special hook that rested in a ring strapped to the long arm of the beam. A short rope attached to the same hook was jerked to release the hook from the ring and so set the beam in motion. The beam rotated, the sling accelerated upwards rapidly, and the missile was discharged. The dynamic system was completely different from that of the traction trebuchet. The beam had to be heavy to support the load of the counterweight; it could be tapered towards the other end, but not drastically so, because it had to take the bending stresses from the spanning rope. It was essentially a compound pendulum, in which the inertia of the beam and the counterweight both affected the terminal speed of the beam. The power of the machine could not be directly augmented by increasing the counterweight, because the size of the beam would then have to be increased, and the inertia effects of both beam and counterweight would be greater. The long sling was therefore essential, both to provide a very light extension to the beam and to produce an acceleration greater than that of the beam. With a short sling, or none, the range of the machine

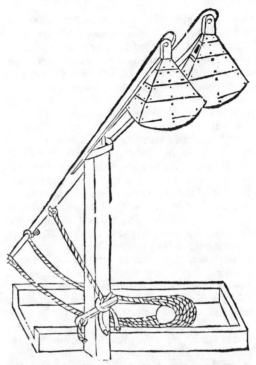

A simple counterweight trebuchet; when untied, the weights drop, whirling the sling and firing the stone (from Valturio).

would have been derisory. These factors may be one reason for the late appearance of this type of trebuchet.

A clear drawing of the counterweight trebuchet is shown in *Bellifortis,* written by Konrad Kyeser [q.v.] in 1405. It is dimensioned, the total length of the beam being 54 feet (16 meters), with a long arm of 46 feet (14 meters) and a short arm of 8 feet (2.4 meters) giving a ratio of 5.75:1. From another source we learn that in England in 1244 stones for the machines made by a certain Gerard were cut from a form and mold supplied by him. Such standardization of ammunition suggests a standardization of weapons, which would never have been possible with traction trebuchets, where the strength of the men and the resilience of the wood were such variable factors. Missiles could be very heavy. During the fourteenth century siege of Tlemcen in present-day Algeria, trebuchets were used capable of bombarding the town with balls made of marble; some have been found there, the largest with a circumference of two meters (6.6 ft) and weighing 230 kilograms (507 lb). At the siege of Hims in 1248, a *manjaniq* was erected that would throw a stone weighing 140 Syrian *ratls* or about 250 kilograms (550 lb). In general, however, missiles were probably somewhat lighter than this, averaging about 100 kilograms (220 lb). We do not have any precise information about the ranges attained by the counterweight trebuchet, but a figure of 300 meters (1000 ft) is probably of the right order. This range is borne out by the results of some nineteenth century experiments and by the calculations of the present writer.

The counterweight trebuchet was invented somewhere in the Mediterranean area in the late twelfth century, and spread very rapidly from its point of origin into northern Europe and western Islam. But the question of the exact provenance of the invention, whether in Europe or in Islam, is not yet resolved. The earliest unambiguous description of the machine in Europe refers to its use in northern Italy in 1199. Writing a few years earlier than this, Murda ibn Ali described a machine that is definitely not a traction trebuchet, and yet the description is too confused for us to identify it for certain as a counterweight machine. Throughout the thirteenth century, however, references to its use, both in Europe and in Islam, are numerous. The inventor of the counterweight trebuchet is therefore unknown, as are the names of most of its constructors. But the trade of "trebuchator" seems to have been well established by the last quarter of the thirteenth century in England, where we have the names of a number of engineers whose chief responsibility was the construction of counterweight trebuchets. Almost certainly, the machine passed to China from Islam. Two Muslim engineers, Ala al-Din and Ismaeel, are honored by a biography in the official history of the Yuan dynasty. They constructed trebuchets for Kubilai Khan at the siege of Fan-ch'eng towards the end of 1272.

Automata

The Arabic word *hiyal* is usually translated as "ingenious devices." It covers a wide range, referring to all machines from trick vessels to siege engines. Here we shall consider machines constructed mainly for entertainment, such as trick vessels and fountains, together with one or two useful devices not included in the preceding sections. In the Muslim world, at different times and places, rulers took an interest in appliances whose main purpose was to amuse and give aesthetic pleasure. The Abbasid Caliphs of Baghdad in the ninth century, patrons of the Banu Musa, encouraged all forms of intellectual activity—literary, scientific, artistic and techni-

cal. To a lesser degree, the Artuqid princes of Mesopotamia, for whom al-Jazari worked in the twelfth century, fostered the intellectual life of the province, and a number of Umayyad rulers in Spain exerted a similar influence. The same can hardly be said of Europe, where there was little time for such urbanities. Rulers were often almost illiterate, and their main pastimes—the tourney and the hunt—were an offshoot of their overriding preoccupation with warfare. Only with the advent of enlightened rulers such as Alfonso X of Leon and Castile (ruled 1252–84) do we find European princes comparable to their Muslim counterparts. Religious orders fostered the branches of learning that were relevant to their calling, and the Cistercians in particular were great promoters of industrial activity. But in Europe, throughout most of the Middle Ages, the engineers were usually anonymous craftsmen who constructed utilitarian machines.

The Banu Musa were three brothers—Muhammad, Ahmad and al-Hasan—who were active in Baghdad from about 830 to 870 as patrons of the sciences and as scientists and engineers in their own right. From historical sources we know that they occupied an honored position at the Abbasid court. Ahmad seems to have been the main author of the *Book of Ingenious Devices,* a work that was much appreciated in Islam during the Middle Ages. His predecessors were the classical writers Philon [q.v.] and Heron [q.v.]. The *Pneumatics* of both were available in Arabic translations, and there are many similarities between the devices described in their works and those in the *Book of Ingenious Devices.* But there are also notable advances on the Greek ideas in Ahmad's work, particularly in the introduction of more sophisticated methods of control. Effects were produced by delicate variations in aerostatic and hydrostatic pressures, using components such as automatically-operating conical valves and the double concentric siphon, neither of which was known to the Greeks. Most of the devices were trick vessels which produced a bewildering variety of effects: pitchers that would not discharge again once pouring was interrupted; basins that replenished themselves if liquid were taken from them; vessels that discharged water if wine were poured into them and vice versa; and so on. Thirty or more different effects could be produced. Indeed, so comprehensive was the treatment of the subject that no similar work was ever written—the subject was exhausted. The Banu Musa also described fountains and musical automata, but these were not as effective as those of al-Jazari. One device of interest is an instrument for recovering articles of value that had fallen into canals. It was a small clamshell grab, almost identical to its modern counterpart.

Al-Jazari's clocks and water-raising machines have already been mentioned, and the unique quality of his book emphasized. The second and third Categories of the work are devoted to trick vessels, water dispensers and phlebotomy measuring devices. These show little development from the designs of the Banu Musa, and indeed are inferior to them in some ways. There is not the same sophisticated use of small variations in pressures; instead al-Jazari relied more upon mechanical means and direct hydrostatic pressures. He made frequent use of the tipping-bucket, along with floats, graduated orifices and special taps. In one vessel the hot water chamber was separated from the cold by two metal plates with an air space between them for minimized heat transfer. This device is clearly an ancestor of the modern vacuum flask.

In Category IV of his book al-Jazari describes alternating fountains and musical automata. His fountains were supplied by two adjoining tanks, from the bottom of which pipes led out; one pipe led to a fountainhead that produced, for instance, a single jet of water, the other to one that emitted multiple jets. Above the tanks was a pipe leading from the water source, balanced on a fulcrum at its center. This pipe discharged water into one or other of the tanks, depending on which way it was tilted. In one variation of this design, water trickled from an orifice into a tipping-bucket; after half an hour the bucket tipped, and a vertical projection on its rear end pushed the pipe and tilted it towards the other tank. In another variation, floats in cages were placed at the sides of the tanks. When the water rose to the top of the tank a vertical rod on top of the float pushed the supply pipe over. Al-Jazari's musical automata worked on similar principles, but in this case water rising in the tanks, from which there was no direct outlet, expelled air into mechanical flutes. When water reached the top of one tank, the supply pipe was tilted towards the second tank as in the fountains, and the first tank was evacuated by a siphon.

The last Category of al-Jazari's work is miscellaneous and strictly speaking not concerned with automata. It describes a large ornamental door made of brass and copper, a protractor, two intricate locks, and a water-clock operated on the submerging bowl principle. The most remarkable feature of this Category is the description of the casting of parts of the door, which was done by using closed mold-boxes with green sand, a technique that al-Jazari did not claim as an innovation. This method was first used in Europe at the end of the fifteenth century.

Conclusion

From this brief survey it can be seen that important engineering ideas originated in Europe and Islam during the Middle Ages. In the use of power, both communities solved their problems with the machines that best suited local conditions. For grist-milling the Muslims had to use complexes of powerful machines to feed their large urban centers, while in early medieval Europe a single mill in a small community served local needs. Later, with population growth and the increase of urbanization, European mills became more numerous and powerful, and the industrial uses of water-power multiplied. It is possible that these industrial applications were not so widespread in Islam. Water supply for drinking and irrigation was primarily a Muslim activity until the later Middle Ages, when Europeans turned their attention to land reclamation and the supply of water to the cities.

The monumental water-clock was characteristic of Islam, as was the mechanical clock of Europe after 1300. It may be stretching the point to regard the water-clock as the precursor of the mechanical clock, with the heavy descending float analogous to the falling weight. The transmission systems were very different, one using pulley-trains, the other gears. It is possible, however, that the elaborate gear-trains of al-Muradi's clocks were transmitted from Spain to other parts of Europe, where they entered the vocabulary of clockmakers. The biological and celestial automata of the water-clocks resembled the representations that appeared later in European mechanical clocks, and these concepts were probably transmitted to Europe from Islam.

Although the automata described by the Banu Musa and al-Jazari were designed mainly for amusement, a number of the components and techniques embodied in them were important in the development of mechanical engineering. All of these were known in Islam before they appeared in Europe. To cite a few examples: conical valves, the crank as a machine part, segmental gears, and the casting of metals in closed mold-boxes using green sand. Even the modern concepts of feed-back control, and indeed automation, can be traced back to the preoccupation of Islamic engineers with self-operating devices.

In the almost total absence of direct evidence, we cannot be sure that Islamic engineering ideas were transmitted to Europe. Re-invention is always a possibility. It does seem likely however, that some Islamic ideas, especially in the field of fine mechanisms and delicate controls, passed into Europe and were an important influence on the development of machine design. In the reverse direction, European ideas for the industrial use of water-power may have influenced Islamic engineers, and the mechanical clock certainly entered Islam from Europe. Information may have been transmitted by travellers' reports, by contacts between the two cultures in countries such as Spain and Sicily, or by craftsmen examining older machines. It is certainly true that the two cultures were closer to each other, in engineering as in other aspects of life, than to any other civilization of the time. ■

DANDIN
fl. 825
Indian Writer on Architecture and Engineering

Life and Times:

Dandin, who flourished in the first half of the eighth century A.D., was one of India's leading writers in Sanskrit. Though he was not himself an engineer, his wide-ranging work provides insights into all aspects of Indian life of his time, including technology. Born in southern India, he apparently held a post at the court of the Pallavi dynasty in Kanci. There he witnessed the struggles for power among the successor states of the Gupta Empire. Though not active in politics, he did participate in the conservative movement to revive the Brahmanistic tradition of Hinduism against the inroads of Buddhism and other influences.

Dandin travelled extensively throughout India and incorporated details of political, social and cultural life in his works. There is some question about the authorship of these writings; as in the case of Prince Bhojadeva [q.v.], books of several writers may have been placed under a single

name. But tradition credits Dandin with three important works in the form of mixed prose and poetry romances: the *Kavyadarsa*, the *Dasakunaracarita* and the *Avantisundarīkathā*. It is Dandin's treatment of the mechanical arts in the *Avantisundarīkathā* that makes his work significant in the history of engineering.

Outstanding Engineering Achievement:

The *Avantisundarīkathā* provides a catalogue of techniques in the applied arts, engineering and architecture. Dandin describes the state of carpentry, including the preparation of wooden building materials, the construction of boats and furniture and techniques for carving and engraving wood. Through the figure of Lalitalaya, the architect, Dandin also records the variety of architectural methods known in his day for building temples and palaces.

Six types of mechanical devices, or *yantra*, are discussed in the *Avantisundarīkathā: sthita*, stationary machines; *cara*, mechanisms for transferring motion from a power source to other objects; *dhārā*, hydraulic devices; *dipa*, methods of lighting lamps (presumably pneumatic devices); *jvara*, a device used for heating; and miscellaneous devices. This division of machines by function and underlying physical principle resembles the practice of classical authors such as Heron [q.v.] and Philon of Byzantium [q.v.]. But it is not clear whether this correspondence represents conscious borrowing by Dandin, a more general Hellenistic influence of which he was not aware, or mere coincidence.

Dandin also refers to a series of mechanical toys, supposedly devised by Lalitalaya, including moving figures of soldiers and jugglers and a cloud-seeding device that produced rain or mist. In the field of military technology he describes a small, mobile catapult designed to fire bolts capable of killing war elephants. Such devices resemble those attributed to many engineers who worked at royal courts in Europe and the Far East. But Dandin also discusses the art of plastering modeled figures, an advanced art form that seems unique to India. ■

Further Reading:

Arthur L. Basham, *The Wonder That Was India*. London, 1954.

D. K. Gupta, *Society and Culture in the Time of Dandin*. Delhi, India, 1972.

BANŪ MŪSĀ IBN SHĀKIR (Muhammad, al-Hasan and Ahmad)
fl. 850 A.D., Baghdad, Iraq
Muslim Astronomers and Mathematicians

Life and Times:

Establishment of the Abbasid Caliphate in 751, with its capital in the new city of Baghdad, began a great cultural flowering in the Islamic world. The caliph al-Ma'mun, who ruled from 811 to 833, created an intellectual center at his court that consolidated and extended the scientific knowledge of the ancient cultures with which the Arabs had come into contact, especially that of the Greeks. Part of this establishment was an academy, the House of Wisdom; here the Banū Mūsā ibn Shākir—the three sons of Mūsā ibn Shākir—played a leading role in the study of mathematics, astronomy, and mechanics. Borrowing extensively from the writers of late antiquity, especially Heron [q.v.] and Philon [q.v.], the Banū Mūsā produced the *Kitab al-Hiyal (Book of Ingenious Devices),* the first work of its kind in the Islamic world and one of two major books on mechanics that appeared in the medieval Islamic world.

The early lives of the Banū Mūsā might see ⅃ taken from a fairy tale. Their father, Mūsā ibn Shākir, was a robber who became a prominent astrologer. After his death the caliph al-Ma'mun supervised the education of the three sons, and placed them in his academy. Muhammad, the oldest and most prominent of the three, concerned himself with geometry, logic and astronomy. Al-Hasan focused on geometry, while Ahmad, the engineer of the group, devoted his attention to mechanics.

The Bānū Mūsa contributed in two ways to the advancement of scientific knowledge. They established a translation bureau at the court in Baghdad which collected and translated ancient scientific texts from the Greek, Aramaic or Syriac into Arabic. With their encouragement the two leading translators of the ninth century, Hunain ibn Ishāq and Thābit ibn Qurra, translated many Greek works, including those of Galen, Euclid and Apollonius. On the other hand, the Banū Mūsā incorporated elements of Greek science, particularly in mathematics and physics, into works of their own. The most important of these was the *Book on the Measurement of Plane and Spherical Figures,* a work on geometry which set forth ways of determining the area and volume of various plane and solid figures. They also wrote about musical theory and methods of weighing objects and precious metals.

Outstanding Engineering Achievement:

In the *Kitab al-Hiyal* the Banū Mūsā provided a technical manual for the construction of practical mechanical devices, such as lamps, pipes in spring wells and drinking vessels. Some of the devices described were viewed on one level as tricks: lamps that refilled themselves with oil or water jugs that poured automatically. In each case, though, the Banū Mūsā demonstrated the basic principles on which these devices operated, essentially those of pneumatics, drawn primarily from the work of Heron. They were the first to record the use of certain devices, such as cone valves which fit into place automatically.

In the case of the lamp, the Banū Mūsā designed an elaborate apparatus in which oil was poured from above into an opening in a gourd and flowed through an aperture near the base into a column leading to the lamp wick. Once the initial flow had been set in motion, sufficient oil would remain to keep the lamp lit. When a certain amount of oil had been consumed, the level of oil in the column would drop below the point at which a second aperture (above the first leading from the gourd) had been cut. The vacuum created by the escape of air when the level of oil dipped below this aperture would cause more oil to flow automatically through the lower aperture and into the column.

Differences in air pressure, differences in the pressure generated by different liquids and gases and the movement of columns of air—in water pipes, for example—through the creation of a vacuum underlay the operation of the various devices. Careful use of systems of pulleys figured in the design of other devices that would, for example, lift objects from the bed of a stream.

In the *Qarastun (Book of the Balance)* the Banū Mūsā expounded the basic principle upon which two objects of different weight could be balanced on a scale: that is, the balance achieved by placing the objects at a distance from the fulcrum in inverse proportion to their weights. ∎

Further Reading:

Dictionary of Scientific Biography, s.v. "Banū Mūsā Ibn Shākir."

George Sarton, *Introduction to the History of Science*. Baltimore, 1927–48.

Heinrich Suter, *Die Mathematiker und Astronomen der Araber und ihre Werke*. Leipzig, 1900.

SUYYA

fl. 860 A.D., Kashmir, India
Indian Civil Servant and Hydraulic Engineer

Life and Times:

Kashmir, in northwest India, is located in the foothills of the Himalayas. Here arise the Indus river and its most important tributaries, including the Jhelum. The Jhelum river valley, better known as the vale of Kashmir, has long been the most populous part of Kashmir. Despite its seeming isolation at a height of six thousand feet (1,829 meters) above sea level, this area formed a part of the various empires that united northern India from the third century B.C. until the sixth century A.D. Only in the seventh century, under the Karkota dynasty, did Kashmir become an independent local power. For generations its rulers warred successfully against their neighbors, built impressive Buddhist temples, and encouraged scholarship. The later kings of this dynasty, however, caused economic difficulties for Kashmir through their oppressive taxation and neglect of flood control measures. In 855 a palace coup brought Avantivarman, the founder of the Utpala dynasty, to power. Avantivarman soon undertook an ambitious hydraulic engineering program, under the direction of his able minister Suyya.

Suyya was of obscure origin. Early in life he supported himself as a tutor of children. His intelligence and learning brought him to the attention of scholars. If legend can be believed, word reached the king that Suyya had a scheme for controlling the Jhelum river. Avantivarman summoned Suyya to court, approved his plan and placed him in charge of the project. Suyya successfully carried out his assignment, the first step of a comprehensive water control and land reclamation program. By the end of Avantivarman's reign hundreds of farming villages stood on former swamp land, floods were infrequent, and the cost of rice had fallen by 80 percent. Little wonder that later generations came to call Suyya the Lord of Food personified.

Outstanding Engineering Achievement:

For part of its course the Jhelum flowed between high mountains. Here fallen boulders partially blocked the stream, so that the villages upstream were flooded. Suyya probably took advantage of this situation to throw a stone barrage across the river slightly downstream of the blockage. For a week laborers cleared the bed of the stream and raised stone embankments to hold back future rock-falls. Then the barrage and boulders were removed, and the Jhelum resumed its normal flow.

In the flatter areas of the valley Suyya's approach was different. Wherever flooding was frequent he carved new channels to lead the water away from low-lying farmlands. Thus he redirected the course of the Jhelum and the Sindhu, one of its tributaries, and made the two rivers flow together at Shrinagar, which became the new capital of Kashmir.

Downstream of Shrinagar was the large Volur (Wular) lake, into which the Jhelum flowed. Suyya directed the river into the lake by the shortest possible course; here and at the point where the Jhelum left the lake, Suyya built 42 miles (68 km) of stone embankments to contain the river and open up new farmland. He also constructed dams around the lake to restrict its frequent overflows. A later chronicler exclaimed that Suyya made the various streams take to any course at his pleasure, as a charmer did with snakes.

Suyya further tested the soil of the reclaimed areas to determine how long it would retain water. Where the soil dried up quickly, Suyya laid down a network of canals for irrigation. Even so, centuries passed before the hundreds of square miles of land which Suyya reclaimed were fully exploited. ■

Further Reading:

R.C. Majumdar et al., *An Advanced History of India*. 1967.

M.A. Stein, ed. and translator, *Kalhana's Rājataranqint, A Chronicle of the Kings of Kashmir*. Westminster, 1900.

BHOJADEVA
b. ca. 980, Dhar, Malwa (India)
d. ca. 1055, Dhar, Malwa
Indian Ruler

Life and Times:

Before the Indian Middle Ages, large parts of the subcontinent had been ruled directly by imperial dynasties. But from the seventh century on, the political structure became increasingly feudal. As a handful of large kingdoms exhausted themselves vying for supreme power, their feudatories rebelled, establishing petty regional states. The Paramaras of Malwa, the area around modern Indore, were one of these newly-independent ruling houses. In the tenth century they freed themselves from the Rashtrakutas, the theoretical overlords of Malwa. The Paramara kingdom was never politically important, but King Bhojadeva is still remembered for learning in a time of decay and social disorganization. Much of our information about Indian achievements in mechanics is a result of his efforts.

Bhojadeva's father, Sindhuraja, was one of the first independent Paramara kings. Bhojadeva succeeded him in 999 or 1000. At about that time raiders from the Islamic kingdom of Ghazni in Afghanistan descended almost yearly into India, and refugees began fleeing south to Malwa. In response, Bhojadeva led forces from several Indian states into the Moslem-occupied Punjab. His success there was temporary, and the Indian kingdoms soon resumed fighting among themselves. Bhojadeva antagonized his neighbors and was defeated by the Chandellas and the Chalukyas.

Though not always successful in battle, Bhojadeva became India's leading patron of scholarship. He established a college for Sanskrit studies and stimulated the revival of Sanskrit culture. To his court at Dhar he drew the leading scholars of India, the most illustrious of whom were known as the "nine pearls." Bhojadeva was himself known as a scholar, although it is doubtful that he wrote many of the twenty treatises attributed to him. These dealt with such varied subjects as rhetoric, poetics, politics and philosophy. The *Rajamriganka*, an influential astronomical work, can be dated on internal evidence to 1042. Other scientific works treated medicine and shipbuilding. The *Samarangana*, on architecture, described a number of Indian

mechanical devices, others being mentioned in a work of fiction, the *Shringaramanjari*.

Outstanding Engineering Achievements:

Chapter 31 of the *Samarangana* discusses *yantras*, or machines. The chapter gives sketchy descriptions of revolving time-keeping devices which strike the "hour," as well as of a revolving astronomical model equipped with needles that trace the movements of the sun and planets. A second class of *yantras* are male and female figures that perform various automatic movements. Multi-storied merry-go-rounds are also described; the rotation mechanism involved a series of gear wheels turned by human labor. Other devices include self-filling oil lamps and birds made to sing by waterworks, both of which were known to Heron of Alexandria [q.v.] and Vitruvius [q.v.] in the classical West. Descriptions of large flying machines found in the *Samarangana* belong to the realm of fantasy.

Both the *Samarangana* and *Shringaramanjari* give details of various types of hydraulic machinery, including underwater conduits, water lifting devices, waterfall machines, showers and elaborate fountains. Many of these mechanisms were intended to entertain the leisured nobility. Nevertheless, a practical outlook is apparent in instructions for the construction of pipes and the height of reservoirs.

Bhojadeva himself contributed to Indian engineering practice by initiating work on the largest irrigation project in ancient India, the 250-square-mile (647 square km) reservoir at Bhojpur. The valley of the Betwa river, almost entirely enclosed by tall hills, was the site of this project. To stop the flow of the river, a dam 300 feet (91 meters) thick at the base and 87 feet (26.5 meters) high was thrown across the mouth of the valley. The dam was made of earth and faced on both sides with immense stone blocks, joined without mortar but so well-fitted as to be watertight. To increase the water content of the reservoir, a second dam was constructed that diverted another river, the Kaliasot, into the Betwa. This dam was similar in construction to the first; 40 feet (12.2 meters) high, it blocked the only other opening to the valley, a gap of 1,500 feet (457 meters). A waste weir cut through solid rock two miles (3.2 km) above the Betwa dam diverted high water from the valley so that the lower dam would not be overwhelmed. The lake was 100 feet (30 meters) deep in places. It might still exist if the lower dam had not been deliberately destroyed in the fifteenth century. ■

Further Reading:

W. Kincaid, "Miscellanea," *The Indian Antiquary,* December 1888.

R.C. Majumdar et al., *An Advanced History of India.* 1967.

V. Raghavan, "Yantras or Mechanical Contrivances in Ancient India," *Transaction 10, Indian Institute of Culture,* 1956.

Mario Vallauri, "Filologia Sancrita Recente," *Archeion.* Vol. XIV (1932).

AL-ZARQĀLĪ
b. 1029, Cordova, Spain
d. 1087, Cordova, Spain
Muslim Spanish Instrument-Maker

Life and Times:

One area of engineering in which the Islamic world produced notable advances was the design of scientific instruments. This work combined the skills of artisans with theoretical concerns developed over several centuries by Islamic scientists from Indian and Greek sources. By the late tenth century Muslim Spain had become a center for sophisticated instrument-making. Artisans and scientists in the Muslim courts of Cordova, Toledo and Seville sought to develop instruments that would precisely indicate the time of day, month and year, establish the relative position of the earth, sun and stars over time, and, secondarily, improve navigation. Perhaps the most innovative of these instrument-makers was al-Zarqālī, who devised the water clocks of Toledo, formulated the Toledan Tables of planetary motions, and constructed the *azafea,* the most advanced astrolabe for the next several centuries in Europe.

Al-Zarqālī (full name: al-Zarqālī abu Ishāq Ibrāhīm ibn Yahyā al-Naqqāsh) was born into a family of Cordova artisans. By his early thirties his skill in making delicate instruments had attracted the attention of Ibn Sā'id, ruler of Toledo, who sét him to work on improving the instruments used in astronomical observations made at the court. Al-Zarqālī's own observations of celestial and planetary motions, especially in 1061 and 1080, were the most precise of his era, and helped provide him with the data from which he developed the tables of planetary motions known as the Toledan Tables. Al-Zarqālī was a central figure in the group of artisans and astronomers that formed at the Toledan court, not only because of his skill as a craftsman but also because of his knowledge of Islamic scientific literature. In the Toledan Tables he drew upon tables developed by al-Khwārizmī [q.v.], the father of algebra; trigonometric relations, especially sines and cosines, played a major role in the operation of al-Zarqālī's *azafea.* Moreover, the inspiration for his construction of the water clocks of Toledo came from his reading of a description of an Indian sun-dial clock in al-Mas'udi's history.

After 1080 the Muslim hold on Toledo weakened, and in the mid-1080s Alfonso VI of Leon and Castile captured the city. In the interim al-Zarqālī had returned to Cordova, and made his last observations in 1087. Historians believe that he died there that year. It should be noted, however, that he dedicated the treatise on the astrolabe, which he apparently completed in the 1080s, to al-Mu'tamid ibn 'Abbād, the ruler of Seville.

Al-Zarqālī wrote, or substantially contributed to, at least seven important treatises. His work on the Toledan Tables and the long-term changes in the position of the solar apogee found their way into the Marseilles Tables, which from the twelfth to the fourteenth century were the standard tables in use in Europe. His treatise on the astrolabe found its way into the courts of western Europe and had a major influence on the construction of astrolabes by sixteenth century astronomers like Gemma Frisius and Juan de Rojas.

Outstanding Engineering Achievements:

Like the standard astrolabe of the period, al-Zarqālī's azafea (or *al-safiha,* meaning flat surface) was designed on the basis of a stereographic projection of the earth. The terrestrial sphere was translated into a circle on a flat surface; lines of longitude formed arcs extending from one polar projection to the other, while lines of latitude curved to meet the equator at the center. The azafea differed from earlier astrolabes in two respects: it used the vernal point, or point of intersection between the apparent path of the sun (the ecliptic) and the equator, as the center of the stereographic projection; and it superimposed a stereographic projection of the celestial sphere directly on that of the earth, rather than using a separate disc for this purpose. Readings on the azafea could be taken by means of three measuring arms: the regulus, equal in length to the diameter of the disc and rotating about its center; the cursor, half the length of the regulus and fixed to it at one end in a perpendicular position; and the brachiolus, attached to the free end of the cursor and rotating so that its tip could touch any point on the surface of the disc.

By manipulating these arms and reading from scales along the edge of the disc, an observer could make a number of astronomical calculations. These included the position of the sun in the zodiac on a given date, the time of the sun's rising and setting on a given date, the declination of the sun in a particular longitude, the declination of a star in a particular geographical latitude, and the geographical latitude of the point of observation. The azafea could also be used to determine the time according to the height of the sun or various stars.

Two other instruments designed by al-Zarqālī are worthy of note. For the water clocks of Toledo al-Zarqālī devised a series of tubes hidden from view that served as adjusting conduits, causing two large tanks to be filled with water over a period of fifteen days and, conversely, to empty at the same rate during the moon's waning. In 1133 the clocks were dismantled at the order of Alfonso VII, but they could not be reassembled. Finally, al-Zarqālī was perhaps the first—along with Ibn as-Samh—to construct an equatorium, a device found on the back of an astrolabe and used to determine the position of the planets. Designed with three sliding discs, representing epicycles in the Ptolemaic construct of the universe, the equatorium provided a geometrical rendering of Ptolemy's theory of the motion of the planets. ■

Further Reading:

Dictionary of Scientific Biography, s.v. "Al-Zarqālī."

Henri Michel, *Traité de l'astrolabe*. Paris, 1947.

J.M. Millas-Vallicrosa, "Un Ejemplar de Azafea Arabe de Azarquiel," *Al-Andalus*. Vol. IX (1944).

George Sarton, *Introduction to the History of Science*. Baltimore, 1927–48.

THEOPHILUS
fl. 1100
German Metallurgist

Life and Times:

Between the time of Pliny the Elder and the Renaissance, only one manuscript is known to have been written in Europe on the subject of metalworking. That one, the *Account of Various Arts,* was probably written in the first quarter of the twelfth century; certainly it was no later, but some have placed it as early as the ninth century. The name of the writer is given in the preface as "Theophilus, a humble priest, servant of the servants of God, unworthy of the name and profession of monk."

Theophilus' origin is as uncertain as his dates. The name is Greek, but it may have been a pseudonym taken by a monk who wished to avoid the personal aggrandizement that authorship might bring. Several of the extant manuscripts have the clause "who is Rugerus" added to Theophilus' name on the title page. This, together with the appearance in the Latin text of occasional German words (such as "meizel" for "chisel") suggest that Theophilus was indeed Rugerus, a monk active as a goldsmith in the Benedictine monastery of Helmershausen near Paderborn. However, the range of techniques discussed in the book suggests that the author had travelled widely; he may have been a Byzantine migrant who taught his art to Rugerus.

Outstanding Engineering Achievement:

The Latin title of Theophilus' work is *Diversum Artium Schedula.* One of the few outstanding medieval documents of technology, its organization and systematic presentation show the influence of Arabic writings, which influenced European writing at the same time that the science of the Arabs influenced that of the Europeans. The book is essentially a manual of practical instruction, explaining to craftsmen how various items were made.

The *Schedula* is divided into three parts. The first deals with painting on the different surfaces of walls, panels, and books. The second describes the manufacture and decoration of glass for vessels, windows, and mosaics. The third part concerns metals, including the refining of gold, silver, iron, and copper, the making of bronze and other alloys, and the construction of chalices, censers, and such musical instruments as church bells, cymbals and organs. a number of devices, which include the rotary grindstone and the wire-drawing plate, are mentioned for the first time in writing.

Most of the processes described were standard metallurgical techniques throughout the Middle Ages. Since Theophilus was writing principally for the builders and decorators of churches, the book contains much detail on the manufacture of gold foil and alloys that have the appearance of gold, lead strips for stained-glass windows, and the coloring of metals. He mentions the use of linseed oil as a painting medium; Jan Van Eyck's use of this technique in the fifteenth century earned him the credit for its origination.

For the refining of copper, Theophilus describes a method that became known as "poling." Crude copper is melted in a clay-lined iron dish and coal ash is scattered on its surface. It is then stirred with a thin, dry piece of wood, causing the impurities to stick to the ash. This ash is then skimmed off, replaced with fresh, and the process repeated until the copper is pure enough. This method, which depends on the reduction of oxides in the copper by the volatile carbon compounds given off by the wood, may have been used by the Romans, but the description in *Schedula* is the earliest on record. ■

Further Reading:

R. P. Johnson, "The Manuscripts of the Schedula of Theophilus Presbyter," *Speculum.* Vol. XIII (1938).

Cyril Stanley Smith, "Life of Biringuccio," in Biringuccio, *Pirotechnia.* New York, 1959.

Theophilus, *On Divers Arts*, trans. by John W. Hawthorne and Cyril Stanley Smith. Chicago, 1963.

AL-KHAZINI, ABUL I-FATH ABD AL-RAHMAN

fl. 1115–1130, Merv, Seljuk (Turkish) Empire
Greek Mathematician and Mechanical Engineer

Life and Times:

The eleventh and twelfth centuries saw a great flowering of interest in mathematics and astronomy in the middle eastern countries that were then under the rule of the Seljuk Turks. An important figure in this development was Al-Khazini, a Greek who had been enslaved and served the treasurer of the court at Merv (now in Turkman SSR). When it was found that he had a knowledge of letters and a grasp of scientific concepts, he was given a thorough education, the mathematical part of which would then have included the Hindu decimal system and algebra, as well as Euclidean geometry and Archimedean mechanics. He became an established mathematician and teacher, constructed precise astronomical tables and wrote a treatise on mechanics, *The Balance of Wisdom*. A Sufi mystic, he led an ascetic life, eating two cakes of bread a day, with meat three times a week. In this way, he managed to live on three dinars a year—and he is said to have refused a gift of 1,000 dinars from the Sultan upon completion of his astronomical tables.

Al-Khazini also wrote a treatise on astronomical instruments, describing the astrolabe, quadrant, an early theodolite, and other devices for sighting objects and measuring the arcs between them. He may have contributed to variations in some of the instruments he described.

Outstanding Engineering Achievement:

The Balance of Wisdom was concerned primarily with specific gravity—the weight of a volume of a substance compared with the weight of an equal volume of water. It was Archimedes [q.v.] who discovered that when a body is weighed in air and then in a fluid, the apparent loss in its weight is equal to the weight of the fluid displaced. Al-Khazini described a very accurate hydrostatic balance with which objects could be weighed in air and in a fluid to compare the specific gravities of solids and fluids with that of water. He also suggested finding the density of water by constructing a hollow brass cube, exactly one cubit on each side, and weighing it filled with water.

The balance was constructed for the court treasury, for testing precious metals, coins, and gemstones. Al-Khazini also used it to produce tables of the specific gravity of a variety of materials, precious and common, for use in analysis. He gave the algebra needed to determine the proportions of two different metals included in an alloy.

The Balance of Wisdom also dealt with the equilibrium of a steelyard, spear, or balance; centers of gravity of bodies of different shapes; and the measurement of time, with a discussion of the water or sand reservoirs of clocks. ■

Further Reading:

M. Clagett, *Science of Mechanics in the Middle Ages.* Madison, Wisconsin, 1959.

Dictionary of Scientific Biography, s.v. "Al-Khazini."

AL-HANAFĪ
b. 1168 (or 1178), Asfūn, Egypt
d. 1251, Rageb, Syria
Syrian-Egyptian Engineer, Mathematician, and Scholar

Life and Times:

The need to irrigate land in order to sustain its fertility has influenced the organization of Middle Eastern society and spawned a millennia-old technology. The waterwheel or *saqiya,* powered by oxen and regulated by the action of cogwheels, played an essential part in the agriculture of the Nile River Valley. Other areas in the Middle East relied on waterwheels not only as an instrument of irrigation, but also as a basis for creating the squares and gardens of urban centers. This was the case in Syria, where the design of water mills often differed from that of Egypt; gearless norias, water-raising devices were more popular.

During the classical and post-classical period of medieval Islam, the design of water mills received the attention of craftsmen who worked at the courts of local rulers. One of the better-known of these figures was the Egyptian-born engineer Ta'asif, or al-Hanafi, who designed several of the water mills along the Orontes River in the vicinity of Homs, in central Syria, during the early part of the thirteenth century.

Al-Hanafi (Sheikh 'Alan-al Dîn Qaisar) came from Upper Egypt, not far from Aswan and the present-day border between Egypt and the Sudan. Born near the town of Asfūn, he studied in both Egypt and Syria. Like many Islamic engineers, al-Hanafi was also a mathematician and an astronomer; he wrote a treatise on geometry based on Euclid's postulates. Like some Islamic scholars of the period, al-Hanafi also devoted himself to the study of religion. In particular, he became a scholar and teacher of Islam as interpreted by the Hanafite school, hence the epithet al-Hanafi. After studying in Syria he went to Mosul, where, under the tutelage of Kemal ad-dîn Mūsā, he studied music.

Chinese drawing (1628) of a noria, the water-raising wheel that was common in the Middle East.

In the early thirteenth century much of the countryside between the Mediterranean and the Persian Gulf had been divided up into small states and petty kingdoms, many of which were ruled by Turkomans who had settled in the region in the previous two centuries. Al-Hanafi placed himself in the employ of the local ruler of Homs, or Hama, and offered his services as an engineer to the kingdom (or *beylik*). He helped construct fortifications for the *beylik* and designed several of the water mills on the Orontes River, along whose banks numerous water mills already existed. Al-Hanafi also constructed a gold-leaf covered globe, made out of wood, which represented on its surface the location of the stars.

Outstanding Engineering Achievement:

The gearless norias, or water-raising wheels, of Homs—many of which are still extant—were water-powered devices. The outer rim of the wheel was fitted with paddles to turn the wheel; the inner rim held a series of pots. As the wheel turned, the pots filled with water at the top. Spillways at the top conducted the water to the populous agricultural region around Homs, which contained a number of famous gardens. ■

Further Reading:

Thorkild Schiøler, *Roman and Islamic Water-Lifting Wheels.* Odense, 1973.

Heinrich Suter, *Die Mathematiker und Astronomen der Araber und ihre Werke.* Leipzig, 1900.

WILLIAM OF SENS
fl. 1150, Sens, France
French Architect

Life and Times:

The early architect was primarily a builder—a man who started in his trade as an apprentice mason and rose through the rank of journeyman to master mason. As such he was responsible for the choice of stone, soundness of the foundations, the overall plan of the building, the efficiency and safety of the hoisting systems, the design of more suitable systems where necessary, the detail of the windows, pillars, arches, and timber work, and for the organization and well-being of the required labor force. He was, in fact, an architect-engineer, carrying his design in his head, for the practice may not yet have developed of drawing a building that did not exist.

In 1140, start was made on the cathedral of St. Etienne in Sens, at the crossing of roads from Paris to Dijon and from Orleans to Troyes. This cathedral was visited by Thomas Becket during his exile and continued its ties with Canterbury even after Thomas' death. It is not known when William became its master mason, but in 1174 he was invited to England to take charge of the reconstruction of the choir of Canterbury Cathedral, which had been badly damaged in a fire. The monk who kept the cathedral archives at that time described William as "a craftsman most skillful in both wood and stone." He was also able to persuade his clients to face the expense of pulling down most of the east end of the cathedral and completely rebuilding it. Wil-

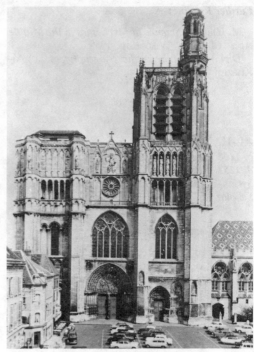

Sens Cathedral, an early Gothic building with vertical lines and a rudimentary form of stone tracery.

liam designed a new choir and apse, but in the fifth year of construction he fell from the scaffolding of the upper vault and was so severely injured that he had to resign and return home to France, leaving the cathedral in the hands of another William.

Outstanding Engineering Achievements:

The cathedral at Sens had originally been designed in the Romanesque style, but William altered the plan and erected a building in the new pointed style that came to be called Gothic, including pointed arches, six-part vaulting, and round piers with foliated capitals placed in pairs. Work in Canterbury began with the selection of stones to be discarded and their replacement with Caen stone that William imported from Normandy. As the engineer in charge, he had to design the cranes used for transferring the stone from ship to river barge.

Canterbury had originally been a Norman church with Romanesque sculpture. The new choir that William built resembled the one in Sens, particularly in its arches, vaulting, and paired piers. The resulting blend demonstrated the possibility of associating Gothic with previous styles and led to the mixed or transitional

The choir (eastern end) of Canterbury Cathedral as rebuilt by William of Sens.

architecture that comprises most English cathedrals. William thus played an essential part in bringing Gothic design as well as construction methods from France to England. ■

Further Reading:

H. Felton and J. Harvey, *The English Cathedrals*. New York, 1950.

E. B. O'Reilly, *How France Built Her Cathedrals*. New York, 1921.

PETER OF COLECHURCH
fl. 1175, London, England
English Civil Engineer

Life and Times:

The River Thames has had a bridge spanning it at London since the days of the Romans. Made of wood, London Bridge was rebuilt several times, but until 1750, it was alone in linking London with Southern England and the Channel ports. Its strategic importance was demonstrated in 1014 when it was deliberately pulled down to stop the Danes from taking the city. The occasion was celebrated with a poem that began, "London Bridge is broken down, Gold is won, and bright renown." The bridge was rebuilt, destroyed, and built again three more times in the eleventh century. In 1163, after a fire, it was rebuilt out of elmwood by Peter, the bridgemaster who was also chaplain of the church of St. Mary Cole.

It was Peter who first conceived of a stone bridge across the Thames. After some initial opposition, King Henry II levied a tax on wool to pay for a new bridge and in 1176 construction began, a few yards upstream of the old one. Just three years before the start, Thomas Becket, the Archbishop of Canterbury who was murdered in his cathedral, had been canonized and had become a popular hero. Since Thomas had been baptized in St. Mary Colechurch, Peter built a chapel dedicated to St. Thomas in the central pier of the bridge. When Peter died in 1205, four years before the bridge was completed, he was buried in this chapel.

Outstanding Engineering Achievement:

Into the soft, muddy bed of the river, Peter drove wooden piles, 10-inch-thick (25 cm) planks of timber. These formed 19 boat-shaped artificial islands, or starlings, to carry the piers of the bridge. Twenty arches varying in width from 17 to 36 feet (5 to 11 meters) spanned the piers, making a bridge that was 926 feet (282 meters) long and 26 feet (8 meters) wide. At low tide there was 30 feet (9 meters) of headroom, but to allow tall ships to sail through, a drawbridge was included towards the northern end. Fortified gateways protected the bridge at either end. In the fourteenth century, traitors' heads began to be impaled on the turrets of the southern gate.

The starlings took up so much of the river that they acted as a dam against the tides. Between ebb and flow the water level rose as much as six feet (1.8 meters) on one side of the piers, falling through the arches in dangerous rapids, swirling in eddies, and often overturning boats that dared to "shoot the bridge." Passengers on river boats frequently preferred to be put ashore on one side of the bridge, walk round and rejoin the boat on the other side. In the fourteenth century waterwheels were built under the arches, at first to grind grain, then to pump water up to serve the city.

Old London Bridge, by Peter of Colechurch, from the south side of the Thames. (The large building on the north side is old St. Paul's Cathedral.)

The bridge was opened in 1209, and in the same year some houses were built, partly on the bridge and partly overhanging the river, supported by struts. Gradually the bridge filled with shops and sumptuous houses, reducing the roadway to 12 feet (3.6 meters) wide, and projecting out above the road, sometimes even touching the house opposite. The cost of maintenance was paid by a toll, until Henry III diverted the revenues to his personal treasury. The consequent weakening of five of the arches allowed them to be knocked down by ice in the winter of 1282, together with the houses built above. "London Bridge is Falling Down," the well-known variant of the older poem, may have been written to commemorate this event.

Occasionally fire swept across the bridge, but it continued to be a favorite shopping street, crowded with travellers, peddlers, sightseers and pick-pockets. The houses were finally removed in 1762, but Old London Bridge remained until 1832, after the opening of the replacement by John Rennie [q.v.]. When Peter's bridge was pulled down, it was simply dropped into the river, along with the St. Thomas Chapel and Peter's bones. ■

Further Reading:

P. Spier, *London Bridge is Falling Down.* New York, 1967.

AL-JAZARI, IBN AL-RAZZAZ
fl. ca. 1200, Mesopotamia
Islamic Hydraulic Engineer

Life and Times:

One of the major treatises on technology in the medieval Islamic world, and probably the most extensive in describing hydraulic devices, was written by al-Jazari, a craftsman who flourished in one of the small Turkoman kingdoms (or *beyliks*) that arose in eastern Asia Minor following the decline of the Abbasid Caliphate. Little is known of al-Jazari, including his real name. His appellation indicates, however, that he came from the region between the upper reaches of the Tigris and Euphrates rivers, homeland of the Kurdish tribes. He apparently entered the service of the Artuqids, the local rulers of Diyar Bakr (a district in the Cilician mountains), sometime between 1179 and 1181. Al-Jazari served as a court craftsman, designer and engineer in the Artuqid capital of Amid for at least 25 years. Under the patronage of Nasir al-Din he completed his treatise on mechanical devices in 1205.

Al-Jazari's treatise, *Kitab fi Ma'rifat al-hiyal al-handasiyya (The Book of Knowledge of Ingenious Devices),* contains descriptions of five kinds of devices: clocks, drinking vessels, bloodletting basins, fountains and water pumps, plus a miscellany of others. Many of the devices reflect the influence of previous works on mechanical theory and design, most notably those of Heron of Alexandria [q.v.] and Philon of Byzantium [q.v.] from late antiquity and the Banū Mūsā [q.v.] from the classical Islamic period. Al-Jazari devoted most of his attention to water-powered mechanisms and to those which moved water. Like many court engineers, he concentrated on the startling or entertaining aspects of his devices rather than on their practical value.

The importance of Al-Jazari's work lies in its close attention to mechanical detail, giving a clear view of Islamic hydraulic engineering of the period. Although much of his material was not original, he suggested many improvements and helped popularize existing devices. These included the conical valve which closes automatically in response to water pressure and the segmental gear. Al-Jazari also provided the earliest surviving description of a crankshaft, and his reciprocating water pump (see below) forecasted the line of development that led to the steam engine.

Al-Jazari's treatise enjoyed great popularity in its own time, and was translated from the original Arabic into Turkish and Persian. The extent of its further influence, however, is uncertain. Several devices described by al-Jazari, including the conical valve and the float valve for regulating water level, were later re-invented by European engineers. The treatise is not known to have been translated into Latin or any other European language. It is possible, however, that knowledge of al-Jazari's devices diffused through personal contacts among craftsmen during the late Middle Ages.

Outstanding Engineering Achievements:

Of the various machines described by al-Jazari, perhaps the most interesting in light of later developments, is the reciprocating water pump. The device was powered by a water wheel, which turned a horizontal axle attached to a toothed wheel. This turned another toothed wheel, to which a lever arm was attached at the center. The rotating motion of the lever moved two rods, attached to opposite ends of the arm. Each rod in turn was fixed to a piston inserted in a cylinder that rested in a body of water. As the lever arm pulled one rod-and-piston up in its cylinder, it forced the other downward. The partial vacuum created by the rising piston sucked water into the cylinder, from which it was diverted into an evacuation pipe. In operation (if not in appearance) the device resembled the later steam pump, using the motion of the water wheel instead of steam pressure to move the pistons. ■

Further Reading:

Dictionary of Scientific Biography, s.v. "Al-Jazari."

Donald R. Hill, trans. and annotator, *The Book of Ingenious Devices*. Boston, 1979.

ROGER BACON
b. ca. 1219, Ilchester, Somerset, England
d. ca. 1292, Paris, France or Oxford, England
English Scholastic Scientist

Life and Times:

Successive generations have seized upon the figure of Roger Bacon as both a symbol of his age and a precursor of another. A thirteenth-century scholar and Franciscan friar, Bacon suggested that experimentation could lead to the practical application of knowledge. He also raised the possibility of making self-powered devices, including self-propelled vehicles operating on land, in the sea, and in the air.

Bacon attended the newly founded university at Oxford. During the 1230s and 1240s he traveled to France and lectured on Aristotle at the University of Paris. He also met Pierre de Maricourt [q.v.] and may have studied with him. Accepting the absolute authority of scripture, Bacon nevertheless stressed the importance of careful observation, controlled experiment, and mathematical analysis in understanding nature. He studied mathematics, astronomy, and astrology, and showed that the current (Julian) calendar was gaining a day every 130 years. He also studied and wrote about the laws of optics, and displayed an interest in alchemy. In 1257 Bacon entered the Franciscan order, but soon found that his views were so unacceptable to those who ran the order that he was restricted in his activities and forbidden to publish. However, between 1266 and 1267, the new pope, Clement IV, allowed Bacon to present three new works: *Opus Majus*, *Opus Minus*, and *Opus Tertium*. These were followed by further elaborations of his theories on the organization of nature (what we would call science).

The death of Thomas Aquinas in 1237 brought to a close much of the independent discussion by cleric-scholars about the structure of knowledge that had characterized previous decades. In 1277 the bishop of Paris labelled a wide range of intellectual propositions as Averroist, and censured them as heretical. Within two years Bacon was imprisoned, most likely on charges of heresy. He remained in prison until his death or shortly before it.

Outstanding Engineering Achievement:

Bacon's primary contribution to the history of technology is contained in his work *De mirabili potestate artis et naturae*, composed between 1256 and 1266. He believed that the ancients had devised a host of self-propelled devices and suggested that modern men should be able to achieve similar results. He mentioned vessels that row without men, carriages that travel without animals, submarines, flying machines, and small instruments with the power to lift heavy weights. Bacon did not present diagrams or sketches, his work thus differing sharply from that of Leonardo da Vinci [q.v.]. Rather, Bacon's description served as a literary goad to future champions of technical progress.

Further Reading:

Dictionary of Scientific Biography, s.v. "Roger Bacon."

JEAN D'ORBAIS
fl. 1212–1231

JEAN DE LOUP
fl. 1231–1247

GAUCHER DE RHEIMS
fl. 1250–1259

BERNARD DE SOISSONS
fl. 1263–1298

ROBERT DE COURCY
fl. c. 1300
French Architect-Engineers

Life and Times:

The names of the architects of Rheims Cathedral, like that of Robert de Luzarches [q.v.] of Amiens, were inlaid in a design on the floor of the nave. The design was that of a labyrinth; in Rheims its shape was octagonal, with octagonal bays in the four corners, filling the shape out into a rough square. The actual floor tiles have been lost, but the pattern has been preserved in old drawings and documents. Each corner contained the name of one of the first four of the architects above. In the center was probably the name of Alberic de Humbert, the Archbishop who laid the foundation stone in 1211.

To the first Jean is credited the overall plan of the cathedral; he was its first directing architect and chief engineer. He had seen, and perhaps worked on, the construction of the abbey church in his native Orbais. That church had been modelled on the early Gothic choir of the church of St. Remi in Rheims. From this background Jean designed one of the great cathedrals of the High Gothic.

Work began at the eastern end, the choir taking thirty years to finish. By then the second Jean had taken over. During his sixteen years in charge, the transept—the north-south wings—was completed, with their portals. Gaucher began the nave and the west portals that form the main entrance to the cathedral. Bernard was the directing architect for the next thirty-five years. He was responsible for the circular rose window in the west facade, and five bays along the nave.

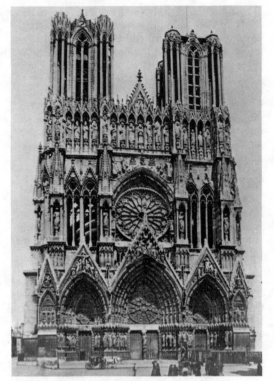

The twin towers and rose window of the western facade of Rheims Cathedral.

By Robert's time the pavement of the nave, with its labyrinth pattern, had been completed, so his name could not be included; he was, however, honored with burial in the church. Villard de Honnecourt [q.v.] visited the site in about 1230 and drew sketches that are sometimes at variance with the building as it now stands. In some cases Villard may have been including his own ideas in his drawings, but there is also the possibility that changes in details were made as the construction progressed.

Outstanding Engineering Achievement:

Although the building of Rheims Cathedral continued for 270 years, it retained a splendid unity of style. The interior of the 460-foot (140 meters) long nave soars 125 feet (38 meters) to its intersecting vaulting. The twin towers of the western façade are 268 feet (81.6 meters) high; spires were never added to them. Since the weight of a Gothic building is supported by piers and flying buttresses, not by bearing walls, large windows could be punched out and later filled with stained glass. In early Gothic the glazed area appears as a hole in the wall, but Jean d'Orbais designed a completely new type of window, which then became typical of Gothic churches. Within the wall opening, independent stonework framing shapes the lancet and rose designs of the glass areas. This stone tracery gave a lightness in appearance and construction that was not equalled until modern concrete and glass was developed.

The cathedral was badly damaged in World War I by shells and incendiary bombs. That it stood and could be restored is a tribute to the work of its original master masons. ■

Further Reading:

John Fitchen, *The Construction of Gothic Cathedrals*. Chicago, 1961.

H. Jantzen, *High Gothic*. New York, 1962.

J. J. Norwich, ed., *Great Architecture of the World*. New York, 1979.

E. B. O'Reilly, *How France Built Her Cathedrals*. New York, 1921.

ROBERT DE LUZARCHES
fl. c. 1220
French Architect and Engineer

Life and Times:

The development of the Gothic style of architecture in Europe coincided with a period of Crusades, both activities exhibiting Christian religious zeal. This fervor is displayed by Gothic, which first appeared in northern France, in an emphasis on the vertical, with arches that come to a point, towers surmounted by spires, thin walls upheld by buttresses and, as the style progressed, taller and taller vaults. One of the tallest vaults in Europe was that over the nave of the cathedral of Amiens.

The master builders of the three classic French cathedrals—Chartres, Rheims, and Amiens—placed their names in labyrinth patterns that were inlaid on the floor of the naves. The circular labyrinth of Chartres has been preserved, and although the square labyrinth of Rheims is lost and the octagonal one of Amiens was destroyed in 1825, their designs are known from drawings and documents. The middle stone of the Amiens labyrinth has been preserved and contains the names of Bishop Evrard de Fouilloy, who laid the foundation stone in 1220,

and of the builders from then until 1288: Robert de Luzarches, and Thomas de Cormant and his son Renaud. Of these Robert is credited with being the premier architect of the cathedral. Nothing else is known of his life.

Outstanding Engineering Achievement:

Typical of the High Gothic, Amiens Cathedral was built on a framework of pillars and arches, which allowed the walls to be far lighter than those of the earlier Romanesque style, and fitted with large stained glass windows. Throughout the Gothic period cathedrals increased in height. The height of the naves of both Paris and Laon, the first to be built, was 78 feet (24 meters), of Chartres 118 feet (36 meters), Rheims 123 feet (37 meters), and Amiens 138 feet (42 meters). A century later Beauvais topped Amiens by 20 feet (6 meters). To counteract the outward pressure that the vaulting produced on its own walls, the Gothic solution was the inward push of buttresses and flying buttresses.

Unlike many medieval buildings which had defective foundations, those of Amiens are unusually elaborate, being comprised of nineteen layers. A bed of compacted clay, about fifteen inches (38 cm) thick, is followed by one of

The choir (eastern end) and south transept of Amiens Cathedral showing the flying buttresses and the high proportion of glass to stone.

concrete of the same thickness. Next are four-teen courses of medium-quality stone, each about one foot (30 cm) thick, and finally three courses of hard sandstone. ■

Further Reading:

H.J. Cowan, *The Master Builders*. New York, 1977.

H. Jantzen, *High Gothic*. New York, 1962.

JORDANUS DE NEMORE
fl. ca. 1230
German Mathematician and Mechanician

Life and Times:

Statics was known in the Middle Ages as the science of weights and was studied in Latin translations of Arabic and Greek works. One such was the *Problems of Mechanics* by an anonymous writer in the school of Aristotle. This accounted for the law of the lever—the fact that unequal weights balance each other if the heavier weight is closer to the fulcrum—by considering the motions of the ends of the arms of an unbalanced lever. The longer arm would sweep through a larger arc than the smaller one, but since both arms take the same time, the longer arm must move faster. The ability to move with a greater velocity was what enabled a lighter weight on the longer arm to balance a heavier one on the shorter arm. In this way, the Aristotelian philosophers explained statics in dynamical terms. However, their account was not a mathematical one. Scholars of the Middle Ages also knew most of the works of Euclid (but not of Archimedes, who treated statics geometrically without reference to motion). Jordanus' work made considerable advances within the Aristotelian framework, and was written entirely in a Euclidean format, with axioms, theorems, and an attempt to prove all its conclusions.

Nothing is known of Jordanus de Nemore, whose name appears as the author of two treatises on mechanics, three on arithmetic, one on algebra, one on geometry and one on astrolabe projections. He has been identified with Jordanus of Saxony, who entered the Dominican order in Paris in 1220, was elected Master-General in 1222, and drowned in a shipwreck leaving the Holy Land in 1237. However, this identification is controversial and uncertain. All that is sure about Jordanus de Nemore is that he completed his work in the decades before 1260.

Outstanding Engineering Achievement:

Jordanus wrote two books on mechanics, the major one being the *Theory of Weights*, which corrected and superseded the earlier *Elements*. He produced an original proof of the law of the lever which contained in it a principle that became known as the principle of Jordanus: that which can raise a one-pound (0.45 kg) weight through a height of 10 feet (3 meters) can raise a 10-pound (4.5 kg) weight through a height of one foot (0.3 meters). Another important result was the law of the inclined plane, stating that if a weight on an inclined plane is connected to another on a plane with a different slope, then they will be in equilibrium if the weights are directly proportional to the slopes. The classical Greek philosophers had tried to prove this law. Only Pappus had appeared to succeed, but his proof was erroneous and, in any case, his work was not known in the Middle Ages. In the late sixteenth century, Simon Stevin [q.v.] and Galileo [q.v.] gave the first proofs after Jordanus'.

The *Science of Weights* was well-known to scholars of the Middle Ages, and was still so important in the Renaissance that it was printed in 1533 and again in 1565.

Other Achievements:

In one of his arithmetic books, Jordanus explained the Hindu decimal system, in another he described arithmetical operations involving fractions, and in the third gave an advanced, formal treatment of theoretical arithmetic which was copied many times and became the standard text of the Middle Ages. It was printed in 1496 and 1514. His algebra was Euclidean in its method of proof, but gave numerical examples after each proof. It was the first work to use letters of the alphabet to represent numbers. ■

Further Reading:

Dictionary of Scientific Biography, s.v. "Jordanus."

M. Clagett, *Science of Mechanics in the Middle Ages*. Madison, Wisconsin, 1959.

E. A. Moody and M. Clagett, *The Medieval Science of Weights*. Madison, Wisconsin, 1960.

R. B. Thomson, *Jordanus de Nemore and the Mathematics of Astrolabes*. Toronto, 1978.

VILLARD DE HONNECOURT
fl. 1235, Honnecourt, Picardy, France
French Architect and Engineer

Life and Times:

No personal sketch-books have come down to us from medieval architects or artists, but there are model-books containing drawings made from life and other drawings, passed on from one craftsman to another through succeeding generations. These could include studies of architecture, religious figures, the geometry of forms, ornamental letters, anything that caught the eye of the artist, noted down in any order, even upside down on the page. The most comprehensive such book is that of Villard, which is comprised of thirty-three parchment sheets, dating from about 1235. Preserved in the Abbey of St. Germain des Pres in Paris, the manuscript was discovered during the French Revolution and eventually deposited in the French National Library, where it is still held.

A little of Villard's life is told by his book. He was evidently a man of some education and means, for he travelled widely in Europe, as far east as Hungary, and drew some of the churches, tombs, and statues that he saw. The remaining facts of his life are unknown.

Outstanding Engineering Achievement:

Villard's sketchbook includes illustrations of buildings, machines and construction or surveying techniques. He was clearly interested in church architecture, but strangely took no notice

The power saw with automatic feet included in the notebook of Villard de Honnecourt.

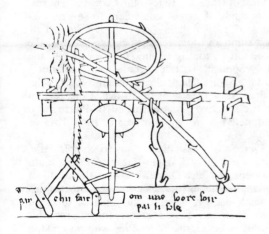

of the great castles then being built in France and other European countries. His drawings of buildings were not done to scale and reveal little of the development of the Gothic style, then at its height in Western Europe.

Perhaps most interesting from the standpoint of engineering history are Villard's drawings of mechanical devices, which illustrate the growing European interest in machines. Villard drew and described a number of large machines, such as a crane and military sling for firing missiles. There is a platform that can be raised by a heavy vertical screw; Villard's note describes this as "one of the strongest machines in existence for lifting weights." Another drawing shows a power saw. It is a straight saw held by a beam at one end and a hinged frame at the other. The frame is pushed by rods attached to the shafts of a waterwheel. The rebound of the beam pulls the saw back. A toothed disc also mounted on the shaft pushes the work forward to the saw. In Villard's drawing, the beam is the limb of a tree, held up by a forked stick. This was either the way he saw it, or the way he recommended it be made. Mechanically improbable as it might appear, this sawmill is the earliest known industrial machine that involves two correlated, fully automatic motions: the sawing and the automatic.

At a time just before mechanical clocks began to appear, Villard drew an early form of the escapement mechanism, a weight-driven system

Villard's perpetual motion machine in which four hammers on one side outweigh the three on the other and turn the wheel.

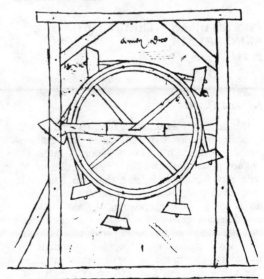

of pulleys turning a vertical axis, in which fashion "one builds an angel whose finger points always towards the sun."

A gadget he may have invented was a hand warmer, for which he says "you should make in copper a sort of apple with two halves" containing pivoting rings (or gimbels) that hold an interior fire-pan level. With this, Villard tells us, a bishop "can cheerfully hold High Mass, protected from cold." The apple warmer may have worked; another of his mechanisms surely did not. It was the first perpetual motion machine illustrated in the West. A wheel has an odd number of hammers attached to its rim with hinge pins. If there are seven hammers, then at any moment there will be four on one side and only three on the other, so the weight of the extra one will carry the wheel round perpetually. The dream of a *perpetuum mobile* continued for centuries. ∎

Further Reading:

T. Bowie, ed., *The Sketchbook of Villard de Honnecourt.* Bloomington, Indiana, 1959.

Dictionary of Scientific Biography, s.v. "Villard de Honnecourt."

Neal FitzSimons, ed., *Engineering Classics of James Kip Finch.* Kensington, Maryland, 1978.

Jean Gimpel, *The Medieval Machine.* London, 1977.

F. Klemm, *A History of Western Technology.* Cambridge, Mass., 1964.

PIERRE DE MONTREUIL (or DE MONTEREAU)
fl. 1245, Paris, France
French Architect

Life and Times:

It is generally agreed that the first true Gothic structure was the abbey church of St. Denis-en-France, dedicated in 1144. A century later, for unknown reasons, the building was almost totally reconstructed. During that time the style had developed towards ever lighter walls, with an increase in the proportion of glass to stone. Another change was that by the thirteenth century the names of the master masons and architects were considered important enough to be recorded. The name of the first master of St. Denis is unknown, but written documents in-

The cathedral of Notre Dame in Paris from the south, with the rose window begun by Jehan de Chelles and completed by Pierre de Montreuil.

clude the name of Pierre, who was responsible for the reconstruction of St. Denis as well as other important works in Paris. (The building was commissioned by Abbott Suger, who may have contributed to its design.)

The villages of Montereau and Montreuil, near Paris, both claim Pierre. There is a possibility that there were two architects named Pierre at the same time, but it is generally accepted that there was only one, known by two names. If there was only one, he was very busy. From 1231 to 1265 he was Master of St. Denis, where he built a new nave, transept, and upper choir. Between 1230 and 1238 he was also commissioned privately by the House of Capet to construct a chapel at the castle of St. Germain-en-Laye. Upon its completion he was employed by the monks of St. Germain-des-Pres to build a new refectory and a chapel to the Virgin.

In 1238 the Byzantine Emperor Baldwin II offered to sell to King Louis of France the holiest of Christian relics—the Crown of Thorns. Thousands of livres—equivalent to several millions of 1950 dollars—were paid, followed by vast sums for other relics, such as a piece of the True Cross, the tip of the Holy Spear, and the Holy Sponge. To house these treasures, Louis had the Sainte-Chappelle built in the court of the Palace, now the Palais de Justice. Construction of the sanctuary was entrusted to Pierre, who completed it in only five years, from 1243 to 1248.

Pierre's last assignment was to complete the rose window and upper facade of the south transept of Notre-Dame following the death of Jehan de Chelles [q.v.]. Pierre died either in his town house or in his country place, south of Paris. He was buried before the altar of his chapel at St. Germain-des-Pres with an epitaph that described him as "a flower overflowing with the perfume of virtue, in his lifetime the Doctor of Masons."

Outstanding Engineering Achievements:

The nave, transept, and upper choir of St. Denis were all rebuilt with slender pillars and flying buttresses that appeared fragile yet supported the roof perfectly. The walls themselves were glass: stained glass windows stretching from pillar to pillar and filling the interior with colored light. For the transept, completed in 1245, Pierre built the largest rose window then existing—36 feet (11 meters) in diameter. Five years later, Jehan de Chelles followed his lead and designed even larger roses for the transept of Notre Dame. Each succeeding ring of these roses, starting from the center, contains twice as many divisions as the preceding inner ring. The roses appear to radiate light outwards from the center, thus being early examples of Rayonnant, the new variant style.

La Sainte-Chappelle, on the Ile de la Cité (the same island of the River Seine on which Notre Dame stands), is constructed of groined vaulting springing from a series of slender shafts built against supporting buttresses. Between the shafts are wall spaces 15 feet (4.5 meters) wide and 50 feet (15 meters) high, totally filled with stained glass. The building houses two chapels, one above the other. Desecrated during the French Revolution, the reliquaries were melted down for their gold and the relics scattered, only the Crown of Thorns being saved. But the Sainte-Chappelle and much of its glass survives. ■

Further Reading:

Yves Bottineau, *Notre-Dame de Paris et la Sainte-Chappelle*. Grenoble, 1966.

Allan Temko, *Notre-Dame of Paris*. New York, 1959.

PIERRE DE MARICOURT (PETRUS PERIGRINUS)
fl. 1269
French Military Engineer and Scientist

Life and Times:

The magnetic compass came to be used in Europe in the twelfth century. It is not known whether the north-pointing ability of the lodestone was discovered independently or was imported from China or Islam, but other properties of magnets were discovered and magnetic instruments were considerably improved in Europe. The man most responsible for this increase in knowledge was Pierre de Maricourt, who wrote the earliest known account of magnetism. After his work no new advances were made until 1600, when William Gilbert wrote his book *De Magnete,* which acknowledged Pierre's work and included some of his experiments.

Maricourt is a village near Honnecourt, and it is probable that Pierre knew Villard [q.v.]. He also knew the visiting Englishman Roger Bacon [q.v.], who referred to Pierre as the Master of Experiments, the greatest living scientist. Bacon described Pierre as gaining medical and chemical knowledge through experiment; studying the work of miners and metalworkers, farmers and surveyors; knowing about warfare, weaponry and hunting; and taking notes of remedies and charms used by old women and wizards. This and other references to Pierre appeared in Bacon's *De Secretis* and three of his *Opera,* written in the mid-1260s.

In 1269, the only date known about Pierre's life, he was accompanying the army of Charles of Anjou at the siege of Lucera, in southern Italy. In view of Roger Bacon's description of him, it seems reasonable to assume that Pierre was an engineer, very likely constructing siege engines and artillery. On August 8, he sent his *Letter on the Magnet* to a friend in Picardy. In it he mentions intending to write a book on mirrors; if he did write it, it has not survived.

Pierre's letter was first printed soon after 1520, before which time it was virtually unknown. The author's name given by the publisher in Rome was Ramon Lull, a thirteenth-century alchemist. The first edition under Pierre's own (Latin) name was in 1558, in Augsburg. The work was at the time still the best available technical description of the compass, its properties and use.

Outstanding Engineering Achievement:

The *Letter* describes the attraction of a magnet for iron, and the attraction of unlike poles and repulsion of like poles; how to find the poles, distinguish between north and south poles and magnetize an iron needle by passing a magnet over it.

In this period, the ever-rotating heavens with their unfailing lights that control human affairs were seen as a source of power that could possibly be tapped. Since the lodestone pointed towards the north star, it was believed to be influenced by this power, and perhaps able to transmit it to a mechanical device. Pierre therefore suggested mounting a spherical lodestone "without friction" parallel to the celestial axis, north pointing to north. He believed that this would rotate once a day, acting as a perfect clock and, if inscribed with a star map, as an automatic armillary sphere.

Another suggestion was for a perpetually moving wheel, in which a magnet was fixed at the rim of a small vertically mounted silver wheel, with its magnetic axis at a slight angle to the diameter of the wheel. Around the wheel a series of iron nails are attached to the wheel's support. As the magnet passes a nail, its outward north pole will induce a south pole in the end of the nail. The wheel's impetus will carry it a little further, so that the south pole of the magnet will be close enough to be repelled by the south pole of the nail. This will keep the wheel turning. Fanciful as the idea may be, it nevertheless shows an understanding of magnetism and magnetic induction. ■

Further Reading:

Jean Gimpel, *The Medieval Machine*. London, 1977.

F. Klemm, *A History of Western Technology*. Cambridge, 1964.

A. Pacey, *The Maze of Ingenuity*. Cambridge, 1976.

JEHAN DE CHELLES
fl. 1260, Paris

PIERRE DE CHELLES
fl. 1300
French Architect-Engineers

Life and Times:

Between 1130 and 1270, 80 cathedrals and 500 large churches were built in France, all in the new pointed style that came to be called Gothic. At the heart of the movement was Notre-Dame of Paris, which served to inspire many other communities to build. The choir of Notre-Dame, built between 1163 and 1182, belonged to the transitional phase; the nave, largely completed before 1200, was in the maturing Gothic; the west facade of 1200–1250 was typical of the High Gothic; and the transept roses of the late thirteenth century are superb examples of Rayonnant, the last flowering of the style before decadence.

As with all buildings of the Middle Ages, the architect was the engineer in charge, as responsible for strength and structure as for design. Very little is known of these men—not even the name of Notre-Dame's first Master. The name of Jehan, however, is inscribed on the foundation stone of the south facade, with a statement that he started that facade on Feb. 12, 1257 (which we would call 1258, since at that time the number of the year did not change until March).

Jehan may have built the church in his hometown of Chelles, just west of Paris. His work on Notre-Dame actually began about 1230 with rebuilding the nave. He enlarged the clerestory, replaced a double row of flying buttresses with ones that cross the double aisle in a single leap of 40 feet, and added seven chapels to each side of the nave.

In 1250 Jehan began work on the northern facade of the transept, after which he turned to the southern facade, but he did not live to complete it. The upper half was probably finished by Pierre de Montreuil [q.v.], who may have been Jehan's cousin. Pierre de Chelles, who must have been related to Jehan, added bays and flying buttresses to the choir, completing the cathedral in 1317.

Outstanding Engineering Achievement:

Before the new facades of the transept of Notre-Dame could be built, the original ones had to be demolished. Each was 45 feet (13.7 meters) in width, and higher than the 108-foot (32.9 meters) vaulting. On both sides of each transept wing, Jehan built powerful pillars to hold the structure erect. A shoring of ash and fir was then built so that, with great care, the facades could be dismantled. After extending each end of the transept, Jehan began work on the new north facade.

Above the portal, he created a wall of colored glass mounted in a net of stone. At the time that the west rose had been built, its 29-foot (8.8 meters) diameter made it the largest window of its type. The window in Jehan's north facade, with a diameter close to 41 feet (12.5 meters), is even larger, but its area of 1,300 square feet (120 square meters) is 80 percent glass. Below it is a row of windows with very little stone visible to support the huge window above. This entire facade has survived for seven hundred years with only minor repairs; even the stained glass is original. ■

Further Reading:

Allan Temko, *Notre-Dame of Paris.* New York, 1959.

LEVI BEN GERSON
b. 1288, Bagnols, France
d. 1344
Judeo-Provençal Astronomer and Instrument-Maker

Life and Times:

As Muslim control receded on the Iberian peninsula after the twelfth century, the Jewish communities of Spain and southern France served as a conduit for the movement of texts and mechanical devices from the Islamic world to the Christian world. In some cases Arabic works were first translated into Hebrew, then translated from Hebrew into Latin. Levi ben Gerson, a Jewish scholar who flourished in Provence in the early fourteenth century, was an important figure in this process: His work on astronomy, including improvements in devices used to measure planetary and celestial motions, had a major impact upon late medieval science. He is perhaps best known for devising—or first reporting on—the Jacob's staff, an astronomical instrument later adopted by mariners for navigational purposes.

Descended from a family of learned men, Levi ben Gerson was born in 1288 in Bagnols, a city in the domain of Provence but under the rule of the king of France. He spent his entire life in southern France, living in Orange, Avignon, and Perpignan. He knew little Arabic or Latin, if any; the availability of Arabic and Greek texts in Hebrew thus proved crucial for his ability to provide commentaries of his own on mathematical, astronomical, and philosophical subjects. For that reason, the work of a previous generation of translators, especially Moshe ibn Tibbon and Jacob Anatoli, set the stage for him.

Between 1317 and 1329 ben Gerson composed his major philosophical and astronomical opus, the *Milhamot Adonai* (*Wars of the Lord*). The work was divided into six books, including one on astronomy, the *Sefer Tekunah* or *Book of Astronomy.* The latter, based heavily on Islamic sources, contained a critique of Ptolemy's *Almagest,* a series of astronomical tables whose base was the meridian on which Orange was situated, and a description of the Jacob's staff. The name of the device was derived from a poem written by ben Gerson, who himself referred to the instrument as a cross-staff. Ben Gerson used the Jacob's staff as an aid in his astronomical observations, which included attempts to measure the diameter of the sun and moon. The instrument was apparently first employed in navigation by Martin Behaim in the fifteenth century, and remained in use until well into the eighteenth century.

Outstanding Engineering Achievements:

The Jacob's staff determined the height of an object by measuring the angle formed by the object, the observer, and the horizon. It consisted of two main pieces; a long graded rod and a plate perpendicular to the rod, held at that angle by a plumb line. The plate could be moved along the rod until, along the line of vision, the top of the plate touched the object measured, generally a celestial body, and the bottom of the plate touched the horizon. Having established the position of the object, the viewer could then determine the angle of the object from the gradations on the rod. These markings were derived from the sine function, since ben Gerson was unaware of the tangent function. The Jacob's staff could be used to find the height of a building or the altitude of the sun and other celestial objects. Ben Gerson also tried to determine the eye's center of vision with the instrument.

Besides the Jacob's staff, ben Gerson helped popularize in Europe the camera obscura, a box with a pinhole in one side which projected on the interior of the opposite side an inverted image of any object outside the box. Of Islamic origin, the device was generally viewed in Europe as a

The Jacob's staff of Levi ben Gerson, drawn in 1633; top, holding the bottom sight along the horizon and the top sight on the star.

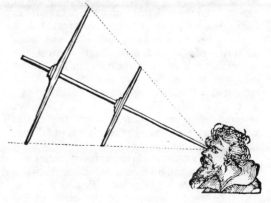

curiosity. But ben Gerson used it in his astronomical observations, and sought to explain variations in the size of the images projected in the box.

Other Achievements:

In addition to his astronomical work, ben Gerson wrote several mathematical treatises. In the *Ma'aseh hoseh* (or *Work of the Computer*), which he completed in the early 1320s, he established some of the rules upon which permutations and combinations were determined. His work on trigonometric functions, which was translated into Latin in 1343 as *De sinibus, chordis et arcabus,* emphasized the use of sines rather than chords, with which European mathematicians of the period were more familiar. ∎

Further Reading:

Dictionary of Scientific Biography, s.v. "Levi Ben Gerson."

George Sarton, *Introduction to the History of Science.* Baltimore, 1927–48.

Inside the 15-foot-thick walls of Conway Castle, built by James St. George.

JAMES ST. GEORGE
fl. 1290
French Military Engineer and Architect

Life and Times:

The medieval castle had a number of functions: while built primarily for defense in war, it could also be the residence of a rich and powerful man, the quarters of a garrison of troops, a base for raids on surrounding villages, a courthouse and jail, and a place for the settlement of disputes and the collection of taxes. Six castles in North Wales, however, were constructed as a group to exert the military, political, and social authority of Edward I of England over the mountainous area of Snowdonia. In 1277, after centuries of sporadic war, Snowdonia was the only part of Wales that had not surrendered to English rule. The area fell in 1283, but revolted again in 1294. Meanwhile the castles were being built. When the revolt was put down, the English victory was final.

The chief architect of this series of castles was James, who began his career in the area between France, Italy and Switzerland, first as a mason and then as the architect of the castle of Es-

The polygonal towers of Caernarvon Castle with, left, the Eagle Tower.

peranche. This castle was in the town of St. Georges, from which James took his last name. The lord of Esperanche, Count Philip, was a cousin of the king of England, who invited James to work in Britain. By 1284 James had risen to the title of Keeper of the Works at Conway, site of one of King Edward's castles, administering six thousand pounds in building funds. In 1290 he was appointed Constable of

Harlech Castle with its fine view of the surrounding area.

Harlech, which placed him as the governor of another of the castles.

Three of the four principal castles, Conway, Caernarvon, and Harlech were under construction at the same time. Between them, they employed 2,500 men from April to November each year. Records of Harlech show that in one week its work force included 170 masons, 90 quarrymen, 28 carpenters, 24 smiths, 520 unskilled laborers, and 26 administrative staff. Workers were conscripted from all over England and Wales, and though they were paid fair wages, the desertion rate was high enough for horsemen to be employed as guards.

With such a labor force, work proceeded apace. James' first project was Rhuddlan castle. He started ground clearance in 1277, and completed work five years later. Conway castle was finished in 1287, less than five years after its start; Harlech took only five years more. Caernarvon was built in the same time, though its Eagle Tower was not finished until 1330. But Beaumaris, which was begun in 1295, never was completed—interest and building funds gradually petered out, and construction was stopped in 1370. The sixth of James' castles was Flint, which had been begun in the previous reign.

The enormous sum of eighty thousand pounds was expended on this project. It is difficult to assess this in modern terms. One estimation is that it was roughly equivalent to twenty million 1970 dollars, but this may be ten times too small. The great hall at Conway cost one hundred pounds. By 1293 James was receiving two-thirds of that amount annually, but this was apart from a lifetime pension that the king awarded him in

1284 of three shillings a day (over fifty pounds a year). His wife was assured of a widow's pension of one-half James' pension.

Outstanding Engineering Achievement:

James was the chief administrator and engineer of all six castles, and the architect of Caernarvon, Harlech, Beaumaris, and Rhuddlan, if not of Conway. They are acknowledged to be among the finest examples of medieval military architecture. Each was built with high, thick curtain walls, so thick that they could withstand iron bolts fired from the giant crossbow called the ballista, or rocks slung with great force from the huge counterweighted seesaw called the trebuchet. The walls of Conway Castle were 12 to 15 feet (3.6 to 4.5 meters) thick, which was enough to withstand cannon fire two centuries later.

As an example of military planning and engineering, Beaumaris is unequalled. Symmetric and almost square, it has an outer wall with 16 round towers, and a higher inner wall with 10 more. Conway is one of the most intimidating of all castles, with 1400 yards (1280 meters) of curtain wall. Its eight huge circular towers and 22 smaller ones are built around two wards, an outer one that still contains the remains of the great hall, and an inner one with the royal apartments.

Caernarvon is strikingly different from the others in having towers that are polygonal instead of round, and in being far from square in its overall shape. It is almost 600 feet (183 meters) long, but its width varies from 120 feet (37 meters) in the middle to nearly 200 feet (61 meters) on each side. The walls have horizontal stripings from differently colored masonry. In this they resemble the walls of Constantinople, which may have been a deliberate reminder of the ancient Welsh tradition that Constantine was born in Caernarvon. An imposing and most unusual feature is the Eagle Tower with its three tall hexagonal turrets.

James St. George's castles have all played a part in British history. Harlech was involved in the War of the Roses in 1468; and Rhuddlan was destroyed by Roundheads in 1646. Caernarvon, which is still manned, was the 1969 site of the investiture of Prince Charles as Prince of Wales. ∎

Further Reading:

Geoffrey Hindley, *Castles of Europe*. London, 1968.

JACOPO DE' DONDI
b. 1290, Padua, Italy
d. May 1359, Padua

GIOVANNI DE' DONDI
b. 1318, Chioggia, Italy
d. June 22, 1389, Milan
Italian Horologists and Physicians

Life and Times:

The development of mechanical clocks brought regular division of time to humanity, not only as a technical ability but also as a concept. Sundial hours varied in duration, being much longer in summer than in winter. Despite all the inaccuracies of the early mechanical clocks, they did divide the day into 24 periods of equal duration. In fourteenth-century Europe it became possible to specify the time for a meeting, say, with some exactness. Consequently, a demand grew for clocks that could be placed in rooms; the necessary technology developed along with the demand. Jacopo de' Dondi and his son Giovanni each built a clock. Jacopo's was a public clock on the outside wall of a tower. Giovanni's was four feet high, standing on its own, and was placed in the library of a castle. It was, moreover, an intricate astronomical clock which was described in such detail by its maker that models of it could be constructed 500 years later.

Jacopo de' Dondi was the son of a physician in Padua. After studying medicine there, Jacopo became the municipal physician at Chioggia, where his son was born. In 1342 the family returned to Padua where, in addition to teaching medicine at the university, Jacopo found a way to extract salt from the mineral springs of Abano, and managed to obtain the privilege of selling the salt without having to pay tax.

Concurrent with these activities, Jacopo designed an astronomical clock which was constructed for the prince of Padua and installed, in 1344, in the tower of the palace. The clock was widely admired, earning the de' Dondi family the additional name of 'Orologio (of the clock).

Jacopo was widowed in 1348 and went to live with his son. That same year, work began on the astronomical clock, called the astrarium, which is attributed to Giovanni. Meanwhile, Giovanni studied medicine at the University of Padua, and became a professor. Father and son worked together on a book on herbals—plants with medicinal value. In 1359, Giovanni was appointed to the faculty in four departments: medicine, astrology, philosophy and logic. That was also the year Jacopo died. Work on Giovanni's clock continued until it was finished, six years later. It is a matter of speculation whether the clock was designed by Jacopo and merely completed by his son, or whether it was entirely Giovanni's work.

In 1381, Gian Galeazzo Visconti, ruler of Milan, having heaped favors on Giovanni, acquired the astrarium for the library of his palace in Pavia. By the next year, de' Dondi was teaching at the University of Pavia, and he and his family were living in the palace. In its new location, the astrarium attracted international attention and wonder. A letter written in 1385 by a friend of de' Dondi describes it as "such a great marvel that the solemn astronomers come from far regions to see in great reverence Master Giovanni of the Clocks and the work of his hands." The German astronomer Regiomontanus saw it in 1463, and Leonardo da Vinci [q.v.] made two sketches of it in about 1492. The astrarium continued to be on display in the castle of Pavia for a few more years, but by

The London Science Museum's working model of the de' Dondi astrarium; top center, the dial of the sun; below it, the 24-hour dial.

1530 it was no longer running. A replica was made by Juanelo Turriano [q.v.] for the Emperor Charles, and taken to his court in Spain. The original may have been dismantled in the process.

Outstanding Engineering Achievements:

The face of Jacopo's tower clock was divided into 24 hours; an inner ring showed lunar phases and signs of the zodiac. As with most clocks before the seventeenth century there was only one hand, the hour hand, but there was also a mechanism for striking. The tower and clock were destroyed in a battle in 1390. A descendant of de' Dondi designed a new clock, which was accepted in 1428. This clock—which still ticks—may be a deliberate duplicate of Jacopo's, and the present dial may be the original dial surviving from 1344.

Giovanni's description of his astrarium was written so that the mechanism could be duplicated. The original manuscript was copied a number of times and preserved in libraries throughout Europe. One copy went to Cracow while Copernicus was there. Later drawings were also made of the clock, so its construction is known in detail. One part, however, was dealt with in only a cursory manner: the dial and gears that showed the time of day. For this, de' Dondi wrote that it was just a common clock, and he advised anyone who was unable to make that part not to attempt the remainder.

The astrarium was built of brass and bronze in its own seven-legged stand, a little over four feet (1.2 meters) high and thirty inches (76 cm) across. At the top, seven dials surrounded the frame, one each for the moon, Mercury, Venus, sun, Mars, Jupiter, and Saturn (the seven planets of the Ptolemaic system). Below them, an open framework revealed the weight drive hanging over a horizontal shaft that carried the crown wheel—a coarsely toothed wheel whose motion was interrupted every two seconds by the rocking of a heavy bar. The hour dial was attached to the frame, as were dials showing the fixed church feasts, the movable ones, and the times when the orbits of the sun and moon intersect so that eclipses can occur. There was also one which showed the rotation of the stars.

No duplicates of the astrarium are known to have been made until 1960, when a working model was constructed in England for the Smithsonian Institution. A second one was made in Milan, and a third, a few years later, in England for the London Science Museum. ∎

Further Reading:

S.A. Bedini and F.R. Maddison, "Mechanical Universe: The Astrarium of Giovanni de' Dondi," *Transactions of the American Philosophic Society*. Vol. LVI, pt. 5 (Oct. 1966).

RICHARD OF WALLINGFORD
b. ca. 1292, Wallingford, England
d. May 23, 1336, St. Albans, England
English Mechanical Engineer and Mathematician

Life and Times:

Before the thirteenth century, the only methods of keeping time were by sundial, hourglass, marked candle, and the water clock. Mechanical clocks developed during a flowering of invention in the late thirteenth and early fourteenth centuries. Their precursors seem to have been, not early timekeepers but mechanical astronomical instruments. A geared calendar was described in an Arabic work of about 1000 A.D.; geared astrolabes exist from about 1300. When clockwork—the regulated release of power to a gear train—was invented in the late thirteenth century, the two traditions of timekeeping and celestial display were united to produce astronomical clocks. These complicated mechanisms showed time and also the positions of the sun, moon, known planets, and stars in an earth-centered system. The earliest one known was a clock built by Richard of Wallingford while he was Abbot of St. Albans.

The son of a prosperous blacksmith in the county of Berkshire, Richard was adopted, upon his father's death, by the local prior, who eventually sent him to Merton College at Oxford University. The philosophers there were studying the motion of a uniformly accelerated body, and deducing a formula for its distance travelled in a given time. Richard came away with an abiding interest in mathematics, although he later regretted not having spent more time on theology. On leaving Merton, he entered the Benedictine order at the abbey of St. Albans, became a priest, then returned to Oxford for nine more years of study. During this period he wrote a four-part treatise on trigonometry, believed to be the first thorough treatment of the subject in Europe outside Moorish Spain. In 1327, Richard returned to St. Albans. The same year, the abbot died and Richard was elected abbot, a position he held for nine years until he died of leprosy.

The abbey had been considerably enlarged during the previous century but a chapel was still to be added. Richard, however, neglected the building, diverting the resources to the construction of his very expensive clock. When King Edward III rebuked him for spending money on unnecessary work instead of on the church, Richard is said to have replied that future abbots would find workmen for the building, but they would not be able to complete his invention. What eventually became of the clock is not known; fortunately, chronicles of the abbey were maintained, and an illustrated manuscript of Richard's own description of his mechanism has survived in the Bodleian Library, Oxford.

Richard also invented a mechanical planetarium called the Albion, which may have been a forerunner of his clock. He also devised a substitute for the armillary sphere, called the rectangulus, and he wrote treatises on his inventions, on mathematics, and on meteorology. Since he was a good administrator, he was able to overcome opposition from the monks, some of whom objected to his being appointed abbot, to deal with the townspeople who were rebelling against the feudal authority of the abbey, and to find acceptance for his scientific pursuits.

Outstanding Engineering Achievement:

Richard's clock showed the canonical hours—the six times of the day when prayers were offered; the chronicles of the abbey record that in 1394 the face was changed to show the twenty-four hours. But it was much more than a clock. Containing rotating disks, gear trains and mechanical linkages, all intricately related to each other, it could be used for predicting eclipses, finding the position of planets and solving other astrolabe problems. An oval gear-wheel varied the speed of solar motion—three centuries before Kepler discovered the elliptical nature of motion in the solar system. Richard's treatise gives little description of the power or regulator of the clock, but it was probably weight-driven with an escapement of the verge and pallet type, as in the clock of de' Dondi [q.v.]. It is also not clear exactly how the movements of the sun, moon, and planets were displayed.

The word "clock" is derived from an earlier word for "bell," and the first mechanical clocks were provided with a bell that would ring at appropriate times. The St. Albans clock, too, could be made to sound a bell. Versions of Richard's clock were made in England and

Germany for two centuries; thirty texts and fragments relating to them still exist. ∎

Further Reading:

S. A. Bedini and F. R. Maddison, "Mechanical Universe: The Astrarium of Giovanni de' Dondi," *Transactions of the American Philosophic Society.* Vol. LVI, pt. 5 (Oct. 1966).

J. D. North, *Richard of Wallingford, an Edition of his Writings with Introductions, English Translation and Commentary.* Oxford, 1976.

HENRY YEVELE
b. ca. 1320, Uttoxeter, Staffordshire, England
d. Aug. 21, 1400, London
English Architect and Military Engineer

Life and Times:

During the fourteenth century the craftsmen of London gradually obtained power over the merchants and took control of the city. The attitude of master masons to their craft can be judged from the articles drawn up in London in 1365 by a committee chosen to represent them. It was agreed that no mason was to take work that he would not be able to complete, and that masters should be chosen and sworn to check on this; that power be given to the mayor and sheriffs to imprison anyone who refused to obey the sworn masters; that an apprentice should serve seven years; that an apprentice or journeyman should be employed only in the presence of his master and not hired away until his time be completed; that journeymen be paid what they deserve "and not outrageously."

The members of this committee were described as "twelve of the most skilful men." Henry Yevele was one of them, probably by far the youngest. Seven years earlier, Yevele had obtained a contract to rebuild parts of Kensington Palace for Edward the Black Prince. In 1360, the prince's father, King Edward III, appointed Yevele "disposer of the King's works pertaining to the art of masonry in the Palace of Westminster and the Tower of London." By 1369 Yevele had been awarded for life the title of "deviser of masonry to the king," or royal architect.

Yevele was the most prominent master mason of his time, and perhaps the greatest English architect before Christopher Wren [q.v.]. As architect and contractor, he was involved in the rebuilding or extension of some of England's most important structures, including Westminster Abbey, Canterbury Cathedral, the Tower of London, Westminster Hall and Savoy Palace. In this period of continual war with France and invasion alarms, Yevele built defensive walls for the city of Canterbury. He also designed the tombs in Westminster Abbey of Edward III, Richard II and his queen Anne, and Cardinal Langham; in St. Paul's, the tomb of John of Gaunt and his wife Blanche; and probably that of Prince Edward at Canterbury.

From 1362 on, work in progress in both London and Canterbury required Yevele to travel between these two cities. At times he must have been accompanied by the man who was responsible for disbursing payments, the Clerk of the Works, Geoffrey Chaucer. There is no record of whether Chaucer passed the time of the journey by reading Yevele the latest of his writings. The road from London to Canterbury goes on to Dover and was therefore extremely important. At Rochester it crosses the Medway, where in 1383 Yevele replaced the old wooden bridge with a stone one, 14 feet (4.2 meters) wide. The structure lasted until the nineteenth century, when it was pulled down to be replaced by an iron bridge.

Westminster Hall, with the world's largest unsupported roof (other than domes and modern structures).

Yevele was a prominent citizen who served on a number of committees. He was one of the two Wardens of London Bridge, reelected annually from 1365 to 1395. In 1384 he was also elected by the guilds to the Common Council. Henry Yevele's father was probably a mason of modest means, but Henry died rich, his property including a number of houses in London and surrounding towns, two quays on the Thames, a brewery, several tenement houses, watermills, lands and a country estate. Childless, he left everything to his wife, and then to the Church of St. Magnus, to the maintenance of London Bridge and to the Hospital of St. Thomas.

Outstanding Engineering Achievements:

When Yevele took charge of work on Westminster Abbey in 1362, the Norman nave was being demolished and replaced with a Gothic one. At the time, English Gothic was moving from Decorated to Perpendicular, with walls of glass held in place by long verticals of stone tracery. But in designing the 102-foot (31 meters) nave of Westminster Abbey, Yevele followed the thirteenth century style of the choir and transepts, to produce a unified whole.

Yevele was also commissioned to replace the Norman nave of Canterbury Cathedral. Here the choir was the early Gothic work of William

The nave that Henry Yevele built for Westminster Abbey.

of Sens [q.v.], and Yevele clearly felt free to build his nave in the new Perpendicular variant.

Westminster Hall had first been built in 1097; Richard II ordering its rebuilding. Yevele cut away the Norman masonry to allow for huge windows. He reinforced the walls to hold an unsupported roof, and relined them to change their styling. The 90-foot-high (27 meters) oak roof, the work of master carpenter Hugh Herland, is a hammer-beam truss in which a series of wooden arches curve gracefully within frameworks that are carved copies of the Perpendicular stone tracery of the windows. With a length of 238 feet (71 meters) and a width of 67 feet (20 meters) it is the largest unsupported roof in the world other than domes and modern steel and concrete structures. It survived World War II, although damaged in air raids, and the oak has been patched with steel. ■

Further Reading:

John H. Harvey, *Henry Yevele, Life of an English Architect.* London, 1944.

GUIDO DA VIGEVANO
fl. 1328
Italian Military Engineer

Life and Times:

Although the Hundred Years War between France and England is generally said to have begun in 1337, it was clearly in the offing for twenty years before that. Control of the wool trade with Flanders and the French desire to regain Guienne from the English were important causes. In 1328 the claim of Edward III to the French throne was blocked when the French invoked the Salic Law, which prevented inheritance through the female line. Instead, Philip VI became the first Valois king of France. In his first year, he put down a rebellion in Flanders and appointed Guido da Vigevano as his military advisor.

Guido had previously been court physician to Jeanne of Burgundy, the queen of Philip V. In this capacity, he had edited a manual of hygiene and a book on medicine. If, as suggested by his name, Guido came from Vigevano, a city in Lombardy near Milan and Pavia, then he may have studied at a university in northern Italy.

Apart from medicine, the education of a physician included astrology with astronomy and mathematics. It would not necessarily have included anatomy. Guido's courses would therefore have provided the foundation for an engineering career, and he followed his medical publications with a treatise on the engines of war.

Guido's treatise is one of a long tradition of illustrated books on military and civil engineering devices. Before Guido were classical authors such as Heron [q.v.] and the medieval architect Villard de Honnecourt [q.v.]. After Guido came early Renaissance writers such as Valturio [q.v.] and Francesco di Georgio Martini [q.v.], leading to the era of printed books, from that of Jacques Besson [q.v.] onwards.

Outstanding Engineering Achievement:

The thirteen chapters of Guido's military treatise are each concerned with one machine. These include boats and chariots, assault towers and bridges, all made to be easily transported. The simplest boat is an inflatable raft made from an animal skin. More complicated is a barge that floats on casks and is propelled by four hand-cranked paddle-wheels. This boat can be dismantled and the parts carried by horseback.

For storming a castle, Guido described an assault tower in which men could be lifted to the top of the wall. Most of Guido's towers contain one or several platforms on vertical shafts. One illustration shows men hoisting themselves on their platform by pulling on ropes that run over pulleys atop the shaft. Another shows a platform that could be winched up through a gearing system by men on the ground. One of Guido's chariots has sails that could be turned by the wind, with a pinion to transmit the turning to an axle and then, by pinions, to the wheels. A crank is provided on the axle so that manpower could be used when there was no wind. Like the other machines, this chariot could be taken apart and reassembled.

Guido's treatise is the first one known that describes transportable machines. It is not known which, if any, already existed or were subsequently built. The subject of transportability was, of course, taken up by Agostino Ramelli [q.v.] and other later engineers. ■

Further Reading:

Bertrand Gille, *Engineers of the Renaissance.* Cambridge, 1966.

KONRAD KYESER

b. Aug. 25, 1366, Eichstätt, Germany
d. 1405
German Military Engineer

Life and Times:

Much of the late Medieval and Renaissance literature of technology was written by men who were first trained as physicians. These include both Jacopo and Giovanni de' Dondi [q.v.], Georgius Agricola [q.v.], and even Galileo Galilei [q.v.]. Kyeser was a physician who also had experience in warfare; his book on military technology was the most influential work of its kind throughout the fifteenth century. Born into a medical family in Eichstätt, between Munich and Nuremberg, Kyeser later moved to Padua, where he studied medicine. He also studied astrology and magic, considered to be a branch of technology, ranked just ahead of the military arts.

In 1396 Kyeser joined the crusade led by King Sigismund of Hungary against the Turkish Sultan Bajazet I, surviving the rout of the Christians at Nicopoli. In his book he claimed to be known and honored by every king, prince, and duke from Sicily to Sweden, Russia to France. He certainly had close connections with Wenceslaus of Bohemia, for, in 1402, when Sigismund deposed that king, Kyeser was exiled to a remote castle. He spent the next three years, his last, writing and illustrating his treatise on warfare.

Outstanding Engineering Achievement:

Kyeser's manuscript, entitled *Bellifortis,* "The Strong in War," came at a time when guns and gunpowder had begun to be used but had not yet displaced medieval weapons. The book showed both. There is, for example, a drawing of a giant trebuchet in which the main part, a horizontally pivoted beam, is some 75 feet (22.8 meters) long. Attached to one end is a heavy weight, and to the other is a cable with a pouch—a sling. The pouch is filled with one or many rocks; the sling

end of the beam is pulled down by a gang of men, and let go suddenly. When properly calibrated and laden with stone balls of equal weight (as much as half a ton), it would fire them in a high, fast trajectory as far as a quarter of a mile (400 meters), each time hitting the same spot on a fortification.

The early cannon described by Kyeser were crude, unreliable, and far less efficient than the trebuchet, but they produced a terrifying bang, a flash, and smoke. *Bellifortis* showed a variety of guns, from a simple tube with a touch-hole for firing lead shot to multiple guns such as one with six barrels mounted along a rotating hexagonal carriage. It even included rockets, one being shown leaving the ramp that was its launching pad, but unfortunately drawn with the smoke and flame coming out of the front.

There were also devices that had important civil applications. Kyeser's account of the Archimedes screw was the first to be included in any book written since Roman times. Another mechanism was fitted to a crossbow so that it could be drawn with a steady force instead of having to increase the force the more the bow was pulled. A drawcord was wound spirally around a conical spindle. The force needed to turn such a spindle decreases as the diameter decreases, thus compensating for the increase in the crossbow's drawing force. This device—the fusee—was later used in mechanical clocks to even the force exerted by the mainspring.

On a larger scale, the 130-page manuscript included a variety of bridges, siege towers, and armored chariots equipped with cannons. For 150 years, the work was consulted as the authority on military technology. Some of its mechanisms were adopted or improved on by Leonardo [q.v.]. ■

Further Reading:

Konrad Kyeser, *Bellifortis*, (new ed.). Düsseldorf, 1967.

Lynn White, Jr., *Medieval Religion and Technology*. Berkeley, California, 1978.

Engineering in the Far East in Historical Times

by Colin A. Rowan

From the earliest times the Far East has been dominated culturally by the immense civilization of China. Certainly there are other cultures with long histories—in Korea, Japan, Mongolia, and Tibet—but even a brief examination of them shows that, on our present understanding, it was not until modern times that they seem to have been in a position to make many advances in engineering.

In Korea lived a people who had a common racial origin with other peoples of North Asia, and who had close links with neighboring peoples during the Neolithic and Bronze ages. Some kin groups apparently migrated southwest from Korea to the Shantung peninsula of northeastern China, thus contributing one element of ancient Chinese civilization; other Koreans moved south to Japan, where they formed an important element of Japanese culture. During the Iron Age, about the fourth century B.C., the Koreans were building wooden houses with a system of floor-heating, but little research has been done to discover any later developments of this kind. There were frequent clashes in early historic times between Koreans and Chinese, who were generally antagonistic to all northern peoples; the famous Great Wall was built not only to prevent northern invaders from entering China, but also to prevent any Chinese from emigrating to the northern lands. By the seventh century A.D. circumstances had changed; friendly relations with China were established, the two countries became allies, and from then on Korea absorbed much Chinese culture.

Japan apparently developed little large-scale or sophisticated technology in early times. Even until the latter part of the nineteenth century it possessed no vehicles except for small wagons; transport was by pack animals and by foot. The country has a long history, its earliest culture, the Jomon, going back to at least the fourth milennium B.C. to be followed in the third century B.C. by the Yayoi. Yet neither seems to have done much, if any, engineering work. Only in the third century A.D. did things change, with the advent of Korean and Chinese influences. Certainly these did not prevent certain Japanese habits from persisting—for instance, the Japanese continued to live on the floor long after Chinese culture developed chairs and beds—but by and large it was the highly developed Chinese culture which held sway. Not until the 250-year period of isolationism, which ran from around 1620 to the late 1860s, did their whole culture receive the hallmark that we would now recognize as particularly Japanese.

Little more in the way of indigenous engineering appeared in Mongolia and Tibet. The people of Mongolia were descended from the Huns, who lived in Central Asia from the third to the first centuries B.C., though the country remained only a loose collection of tribes long after this. A single Mongolian state appeared in the thirteenth century A.D., the time of Genghis Khan, and vanished when the Manchurians overran the area in 1609. There was little stimulus to the undertaking of large engineering works in what was mainly a land of mountains, desert and undulating steppe-land.

Tibet, the "Roof of the World," has a recorded history dating only from about 600 A.D., though this land of mountains and high plateaus bordering southeastern China was populated long before this. Cultural contacts with the Chinese developed early, and such engineering as there was—the iron suspension bridge is a prominent example—came from them. Tibet became Buddhist early in the Christian era, first by way of China and later by missionary zeal direct from India; but in general Tibetans sought to isolate themselves from other countries and from cultures foreign to their own.

It becomes clear, then, that for engineering in the Far East before the nineteenth century we must turn to China, and here the situation is very different. The Chinese have a long and enviable cultural history which stretches back well into the second millennium B.C., if not earlier, and though disrupted by periods of internal conflict and invasion, there was a constant thread of development. To see this in its perspective, though, it is necessary first to glance briefly at the geography of China and then at the general cultural picture of a civilization which is in so many ways different from our own.

China can be said to be divided from west to east by its two great rivers, the Yellow River and the Yangtze. The Yellow River flows first through mountainous country, then past the Gobi Desert to the north, and, still in a generally easterly direction, it curves round a vast fertile area before emptying into the Pei-chi li Gulf. North and east of the river are vast areas covered with loess, a compacted dust blown from the northern deserts, which forms a self-contained region surrounded by mountains to the west, the south and the southeast. Several hundred miles south of the Yellow River flows the Yangtze, which empties into the Pacific near Shanghai. It too originates in high western mountains, but after passing through mighty gorges, it finds its way through level country, like the Yellow River, its course is somewhat isolated, divided from the country's southeastern coast by more mountains. In brief, then, China is a country of vast mountain ranges, with large flat and fertile areas as well as a long coastline. The semi-isolation of these different areas made it necessary from early times for the engineer to improve communications either by roads or by waterways. Although Chinese road building was prodigious, the waterways proved even more important, since heavier loads could be carried than by land. The growth of canals and water transport, as well as the need for irrigation, brought about great feats of hydraulic engineering. China's population, constantly increasing despite natural disasters and wars, has made not only irrigation techniques but also agricultural engineering a very important development.

As Chinese society developed and gave rise in the third century B.C. to the country's first great empire, Confucianism and Taoism emerged as the two dominant cultural attitudes. They continued to develop and diverge in the centuries that followed, a process that formed the background against which much Chinese engineering

was carried out. The Confucian approach, which originated in the sixth century B.C. with K'ung Fu Tzu, or Confucius, was concerned above all with just and harmonious social relationships; it has been termed a "worldly social-mindedness." It arose at a time of perpetual warring between powerful states, when life was held cheap, and it sought to bring order and respect for the individual. It promoted a paternalistic form of government, run by an academically trained and qualified bureaucracy. But in doing this, Confucianism gave rise to a certain amount of intellectual elitism. The scholar knew best, because of his greater mental ability; he was superior to the artisan, to the man who worked with his hands, however skilled those hands might be.

The social superiority of the Confucian scholar sometimes tempted him to go further than his knowledge warranted. There are many stories in Chinese literature telling of the discomfiture of the theorist in the face of the practical experience of the skilled craftsman. One such tale is found as early as the third century B.C. in a work called *Master Lü's Spring and Autumn Annals*, where it is recounted how a certain Kaoyang Ying was having a house built. His mason advised that the wood used should not be too green because, if it were, it would warp when plastered: it would look all right for a short time, but then the house would collapse. Kaoyang Ying argued that, according to the mason's own statement, the house could not fall down. The drier the wood became, the harder it would get, and the drier the lime the lighter it would become. If something that is getting harder (the green wood drying out) is combined with something getting softer (the lime which is drying out and becoming lighter), it could not possibly be damaged by it—such was the scholar's reasoning. The mason could find no argument with which to counter this, but by experience he knew that Kaoyang Ying was wrong. Nevertheless, he did as he was told and the house was built. It looked well, but soon fell down. As the author, "Master Lü," remarks, while Kaoyang Ying liked such sophistries, his fault was that he did not understand the "principles of Nature."

The Taoists took a different approach. Theirs was a mixture of philosophy, religion, and science. Their name was derived not from any founding father, but because they followed the Tao, a virtually untranslatable word that can perhaps best be rendered as "The Way" or the "Order of Nature." They sought peace and harmony with the natural world. This in turn brought some real appreciation for the skill of the craftsman and of the engineer, who had a feel for his materials, knew their capabilities and their limitations, and knew what was practical and possible in a given situation. The Taoist was not averse to using his hands—the alchemists of China who made practical experiments in their laboratories were Taoists—and had no disrespect for those who earned their living by doing so. But as it turned out, the development of the elaborate Chinese bureaucracy which ran this vast country, one-and-one-quarter times the area of the continental United States, was Confucian by training and, by and large, in outlook. What then was the standing of the engineer?

To begin with it must be appreciated that engineering in China was in what is sometimes known as the "eotechnic" stage, a term coined by the American Lewis Mumford (see his *Technics and Human Development*). In Mumford's scheme our modern era is called "neotechnic," its predecessor, when iron and coal were the chief substances, "palaeotechnic." Before this was a very long period, the "eotechnic," the age of wood and of human, animal and water power. In China not only wood but also bamboo was an important material. That is not to say that metals were not available; bronze was used at least as early as the first millennium B.C., and during Han times (third century B.C. to third century A.D.) iron ploughshares were common. But all large engineering projects were done in bamboo, wood and stone. It was with these materials that the Chinese engineers of the past achieved such great success.

Some parts of Chinese scientific and technical culture were intimately concerned with the governing bureaucracy. Astronomers and astrologers were lodged in the imperial palace and considered civil servants; their work was considered to have a special "state security" status, for it was vital in maintaining an accurate calendar, without which the emperor could not claim the Mandate of Heaven. Many artisans and engineers were also part of the bureaucratic machine, which operated Imperial Arsenals and Workshops. During certain periods of Chinese history, some advanced techniques like salt manufacture and iron founding were "nationalized" industries. As the administrative structure developed, technicians gathered around official patrons who encouraged them.

The most important document about the standing of ancient Chinese technology is generally agreed to be the *Artificers' Record,* part of the *Record of the Institutions of the Chou Dynasty*. The book was mostly compiled during the Han period, but it may well reflect the feudal conditions of the earlier Warring States period (fifth to third centuries B.C.). In any event it was the basis for later commentaries. It defines six classes of workers, beginning with the princes who deliberate on the Tao of society and the ministers and officials who carry out their decisions. The third class consists of the "hundred artisans" who examine raw materials and make useful devices—i.e., engineers. Fourth come the merchants and travellers who deal with the transport of goods. At the bottom of the scale are those who till the soil and, lastly, the women workers whose responsibility is weaving. Concerning the work of the third class, the text explains that tools and machines were invented by men of intelligence and maintained by men of skill. Smelting metal to make swords, hardening clay to make vessels, constructing chariots for transport by land and boats for crossing water— all these were once the work of the sages. Those who preserve these techniques generation after generation are the "hundred artisans." The *Record* then goes on to specify various kinds of work, and it is interesting to note that at different times different crafts were more valued than others. For example, during the second millennium B.C. the most highly regarded activity was house building; in the next historical period it was pottery; while during feudal times it was the construction of chariots.

All dynasties had their Imperial Workshops, and it seems that these institutions had large administrative staffs. The ratio of bureaucrats to artisans is difficult to determine, though in one early case artisans outnumbered bureaucrats only by seven to five. But by the eighth century A.D., every kind of technique was in use, from metallurgical and engineering to purely artistic processes, and some six to seven thousand artisans are spoken of. Periodic examinations of technical skills were made, and every object produced was stamped with the name of the artisan responsible for it.

The Imperial Workshops were not the only state organizations that fostered engineering. There were the Arsenals where crossbows, catapults and other types of military equipment were made, the Office of Works which was responsible for buildings and ceramics, and the General Water Conservancy which supervised the maintenance and construction of irrigation works, canals and bridges. Government support also went to ship-builders, road-makers and centers for textile manufacture. The engineer entered the service of the state in every field and, as the *Artificers' Record* clearly shows, was a well-respected member of society, especially if he was an inventor or innovator. Yet there was always a gap between the skilled manual worker and the administrator, and even important engineers seldom held high administrative positions.

There were exceptions, as in the case of Yüwên K'ai [q.v.], who lived about 610 A.D. and was for 30 years the chief engineer of the Sui dynasty. He carried out irrigation and conservation works, superintended construction of part of China's Grand Canal, built new capital cities, invented a special clepsydra, and so on; besides being an extremely able engineer he was also a senior official, serving for many years as Minister of Works.

At the time of the Sung (tenth to twelfth centuries) lived and worked Shen Kua [q.v.], sometime ambassador and Assistant Minister of Imperial Hospitality. He too was an engineer, famous for his many-sided scientific book containing much technical detail and, incidentally, providing what has been termed the best authentic evidence of the beginning of printing in China. During the Ming dynasty (fourteenth to seventeenth centuries) it became possible for more artisans to move into administration, a change probably brought about by the importance of hydraulic engineering at this time. It was during the Ming, too, that senior officials acted as patrons to groups of artisans.

It was possible, then, for engineers to reach high office, though this did not happen frequently. But on the other side of the coin, some brilliant inventors and engineers, whose reputations still live on, were lowly menials in their own day. Thus in the sixth century Hsintu-Fang entered a prince's household as a dependent or retainer. Though not an engineer as such, he ministered to the scientific interests of his master and, when the letter fled for political reasons, stayed on to write the books the prince had intended to do himself, living in poverty to do so. His case is typical of what could happen. There was also the technologist and horological engineer Kêng Hsün [q.v.], who became a slave to the Chinese general Wang Shih-Chi. His story has a happier ending, for his abilities were so remarkable that he was freed by the emperor and later became Acting Superintendant of the Imperial Workshop.

In China, as in most other civilizations, engineers inherited a certain amount of tradition about their calling. The oldest were stories of legendary inventors, such as Po I, who dug the first well, or Hu Ts'ao, who is reputed to have invented clothing. Most of these legendary inventors appear in the records as ministers of the totally legendary Yellow Emperor, Huang Ti.

The Taoists also revered a number of engineering patrons, including Ko Yu, a maker of mechanical toys who brought one to life and rode away on it. The most notable of this company was Kungshu P'an [q.v.], the patron saint of all artisans and engineers. Much legend is attached to him; he was supposed to be the inventor of rotary grain-mills and automata, siege engines and man-lifting kites. But he certainly existed in the fifth and fourth centuries B.C. and worked as an engineer in the state of Lu—hence his other name, Lu Pan. His reputation was such that there is even a well-known expression involving him: "brandishing one's axe at the door of Lu Pan," the equivalent of our "teaching your grandmother to suck eggs."

Besides traditions, all Chinese engineers were familiar with various basic concepts that dealt with the physical facts of their crafts, or what we would today call basic mechanics. These principles included the power of the lever and the mechanical advantage of pulleys. Knowledge of the lever is very old, and in China seems to go back to the Mohists, followers of the philosopher Mo Ti who flourished during the third century B.C. These scholars and craftsmen were apparently acquainted with most, and perhaps all, of the ideas of equilibrium which, in the Western world, were discussed by Archimedes [q.v.] at about the same time. In China the lever was soon put to great use, most notably in the making of bronze trigger mechanisms for crossbows, which were used as personal weapons in China 1,400 years before they appeared in the West. Chinese engineers also devised a version of the shaduf, a counterweighted lever with a bucket at one end used for raising water, and employed the lever in the trip hammer for pounding. Later, the lever was applied with great ingenuity to textile machinery, where it was combined with the treadle. Indeed, the Chinese were ahead of the West in the construction of looms by 400 years, having the essential principles of the draw-loom in the first century B.C. or possibly as early as the fourth. Links and hinges were also used very early in China.

The wheel was known in China in the second millennium B.C., when it was introduced in the form of the chariot from Mesopotamia, the area of Sumerian civilization. Chinese officials considered chariot and carriage wheels important, and laid down elaborate testing procedures for completed wheels. Such tests make it clear that the standards of Chinese wheelwrights were very high and their techniques sophisticated. Dished wheels, developed in Europe in the fifteenth century because of the strength they gave against sideways thrusts, were already used in China in the first century A.D. Gear wheels were known in China early in the third century B.C., certainly as early as they seem to have been known in the West. One other engineering feature connected with the wheel and known in ancient China seems to have been the use of roller bearings, which appeared as early as the second century B.C.

Pulleys, driving belts and chain-drives were also familiar to the ancient Chinese engineer. Pulleys were known from very early times, in China certainly by the fourth century B.C., if not before. The use of a small windlass on a fishing rod to reel in the line seems to be a Chinese invention. The driving belt was used in textile machinery in China, its development perhaps stimulated by the very long fibers which come from silk cocoons and require mechanical reeling. This innovation appears in the eleventh century A.D. but may well go back before this. The first use of the chain-drive, in the true sense of a device for transmitting motion rather than an endless chain of pots for raising water, dates in the West from the eighteenth century, although a small chain-driven hoist appeared in the fifteenth. But in China an early water-raising device known as the square-pallet chain-pump, powered by an endless chain which passed over sprockets at each end, was developed by the first century A.D., 1500 years before it was known in the West. Certainly it did not use a chain for the true transmission of power, but it probably inspired later Chinese engineers to use a chain for this purpose. They did in fact do so in their mechanical clocks, probably as early as the tenth century, and certainly during the eleventh.

Chinese engineers thus had a legendary tradition of archetypal inventors and a body of techniques which were a sound basis for further progress. Their innovativeness extended to all areas of engineering, and they arrived at many results long before their counterparts in the West. Yet, strangely enough, there were three basic techniques which the Chinese, for all their practical ingenuity and ability, did not discover. These were the screw, the force pump for liquids and the crankshaft. The screw was unknown in China until the seventeenth century, yet it had been used in the West before the time of Archimedes (third century B.C.)—first probably in the screw press for squeezing the juice out of olives, then as the Archimedean screw for raising water, and later as a wormwheel for driving a gearwheel. Although the Chinese had efficient pumps, they do not seem to have arrived at the idea of a force pump for liquids, which Ktesibios [q.v.] had developed in Alexandria in the third century B.C. This invention did not reach China for some 1,800 years. The crankshaft was also unknown to Chinese engineers until the seventeenth century, 300 years after its development in Europe. But if the Chinese were indebted to the West for these three important inventions, the West has been in China's debt for a host of engineering developments. The individual crossbow, the draw-loom, dished cart and chariot wheels and the driving belt have so far been mentioned, but the Chinese led the West in many other ways up to the eighteenth century. Their long-standing technical superiority is a tribute to their practical engineering abilities.

Sericulture, the art of breeding silkworms for the fibers of their cocoons, demanded engineering help from the time of its origin around 1,500 B.C. The vast quantity of silk in a cocoon (varying between one-third and two-thirds of a mile) and the fact that it comes away from the cocoon in one thin continuous fiber necessitated some mechanical means of reeling. Though the earliest detailed records of such machines do not go back before the eleventh century, they were clearly much older than this. By the time written descriptions appear, techniques of silk-processing show great sophistication. The cocoons were unwound in a heated water bath, after which the thread was distributed across the take-up reel by a "flyer" so that it wound evenly. The machine was operated by a treadle; although the Chinese did not know of the crankshaft, they were well aware of the use of a treadle and crank arm to turn reciprocating into rotary motion. Waterpower was applied as a driving force in the eleventh century, 300 years before power reeling machinery was known in the West. Mechanical reeling of course was older and the time-lag between China and the Western world correspondingly greater, perhaps as much as thirteen centuries.

Another field that stimulated engineering innovation from early times was metallurgy. Although iron smelting appeared later in China than in the West, a number of factors combined to encourage its rapid development. In China the iron age arrived in the sixth century B.C., and within 200 years cast iron was in use. In the Western world smelting consisted of heating the iron to a plastic or pasty state so that impurities could be removed as slag. The heat was not sufficient to melt the iron, however, so that some slag invariably remained. In China, on the other hand, true smelting took place, and the iron was brought to a liquid state. This was partly because the small and efficient Chinese blast furnaces either used an iron ore which was rich in phosphorus or had phosphorus added to the melt; in either case this had the effect of lowering the temperature required for liquefaction. Clays which could resist high temperatures were also available to the Chinese, who used them to improve the efficiency of their blast furnaces. A third important factor was the invention of the double-acting piston bellows in the fourth century B.C. This consisted of a long box containing a piston and an air channel with valves. On the forward stroke the piston drew in air behind it by way of a valve, at the same time pushing out the air ahead of it through an exit valve. On the reverse stroke, air was drawn into the now empty chamber which had been in front of the piston, and at the same time the air previously drawn in behind the piston was pushed out. The double acting bellows thus gave a continuous stream of air, which could be directed to a precise point in the furnace with an iron nozzle. No equivalent device appeared in the West for 2,000 years.

Chinese engineers were adept at applying and controlling air in other fields as well. Before the Han (i.e., sometime in the third century B.C. or earlier) they had developed rotary winnowing fans for separating chaff from grain. Treadle-operated, the fan had either four or six blades in an open framework. During the Han certain improvements were made; the machine was totally enclosed, the treadle was replaced by a cranked handle, the grain was put into a hopper, and when the husks were driven away the husked grain dropped through a sieve. Such machines can still be found in Europe, although they did not reach there until the eighteenth century. Other uses of air by the Chinese can be seen in their kites and "bamboo dragonflies." Kites were used not only as toys but also by the military; even if the legend of man-lifting kites is untrue, they were certainly used for signalling and for dropping leaflets on the enemy. The "bamboo dragonfly" was a helicopter top, a small framework with rotating blades set in motion by unwinding a long string. The kite was first used in China in the fourth century B.C., the helicopter top some 800 years later. Both took a long time to reach the West (1,900 years for the kite, 1,100 years for the helicopter top), but influenced the development of aeronautics when they finally arrived.

Some of the earliest sophisticated agricultural machines also originated in China. These included the seed drill plough, a range of harrows and rollers, and a device to which hoes were fitted so that they could be pulled between rows of crops. All this was developed by the ninth century A.D., undoubtedly stimulated by increasing population pressure and by the fact that Chinese agriculture was, in a sense, a form of intensive market gardening. In the West, larger areas of less intensive cultivation necessitated larger agricultural machinery, which could not be constructed until much later.

Grinding mills existed in most agricultural societies, but the Chinese developed some interesting variations. The edge-runner mill was one of these; here the grinding stone was held vertically and ran around a circular groove. This type of mill was much used by metallurgists and grinding medicinal substances. Common during Han times and possibly devised during the preceding Warring States period, it did not reach Europe for some 1,200 years. A water-powered model later appeared in a variety of designs, some utilizing two vertically mounted grindstones working on opposite sides of the circular groove. The Chinese also developed the "camp mill" or "field mill." This was a mill mounted on wagon wheels which moved the millstone as they turned by means of a rope drive or a chain and gearing. Such mills were used by armies and were well-known in China a millennium before they arrived in the West. A similar Chinese invention was the "pounding cart," which used hammers driven in a similar way by road wheels to hull rice.

In the area of transport and load-carrying, Chinese engineers were responsible for two important developments; the horse harness and the wheelbarrow. In the days when animal power was the chief means of drawing loads on land, it was vital that any harness fitted to a draught animal should be as efficient as possible. In the West the harness used on horses fitted around the animal's throat and girth; when the horse pulled a heavy load, the throat strap nearly strangled it by pressing on its windpipe. The Chinese used the same kind of harness to begin with, but soon changed it. By about the third century B.C. they had already developed a breast-strap harness which shifted the pull from the shafts of a cart from the horse's throat to its chest. Chinese living in Central Asia developed a separate idea, the horse-collar. This seems to have been derived from the padded saddle used on camels. The horse-collar probably originated in early Han times, though it only came into general use in China around the fifth century A.D. and did not reach the West for another 500 years.

The wheelbarrow used today in the West

became a familiar sight in the twelfth or thirteenth centuries, but it is not very efficient for lifting heavy loads. This is because, with the wheel in the front, the load puts a great strain on the person lifting the handles. The Chinese did not make this mistake; they placed the wheel in the center of the wheelbarrow so that the barrow itself balances around it. Such a device can carry really heavy loads and can be pulled by men or animals, or even fitted with sails to help it along. Sails were certainly used by the sixteenth century, though they may have been introduced earlier. The Chinese wheelbarrow itself is much older, dating from around the third century A.D.

Another invention which the West usually thinks of as its own is the gimbals mounting, sometimes called the Cardano suspension after Girolamo Cardano [q.v.] who, in the sixteenth century, described a sedan chair which would remain upright even if the bearers carrying it tilted the supporting handles. Cardano did not claim the invention as his own; it had, as he knew, been used by the Arabs for suspending oil lamps. But the invention came originally from China, where, in the second century A.D., it was used in bedwarmers which carried hot coals, and for incense burners that could not be spilled.

Of all Chinese mechanical devices, perhaps the most ingenious, and certainly one of the most important, was the mechanical clock. The basic problem with all mechanical clocks is to ensure that the driving mechanism runs at a steady rate. To achieve this the clock must have an escapement which regulates the driving mechanism and transmits its motion step by step to the gearwork. This the Chinese did by using a waterwheel with a scoop at the end of each spoke; when one scoop was filled, a system of weights and levers permitted the wheel to move just far enough for the next scoop to receive water. Power came not from a natural stream but from a constant level tank which was constructed to pour a certain amount of water into each scoop, the wheel remaining stationary while this was happening. As a result, the wheel rotated spoke by spoke with a regular pause between the movements. This arrangement solved the basic problem of mechanical timekeeping. The Chinese mechanical clock was developed in the eighth century A.D. in an effort to ensure accurate measurement and prediction of celestial motions; it reached its peak in a public astronomical clock tower constructed in 1090 in K'aifeng, capitol of the Northern Sung dynasty. Mechanical clocks did not appear in Europe until early in the fourteenth century.

Enough has probably been said to make it clear that the Chinese were advanced mechanical engineers, but it must not be forgotten that they were also first-class civil and nautical engineers. Chinese road-building was highly developed, though the country's difficult terrain and extensive inland waterways meant that road mileage did not equal that of the Roman Empire. Nevertheless, political unification was a strong stimulus to road construction in China as in the Mediterranean area. The Chinese road system grew from some 4,000 (6,400 km) miles in the third century B.C. to 20,000 miles (32,000 km) a century later, though by the third century A.D. Chinese roads still totalled less than three-quarters of the Roman mileage. But the Chinese did invent what can best be described as a waterbound macadam surface which made their roads light and reasonably flexible.

Chinese inland waterways and irrigation systems were vital to the state. Certain fertile areas required constant irrigation if they were to produce enough food for the growing population, and as early as the eighth century B.C. some irrigation projects had been started around the Yellow River with the construction of reservoirs. By the third century B.C. an artificial waterway almost 100 miles (160 km) long had been constructed from Chengkuo—it is still in use today—while the Kuanhsien system in the Szechuan area prevented flooding and irrigated some 3,000 square miles (4,800 square km). Transport canals were also important, beginning in the second century B.C. with the "Magic Transport Canal." By the sixth century A.D. the Grand Canal had been constructed, covering over a thousand miles from Hangchow on the east coast to Ch'ang-an in north-central China. The Grand Canal incorporated many existing minor waterways, but much new building was still required for such an enormous project. This involved not only digging level channels but also the design and building of locks, slipways and pumping stations, for the highest point of the Grand Canal was about 140 feet above sea level. By the tenth century the Chinese had designed the vertically moving lock-gate, an invention which was not to reach the West for another four centuries.

With China's enormous transportation network and rough terrain, the fact that Chinese civil engineers were great bridge builders should come as no surprise. But the magnitude of their achievements in this area is still astonishing. It was the Chinese who invented the suspension bridge no later than the third century B.C. The suspension was first made of bamboo fibers

Timber bridge in Tibet showing the ancient method of cantilever construction.

woven together in such a way as to give three times the tensile strength of hemp; by the sixth century A.D. but possibly as early as Han times, iron chains replaced the bamboo ropes. The cantilever bridge is another Chinese invention. Dating from the fourth and fifth centuries, it may have been derived from the Han practice of constructing buildings on cantilever supports so that they could project over the edges of lakes. The beauty of many Chinese arched stone bridges is also well-known. Their aesthetic elegance is due not only to the artistic flair of their builders but also to the invention of the built-in shear wall, which helped resist deformation and allowed designs using a minimum of material in their construction.

With a coastline of over 3000 miles and two extensive navigable rivers, Chinese shipbuilding had flourished from the very earliest times. Its development was encouraged by the availability of an ideal shipbuilding material, bamboo. Both light and strong, bamboo has advantages even today and is still used in China for building large shallow-draught rafts. The structure of bamboo, with its short sections separated by septa (which from the outside look like rings), led Chinese nautical engineers to build boats like the junk, which has no internal skeleton but is in effect a hollow cylinder braced by solid partitions. This led to the invention of separate watertight compartments within the hull. Noticed and remarked upon by Marco Polo in the fourteenth century,

this important design was not adopted in the West for some 400 years. Chinese shipbuilders later used this structure of bamboo to develop free-flooding compartments, sections fore and aft of a boat into which water could pass in and out freely. This made it possible to sail boats down rapids and, so Chinese sailors claimed, prevented junks from flying up in the wind. It also allowed fishing boats to bring their catches to port in live condition.

Many problems faced Chinese nautical engineers, not least the necessity for craft that could navigate winding channels too shallow for ordinary shipping. They responded to this by designing the articulated junk—a shallow-draught vessel built in two sections which could be coupled together—which came to be much used on the Grand Canal. By the fifth century A.D. the Chinese had also invented the paddle wheel for propulsion, some 1,100 years before the idea was put to practical use in the West. Most shipping in China, as elsewhere in the world, was wind-powered, yet even here the Chinese had their own contributions to make. Their sails were made of bamboo matting and braced with bamboo poles, another way of exploiting the material's lightness and strength. Chinese sails also had certain navigational advantages and could be easily lowered—they collapsed concertina-fashion into pleats—thus obviating the need to send men aloft in stormy weather.

Lastly, it is to the Chinese that we owe the first use of axial rudders fitted to a post at the stern of a ship. These were in use at least by the first century A.D. though it was to be eleven centuries before the West adopted them. Other original Chinese developments were the balanced rudder, with an equal amount of rudder blade on each side of the pivoting axis, and the fenestrated rudder, with holes drilled through it. Both inventions, again, took a long time to reach the West.

It can safely be said that, until the advent of the Industrial Revolution in the West, the Chinese led the world in many inventions and techniques, and excelled over the whole range of civil and mechanical engineering. All through ancient and medieval times they displayed great practical sense, immense ingenuity and the genius to make far-reaching innovations. That these advances did not cohere into a process of self-sustaining change lay in the nature of Chinese society, not in the technical ability of Chinese engineers. The staggering recent development of the West should not blind us to the fact that elsewhere in the world people of equal or superior skill were at work. ∎

KUNGSHU P'AN
fl. 470 B.C., Lu (Central China)
Chinese Engineer and Artisan

Life and Times:

The sixth and fifth centuries B.C. were years of political disunity and strife in China, but also a formative period for Chinese culture. Confucius, the country's leading moral philosopher and political theorist, lived during the late sixth century in the small central Chinese state of Lu. A generation later Kungshu P'an, one of China's earliest known engineers and craftsmen, began his career, also in Lu. Over the years numerous inventions were attributed to Kungshu P'an, who came to represent the traditions and achievements of Chinese artisans. In effect, he became the "patron saint" of artisans and engineers, part historical figure and part myth.

Kungshu P'an apparently spent much of his career as a minor official at the court of Lu—hence his appellation Lu Pan. But like many talented men of his time, he was also something of a freelance adviser. In 445 B.C. he designed armaments for the large southern state of Ch'u, often a military ally of Lu. Among his inventions were grappling hooks for use in naval campaigns. Meanwhile, at the court of Lu he designed devices for the entertainment of officials. One of thse was a wooden kite in the shape of a bird which, the annals report, remained aloft for three days. Though he missed Confucius by a generation, Kungshu P'an did associate with another famous moral philosopher, Mo Tzu, who shared the engineer's interest in lighter-than-air devices.

Among the inventions attributed to Kungshu P'an are the rotary grain mill and the tumbler lock. A classic Chinese text on carpentry, *The Manual of Lu Pan,* is named for him, though the origin of his material is obscure. Colored pictures of Kungshu P'an formerly hung in the workshops of many Chinese artisans, who burned incense to honor their tutelary deity.

Outstanding Engineering Achievements:

Both the rotary mill and the tumbler lock deserve serious attention, even if their attribution to Kungshu P'an is less than certain. Early rotary mills consisted of two stones, one of which turned against the other. The rotating stone was mounted on an adjustable central pin, making it possible to vary the space between the stones when grain was poured into the mill. Previously, wheat and rice were ground into flour with a mortar and pestle. The rotary mill considerably sped up this process and made it semi-automatic. Early mills were turned by hand; as they became larger, they were adapted to water and animal power.

The early tumbler lock attributed to Kungshu P'an consisted of several pegs that fit into corresponding loops. A properly-shaped key lifted all the pegs from the loops, making it possible to throw the bolt. ■

Further Reading:

Needham, *Science and Civilization in China,* Vol. IV, pt. 2.

SHIH CH'I
fl. 300 B.C.
Chinese Hydraulic Engineer

Life and Times:

Irrigation of the land was a precondition for extending the agricultural domain of Chinese states and empires. Between the sixth and fourth centuries B.C., the competing rulers of the "Spring and Autumn" period in north and central China vied with one another in fostering the development of irrigation networks. The creation of reservoirs and channels not only supplied adjacent lands with water but also opened the possibility of controlling the destructive flooding of major rivers. This was especially true in the case of the Yellow River, north China's largest waterway.

At the end of the fifth century B.C., Duke Wen of the state of Wei embarked on a major hydraulic project: the diversion of the Chang River, which flowed southeast from Shansi into the Yellow River, into a northeastern course that met the Yellow River not far from the modern city of Tiensin. Delayed by difficulties in mobilizing labor, the project was completed two generations later under the supervision of the official Shih Ch'i. The resulting canal irrigated a substantial part of the province of Honei, in the northeastern part of Wei. It also helped reduce the danger of flooding along an important part of the Yellow River, which was no longer swollen by the waters of a large tributary. For these reasons, the Chang River canal is regarded as one of the two major irrigation projects of the period and one of the earliest recorded efforts at large-scale irrigation in China.

Outstanding Engineering Achievement:

It is uncertain how much of the canal Shi Ch'i himself designed and to what extent he relied on the plans of his predecessors. In any event, the watercourse was notable for its use of lateral contours; the sides of the channel were graded along an incline so that water ran through the canal much as it might pass along a river bed. Existing records give no indication of how the Chang River was diverted into the completed channel. Shih Ch'i may have constructed dams to alter the river course, or simply relied on the normal flow of water to fill the new canal. ■

Further Reading:

Needham, *Science and Civilisation in China.* Vol. IV, pt. 3.

CHENG KUO
fl. 246 B.C.
Chinese Hydraulic Engineer

Life and Times:

A hydraulic engineer during the Period of Warring States in ancient China, Cheng Kuo became involved in an unusual way in the political rivalries of his time. The prince of Han, fearing the growing strength of the neighboring state of Ch'in, hoped to divert his rival's energies into a mammoth construction project. He therefore sent Cheng Kuo to persuade the Ch'in ruler to build a canal through his territories. The king of Ch'in assented and commissioned Cheng Kuo to supervise the project. Before work was half completed, however, the king discovered the scheme and threatened to execute Cheng. The engineer did not deny his deceit, but defended the project on ground of its utility. "I have by this ruse prolonged the life of the state of Han for a thousand years, but [my] work will sustain the state of Ch'in for ten thousand generations." The king agreed, reprieved Cheng and ordered the canal completed.

Outstanding Engineering Achievement:

The Chengkuo canal, named for its builder, carried water along the foot of mountains in northern China into the eastern river Lo. Opening in the west from the Ching River near modern Ching-Yang, the canal waters bore rich silt and irrigated an estimated 667,000 acres (270,000 hectares) of land. Partly as a result of the irrigation system fed by the canal, Ch'in grew into a powerful state, eventually strong enough to conquer all its rivals and unify China. ■

Further Reading:

Needham, *Science and Civilisation in China.* Vol. IV, pt. 3.

SHIH LU
fl. 220 B.C.
Chinese Hydraulic Engineer

Life and Times:

A contemporary of Li Erh-lang [q.v.], Shih Lu served the emperor Shi Huang-ti during the struggle for China's unification under the Ch'in dynasty. Around 220 B.C., when the emperor planned a campaign against the southern state of Yüeh, he commissioned Shih Lu to build a canal in present day Kwangsi province connecting the river systems of north-central and south China. The canal, called the Ling Ch'u or Magic Transport Canal, was the first work of its kind in history. The emperor used it to transport troops and supplies southward during his successful campaign against Yüeh.

Outstanding Engineering Achievement:

The Ling Ch'u extended for about 20 miles (32 km) through a range of hills, connecting the Hsiang river in the north with the Kuei Chang river in the south. It made possible for the first time direct water transportation between the Yangtze river and the southern port of Canton. To construct the canal, Shih Lu diverted the headwaters of the Hsiang and Li rivers, the latter a tributary of the Kuei Chang. He was careful to avoid sudden changes in the level of the canal by closely following the contours of the hilly region through which it passed. Even so, some sources maintain that a system of 35 lock gates had to be constructed to cope with some of the sharper rises and falls in the land. The canal was no more than a few feet in depth, enough to accommodate broad-bottomed vessels holding 1,000 bushels (36,000 l) of cargo.

The campaign against Yüeh was not the last time that Shih Lu's canal was used for military purposes. As the Chinese prepared in 40 A.D. to conquer northern Vietnam, Ma Yuan, a general of the Han dynasty, extended the canal northward by excavating the bed of the Hsiang river in an effort to facilitate troop movements. ■

Further Reading:

Needham, *Science and Civilisation in China*. Vol. III.

MENG T'IEN
fl. 220 B.C.
Chinese General

Life and Times:

A successful military leader during the Ch'in dynasty, Meng T'ien commanded forces that repelled incursions of Mongolian nomads into northern China. Though not an engineer, he was then commissioned by the Ch'in emperor, Shih Huang Ti, to build the first section of what later became known as the Great Wall of China. The idea behind the project, conceived by the emperor himself, was to join the fortresses guarding China's northern border into a continuous system capable of preventing Mongolian raids from Central Asia. The task was completed, but its very success proved Meng T'ien's undoing. Apprehensive contemporaries believed that such a cast man-made work disrupted the natural pattern of the landscape. Their fears were strengthened when Shih Huang Ti reportedly died while inspecting a section of the rampart. The emperor's successor ordered Meng T'ien, as overseer of the unlucky project, to commit suicide. Conceding that the wall probably "cut through the veins of the earth," Meng swallowed poison. (This demonstrates the probable influence of the ancient Chinese occult science of geomancy.)

Outstanding Engineering Achievement:

Archeological evidence suggests that the original Great Wall, known as the Great North Wall,

Part of the Great Wall of China, the only man-made feature visible from earth orbit.

took an immense detour north of the great bend of the Yellow River. The ancient wall is estimated to have been 3,080 miles (4950 km) in length, while the modern wall runs about 1,700 miles (2740 km). The Ch'in wall, so-called after the dynasty during which it was built, is believed to have passed Ninghsia, continuing north of the river and then running east through the southern steppes of Mongolia at a line north of the present Great Wall. It is believed to have reached the sea near Shan-hai-huan. The wall apparently created an elliptical line of defense which included the lower valley of the Liao River in Manchuria and extended to the coast near the mouth of the Yalu River.

After six centuries of use, the wall suffered neglect until the sixth and seventh centuries A.D., when it underwent major reconstruction under the Wei, Ch'i and Sui dynasties. Historians and archeologists agree that most of the present structure is the work of Ming dynasty builders dating from the sixteenth century. By the time of China's last dynasty, the Ch'ing, the vast structure had lost all military significance. ■

Further Reading:

John Miller, *Master Builders of Sixty Centuries*. New York, 1938.
Needham, *Science and Civilisation in China*. Vol. IV, pt. 3.

YANG CH'ENG YEN
fl. 200 B.C.
Chinese Civil Engineer

Life and Times:

The art of fortifying towns in China developed during the Period of Warring States, as rival princes sought to protect their capitals and market centers from attack. The earliest Chinese symbol for capital city, in fact, is a drawing of a guard house surmounting a city gate. Shortly after the unification of China, the newly-founded Han dynasty established its capital at Ch'ang-an in the east-central part of the empire. Construction of the capital's massive fortifications was entrusted to the civil engineer Yang Ch'eng Yen.

Outstanding Engineering Achievement:

The work undertaken by Yang Ch'eng Yen was far more extensive than any previous city defense system. This was a direct response to increasingly sophisticated techniques of siege warfare, including the digging of tunnels to undermine city walls and the diversion of waterways to wash away the foundations of a fortress. The remains of Ch'ang-an's fortifications are still visible today near the modern city of Sian.

Laid out in a square grid pattern, Ch'ang-an was surrounded by walls running 16 miles (26 km) in any direction. Ancient sources report that the walls measured 50 feet (15 meters) high and 40 feet (12 meters) wide, and were backed by a terreplein, or reinforcing rampart, that extended 200 feet (60 meters) into the city. Yang Ch'eng Yen also had a protective moat, measuring 15 feet (4.5 meters) deep and 150 feet (45 meters) wide, dug around the fortifications. The entire line of defense, including barracks for the city garrison, is estimated to have been 480 (145 meters) feet wide around the perimeter.

Originally made of an earthen or rubble core, the city walls were later reconstructed with large burnt bricks set in lime mortar. The bricks were reinforced with stone blocks placed in the wall at regular intervals. ◼

Further Reading:

Needham, *Science and Civilisation in China.* Vol. IV.

CHENG TANG SHIH
fl. 130 B.C.
Chinese Hydraulic Engineer

Life and Times:

Chang Tang Shih was an engineer during the early Han dynasty, a time of rapid economic growth following the unification of China. As commerce grew, the country's transportation network became increasingly inadequate; this was especially true of the clogged routes to the capital, Ch'ang-an. Cheng Tang Shih conceived the idea of building a canal between the Yellow River and Ch'ang-an running parallel to the Wei river, a major artery of grain shipments to the capital from the empire's rich eastern provinces. The emperor Wu Ti, a vigorous ruler who sponsored an extensive program of public works, supported Cheng's plan and made arrangements to have it carried out.

Outstanding Engineering Achievement:

The transport canal proposed by Cheng Tang extended about 100 miles (160 km), reducing the water route from Ch'ang-an to the Yellow River by two-thirds and the travel time by half. Water from the canal was also used to irrigate about 166,000 (67,000 hectares) acres of farmland. Actual supervision of the canal's construction was assigned to the hydraulic engineer Hsü Po. Some 30,000 laborers worked on the project, which was completed in three years. With the canal in operation, traffic to Ch'ang-an increased significantly. ◼

Further Reading:

Needham, *Science and Civilisation in China.* Vol. IV, pt. 3.

CHUANG HSIUNG-P'I
fl. 120 B.C.
Chinese Hydraulic Engineer

Life and Times:

The reign of the Han emperor Wu Ti, at the beginning of the first century B.C., brought the extension of imperial authority into Central Asia north and west of the old Chinese heartland.

Territorial expansion brought China closer to other culture centers such as the Middle East, increasing the opportunity for diffusion of ideas and techniques. One area in which this process can be traced is irrigation technology, a matter of vital concern to both civilizations.

An early sign of possible Middle Eastern influence in China was the proposal of an official named Chuang Hsiung-P'i to construct a subterranean canal in Shensi province. Chuang's actual position is not known, nor is it clear whether he initiated, supervised or designed the project. What is clear from existing records is that about 120 B.C. Chuang Hsiung-P'i argued the desirability of building a canal that would irrigate lands in southern Shensi, northeast of the Han capital of Ch'ang-an, and described its specifications. Using water that came from mountain streams, the canal flowed at least in part through tunnels to avoid erosion of the area's porous surface soil. Chuang hoped to transform a salty terrain into one able to sustain well-developed agriculture, but the project proved of limited practical value. The distinguishing feature of these tunnels was a series of shafts dug to give the workers air and to allow for the removal of rubble.

Although Chuang's canal was the first of its kind in China, its system of wells and tunnels resembled a method of irrigation already long practiced in western Asia. In Persia such a canal, known as the *quanat,* was the standard method of irrigation. There, as in Shensi, underground irrigation was a response to the problem of porous valley soil that absorbed water flowing down from the mountains.

Outstanding Engineering Achievement:

The "Dragon-Head Canal," so called because of fossil bones found during its excavation, ran from Ch'eng ch'eng to Shang-yen mountain. The tunnel was dug above fairly impervious clay soil; vertical shafts were dug at intervals to tap the water, catch the run-off and ventilate the underground passageway. Starting in the foothills of Shensi, the canal ran to another set of hills, at which a reservoir had been created. This then served as a source of water for irrigating the adjacent region. ∎

Further Reading:

Needham, *Science and Civilisation in China.* Vol. I.

YANG YEN
fl. 26 B.C.
Chinese Hydraulic Engineer

Life and Times:

One of the most common flood-control devices in dynastic China was the gabion, a huge open-ended bamboo basket filled with stones. Large gabions emplanted against dikes and dams succeeded in shoring up these structures against floodwaters that would break through barriers of solid stone. The strength and resilience of bamboo were well-known to the ancient Chinese, and the use of gabions was probably as old as hydraulic engineering in China. But gabions first served as the main element of a massive flood control project during the late first century B.C., when the Yellow River broke through its dikes in several places, flooding up to 2.5 million acres (one million hectares). The work of containing and repairing the damage was supervised by two men, the bureaucrat Wang Yen-Shih and the engineer Yang Yen.

Himself an important official, Yang Yen served at the imperial court as vice minister and director of engineering works. In 26 B.C., when the Yellow River flooded for the second time in three years, he was detailed to assist Wang Yen-Shih, comptroller of water conservancy works, in the reclamation effort. It was Yang who proposed and directed the systematic placement of large gabions to reinforce the breached dikes; Wang apparently mobilized labor for the project and saw to the movement of supplies. Work was completed in six months.

Yang Yen also supervised another major hydraulic project, an effort to improve navigation on the upper reaches of the Yellow River by widening the San-Men (or Three Gates) gorge. To remove rock from the gorge, Yang proposed that large stones be fractured by applying extremes of heat and cold. This technique, which involved lighting fires on the rock and then dousing it with cold water, was later applied on a larger scale by Yü Hsü [q.v.]. Yang succeeded in widening the gap, but this failed to eliminate the river turbulence which had caused him to undertake the project.

Outstanding Engineering Achievement:

The gabions designed by Yang Yen to control the Yellow River were sausage-shaped structures, about 40 feet (12 meters) long and 17 feet

(5 meters) in diameter. Even when filled with stones, they weighed less than stone or wooden barriers; as a result, it was possible to sink gabions in alluvial soils which would not support heavier emplacements. Gabions were also porous and relatively flexible, which made them effective shock absorbers able to withstand sudden increases in water pressure when the Yellow River flooded. ■

Further Reading:

Needham, *Science and Civilisation in China*. Vol. IV, pt. 3.

CHIA JANG
fl. 6 B.C.
Chinese Hydraulic Engineer

Life and Times:

A prominent engineer and civil servant in the final years of the Former Han dynasty, Chia Jang grappled with the problem of how to maintain the empire's extensive flood control and irrigation systems with declining and increasingly sporadic revenues from the central government. In this effort he became involved in a long-standing controversy over flood control along rivers. One school of thought, known as the Taoist school (due to its preference for minimal action), favored allowing a river to flow in its existing channel; floods were to be prevented through periodic dredging of the river bed. The opposing Confucianists, who advocated a more activist approach, urged that the river be periodically diverted by means of dykes into a deeper and more secure channel. Chia Jang gave his influential support to the Taoist school, which had the advantage of requiring less maintenance work than its rival. This was the approach that dominated Chinese flood control technology during Chia Jang's lifetime and for several decades after.

Outstanding Engineering Achievement:

Chia Jang is best known for a report to the emperor which he wrote in 6 B.C., revealing the state of disrepair into which the Yellow River flood control system, the most extensive series of waterworks in China, had fallen. Not only were dykes not maintained, he complained, but new embankments were being erected haphazardly to contain the damage caused by neglect of older works. Chia Jang went so far as to recommend resettlement of populations living along the river. Although this proposal was not adopted, his report was influential in the shaping of Chinese flood control policy. ■

Further Reading:

Needham, *Science and Civilisation in China*. Vol. IV, pt. 3.

CHANG JUNG
fl. 1 B.C.
Chinese Hydraulic Engineer

Life and Times:

The accumulation of silt in the Yellow River and other major waterways of northern China posed a constant dilemma for early Chinese hydraulic engineers. On the one hand, topsoil carried by the river enriched the surrounding farmland when diverted into irrigation channels. On the other hand, silting caused the level of the river to rise until it broke through its dikes in devastating floods. Taller dikes were then built and the process continued, until the level of the Yellow River was actually higher than that of the surrounding countryside. By the end of the first century B.C., the problem had become so acute that hydraulic engineers began to seek a systematic approach to river control which would avert emergencies and stopgap solutions. This led to the first general sutdy of soil erosion and silting on the Yellow River. Completed in 1 B.C., it was the work of a palace official of the Former Han dynasty named Chang Jung.

Outstanding Engineering Achievement:

Chang Jung's study estimated the silt content of the Yellow River at a surprisingly high 60 percent. It also concluded that silt content was proportional to the speed of the river flow. To limit the accumulation of silt, Chang Jung proposed what came to be known as the self-scouring method of flood control. Rather than building ever-taller dikes, he urged, the flow of the river should be narrowed and its speed increased by means of dams and dikes constructed closer to the river's center. In this way, the river would scour silt from its own channel and deepen its bed. The idea of self-scouring came to be embodied in the maxim: "A good canal is scoured by its own water; a good embankment is consolidated by the sediment brought against it."

Chang Jung's ideas exerted great influence on later Chinese hydraulic engineers, especially those of the so-called Confucianist school, who advocated energetic and extensive flood control measures. Self-scouring found less favor among engineers concerned with crop irrigation, who realized that the system would carry valuable silt past farmlands. Much of Chinese hydraulic engineering history is the story of various compromises between these opposing viewpoints. ∎

Further Reading:

Needham, *Science and Civilisation in China.* Vol. IV, pt. 2.

TU MAO
fl. 25 A.D.
Chinese Military Engineer

Life and Times:

Tu Mao was a military engineer in the first years of the Later Han dynasty, a time of restoration and consolidation of central government power following the collapse of the Former Han line. Kuang Wu Ti, the emperor under whom he served, was occupied chiefly with recovering lands in the south and north lost during the interregnum. Tu Mao played a major role in the strengthening of China's northern frontier, then beset by barbarian incursions from Central Asia. Among the invaders were tribes known to the Chinese as the Hisung-nu. Pushed back across the border, they appeared three centuries later in southeastern Europe as the Huns; this time their invasion was successful, contributing to the collapse of the Roman Empire. Tu Mao's work thus helped influence events far beyond the frontier which he defended.

Outstanding Engineering Achievements:

Tu Mao's defense works included numerous beacon stations, transport depots and fortifica-

tions. He is particularly remembered for building a strategic road along the northern frontier. Called the Flying Fox Road, after the Fai-hu Pass through which it wound, the road began at the city of Tai on the Shansi road to Peking and wound through the Fei-hu Pass to the north of Wu-t'ai Shan, ending at P'ing-Ch'eng near Ta-shung. The Flying Fox Road traversed over 200 miles (320 km) of mountainous territory. ∎

Further Reading:

Needham, *Science and Civilisation in China.* Vol. IV, pt. 3.

HSÜN MAO
fl. 50 A.D.
HAN TS'EN
fl. 50 A.D.
Chinese Civil Engineers

Life and Times:

China's road network has traditionally been shaped by the country's water transportation system. Major rivers such as the Yellow and Yangtze rivers and their tributaries flow in a general easterly direction. Therefore, efforts were made from earliest dynastic times to construct north-south roads linking river transit points. The rulers of China's first dynasty, the Ch'in, ordered the construction of three roads between the Wei River, a tributary of the Yellow River, and the Han, a tributary of the Yangtze. These routes were difficult both to build and to travel, for they crossed the Sinling Mountains, an eastward extension of the massive Kunlun chain in Tibet. The engineers responsible for the Ch'in roads are unknown. But during the first century A.D. one of the routes, the Pao-yeh Road, was reconstructed at enormous cost in labor and material. The engineers in charge of the project, whose names were recorded in an inscription, were Hsün Mao and Han Ts'en.

Outstanding Engineering Achievement:

The Pao-yeh Road ran some 125 miles (200 km) from the town of Mei-hsien on the Wei River to Pao-ch'eng on the Han River. For most of its length it was a mountain road, either excavated into vertical rock faces or supported on wooden brackets (or galleries) driven diagonally into the rock. As rebuilt by Hsün Mao and Han Ts'en, the road crossed 623 small trestle bridges and five large bridges. Sixty-four rest houses were also built for travellers. The entire reconstruction project involved 2,690 forced laborers working a total of 766,800 man-days. ∎

Further Reading:

Needham, *Science and Civilisation in China.* Vol. IV, pt. 3.

WANG CHING
fl. 70 A.D.
Chinese Hydraulic Engineer

Life and Times:

One of the earliest major Chinese canals was the Hung Kou or Pien Canal, which flowed 500 miles (800 km) through east-central China to join the Yellow River. Built between the sixth and fourth centuries B.C., it was equipped with numerous flash locks to help small vessels over gradients. During the Former Han dynasty the Pien Canal became an important access route to the capital city of Ch'ang-an; boats bearing some 122,000 tons of grain passed along it annually. But in 11 A.D. extensive flooding along the Yellow River blocked the mouth of the canal, caused it to deviate from its bed and overwhelmed most of the flash locks. Efforts to restrict both the river and the canal with stone embankments failed, and some 50 years later the emperor Ming Ti ordered a thorough reconstruction of the canal. As often the case in large public works, the project was headed by a two-man team—a bureaucratic official to coordinate labor and supply, and an engineer to supervise technical operations. The engineer in charge of the Pien Canal reconstruction was Wang Ching.

Descended from a family that had gained some engineering distinction in Korea, Wang Ching entered the emperor's service in the mid-first century A.D. He was an influential proponent of the so-called Confucianist viewpoint in hydraulic engineering, which favored larger and more extensive works to control major waterways. The opposing Taoist school generally advocated less heroic measures, and in extreme cases simply urged the removal of population from flooded areas. Indeed, a Taoist engineer would have refused to undertake much of the work involved in the Pien Canal project.

Reconstruction of the Pien Canal, completed in 70 A.D., was Wang Ching's most important achievement. Eight years later he began to rebuild the Peony Dam, a project still under way at the time of his death in 83. Following his work on the Pien Canal, Wang was named Inspector General of Rivers and Dikes. The emperor, impressed by an inspection tour of the rebuilt canal, also presented Wang with gifts of money, goods and books.

Outstanding Engineering Achievement:

In reconstructing the Pien Canal, Wang Ching had large dikes erected at the canal's junction with the Yellow River. He also restored and added to the canal's system of flash locks, which totalled 200 when his work was completed. Wang almost certainly went further than any other contemporary engineer in his reliance on flash locks, for many centuries the primary means of canal navigation in China.

Flash locks were large gates set across the canal, generally made of logs that fell into place between two stone or wooden grooves set on either side of the waterway. The logs could be lifted or dropped into position by ropes, although in later versions windlasses were used. When the flash lock was opened water coursed into the adjacent section of the canal, propelling vessels up- or downstream. It was necessary to set the gates at a substantial distance from one another; once the stream of water had abated, it often took hours to build up sufficient volume and pressure to propel a vessel further along the canal. As a result, traffic in the canal could move in only one direction at a time. A canal equipped with flash locks could also handle only fairly small vessels, which could be moved by a single rush of water. These difficulties were overcome only in the eleventh century with the invention of the pound lock, which could substantially raise or lower the water level in small sections of the canal. ∎

Further Reading:

Needham, *Science and Civilisation in China.* Vol. III.

CHANG HENG
b. 78 A.D.
d. 139 A.D.
Chinese Clock and Instrument Maker

Life and Times:

Early engineers were commonly active in several fields, and a single invention often found unexpected adaptations. A technique introduced to improve the processing of wheat might be incorporated into the design of astronomical instruments. Yet even by these standards, Chang Heng, an important scholar-official of the Later Han dynasty, was an unusually protean and original figure. Active in mathematics and astronomy as well as engineering, Chang devised one of the first water clocks that made use of a compensating tank to ensure accuracy. He also improved the design of the armillary sphere, used to chart the motion of celestial bodies, and even developed an early seismograph. His activities both as an engineer and as a civil servant reveal the close connection between politics, astronomy and engineering in dynastic China.

Chang Heng was born in Wan—modern-day Nanyang—and rose to prominence as an official in the Han capital of Ch'ang-an. Adept at political maneuvering, he also won respect for his scientific skills. At a fairly early age he was named Astronomer Royal, a position that gave him responsibility for the astronomical observations which regulated court life and were thought to form the basis of the emperor's moral authority. Chang Heng's political career reached its zenith with his appointment as President of the Imperial Chancellery, making him one of Emperor Shun Ti's leading officials. Whether in office or out, Chang devoted himself to writing and experimenting. As a result, he left behind a large body of writings, including two books: *Ling Hsien* (Spiritual Constitution of the Universe) and *Hun I Chu* (Commentary on the Armillary Sphere).

Much of Chang Heng's scientific work was obviously related to his official duties. His success as Astronomer Royal depended on the accuracy of the instruments at his disposal, directing his attention to both the armillary sphere and the water clock. His seismograph informed officials in the capital that an earthquake had occurred and indicated its general location, allowing relief efforts to be organized even before messengers from the affected area had arrived. A leading exponent of the Hun T'ien (or Celestial Sphere) school of astronomy, Chang maintained that the heavens and earth were both spherical, with the earth at the center of the system. This belief led him to seek improved methods of measuring terrestrial distance, and he devised the first coordinate maps used in China. But Chang had less immediate interests as well. He studied the principles of flight, and his writings refer to a flying wooden bird which he designed, apparently powered by a spring-driven air screw resembling a helicopter propeller.

Outstanding Engineering Achievements:

The simple water clock, which measured time by means of the flow of water from one vessel into another, had been used in China since ancient times. This instrument had one important disadvantage: as water drained from the outflow vessel, its rate of flow decreased and time-keeping became increasingly inaccurate. Chang Heng developed one means of solving this problem. His water clock consisted of three vessels. The flow of water from the topmost vessel was adjusted so that the water level of the middle vessel, or compensating tank, remained constant. Water thus entered the bottom vessel at a uniform rate, raising a float which moved an indicator-rod on the water clock's exterior. This was the basis of later, more sophisticated designs, including the giant steelyard-balance water clocks of Yüwen K'ai [q.v.] and Liang Ling-Tsan [q.v.].

Chang Heng made several important improvements in the armillary sphere.

He added two rings, representing the horizon and meridian, to the two already in use. His armillary sphere was also the first that could be used entirely as a demonstrational device, showing the movements of celestial objects rather than simply helping an astronomer to observe them. For this purpose it was equipped with a model earth at the center and colored beads representing planets and major stars, features that became standard in later armillary spheres. Chang's instrument, some 14½ feet (4.4 meters) in circumference, was housed in a closed chamber with an attendant who called out the positions of celestial objects for verification by an observer on a platform outside.

The device was also important for being the first mechanical armillary sphere, with rings turned automatically by a water-powered system. To ensure the even movement of the water wheel which provided the motive force, Chang designed a mechanism with certain features of the water clock. Water from a tank emptied at a constant rate into scoops fastened along the periphery of the water wheel. As each scoop in succession filled with water it overturned, tripping a lever that rotated the wheel one notch along a ratchet. A series of gears and pinions transmitted the motion of the water wheel to the rings of the armillary sphere. Water from the overturned scoops meanwhile dropped into a drainage tank, from which it could be recycled into the outflow tank. This closed system, which regulated the movement of the wheel by weighing controlled amounts of water, was a direct predecessor of the linkwork escapement used by I Hsing [q.v.] and other Chinese horological engineers in the first mechanical clocks.

The exact structure of Chang Heng's seismograph is not clear from the records which describe it, and modern scholars have made plausible reconstructions. All agree that the central component was a pendulum set in motion by an earthquake shock. The pendulum was housed in a bronze jar some four feet tall; around the sides of the jar were fastened eight movable figures representing dragon heads, each holding a ball in its mouth. Directly beneath each dragon head at the base of the jar was the figure of a toad with an upturned, open mouth. An earthquake was registered by the fanciful means of a ball dropping from one of the dragon heads into the mouth of the corresponding toad. This was done by the action of the pendulum, which tripped the dragon head through a system of levers or by means of a rotating plate. The direction of the quake's center could be determined by the swing of the pendulum and the position of the ball that was dislodged. The instrument evidently included a locking mechanism so that it could not be set off by secondary tremors following the main quake. ■

Further Reading:

Needham, *Science and Civilisation in China.* Vol. IV, pt. 3.

YÜ HSÜ
fl. 110 A.D.
Chinese Civil Engineer

Life and Times:

The early emperors of the Later Han dynasty, ruling in the first century A.D., made great strides in consolidating the power of the central government. An essential part of their efforts to bind the empire together was a vigorous pro-

gram of canal construction and road-building. Special attention was given to improving the system of roads along the southern and northern frontiers, where expanding Chinese power came into conflict with tribal peoples. Much of the terrain here was wild and difficult, challenging Han civil engineers to develop new techniques of highway design and construction.

One of the most significant road-building efforts on the northern frontier was undertaken by an official and engineer named Yü Hsü. During the first decades of the second century, Yü planned and supervised the cutting through of a path along the Chia-ling River, in the mountainous northwestern region near the approaches to Sinkiang province. He succeeded in both constructing a pathway capable of bearing wheeled vehicles and clearing the river of obstructions to water-borne traffic, especially in a rock gorge east of Hsia-pien. As a result, the river no longer flooded.

Outstanding Engineering Achievement:

Yü Hsü's main problem in opening the Chia-ling valley to road and river traffic was removing massive rock obstacles. He was among the engineers who developed what became the standard method of rock removal in China: splitting the rocks apart by applying extreme heat and cold. He first had his crews spread kindling and light fires on rock formations; when the fires had burned down, water was poured over them. The sudden change in temperature fractured the rocks, which were then pried loose with crowbars and removed. In the absence of effective blasting techniques, this procedure was still used in China during the eighteenth century. ■

Further Reading:

Needham, *Science and Civilisation in China.* Vol. IV, pt. 2.

TING HUAN
fl. 180 A.D.
Chinese Mechanical Engineer and Instrument Maker

Life and Times:

In the ancient world the design of household devices, including those meant only for entertainment, often involved engineering innovations that went far beyond the immediate purpose for which the item was intended. Royal courts in particular encouraged the creation of such contrivances, often as luxuries or curiosities, and relied on groups of artisans to produce them. The Chinese court of the Later Han period—the first centuries A.D.—became a center for such activity. Visiting troupes of entertainers and travelling artisans were invited to the empire's eastern and western capitals from areas well outside the domains of China. At the western court the creations of Ting Huan, a craftsman and designer of mechanical devices, became famous. The incense burner he devised for use at court embodied the principle of design later found in the free-floating compass, the gyroscope and the universal joint: what in the west is known as the Cardan Suspension.

The details of Ting Huan's life are obscure. He lived during the second half of the second century; his major work was produced about 180. By class he was an artisan, neither from one of the gentry families nor of servile status. His interest in free-floating devices may have resulted from work on instruments used for astronomical observation, especially the armillary sphere, which consists of a system of rings similar to those in the Cardan Suspension. Some scholars believe that Ting Huan was attached to the staff of the Bureau of Astronomy and Calendar, where the instruments were made. Moreover, Ting Huan designed a huge rotary fan with seven interconnected wheels for the Han palaces, which suggests that he served as a court artisan for some time.

In addition to the incense burner (known as the "perfume burner for use among cushions" or "bedclothes censer") and the huge rotary fan, Ting Huan constructed several—often quite large—zoetrope lamps. These lamps provided a moving picture through the rotation of a thin umbrella about a light source, which illuminated through slits in the umbrella what appeared to be a coherent series of images.

Outstanding Engineering Achievements:

Ting Huan's incense burner was constructed in a system of rings that freed the central object from any disruption or displacement by the support upon which it rested. At least three concentric rings were used in the device. The incense burner had to be free to move on the axis of the pivot of the inner ring. The pivot of the axis of the middle ring had to be set at right angles to that of the inner ring; the pivot of the axis of the outer ring, if set at right angles to that

of the center ring, would then protect the burner from changes in the position of its external support. Ting Huan's incense burner represents perhaps the first application of this arrangement of rings in a mechanical device.

Ting Huan's zoetrope lamp operated through the movement of warm currents of air towards the covering or umbrella of the lamp. The vanes or wheels at the top of the lamp—here the similarity with the design of the rotary fan should be noted—were affected by the current of air and set the umbrella in motion. Occasionally, the lamp would also serve as a censer, and Ting Huan constructed a massive censer that also provided a light show. ■

Further Reading:

Needham, *Science and Civilisation in China.* Vol. III.
The Grand Titration: Science and Society in East and West. London, 1969.

CH'EN TENG
fl. 190 A.D.
Chinese Hydraulic Engineer

Life and Times:

The most extensive hydraulic works of China's early dynastic period were generally undertaken during the Former Han dynasty, between the third and first centuries B.C. In the later years of Han rule the scope of hydraulic projects diminished somewhat, and the focus of activity shifted south and east, away from the upper reaches of the Yellow River and the Lo River to the Yangtze. Nevertheless, the Later Han period could boast the construction of some major waterworks. One of these was an irrigation system west of Shou-hsien, planned and built by the engineer Ch'en Teng.

Outstanding Engineering Achievement:

In 189 A.D. Ch'en Teng constructed a system of weirs, or small dams, that blocked and redirected the flow of 36 streams in order to irrigate an area about 20 miles (32 km) in diameter. Each weir was constructed of alternate layers of rice straw and clay soil, resting on a gravel base reinforced by wooden pilings. The layers of rice stalks were carefully laid parallel to the current. Because of this feature and the porous materials used in construction, the dams were flexible, resistant to erosion and sudden changes in water pressure. ■

Further Reading:

Needham, *Science and Civilisation in China.* Vol. IV, pt. 3.

MA CHÜN
fl. 250 A.D., Loyang, China
Chinese Mechanical and Hydraulic Engineer

Life and Times:

Technological innovation proceeded in China even as the Later Han dynasty declined in the late second and early third centuries. Imperial workshops were established at the various courts that emerged, often in emulation of the imperial workshop of the Han. Attached to the workshop of the state of Wei—whose capital was Loyang— was Ma Chün, one of China's early leading engineers. Active during the middle of the third century, Ma Chün contributed to the design of the square-pallet chain pump, the standard water-raising device in China, and experimented with the early forms of several other important mechanisms.

Ma Chün's major activities have been set in the 220s and 230s, although he remained active past 260. He is known to us through the memoirs of a friend, who describes him as a modest, reticent individual who had difficulty advancing at the Wei court. Ma Chün's highest position was that of court adviser, and he never held a post in the Ministry of Works, where his talents would have been more fully utilized. Nonetheless, he was commissioned by the emperor, Ming Ti, to devise an assortment of inventions and curiosities for the amusement of the court. Among these was an elaborate theater of mechanical puppets, whose movements were powered by a horizontal waterwheel. Known earlier in the Near East, this is the first known use of this type of waterwheel in China, and the entire apparatus can perhaps be regarded as a precursor of the elaborate systems of jacks which marked the passage of time in the clocks of Su Sung [q.v.] and other horological engineers.

Ma Chün was also commissioned by Ming Ti to construct a "south-pointing carriage," a vehi-cle in which a pointer, generally in the shape of a human figure, continued to indicate the direction of true south no matter what the course of the vehicle. This was one of the first in a series of non-magnetic directional devices, which are still used in modern military tanks.

Asked to devise a means of irrigating land for a garden in Loyang, Ma Chün designed an improved version of the square-pallet chain pump. Though the chain pump had almost certainly been used by Chinese peasants (who called it the "dragon backbone machine") since earlier Han times, the description of Ma's work is one of the first positive references to the device still existing. The square-pallet chain pump was important not only for its widespread use but also as the likely inspiration for the first endless chain drives, developed by Chinese clock-makers of the Sung period.

Outstanding Engineering Achievements:

The effective operation of the south-pointing carriage depended on some method of feedback between the wheels and the pointer, so that changes in the direction of the vehicle would be transmitted to the pointer. In Ma Chün's invention a simple form of differential gearing probably served as the feedback mechanism, although the system did not always work properly and had

Conjectural model of the south-pointing carriage of Ma Chun, with a possible feedback gearing system.

to be adjusted periodically by hand. The wheels were connected by axles or shafts, which rotated in the same plane—in front and in back—but whose rotating speeds differed as the vehicle moved through a curve. The gears—perhaps toothed wheels—meshed with the horizontal shafts and moved at a rate equivalent to their rotation. Presumably both gears were attached to a bar or some other indicator, whose resulting movement and position served as the basis for adjusting the direction of the pointer.

The square-pallet chain pump resembled a conveyer belt which raised water in a series of rectangular units open at one end. In Ma Chün's machine, the belt was turned by an attendant operating a foot-pedal. Water was scooped from a spring by the rectangular units, raised up a 45-degree grade and deposited in an irrigation ditch as each unit turned over to begin its downward journey.

Two other inventions of Ma Chün's are worthy of note: a drawing-loom for weaving silk in which the number of treadles was reduced from 60 to 12, and a rotary ballista, an engine in the shape of a cross-bow which hurled stones or other missiles. The rotary ballista pivoted about in a circle, creating a side-arm throwing effect. ∎

A battery of hydraulic trip-hammers worked by an undershot vertical waterwheel.

Further Reading:

Needham, *Science and Civilisation in China.*

TU YÜ
fl. 250 A.D.
Chinese Mechanical and Civil Engineer

Life and Times:

Tu Yü was a prominent figure in the Chin state that succeeded the defunct Han empire in east-central China. An astronomer and military leader as well as an engineer, he commanded Chin forces in a successful campaign against the state of We. He was also a confidant of the Chin ruler who used his position to initiate ambitious public works. He was best known in his own time for designing and building the Ho-Yang bridge over the Yellow River near Loyang. But Tu Yü also made important contributions to mechanical engineering, developing new tools and designs for the water mills which were common in his area.

Outstanding Engineering Achievements:

Tu Yü's Ho-Yang bridge, completed in 247, was the second structure built across the Yellow River. The first, the P'u-Chin bridge in Shansi, was a floating bridge constructed during the Ch'in dynasty in the third century B.C. Like its predecessor, the Ho-Yang bridge consisted of a row of boats lashed side-by-side and covered with wooden planking. Despite their apparent fragility, these bridges were well-maintained and lasted many centuries; references to them are found in the annals of the T'ang and Northern Sung dynasties.

Tu Yü's most important contribution to hydraulic power technology was the trip-hammer, which he introduced in water mills about 260. Powered by a water wheel, trip hammers could be installed in series and coordinated by a system of gears and shafts. They were used most often to pound or pulverize materials such as grain; but they could also be adapted to rotary motion and used to power other devices. ∎

Further Reading:

Needham, *Science and Civilisation in China.* Vol. III.

WEI MENG-PIEN

fl. 340 A.D., northern Honan
Chinese Mechanical Engineer

Life and Times:

The numerous petty states that appeared in northern China during the fourth century, though unstable and short-lived, produced some notable engineering works. Rulers sought to increase their prestige—and encourage inventions of military value—by establishing state workshops on the model of the defunct Han dynasty. One of the most important of these was the workshop of Shih Hu, a king of the Later Chao dynasty that ruled in Honan province. Director of the workshop was Wei Meng-Pien, who cooperated closely in his work with a palace official named Hsieh Fei. Both Wei and Hsieh were Chinese, but the Later Chao house that they served had been established by Hunnish nomads. Interaction between Chinese and barbarian at the Later Chao court was undoubtedly important for Wei, providing an environment that stimulated new ideas and minimized the constraints of traditional literary culture.

Outstanding Engineering Achievements:

Most of Wei Meng-Pien's work mentioned in surviving records involved the construction of various wheeled vehicles. It is known that Shih Hu possessed a hodometer, which measured distance, and a south-pointing carriage, which indicated true south by means of a non-magnetic pointing figure. Both were probably designed by Wei, though he did not invent them; an earlier south-pointing carriage has been attributed to the engineer Ma Chün [q.v.]. More original was a ceremonial vehicle of Shi Hu that featured an elaborate set of moving jack figures, activated by the rotation of the wheels.

Though such devices were purely for the entertainment of the court, others invented by Wei had practical value. The most noteworthy of these was the so-called wagon-mill or camp-mill, a wagon equipped with rotating millstones and tilt-hammers that hulled and ground grain. According to some sources, the wagon's right wheel turned gears that operated the tilt-hammers, while the left wheel activated the millstones. If not the first, this was certainly the most novel automatic device for processing grain; it cleverly suited the needs of a military column, nomadic population or other frequently moving group. But sedentary Chinese peasants were better served by the traditional hand- or water-powered rotary mill, and Wei's invention never gained wide application. ■

Further Reading:

Needham, *Science and Civilisation in China.* Vol. IV, pt. 2.

SHOTOKU TAISHI

b. 574 A.D.
d. 622 A.D.
Japanese Prince and Architect

Life and Times:

A decisive moment in Japanese history occurred when Prince Shotoku Taishi assumed political control of the country in 592. With his encouragement and direction Japanese society underwent a transformation of its religious beliefs, its favored art styles, and its standard architectural forms. Under Shotoku, ideas and techniques current in China and Korea entered the mainstream of Japan's social life. More directly, he centralized the organization of the state in the emperor and an imperial bureaucracy. His sponsorship and supervision of the construction of a Buddhist temple, known as the Horyuji, in the city of Nara (soon to become Japan's capital) established a new architectural standard for the Japanese, one which merged Chinese styles of the Sui period with indigenous Japanese ones.

Shotoku came to prominence early in life. Before he had turned twenty he was chosen as Japan's regent, ruling in place of his aunt, Empress Suiko. As the chief administrator of the government he devised a set of constitutional precepts, in the spirit of Confucianism, to guide the running of the state. He sought to weaken the power of Japan's nobility; to that end he introduced court ranks, in which various members of the bureaucracy were identified by their headgear, or caps. He also strengthened cultural ties with the East Asian mainland, sending several Japanese embassies to China and welcoming Chinese and Korean artisans to Japan. A devout Buddhist, Shotaka encouraged the spread of the religion, brought to Japan from China in the previous century. These developments in turn strongly influenced Japanese art

The Horyuji temple built for Shotoku Taishi, an example of early Buddhist architecture in Japan.

and architecture. Indeed, the general course of Japanese culture in the next several centuries can be traced to a significant degree to Shotoku's influence.

Outstanding Engineering Achievement:

The Horyuji temple is the best surviving example of early Buddhist architecture in Japan. On the grounds of the monastery Shotoku constructed his own quarters and a chapel, known as the Yumedono, or Hall of Dreams. The central building in the monastery complex was the Golden Hall, or Kondo. Made of wood, the Golden Hall had two tiled roofs and was supported by substantial pillars. The latter were fashioned with a technique known to the Greeks as entasis, curving outward in the middle to avoid an appearance of fragility. The two-tiered roof and the balance of longitudinal and altitudinal elements became characteristic of Japanese architecture. The monastery grounds included a pagoda as well. Within each of the buildings Japanese sculptors and artisans, most notably the sculptor Tori Busshi, carved numerous pieces of statuary, mostly of bronze or wood. Destroyed by fire in 670, the monastery was rebuilt along the same lines as the original structure in the early eighth century. The complex of buildings has survived into the twentieth century, allowing some scholars to claim that the temple contains the oldest wooden building in the world. ■

Further Reading:

George B. Sansom, *Japan: A Short Cultural History.* London, 1931.
W. Scott Morton, *Japan: Its History and Culture.* New York, 1970.

YANG SU
fl. 590 A.D.
Chinese Military Engineer and Admiral

Life and Times:

A prominent naval commander and military engineer, Yang Su served the emperor Wen Ti, who reunited China under the Sui dynasty after nearly four centuries of division. Yang Su commanded imperial forces in the campaign against the Ch'en, last of the fractionary dynasties that opposed the Sui in southern China.

Outstanding Engineering Achievement:

Yang Su is best known for designing and commanding a fleet of enormous war junks, built in 584 on the orders of the emperor. The biggest of the ships, known as "five-ensign battleships," had five decks and carried a complement of 800 marines. Over 100 feet (30 meters) high, the ships were equipped on each side with grappling hooks and large striking arms capable of smashing through the decks of enemy vessels. A number of smaller but still sizeable war junks were also built; called yellow dragon ships, each carried 500 marines. With these forces, Yang Su routed the Ch'en and cleared the rivers of southern China for the Sui. ■

Further Reading:

Needham, *Science and Civilisation in China.* Vol. IV, pt. 3.

LIANG JUI
fl. 600 A.D.
Chinese Civil Engineer

Life and Times:

A prominent engineer of the Sui dynasty, Liang Jui lived at the time of China's reunification after nearly four centuries of division and civil strife. It was a period of greatly expanded trade and military activity, accompanied by reconstruction of the country's system of canals and waterworks. With Ch'ang-an in central China restored as the capital, the Yellow River assumed renewed importance as a trade artery and route for movement of tax payments to the empire's treasury. This was the time when the so-called first (or Sui) Grand Canal was built to connect the capital with the agricultural lands of the Yangtze River to the south. For about a quarter of its length, the canal followed the course of the Yellow River, dredged and provided with flash locks to speed the movement of boats, Liang Jui played an important part in restoring and extending these waterworks, which had fallen into neglect during the preceding centuries of national disunity.

Outstanding Engineering Achievement:

Liang Jui's most important work was a westward extension of the Metal Dike, later called the Liang Kung Yen. Built on the southern bank of the Yellow River, the dike regulated water levels by means of lock gates which conducted water into subsidiary channels. It also contained double slipways for hauling boats in the event that the lash locks became inoperative. ■

Further Reading:

Needham, *Science and Civilisation in China.* Vol. IV, pt. 3.

LI CH'UN
fl. 610 A.D.

LI CHAO-TE
fl. 690 A.D.
Chinese Civil Engineers

Life and Times:

Until the eighteenth century, European bridges were generally clumsy structures, with thick piers and numerous semicircular arches. Only the work of Jean-Rodolphe Perronet [q.v.] convinced European bridge builders that arches could be much shallower and piers more slender than previously believed. Chinese engineers,

however, made this discovery a full milennium earlier, during the Sui and early T'ang periods. Pioneering work in bridge design was done in the seventh century by Li Ch-un and Li Chao-Te.

Both men lived at a time of vigorous building activity that followed the reunification of China under the short-lived Sui dynasty. Though both were prominent engineers, little is known of their lives. Li Chao-Te built a number of bridges in the former imperial capital of Loyang, while Li Ch'un was active over a wider area in Hopei and Shansi provinces. Li Ch'un trained a group of younger engineers, who applied his techniques in their own work. It is not known whether Li Chao-Te was part of this school; but his work was certainly based on the innovations of Li Ch'un.

Outstanding Engineering Achievements:

Li Ch'un's most important work was the Great Stone Bridge over the Chiao River near Chaohsien. Still in existence, the bridge is a single-arch structure that represented in its time a major advance in design. Earlier single-arch bridges were limited in length by the semicircular shape of the arch. It was Li Ch'un's insight that the arch need not be semi-circular; rather, it was possible to design the arch as a segment of a much larger circle, hence the name segmented arch bridge. The segmented arch allowed the curve of the bridge to be flattened out considerably, so that the span could be extended.

The Great Stone Bridge is 123 feet (37 meters) long; its roadway rises 237 feet (72 meters) above the chord-line of the arch. To strengthen the attenuated main arch, Li Ch'un built 25 small interior arches into its lining. On either side of the bridge he inserted two arch-shaped holes in the spandrels to limit the build-up of water pressure on the bridge during floods. In this way Li Ch'un also tightened up the design of the bridge, reducing the amount of stone and other materials needed for construction and lessening some of the tension on the arch.

Some three generations later during the early T'ang period, Li Chao-Te applied many of Li Ch'un's innovations to the design of longer bridges. His most famous work, the T'ien-chin bridge in Loyang, demonstrated that a bridge with multiple segmented arches could be supported without difficulty on relatively slender piers. The structure was not only more elegant but also safer than earlier bridges with their semicircular arches and massive piers. Since the piers were both thinner and more widely spaced, far less masonry was exposed to the eroding action of water; the design also minimized obstruction of the river current during periods of heavy flow, a problem which often caused flooding near more conventional bridges. ■

Further Reading:

Needham, *Science and Civilisation in China*. Vol. IV, pt. 2.

Henry G. Tyrrell, *History of Bridge Engineering*. Chicago, 1911.

YÜWÊN K'AI
fl. 610 A.D., Ch'ang-an and Loyang, China
Chinese Engineer and Architect

Life and Times:

The brief reign of the Sui emperors near the end of the sixth century and the beginning of the seventh provided the impetus for the reconsolidation of political power in a more formidable dynasty, the T'ang, and laid the basis for the reemergence of the Chinese imperial bureaucracy. As such, the Sui emperors were transitional figures whose plans and programs outlasted them. The Sui came to power in the mid-500s; during the early seventh century they tried to push back the various Turkic tribes that had gained control of much of northern and western China. At the same time they encouraged the development of extensive irrigation works, both to increase crop yields and to concentrate political power in the central government.

A prominent role in these tasks was assigned to Yüwên K'ai, who was most likely a member of the Yüwên tribal group that usurped the throne of the western Wei in the mid-500s. As chief engineer and architect for both Sui emperors, Yüwên K'ai directed the reconstruction of the capital cities of Ch'ang-an and Loyang. In collaboration with another engineer, Kêng Hsün [q.v.], he also devised a monumental water clock similar to those which appeared later in the Islamic world.

Yüwên K'ai first served as director of the Architectural and Engineering Department of the Imperial Palace in the 570s; he was then Minister of Works under the two Sui emperors for roughly thirty years. As a civil engineer and public official he worked extensively to prevent silting and flooding in the empire's canal network. In particular, Yüwên K'ai supervised the construction of part of the First Grand Canal, which ran from the capital, Ch'ang-an, to the port of Hangchow in the central coastal region of China. He also worked as a military engineer, designing large land-roving carriages with sails that could transport hundreds of soldiers along China's steppe frontier. His "mobile wind-facing palace" was the size of a small building, with guards stationed on the upper deck while the main body of troops travelled below. The undercarriage was an assemblage of wheels and axles.

Yüwên K'ai's skills as an architect found outlet in large and small-scale projects. He prepared a wooden model of the Buddhist temple, Ming T'ang, and redesigned the cities of Ch'ang-an in 583 and Loyang in 606. But his most notable feat as an engineer was his work on the design of the balance clepsydra, or water clock. Encouraged by the emperor around 610, he and Kêng Hsün [q.v.], an engineer known for devising water-powered astronomical instruments, translated the design of the portable, steelyard balance water clock into instruments large enough to serve as public and palace clocks, which became famous during the T'ang and Sung dynasties that followed the reign of the Sui.

Outstanding Engineering Achievement:

The accuracy of water clocks depended on the steady flow of water through a tank. Various means could be used to measure the passage of time on the basis of the water flow. Yüwen K'ai and Kêng Hsün weighed the amount of water in the tank by suspending the vessel from the short arm of a steelyard balance; changes in water weight were registered by a pointer attached to the long arm. Since Chinese hours varied seasonally according to the length of the day, the rate of water flow through the tank was adjusted periodically by changing the position of a weight that slid on the long arm of the beam.

Though steelyard-balance water clocks had been constructed before Yüwên K'ai and Kêng Hsün, their device was the first to use a compensating tank, i.e., once that both received and ejected water, rather than a simple inflow tank.

This change had two advantages: it permitted seasonal adjustment of the device, and it required the use of a larger tank (necessary to maintain a constant throughflow of water), resulting in a water clock suitable for public display. But the innovations of Yüwên K'ai and Kêng Hsün had even greater ramifications; for the technique of weighing water as it flowed through a vessel was later incorporated into the first true mechanical clocks constructed by I Hsing [q.v.] and other engineers of the T'ang and Sung periods. ∎

Further Reading:

Needham, *Science and Civilisation in China.* Vol. III.

KÊNG HSÜN
fl. 610 A.D.
Chinese Horological Engineer

Life and Times:

The reunification of China under the Sui and T'ang dynasties brought a renewed interest in clock-making as the new emperors sought to restore order to calendrical and astronomical computations, upon which the stability of the state was thought to depend. In the early seventh century, the technology of waterwheels was wedded to that of water clocks; the result was a continuously rotating armillary sphere, or celestial globe, designed by Kêng Hsün. Working with Yüwên K'ai [q.v.], Kêng Hsün also built an improved version of the steelyard waterclock, and so doing set the stage for construction of the first true mechanical clock with an escapement a century-and-a-half later.

Kêng Hsün lived at a time of intrigue and unrest as the new Sui dynasty sought to reassert Chinese control over tribal peoples along the country's borders. Kêng's skills as an engineer, particularly in the application of water power, brought him a position in the retinue of the imperial governor of Ling-Nan. After the governor's death, Kêng Hsün headed south and made common cause with one of the tribes living in the region. He played a prominent role among the tribespeople, finally leading them in a revolt against the central government. Captured by the general who quashed the uprising, Kêng Hsün was spared, apparently because of his engineering abilities. He was attached to the general's staff as a slave.

With the assistance of an old friend, Kao Chih-Pao, who had become Astronomer-Royal at the court, Kêng Hsün learned about astronomy and honed his skills as an engineer. He put these to good use when, with Kao's encouragement, he devised a water-powered armillary sphere, a globe composed of rotating rings representing the great circles of the heavens (given the earth as a stationary body). Kêng Hsün's ingenuity came to the attention of the emperor, who made him a government slave.

Now able to advance within the imperial bureaucracy, Kêng became assistant director of the Bureau of Astronomy and Calendar, and devised a series of hydrostatic tricks called "advisory inclining vessels," which tipped over when full. More importantly, he was commissioned along with Yüwên about 610 to design large water clocks for use at the imperial court. The clocks they built were placed prominently in the palace at Loyang, and served as models for public and palace clocks throughout the T'ang and Sung periods.

Later posts held by Kêng Hsün included acting superintendent of the imperial workshops and acting executive assistant in the Bureau of Astronomy.

Outstanding Engineering Achievements:

The water clocks designed by Kêng Hsün and Yüwên K'ai measured time by weighing the amount of water passing through a vessel attached to one arm of a steelyard beam, Kêng Hsün also used the principle of measuring water weight in the design of his armillary sphere. Here water dripping from a tank at a carefully controlled rate entered scoops attached to the periphery of a water wheel. Each scoop moved only when filled with a certain amount of water. The water wheel was joined through a cogwheel gear with a ratcheted, toothed wheel which turned one tooth for every movement of a scoop. The toothed wheel turned a vertical shaft, attached through other cogwheels to the various rings of the armillary sphere. The entire mechanism foreshadowed the true mechanical clocks constructed by I Hsing [q.v.] and other engineers of the T'ang and Sung dynasties. ∎

Further Reading:

Needham, *Science and Civilisation in China.* Vol. III.

I-HSING
b. 682 A.D.
d. 727 A.D.
Chinese Horological Engineer

Life and Times:

From the last days of the Later Han (the early 200s) until the later days of the T'ang (the early 900s) China was transformed by the infusion of Buddhism into its political, cultural, and religious life. In some respects Buddhism reached the height of its popularity during the period of barbarian rule in the 500s, but it received the highest sanction of state during the period of T'ang rule. With the encouragement of the T'ang emperors Buddhist monasteries were founded throughout China; these often became centers of learning. Buddhist influence gave new direction to Chinese science and engineering, in part because of new astrological (and astronomical) concerns raised in Buddhist texts and in part because Buddhism's Indian roots tended to strengthen the cultural line of transmission between India and China—and through India to the Hellenistic world.

Chang Sui, who assumed the religious appellation I-Hsing, left his mark as a Buddhist holy figure, astronomer, and engineer for the court of the emperor Hsüan Tsung in the first decades in the eighth century. I-Hsing's interest in the movement of heavenly bodies, at once religious, scientific and political, led him to devise the first true clock: an astronomical timepiece whose motions were automatically maintained at a constant rate by a combination of gearing and linkwork which regulated the movement of the time-indicator. In the West this arrangement is known as an escapement, the technical breakthrough that made the construction of clocks and other timepieces possible.

Our knowledge of I-Hsing's life is a mixture of fact and legend. Born in 682, he wandered about the Chinese countryside, establishing his reputation as a spiritual "holy man" and intellectual prodigy. He became a Tantric Buddhist monk, but that did not prevent him from having an active career at court. There he assumed the role of a seer, predicting the fall of the emperor Esüan Tsung, known for his tragic involvement with the concubine Yang Kuei Fe. He also explored the possibility of improving astronomical measurements, and one result of his efforts was a new calendar, the Ta Yen, which was adopted by the T'ang government in 724 and which reflected Indian Buddhist influences.

Rivals of I-Hsing among Chinese Buddhists charged that he had merely stolen the Navagraha system devised centuries before in India and translated into Chinese by a contemporary of I-Hsing, Ch'üt'an Hsi-Ta. Nonetheless, the calendar remained in place and the claims against I-Hsing were eventually disproven.

I-Hsing wrote several mathematical treatises and contributed several works to the holy texts, or Tripitake, of Chinese Buddhism, most notably the *Hsiu Yao I Kuei (The Tracks of the Hsiu and Planets)* and the *Pei Tou Ch'i Hsing Nien Sung I Kuei (Mnemonic Rhyme of the Seven Stars of the Great Bear and Their Tracks)*. It was his attempt to make more precise astronomical observations that led I-Hsing to experiment with new devices and instruments. To improve the accuracy of land-based measures of earth meridian I-Hsing went on an expedition in the early 720s to obtain new data for his calendar. He was willing to rely upon measurements based on ecliptic coordinates, popular among Hellenistic but not among Chinese astronomers; the former were inclined to make measurements based upon the relation between the path of the sun and the position of the earth, assuming that the earth remained stationary. In 724, with the assistance of a court official, Liang Ling-Tsan [q.v.], I-Hsing then devised armillary spheres which had ecliptically mounted sighting-tubes. More importantly, I-Hsing collaborated with Liang-Ling-Tsan in making improvements in the operation of a water-powered celestial sphere. Together they produced a clock, a water-driven device with an escapement, in 725.

Outstanding Engineering Achievement:

The clock designed by I-Hsing and Liang Ling-Tsan, known as the "Water-Driven Spherical Bird's-Eye-View Map of the Heavens," was a major achievement in several respects. It was the first device in the world to make use of an escapement (or "coupling devices and locks checking mutually," in the words of a contemporary description); the first armillary sphere to incorporate an "orrery" system of concentric gears and shafts that automatically regulated the pieces depicting the motions of various heavenly bodies; and the first timepiece in China that featured striking jacks to mark the passage of time.

Power for the clock was provided by a water wheel, which turned the main shaft. The motion of this shaft, regulated by a system of gears and balances forming the escapement, turned a model of the celestial sphere. Two wheels rotated about the sphere, representing the motion of the sun and moon. Each was turned by a shaft running parallel to the main shaft and connected to gears with an odd number of teeth. These gears were attached to the main shaft, so that the rotation of the celestial sphere, the sun and the moon was automatically coordinated. For each revolution of the celestial sphere, which took one day to complete, the sun moved one degree in the opposite direction, and the moon 13.37 degrees in the same direction as the sun.

The lower half of the armillary sphere was enclosed in a wooden case, the surface of which represented the horizon. By observing the relative positions of the celestial sphere, sun and moon, it was possible to determine the time of day as well as changes in lunar phase. Passage of time was marked by two jacks on the surface of the case, which sounded a bell on the hour and a drum on quarter-hours.

Despite its ingenuity, I-Hsing's clock was in use for only a short time. The bronze and iron parts of the mechanism corroded quickly, and the device was soon placed in a museum. It served as a model, however, for the later escapement clocks of Chang Sau-Hsün [q.v.] and Su Sung [q.v.]. ▮

Further Reading:

Kenneth S.H.A. Giles, *Chinese Biographical Dictionary*. London, 1898.

Ch'en, *Buddhism in China, A Historical Survey*. New Jersey, 1964.

Needham, *Science and Civilisation in China*. Vol. IX, pt. 3.

LIANG LING-TSAN
fl. 725 A.D.
Chinese Horological Engineer

Life and Times:

A major advance in the design of time-keeping devices occurred in the early eighth century when a Buddhist monk, learned in mathematics and astronomy, joined with a minor official of the T'ang court whose talents lay in engineering, to create the first true clock. These two men, I-Hsing and Liang Ling-Tsan, built an armillary sphere—used for tracking celestial bodies—whose time-keeping mechanism was based on the action of linked gears. This device included

an escapement that regulated the speed of the clock, serving the same function as the verge-and-foliot mechanism of European clocks made in the thirteenth and fourteenth centuries.

It is an interesting feature of Chinese horological history that several important developments were the work of two-man teams consisting of a prestigious scholar and a lesser-known, often younger, technical expert. This was true of the steelyard balance clepsydras constructed in the seventh century by Yüwên K'ai [q.v.] and Kêng Hsün [q.v.] and of the enormous eleventh-century clock of Su Sung [q.v.] and Han Kung-Lien [q.v.]. The senior member of the partnership considered here was I-Hsing, a favorite of the famous T'ang emperor Hsüan Tsung. Liang Ling-Tsan was a civil servant who served in the War Office as chief secretary of the Left Imperial Guard. Though less promising than I-Hsing, Liang had wide-ranging interests that gained him a position in the College of All Sages, an imperial academy whose members advised the emperor. An astronomical treatise attributed to him, the *Spirits of the Five Planets and the 28 Hsiu,* was well-regarded at the time.

It was Liang's technical skills, however, that helped determine the design and construction of the first clock. I-Hsing recognized the need for a more accurate mounted sighting-tube, which included a fitting for the ecliptic (the path of the sun). Liang devised the working model, made out of wood. When I-Hsing assessed the work of his junior partner as accurate, the two devoted the next two years to the construction of the full-scale version, completed in 725. Liang also supervised the construction of a demonstrational celestial globe, whose readings could be confirmed by the sighting tube. Like Han Kung-Lien two centuries later, Liang handled problems of technical design while I-Hsing developed the theoretical perspective and purpose of the project. Their instrument served as the model for clocks made in China, Mongolia and Korea over the next six centuries.

Outstanding Engineering Achievement:

In constructing their armillary sphere, I-Hsing and Liang Ling-Tsan drew upon the technology of water clocks that had developed from the time of Chang Heng [q.v.] in the second century. The device was powered by water dripping at a controlled rate from a tank into scoops fastened to the periphery of a water wheel. The wheel's rate of rotation was regulated by a system of interlocking levers that formed the escapement. The motion of the wheel was transmitted by a pinion and shaft to a series of concentric gears that rotated the three separate circles of the armillary sphere. (This arrangement, which came into use in Europe some 600 years later, was known in the West as an "orrery" system.) Through a second shaft, the water wheel also tripped levers that regulated the movement of two jack figures. The purpose of these was to indicate the hours, one by striking a gong, the other by ringing a bell—the first such use of jack figures in China. ■

Further Reading:

Needham, *Science and Civilisation in China.* Vol. III.

KIMI-MARO
fl. 750 A.D.
Japanese Metal-Worker

Life and Times:

The eighth century was a time of important developments in several areas of Japanese life. The population was expanding and new territories were opened to settlement, especially on the southern island of Kyushu and the northern island of Honshu. The central government, under the influence of China's example, grew in power and in the elaborateness of its institutions. And Buddhism, which had spread to Japan from China in the sixth century, gained great influence under state patronage.

These trends influenced one another in many ways. The Buddhist clergy was active in the construction of roads and bridges, which helped expand settlement. The opening of new lands led to the discovery of new mineral deposits, most important of which was a copper ore field in the Chichihu mountain range. The increased availability of metal in turn encouraged the development of metal-working, and the state for the first time began to mint coins. More generally, the growth of the country's population and wealth made it possible for the central government to sponsor ambitious construction projects. The capital city of Nara was built in the early eighth century, and many Buddhist temples and monasteries arose with state support throughout Japan.

The interaction of politics, religion and technology was most obvious during the reign of the Emperor Shomu, which lasted from 724 to 749.

It was at this time that Buddhism became a true state religion, with buildings and lands in every province. For the greater glory of both church and state, Shomu commissioned lavish works of religious art, the most impressive of which were gathered at the Todaiji (Great Eastern Temple) on the outskirts of Nara. One of these was the great temple bell, completed in 732; weighing 49 tons, mostly of copper, it was the first giant bell ever cast and remains to this day the fourth largest bell in the world. But even this project was dwarfed by the Daibutsu (Great Buddha) of Nara, an enormous bronze statue housed in the Great Hall of the Todaiji.

According to tradition, Shomu conceived the idea of casting the huge image of Vairocana, the Eternal Buddha, during Japan's first smallpox epidemic, which struck the capital in 734. Work on the project, delayed by a revolt in Kyushu, began in 744 with construction of a scale model. Seven unsuccessful attempts to cast the full statue had been made by the time Shomu's reign ended with his abdication in 749. But he did not leave office before appointing the metal-worker Kimi-maro to supervise the eighth and finally successful casting of the Daibutsu. The statue was dedicated in 752 with an elaborate ceremony at the Todaiji presided over by Shomu's successor, the Empress Koken.

Little is known of Kimi-maro's life aside from the fact that he was the grandson of a Korean immigrant to Japan. But the very survival of his name indicates the importance both of the project and of his role in it. The Nara Daibutsu rivalled in size the greatest monuments of antiquity; the work of Kimi-maro and his assistants might be compared to that of Chares of Lindos [q.v.] in constructing the Colossos of Rhodes. It was evident from the seven unsuccessful attempts to cast the statue that traditional metal-working techniques were completely inadequate for so large a project. New methods had to be devised, and fortunately some record of these has survived. The statue itself, damaged by fire in 1180, was repaired and remains on view to this day.

Outstanding Engineering Achievement:

The Daibutsu of Nara is a seated figure about 53 feet (16 meters) tall, weighing over one million pounds. It is made primarily of bronze, consisting of copper (986,180 lb; 447,330 kg), tin (16,827 lb; 7633 kg), and lead. In addition, 500 lb (227 kg) of gold and 1,954 lb (886 kg) of mercury were used to gild the image.

A statue of this size obviously could not be

The Daibutsu, the 53-foot (16.2 m) statue of Buddha, the world's largest bronze statue.

cast by normal methods in a single mold. Instead, Kimi-maro and his assistants cast multiple rectangular segments in layers to form the main part of the statue. Each segment was 10 inches by 12 inches (25 cm by 30 cm), with a depth of six inches (15 cm); they were cast in 41 layers from feet to shoulders, the clay mold being built up one layer at a time as the previous layer cooled. The head and neck of the statue, about 12 feet (3.6 meters) high, were cast separately in a single mold and fitted into a socket atop the trunk. ■

Further Reading:

Frank Brinkley, *A History of the Japanese People.* New York, 1915.

James Murdoch, *A History of Japan.* New York, 1964.

LI P'O
fl. 800 A.D.
Chinese Hydraulic Engineer

Life and Times:

As early as the third century B.C., Chinese hydraulic engineers had created an enormous north-south system of waterways, extending over 2,000 miles from the lower reaches of the Yellow River to the mouth of the West River at present-day Canton. Much of this network consisted of navigable rivers, but these were linked by three canals. The southernmost of these, the Ling Ch'ü canal, connects the West River with the Hsiang River in south-central China. Still in use today, it has undergone repeated repairs and improvements in the course of its 2,000-year existence. One of the most extensive of these operations was undertaken in the early ninth century, after collapse of the canal's banks blocked the passage of ships.

Restoration of the Ling Ch'ü was put in the hands of Li P'o, Inspector General of Waterways in the early part of the T'ang period. Li took this opportunity not only to repair the canal's banks but also to alter its course and add a system of locks to improve navigation. The resulting project, completed in 825, was one of the most ambitious hydraulic works of the T'ang dynasty.

Outstanding Engineering Achievement:

Before Li P'o's time, the main obstacle to navigation on the Ling Ch'ü was the swift current of the Hsiang River at the canal's northern entrance. Earlier engineers had built a spillway here to prevent flooding, and had also dug the northern end of the canal in a winding course to slow the incoming water. Nevertheless, navigation was hazardous at this point, and south-bound vessels had to reverse direction carefully upon entering the curved canal. Li P'o improved this situation by building a triangular dam that divided the Hsiang River just before the canal's entrance. Gates on both sides of the dam helped control the water; boats entering or leaving the canal passed through the south gate, which could otherwise be kept closed to reduce the flow of water into the canal. This improvement, combined with the already-existing spillway, eliminated the need for curves at the canal's northern end. Li P'o bypassed them by digging a straight channel 175 feet (52.5 meters) long between the river and the main body of the canal.

Another part of Li P'o's reconstruction plan was the installation of 18 flash locks to help boats along gradients of the Ling Ch'ü. Most of the locks were located near both ends of the canal, where it rose from the Hsiang and West river valleys. This change permitted a considerable reduction of manpower along the canal, for boats could now be hauled up gradients by windlass rather than by teams of laborers. Flash locks were replaced in the tenth or eleventh century by pound locks, which further reduced the manual labor involved and enabled the canal to handle heavier vessels.

Following its restoration by Li P'o, the Ling Ch'ü canal was about 20 feet (6 meters) wide with a depth of several feet. Peasants of the surrounding countryside used its water for irrigation. ■

Further Reading:

Needham, *Science and Civilisation in China.* Vol. IV, pt. 3.

CHANG SSU-HSÜN
fl. 975
Chinese Horological Engineer

Life and Times:

Chinese clock-making developed largely from efforts to improve the accuracy of the calendar. Astrology was a highly esteemed study, and the correct prediction of celestial events was held to confirm the ruling dynasty's claim to the Mandate of Heaven. On the other hand, a calendar which did not fulfill these functions meant disaster, for the actions of the emperor and his officials no longer conformed to the celestial pattern. Thus it is not surprising that the Chinese calendar underwent periods of frequent revision caused by political events or contact with foreign astronomical ideas. Beginning with the T'ang dynasty, this process was sometimes accompanied by the construction of new armillary clocks, which indicated both the time and prevailing celestial configurations. One such clock, which came at a time of calendrical revision near the start of the Sung dynasty, was the work of Chang Ssu-Hsün.

Chang grew up in Szechuan province, an area noted for its role in the early growth of block printing. Printed treatises of the time were devoted mainly to astrology and related fields, and the availability of such works may well have influenced the development of Chang's mechanical ability. Nevertheless, like many of China's most ingenious engineers, Chang never attained high office. He was a student in the Bureau of Astronomy when he designed his clock in 976, and his final position was apparently assistant at the bureau in charge of clocks and armillary spheres. For this reason, construction of his

clock was accompanied by little of the pomp and circumstance occasioned a century later by Su Sung's [q.v.] famous clock. Though the latter was far larger and more complex than any previous clock, most of its parts—particularly the escapement mechanism—were apparently modelled closely on Chang's design. Chang was thus an important figure in the transmission of the Chinese horological tradition to later generations.

Outstanding Engineering Achievement:

In appearance as well as function, Chang's clock resembled Su Sung's. The mechanism was housed in a tower some 10 feet (3 meters) tall. In the lower part of one wall were windows at which 19 jacks appeared at intervals, sounding gongs, beating drums and showing placards to mark the passage of time. Chambers in the upper part of the tower contained a celestial globe and an armillary sphere with which the motions of celestial objects could be depicted and observed.

Like the earlier clock of I Hsing [q.v.] and the later clock of Su Sung, Chang's mechanism was powered by the motion of a water wheel. It was unique, however, in using mercury instead of water to provide the drive. In this way Chang avoided the problem of freezing or reduced water flow during cold weather. The mercury evidently circulated through a closed system within the tower; like the water which powered Su Sung's clock, it probably passed through several tanks before passing into scoops attached to the wheel's rim. This technique, adapted from the structure of water clocks, ensured a uniform flow rate and a constant rate of rotation for the wheel, upon which the accuracy of the mechanism depended.

Chang's clock was also important as probably the first device that used a chain drive to transmit motion from the power source to the mechanism. In this case, the chain connected the main transmission shaft projecting from the water wheel to gears that turned the armillary sphere and, possibly, the celestial globe. The device may well have been derived from the treadle-operated chain pumps used for centuries previously by Chinese peasants to raise water. Whatever his inspiration, Chang was well ahead of European engineers, who only began to design machines with chain drives during the Renaissance.

Another important feature of Chang's clock was the escapement, a device which slowed

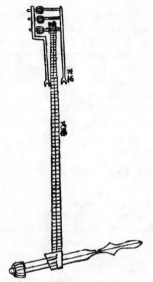

Chain-drive for transmitting power. This one is from Su Sung, but is probably similar to one in Chang's clock.

the motion of the water wheel so that the time-keeping mechanism could operate at an appropriate speed. As in Su Sung's clock, the escapement consisted of a series of weighted levers which obstructed the motion of the water wheel, and were set to trip only when a certain weight of mercury had accumulated in the wheel's scoops. After the wheel had moved through a partial rotation, the levers locked into place and the cycle began again. ■

Further Reading:

Needham, *Science and Civilisation in China.* Vol. IV, pt. 2.

CH'EN YAO-TSO
fl. 1000
Chinese Hydraulic Engineer

Life and Times:

Chinese engineers made extensive use of bamboo in their flood control projects. Strong, light and readily available, it was an ideal framework for holding structural materials in place. As early as the Former Han period, the engineer Yang Yen [q.v.] made extensive use of stone-filled

bamboo baskets, or gabions, to repair breaches in the Yellow River dikes. A milennium later, during the Northern Sung dynasty, the engineer Ch'en Yao-Tso developed a larger and more complicated bamboo framework, known as the *mu lung* or wooden dragon.

Outstanding Engineering Achievement:

The wooden dragon was an early form of sheet piling used in extensive dike repairs. It consisted of a many-layered bamboo raft held in place by cables along the weakened section of a dike. Through holes in the raft, bamboo poles were thrust into the bed of the waterway to form a framework. The space between the framework and the dike was then filled with stones or earth, which was held in place by the bamboo until it settled into a solid mass. Unlike gabions, the wooden dragon could not be used in emergency to fill already-existing breaches. Its invention indicates that Northern Sung engineers had developed a system of inspection aimed at identifying and reinforcing weak spots in waterways before the onset of a crisis. ■

Further Reading:

Needham, *Science and Civilisation in China.* Vol. IV, pt. 3.

SU SUNG (SU TSU-JUNG)
b. 1020, Fukien Province, China
d. 1101, K'aifeng, China
Chinese Astronomer and Horological Engineer

Life and Times:

From its beginnings during the T'ang dynasty, Chinese clock-making was closely associated with the imperial court. The lives of the emperor and courtiers were strictly regulated by astrological considerations, which determined among other things the order in which the emperor slept with his many consorts. The celestial signs prevailing when a potential heir to the throne was conceived were also vital in choosing a new emperor. All this demanded accurate time-keeping and a precise knowledge of stellar and planetary positions, regardless of the weather. For this reason Chinese clocks became more and more elaborate, commanding all the mechanical ingenuity available at the time. By far the most impressive of these devices was built during the Northern Sung dynasty by the scholar-official Su Sung, or Su Tsu-Jung.

A member of the ruling gentry class, Su Sung rose in the imperial bureaucracy as an administrative and financial expert. By the time his clock was finished, he had been promoted to vice president of the chancellery secretariat. He also had broad scientific interests, ranging from mathematics and astronomy to botany. Around 1070 he wrote an "Illustrated Pharmacopoeia," which provides valuable insights into the period's knowledge of drugs, zoology, metallurgical techniques and other topics.

The first impetus for construction of Su Sung's clock came in 1077, when Su was sent to offer birthday congratulations to the emperor of the barbarian Liao state on China's northern border. Due to discrepancies between the Chinese and Liao calendars, he arrived one day before his host's celebration. Though able to obtain an audience with the Liao emperor in accordance with the Chinese reckoning, Su realized that the Liao calendar was in fact correct. He reported this to his own emperor, who punished the officials responsible for calendrical computations and decreed that all foreign ambassadors in China could follow their own calendars in celebrating festivals.

Nine years later, Su Sung was ordered by the emperor to construct an armillary clock that would serve as a basis for calendrical reform. The specifications called for a far more elaborate device than those constructed previously by I Hsing [q.v.] and Chang Ssu-Hsün [q.v.]. Despite his knowledge of mathematics and astronomy, Su Sung was too occupied with his official duties and lacked the mechanical training necessary to complete the task himself. Fortunately, however, he knew a minor clerk in the Ministry of Personnel, Han Kung-Lien [q.v.], whose learning and experience enabled him to undertake much of the instrument's actual design and construction. Su named a ten-member board of advisers, including Han, to see the project through its initial stages. Only after the construction and testing of a full-size, operating wooden model were the metal parts of the clock cast in 1090, four years after Su had received the emperor's orders. In 1094 Su Sung completed and presented to the emperor a monograph describing the clock's operation. So detailed was this account that in 1961 a British scholar was able to reconstruct a functioning, accurate model of part of the mechanism.

Model of Su Sung's astronomical clock tower, built 900 years later from Su Sung's own description.

Su Sung's clock recorded not only the passage of time but also the position and movement of heavenly bodies. Given the vital political importance of these functions, it is not surprising that the device soon became embroiled in factional disputes at the Chinese court. Though Su Sung did not belong to any particular faction, he had friends among the so-called Conservatives who dominated the court when the clock was built. Opposition Reformist officials came to power in 1094, at the beginning of a new reign-period; they immediately began to press for removal of the clock as a remnant of the previous reign-period. Fulfillment of their desire was only narrowly averted.

The destruction of Su Sung's masterpiece finally resulted not from factional politics but from the fall of the Northern Sung. When Tartar invaders captured the Sung capital of K'aifeng in 1126, they quickly dismantled the clock as a symbol of the defunct dynasty's claim to the Mandate of Heaven. Parts of the mechanism were reconstructed in Yen (modern Peking), capital of the new Ch'in dynasty. But they apparently lacked proper maintenance, and were destroyed when the Ming dynasty re-established Chinese control over northern China in the fourteenth century. Indeed, Chinese horology never again reached the level it had attained with Su Sung.

The armillary clock was not the only product of Su Sung's collaboration with Han Kung-Lien. Shortly after the clock was completed, a scholar named Hsu Chiang suggested that the knowledge applied in the project could also be used to construct a device for demonstrating celestial configurations at the latitude of the capital for any time and season. When Su Sung accepted the proposal, Han undertook the necessary calculations and designed the object—a small room with walls of silk and paper, into which holes were cut to represent heavenly bodies. The configurations could be changed by means of a hand crank. This was the origin of history's first planetarium.

Outstanding Engineering Achievement:

Su Sung called his clock a "Tower for the Water-Powered Sphere and Globe." As the name indicates, the entire mechanism was housed in a tower some 30-40 feet (9-12 meters) tall. The bottom part of the structure was occupied by five flights of windows in which jacks appeared, sounding gongs, beating drums and showing placards to mark the passage of time. There were far more jacks—133 in all—than in any previous clock, and the divisions of time recorded were correspondingly more complex. Above the jacks was an enclosed room with a rotating celestial globe; as in I Hsing's clock, the globe's bottom half was encased in a wooden box to simulate the horizon. Finally, the semi-enclosed roof of the tower housed a mechanized armillary sphere with which the positions of celestial objects could be observed.

The clock's equipment weighed some 20 tons (18 metric tons). Power for this enormous mechanism was provided by a water wheel at the base of the tower, 11 feet (3.3 meters) in diameter with 36 scoops along its periphery. The wheel was turned not by a natural or free-flowing source but by a closed system in which water flowed into the scoops from a constant-level tank mounted about midway up the wheel. From the scoops the water emptied into a drainage tank beneath the wheel; the water was then lifted manually by attendants operating two water-raising wheels, finally passing through a series of intermediate tanks back into the constant-level tank. This elaborate apparatus was necessary to ensure a constant flow rate, upon which the clock's accuracy in large part depended. In design and effect, the system resembled a water

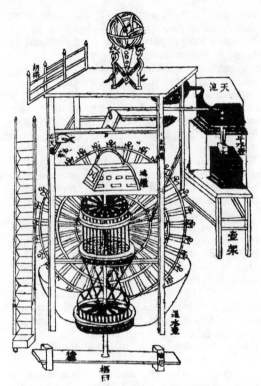

Diagram of the clock tower that appeared in Su Sung's monograph. Right, constant-level tank below reservoir tank.

clock—with the difference that it was merely the power source rather than the time-keeping mechanism itself.

Attached to the axle of the water wheel was the main drive shaft, made of iron. This ended in a pinion which turned a gear wheel at the bottom of the vertical transmission shaft, some 20 feet (6 meters) long and made of wood. The top of the transmission shaft ended in a gear wheel connected through intermediate pinions to an oblique, toothed ring which surrounded the middle section of the armillary sphere. About mid-way on the transmission shaft was a pinion that rotated a large gear wheel on the time-keeping shaft, a vertical pole upon which were fixed eight horizontal wheels. Seven of these wheels, six to eight feet (1.8 to 2.4 meters) in diameter, turned the jacks at their proper rate of rotation; the eighth and topmost engaged an oblique gear wheel at the bottom of the polar axis of the celestial globe.

About ten years after its construction, the clock's drive mechanism was modified. Apparently the long wooden transmission shaft had proven unequal to stresses placed upon it, for it was first shortened and then eliminated entirely. The time-keeping shaft was now turned directly by a pinion at the end of the horizontal main drive shaft. Su Sung also introduced a chain drive (or "celestial ladder"), turned by another pinion on the main drive shaft, to transmit power to the armillary sphere. This last feature is especially important, for operational chain drives did not appear in Europe until shortly before the Industrial Revolution. Su Sung may actually not have been the first Chinese horologist to make use of the device; but the monograph which he presented to the emperor contains what is undoubtedly the first illustration of a chain drive in history.

Another important feature of Su Sung's clock was the escapement, a mechanism that slowed the action of the power source and enabled the timekeeping wheels to rotate at an appropriate rate. Here again Su Sung anticipated European practice, though he was not first in China to design such a device. His escapement (or "celestial balance") was a set of finely-adjusted, weighted levers which locked against certain spokes of the water wheel and obstructed the wheel's motion. The levers were set to trip and allow a spoke to pass only when a certain weight of water (about 100 pounds; 45 kg) had accumulated in the wheel's scoops. In this way, the wheel's rate of rotation was slowed to roughly once every quarter-hour.

The escapement and the elaborate system of tanks which fed the water wheel apparently produced a high level of accuracy required by the clock's vital political function. The mecha-

Close-up of the water-balance escapement in the model of Su Sung's clock tower.

nism reconstructed in Britain indicates that the original gained or lost less than 100 seconds a day, a figure well in advance of the performance of early European clocks. ∎

Further Reading:

Needham, *Science and Civilisation in China.* Vol. III.

LU TAO-LUNG
fl. 1025, K'aiffeng, China

WU TE-JEN
fl. 1107, K'aiffeng, China
Chinese Mechanical Engineers

Life and Times:

From the time of the Han dynasty in the first century B.C., the processions of emperors and high officials included carriages designed to impress onlookers with visual or auditory effects. At first simply moving platforms on which musicians and acrobats performed, these vehicles gradually developed into mechanical devices which performed their functions automatically. One such device was the "mile-measuring drum carriage," an early odometer featuring a jack-figure that beat a drum or sounded a gong when a certain distance had been traversed. Another popular vehicle was the "south-pointing carriage," which used differential gearing to keep a jack-figure pointing south regardless of the direction of travel. Ma Chün [q.v.], a leading mechanical engineer of the Later Han period, was probably involved in the development of both vehicles. Though it must have been evident that these inventions could have other than ceremonial uses, their practical aspects never seem to have been developed to any great extent. Nevertheless, engineers of subsequent dynasties sought to improve the odometer and south-pointing carriage for the greater glory of their emperors. Important work on both devices was done during the Northern Sung period and recorded in the court annals by the engineers Lu Tao-Lung and Wu Te-Jen.

Both Lu and Wu were apparently minor officials at the imperial court in K'aiffeng, living and working three-quarters of a century apart. Lu left a detailed description of the odometer, while Wu worked mainly on the south-pointing carriage. Both vehicles operated by means of a gear train turned by the motion of the carriage wheels. The south-pointing carriage was the more complex of the two, since its operation was discontinuous and gear wheels had to engage and disengage at the proper time. Indeed, the system of differential gearing recorded by Wu Te-Jen can be regarded as a remote predecessor of the differential drive used to power the wheels of modern automobiles.

On the basis of Northern Sung records, modern scholars have been able to reconstruct both the odometer and the south-pointing carriage.

Outstanding Engineering Achievements:

The odometer described by Lu Tao-Lung was a large, horse-drawn vehicle with two stories and wheels six feet (2 meters) in diameter. Each story housed a jack-figure; one struck a drum when the carriage had travelled one *li* (about one-half mile; 1 km), while the other sounded a gong when ten *li* had been completed. A vertical toothed wheel attached to one of the carriage wheels provided the main drive for the mechanism, turning a horizontal, toothed wheel. This rotated a vertical shaft upon which two horizontal wheels were fixed, differing in size and number of teeth. The shaft wheels measured distance with their revolutions. The lower one rotated once every *li*, turning a shaft which tripped a wire and triggered the drum-striking jack. The upper wheel, connected to the gong-ringing jack, performed the same operation every ten *li*.

Wu Te-Jen's south-pointing carriage was also a large vehicle, with wheels 5.7 feet (1.7 meters) in diameter. The carriage body was some 11 feet (3.3 meters) long, 9½ feet (3 meters) wide and 11 feet (3.3 meters) high; a pole 10½ feet (3 meters) long, pulled by horses, ran the length of the underside of the carriage. As in the odometer, the main drive was provided by a vertical, toothed wheel attached to the carriage wheel. In this case, however, there were two drive wheels, one for each carriage wheel. At the center of the carriage, level with the top of the vertical drive wheels, was a horizontal, toothed wheel about four feet in diameter. This was attached to a vertical pole extending upward to the top of the carriage, where it was fixed to the south-pointing jack-figure. The central horizontal wheel was connected on either side to the two drive wheels by a smaller horizontal, toothed wheel. Each of these smaller horizontal wheels was weighted and set on a short vertical shaft, so that it could engage and disengage the vertical drive wheel. This was done by a bamboo cord joining the top

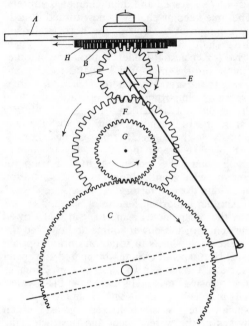

Possible gearing for the south-pointing carriage of Wu Te-Jen.

of each smaller horizontal wheel to the rear of the horse-drawn carriage pole, which was mounted slightly above the horizontal wheels. The two cords were adjusted so that, when the carriage was moving in a straight line, both smaller horizontal wheels were held up at the top of their shafts, disengaged from the drive wheels. But when the horses turned right, the rear of the carriage pole swung left; this relaxed the tension on the left-hand bamboo cord, allowing the smaller horizontal wheel on the left to drop down on its shaft. In this position it engaged both the left-hand drive wheel and the central horizontal wheel, turning the latter to the right. This caused a corresponding movement of the central vertical pole, and finally of the south-pointing jack-figure. The reverse process was set in motion by a left-hand turn of the horses. Every deviation of the carriage from a straight line thus caused the jack-figure to turn through the same angle in the same direction. Once set to point south, it would maintain that orientation indefinitely. ■

Further Reading:

Needham, *Science and Civilization in China.* Vol. IV, pt. 2.

SHEN KUA

b. 1031, Ch'ien-t'ang (Hangchow, Chekiang
province)
d. 1095, Ching-K'ou (Chinkiang, Kiangsu
province)
Chinese Civil Engineer

Life and Times:

One important feature of Chinese science and technology throughout the dynastic period was the involvement of members of the civil service in the study of natural phenomena and the writing of scholarly treatises. One of the most notable scholar-officials of the Northern Sung period (960–1126) was Shen Kua, who left his mark in such diverse fields as astronomy, medicine, cartography, hydraulics and military fortification.

Shen Kua was born into the lesser gentry, a class that first gained admission into the civil service under the Northern Sung. Shen's father, a minor bureaucrat, took the youth with him as he travelled through the empire on official business during the 1040s. Beginning in 1054 Shen was assigned to several minor provincial posts, at which he applied himself to problems of land drainage and flood control. His work came to the attention of the emperor, and after passing the national civil service examination he was made a financial administrator, first in Yangchow and later at the imperial court.

As a rising young official, Shen became closely associated with Wang an-Shih, an imperial councillor whose so-called New Policies aimed at centralizing and strengthening the bureaucracy. In an effort to improve the flow of traffic to and from the imperial capital, Shen undertook in 1072 to survey and dredge the Grand Canal over a distance of about 150 miles (240 km). Also in 1072, he was named director of the Astronomical Bureau, a post in which he planned—but did not have a chance to complete—major changes in the computations used to predict celestial events. In addition to his work in the capital, Shen undertook several diplomatic and military missions along China's northern frontier, where the nomadic Liao tribes posed a constant threat to the empire's security. In 1075 he compiled a series of relief maps of the frontier area, and later designed fortifications that served as a base for successful military operations against the nomads.

Despite these achievements, Shen was too closely identified with the New Policies to survive their decline amidst court intrigue after the mid-1070s. In 1082 he was forced to resign from government service following a military defeat on the frontier for which he was not responsible. But Shen did not abandon his scholarly activities in retirement. Resuming his cartographic work, he compiled a large atlas of the entire Chinese empire. Shen also wrote a collection of epigrams and brief essays, "Brush Talks from Dream Brook," which provides valuable insights into Chinese science and technology of the period. Among the vast array of topics discussed are metallurgical and water-control techniques, printing with movable type and the recovery of ancient technological processes through archeological and literary sources. Shen also proposed a thoroughgoing reform of the Chinese calendar, with the substitution of solar for lunar months. Shen's writings have a breadth of vision which illuminates the assumptions behind the scientific thought of his time, showing both its limitations and accomplishments.

Outstanding Engineering Achievements:

Shen Kua did his most notable engineering work in the area of hydraulics. In addition to supervising reclamation projects and the dredging of the Grand Canal, he directed the closure of breaks in the barriers controlling the flow of the Yellow River. Large baskets or cages, open at the base and known as gabions, were filled with stones and dropped to the bottom of the river, section by section. Where possible, wood piles, set at varying angles, were used to reinforce the large gabions and diminish the force of the waves breaking against the barrier. Shen also made use of large, cylindrical wicker bundles, up to 300 feet in length, to close gaps on an emergency basis.

Shen's duties as head of the Astronomical Bureau also drew his attention to the design of several scientific instruments. He discovered that the radius of the sighting tube used for astronomical observation in the armillary sphere needed to be enlarged to accommodate changes in the position of the pole star that had developed since the time of the instrument's original design. Shen also discovered the usefulness of multiplying the number of roses of the compass, increasing the number of directional bearings (that is, azimuths) from the traditional eight to twenty-four. ∎

Further Reading:

Dictionary of Scientific Biography, s.v. "Shen Kua."

Needham, *Science and Civilisation in China.*

LI SHIH-CHUNG
fl. 1059
Chinese Hydraulic Engineer

Life and Times:

Along with the Grand Canal in northern China, the Ling Ch'ü canal in south-central China proved to be one of the most durable parts of the country's vast system of waterways. Constructed in the third century B.C., the Ling Ch'ü was revamped over the centuries as improvements were made in its design and obsolete parts were reinforced or rebuilt. Many innovations in Chinese canal design took place in the Ling Ch'ü; one of the most significant was apparently the work of Li Shi-Chung, a hydraulic engineer of the Northern Sung dynasty.

In 1059 Li supervised a series of repairs on the Ling Ch'ü canal. At this time he may well have introduced pound locks, for the records of the period indicate a sudden doubling in the number of locks in the canal—what would be expected if every single-gate flash lock were converted into a pound lock. So equipped, the canal could move boats across gradients more efficiently (see below). Pound locks were used in Chinese canals through the Yüan dynasty in the fourteenth century; they apparently disappeared in later years due to a decline in the volume and importance of inland waterway traffic. But it is interesting to note that pound locks appeared in Europe during the mid-fifteenth century, when they were used by Bertola da Novate [q.v.] in two Italian canals. Though there is no proof of cultural diffusion, it is at least possible that knowledge of the pound lock came to Europe from China at the time when Mongol domination of Central Asia formed a link between East and West.

Outstanding Engineering Achievement:

Unlike flash locks, which moved boats along a gradient with a sudden rush of water, pound locks raised and lowered boats by changing the water level between two closely-spaced gates. This method had several advantages over the earlier one. In the first place, pound locks could handle larger and heavier vessels than flash locks, since they did not depend on the limited momentum of a single spurt of water. Pound locks also reduced the need for canal laborers, who often had to haul boats through flash locks. Finally, pound locks could be built on far steeper gradients than flash locks, moving boats up and down in a terrace-like series of steps. This made possible the first so-called summit canals across a range of hills, built in China during the Yüan dynasty and in Europe during the seventeenth century. ■

Further Reading:

Needham, *Science and Civilisation in China*.
Singer et al., *A History of Technology*, Vol. III.

YING SHUN-CH'EN
fl. 1071
Chinese Hydraulic Engineer

Life and Times:

As the population of southern China expanded during the fifth and sixth centuries, it became increasingly important to ensure efficient transportation between the Yangtze river valley and the north China plain, traditional center of Chinese civilization. One response to this need was the so-called First Grand Canal, built during the Sui dynasty between Ch'ang-an on the Yellow River and Hangchow, a port city south of the Yangtze. Though vital for the movement of supplies to the imperial capital, the canal was repeatedly blocked by silting and flooding along the Yellow River. Engineers of the Sui and T'ang dynasties kept the canal open by building new dikes, dredging and periodically altering the canal's junction with the river. But no one succeeded in doing away with periodic crises until the Sung dynasty, when the engineer Ying Shun-Ch'en developed a self-regulating system of water control along the canal.

Outstanding Engineering Achievement:

Ying Shun-Ch'en's system, completed in 1071, was essentially an effort to maintain a constant water level on the Grand Canal and the adjoining section of the Yellow River. He did this by constructing a network of sluice gates to control the overflow of water during floods, retarding the accumulation of silt. This was accompanied by a network of feeder canals that supplied the main canal with water when the water level dropped during dry seasons. The system served its purpose as long as it was maintained during the Sung period. Ying's work was the last improvement in the technique of constructing sluice-gates and flash locks to control the flow of water before the introduction of pound locks, which allowed engineers to isolate segments of a waterway and adjust the water level within each. ■

Further Reading:

Needham, *Science and Civilisation in China.* Vol. IV, pt. 3.

HAN KUNG-LIEN
fl. 1090, K'aifeng, China
Chinese Horological Engineer

Life and Times:

When the emperor Shen Tsung ordered Su Sung [q.v.] to construct a monumental armillary clock in 1086, the detailed mechanical knowledge necessary for such a project was not readily available. For all his learning, Su Sung could not have completed the task by himself. Fortunately, he happened to become acquainted with a minor clerk in the Ministry of Personnel, Han Kung-Lien, whose technical background and ingenuity were such that he could handle the details of the clock's design and construction. To Han Kung-Lien thus belongs much of the credit for what Joseph Needham has called "one of the greatest technical achievements of the medieval time in any civilization."

Our sparse knowledge of Han Kung-Lien derives from the chronicles and memorials that describe the armillary clock. Han was apparently an auto-didact who had thoroughly studied the "Nine Chapters of Mathematical Art" *(Chiu Chang Suan Shu)* and other standard scientific works of the period. He was especially interested in solving astronomical problems by means of geometry. Han's humble bureaucratic position provided no outlet for his talents, and he owed his fame entirely to his contact with Su Sung.

Outstanding Engineering Achievements:

After receiving the emperor's instructions, Su Sung gave Han a description of earlier armillary clocks designed by I-Hsing [q.v.] and Chang Ssu-Hsün [q.v.]. Han advised that the project was feasible in light of past experience, "if mathematical rules were followed." He then wrote a memorandum, "Verification of the Armillary

Clock by Geometry," setting forth his own design. Su Sung accepted the proposal after seeing a small wooden model of the device.

The project was of such importance that it went through several stages before construction of the final mechanism began. A functioning scale model was first built under the supervision of a board of ten scholars, including Han. A full-size wooden model was then built and elaborately tested for accuracy. Only in 1090, four years after inception of the project, were the bronze and iron parts of the clock finally cast.

Han also collaborated with Su Sung to build the first planetarium, a small chamber with walls of silk and paper into which were cut the positions of stars and other heavenly bodies. The positions could be altered, apparently by hand crank, to account for changes in hour and season.

(For further description of this device and of the armillary clock, see profile of Su Sung.) ■

Further Reading:

Needham, *Science and Civilisation in China.* Vol. IV, pt. 2.

LI CHIEH
fl. 1100
Chinese Architect and Civil Engineer

Life and Times:

In China as in Europe, architecture and engineering did not become distinct professions until the modern period. Much of our knowledge of architectural ideas in medieval China comes from two treatises written by engineers of the Northern Sung dynasty. These works attested to growing interest in problems of construction, and both were attempts to derive general rules from practical knowledge. The first treatise, the *Mu Ching* or *Timberwork Manual,* was written by Yü Hao in the first years of the Northern Sung. A century later it was superseded by the work of Li Chieh, the *Ying Tsao Fa Shih* or *Treatise on Architectural Methods.*

Li Chieh began as a minor official in the Bureau of Imperial Sacrifices at the Northern Sung capital of K'aifeng. In 1092 he was transferred to the Directorate of Buildings and Construction, where he demonstrated an interest in carpentry and design. This led five years later to an assignment revamping previous texts on architectural methods.

Outstanding Engineering Achievements:

Li Chieh's *Treatise on Architectural Methods* contains information on basic construction and woodworking techniques that does not appear in comparable European building texts until the eighteenth century, or for that matter in later Chinese texts. Of special significance are the drawings, which resemble the projective, two-part mechanical drawings that developed in France during the early nineteenth century. The text itself describes building techniques and regulations of Li Chieh's own time and of previous dynasties. Among the topics discussed are construction of moats and fortifications, shipbuilding, stonework, woodwork, tiling, painting and decorating, brickwork and wall construction. The text also describes job accounting and common building.

As a builder, Li Chieh planned the construction of numerous buildings of state including gates, temples (among them the ancestral temple of the Northern Sung) and palace apartments and offices. ■

Further Reading:

Needham, *Science and Civilisation in China*.

KAO HSÜAN
fl. 1130
Chinese Nautical Engineer

Life and Times:

The collapse of the Northern Sung dynasty in 1126 and the reconstitution of a Sung state south of the Wei and Huai rivers provided the impetus for the development of a Chinese navy. Seafaring had traditionally been important in southeastern China, which faced the sea lanes leading to India and West Asia and which now became the center of the Chinese state. To protect their coast and rivers against the northern barbarians, Southern Sung rulers encouraged maritime technology and built fleets far larger than those of preceding dynasties. Among the engineers enlisted in this effort was Kao Hsuan, builder of ingenious war junks powered by paddle-wheels.

Kao Hsüan was an artisan as well as engineer, and he began his career as a carpenter in several government offices. Drawn into military service, Kao was assigned to make plans for a fleet of ships to be used against a peasant uprising that had broken out around Tung-t'ing Lake in south-central China. In 1130 he designed a ship with eight paddle-wheels powered by the pedalling of the crew. He soon enlarged the scope of his efforts and supervised the construction of 20-wheeled and 23-wheeled ships.

Kao's work at first gave the Sung government the upper hand. But the rebels soon succeeded in capturing part of the government fleet, stranded at low tide on a river bank; among the prisoners was Kao Hsüan himself. Kao then entered the service of the rebels, and the 22- and 24-wheeled ships which he built enabled them to hold out for some five years. The struggle encouraged a naval armaments race, with both sides vying with one another to develop such weapons as poisonous bombs and giant shipborne trebuchets. Ultimately, the superior resources of the government won out. Whether Kao Hsüan was ever recaptured and brought to justice for treason is unknown.

Outstanding Engineering Achievement:

Paddle-wheel ships had been used in China before Kao Hsüan. But these were generally small and relied primarily on sails. Kao increased the size of the ships; some were several hundred feet and equipped with metal armor, weighing up to 200 tons. Kao also revamped the method of powering the ships, designing a treadmill for this purpose. The pedalling of the crew turned the paddle-wheels, symmetrically placed on both sides of the ship and sometimes at the stern as well.

Although the arrangement of treadmill shafts was a military secret, it is likely that each paddle-wheel was equipped with a separate shaft. By ordering crew members on one side of the ship to pedal backwards while those on the other side pedalled forwards, a captain could turn his vessel sharply without use of a rudder. This greatly enhanced its maneuverability in close-quarter combat. Kao may also have devised means of turning a single paddle-wheel with several shafts, proportionately increasing its power. It is certain at any rate that Kao's ships were surprisingly fast; the nomads who ruled northern China, unaccustomed to naval warfare, asserted that they moved by magic.

Kao designed his ships with the body of a standard Chinese junk. The crew numbered up to 200 sailors and marines. Most of the ships were equipped with a ram at the bow to take advantage of their maneuverability. The paddle-wheels were covered with a protective wooden framework, which hid them from view and probably encouraged the superstitious fear of the northern barbarians. ■

Further Reading:

Needham, *Science and Civilisation in China.* Vol. IV, pt. 3.

CHANG JUNG
fl. 1220
Chinese Civil Engineer

Life and Times:

Cultural interaction between the Chinese and Mongols played an important part in the emergence of Chinggiz Khan and the establishment of Mongol power in Asia during the early thirteenth century. One area in which the Mongols borrowed heavily from China was civil and military engineering. Not only the techniques used by the Mongols but also the engineers who applied them were frequently Chinese. As Mongol armies moved across Central and Western Asia, the bridges and highways designed by a Chinese engineer named Chang Jung facilitated their advance.

Little is known of Chang Jung's life. He entered the service of Chagatai, one of Chinggiz's four sons and generals, near the beginning of Mongol expansion. The gateway to the Middle East lay to the west of the T'ien Shan Mountains, in the Central Asian region bounded by the Amu Darya (Oxus River) and the Syr Darya (Jaxartes River) and ruled in the early thirteenth century by the Khworezm kings. Chang Jung built a wooden trestle bridge in a defile of the T'ien Shan Mountains east of Kuldja; the passageway was large enough to carry two lanes of traffic, including Mongol troops. As the Mongols approached the leading cities of Khworezm, Chang Jung designed a pontoon bridge over the Amu Darya. By the time the first Chinese embassy to Chinggiz arrived at the newly-conquered capital of Samarqand in 1221, Chang Jung's work had demonstrated the ability of the Mongols to make use of Chinese civil engineering practice.

Outstanding Engineering Achievement:

Chang Jung's pontoon bridge drew upon Chinese technology of bridge design developed during the Three Kingdoms period nearly a millennium before. The trestle bridge in the T'ien Shan chain was part of a two-lane mountain road constructed for Chinggiz by Chang Jung and other engineers; it was notable less for innovation in design and technique than for the sheer audacity of undertaking such a project amidst the world's tallest mountains. ■

Further Reading:

V.V. Barthold, *History of Turkestan Down to the Mongol Invasion.* London, 1928.

TAO HSÜN
fl. 1250
Chinese Civil Engineer

Life and Times:

The last century of the Southern Sung dynasty, from about 1150 to 1250, saw an upsurge of bridge-building in the coastal regions of southeastern China. Fukien province, on the coast opposite Taiwan, was the center of this activity. Many of the bridges built there were enormous structures made of massive stone blocks—hence their name, "megalithic" bridges. The engineers associated with these bridges were often Buddhist monks, who viewed the construction of public works as a "beatific act." Perhaps the most prominent of them was Tao Hsün, who lived during the first half of the thirteenth century.

Tao Hsün's work as a civil engineer was prodigious. Within Fukien province he built over 200 bridges; the most noteworthy of them was the P'an-Kuang bridge near Ch'uanchow, the main foreign trade port of the Southern Sung. Tao also devoted himself to problems of hydraulic engineering, contributing to the design of harbor works and sea walls. The increased importance of controlling the sea reflected the shift in the focus of Chinese life at this time to the coastal regions.

Outstanding Engineering Achievements:

The megalithic bridges of Fukien province were beam bridges, long, flat structures with many piers. The longest such bridge spanned more than 4,000 feet (1200 meters), with individual segments nearly 70 feet (21 meters) in length. The stone blocks used in these structures weighed up to 200 tons. The construction techniques of Tao Hsun and other megalithic bridge builders are unknown, though they must have been sophisticated. Small beam bridges were often built by temporarily diverting a stream by means of a dam. This method obviously could not be used in large rivers; it has been suggested that in such cases engineers somehow took advantage of the tidal movements of water. As the pace of bridge building declined towards the end of the Southern Sung dynasty, interest in megalithic bridges—and perhaps the techniques involved in their construction as well—faded. ■

Further Reading:

Needham, *Science and Civilisation in China.* Vol. IV, pt. 3.

ONO GOROEMON
fl. 1250
Japanese Architect and Sculptor

Life and Times:

During the twelfth and thirteenth centuries, as feudalism became established in Japan, a Buddhist revival invigorated the country's religious and cultural life. New Buddhist sects, including Zen and the Amida (or Pure Land) sect, won converts in all parts of Japanese society. Buddhist themes flourished in Japanese art, and sculptors turned in great numbers to producing deities for temple use. Among the most famous and technically accomplished statues of this period was the Great Buddha, or Daibutsu, of Kamakura.

Completed in 1252, the Daibutsu was commissioned by Tokiyori, head of the Hojo family which dominated Japan's feudal government from its headquarters at Kamakura. Tokiyori wanted a statue that would rival the Daibutsu of Nara, built in the eighth century by the metalworker Kimi-maro [q.v.]. To design the model and supervise the casting, Tokiyori chose the sculptor Ono Goroemon. Little is known of Ono's life and career; but his representation of Amida, or the Buddha of Endless light, has survived the destruction of the temple in Ka-

The statue of Buddha at Kamakura, a hollow bronze casting, 42-ft (13 m) high, with a staircase within it.

makura which originally housed it. Like its inspiration, the Daibutsu of Nara, it is important as both a work of art and a feat of engineering.

Outstanding Engineering Achievement:

Both the Nara and Kamakura Buddhas are cast mainly of bronze. Here the similarity ends, however, for Ono's work reflects a far more sophisticated metal-working technology. Unlike the Nara Daibutsu, the Kamakura statue is hollow; though nearly as tall as the older work (42 feet or 13 meters), it weighs less than one-fiftieth as much (103 tons). A staircase within the Kamakura Daibutsu connects the base with the shoulders. The techniques used to cast large bronze statues like the Daibutsu were applied by Japanese engineers in the late sixteenth century to produce muzzle-loading cannon, which were initially made of bronze. ■

Further Reading:

Frank Brinkley, *A History of the Japanese People.* New York, 1915.
Daisetz Suzuki, *Zen and Japanese Culture.* New York, 1959.

KUO SHOU-CHING
fl. 1290
Chinese Hydraulic Engineer and Astronomer

OQRUQCI
fl. 1290

LOQSI
fl. 1290
Mongol Hydraulic Engineers

Life and Times:

In 1279, the Mongol armies of Khubilai Khan completed their conquest of China and unified the country under the Yüan dynasty. To link their Chinese possessions with their base of power in Mongolia, the new rulers established their capital at Peking, on the northern end of the North China Plain. The rapidly growing city had to be supplied with food and other necessities; but, since it lay well beyond the traditional Chinese area of settlement, there were no direct transport routes connecting it with the agricultural regions of central and southern China. The Mongols had to find an immediate solution to this problem, for the resentful Chinese were not likely to tolerate an alien dynasty isolated in the north by poor communications.

Peking's connection with the rest of China soon became the focus of a political dispute at the Mongol court. One party advocated supplying the capital by sea around the Shantung peninsula; the other urged that China's centuries-old system of inland waterways be expanded and renovated to cope with the problem. At issue was more than just a technical decision, for the sea route group consisted of officials who favored developing the empire's naval strength. This course was alien to the traditions of the Mongols and northern Chinese, but its advocates could be ruthless; a leader of the inland waterway party, the former governor of Shantung province, was evidently assassinated by his opponents while travelling to Japan on a diplomatic mission. Nevertheless, partisans of the sea route had against them not only the weight of tradition but also the fact that the passage around the Shantung peninsula was stormy and unsafe. Failure of a Mongol naval expedition against Japan in 1274 may also have influenced the dispute. Ultimately, the inland waterway group won the emperor's consent to a mammoth canal construction project. The result became known as the Yuan (or modern) Grand Canal.

Much of the Mongols' canal work involved not new construction but the repair and restoration of existing routes. Indeed, a waterway system known as the Grand Canal had already been built in the early seventh century to connect the agricultural lands south of the Yangtze with Loyang and Ch'ang-an, principal cities of the Sui dynasty. A northern extension of this old Grand Canal, also built under the Sui, ran from Ch'ang-an northeast to the area around Peking. The entire system formed an enormous Y extending 1,560 miles (2500 km), with Ch'ang-an situated at its base. During the Southern Sung dynasty, when semi-nomadic tribes from Central Asia overran northern China, the old Grand Canal had fallen into disuse. The task of the Mongols was to restore parts of it and to create a new system between the arms of the Y, establishing a direct link between Peking and the south.

Once the Mongol leaders had decided on the canal, they moved rapidly. Work on the modern Grand Canal began in 1279 and was completed by 1293. The waterway, together with a paved highway at its side, extended some 1,100 miles (1770 km) from Peking in the north to the port city of Hangchow in the south. For 650 miles (1050 km), over half its length, it followed the line of the old Grand Canal. The new sections, which skirted the mountainous Shantung peninsula and crossed the Yellow River, were the work of both Chinese and Mongol engineers. Among the former was Kuo Shou-Ching, a prominent astronomer who served Khubilai as Intendant of Waterways. The Mongol engineers involved in the project are unfortunately known to us only by name: Loqsi and Oqruqci.

Outstanding Engineering Achievements:

Though they comprised less than half its total length, the new sections of the Grand Canal were important because they presented new engineering problems. This was especially true of the 56-mile (90 km) section known as the Chi Chou Ho, which passed through western outriders of the Shantung mountains. At its highest point, the land to be excavated rose 170 feet (51 meters) above the mean level of the Yangtze River. This made the waterway the world's first true summit canal, requiring special provisions for maintaining its water supply on high ground.

The summit excavation of the Chi Chou Ho, begun in 1283, was planned by Kuo Shou-Ching and carried out by Oqruqci. To keep the summit level supplied with water, the nearby Wen and Kuang rivers were tapped by means of dams and a feeder canal. Oqruqci also installed at least seven pound locks, first used some two centuries before in the Ling Ch'u canal, to keep boats moving over the hills and to retard the run-off of

Stop-log gate on the Grand Canal in 1797, with a barge and other boats passing through.

water. This first effort at construction of a summit canal was not entirely successful; the supply of water at the summit level in particular was inadequate, and this part of the works had to be reconstructed some 130 years later under the Ming dynasty. Until this was accomplished, the canal could not handle the volume of traffic anticipated by its planners. As a result, the sea route to Peking remained important throughout the Yuan period.

The other new sections of the Grand Canal, though not unique like the summit level, still presented great engineering challenges. Just north of the summit section, the Hui T'ung Ho (Union Link Channel) extended some 80 miles (128 km) over only slightly less hilly terrain. It was completed in one year (1289) by a work force of 2.5 million under the Mongol engineer Loqsi. With 31 pound and flash locks, it joined the summit section with the northern part of the old Grand Canal, which followed the course of the Wei River for some 250 miles (400 km). Another new section connected Peking with the terminus of the old canal north of Tientsin. Built by Kuo Shou-Ching, it extended some 20 miles (32 km) and covered a steep ascent with 20 pound and flash locks. This was the last part of the modern Grand Canal to be opened; after 1293, the entire waterway was in operation. ∎

Further Reading:

Needham, *Science and Civilisation in China.* Vol. IV, pt. 3.

John K. Fairbank and Edwin O. Reischauer, *East Asia: the Great Tradition.* Boston, 1960.

MASAMUNE (OKAZAKI GORO NUIDO)
fl. 1300
Japanese Swordsmith

Life and Times:

The characteristic Japanese sword, single-edged with a curved blade, first appeared in the seventh century. By the thirteenth century, swordmaking had become a highly developed art in Japan, practiced by a class of swordsmiths known as *Katana-kaji.* As with most professionals, these artisans varied considerably in their techniques and level of skill. Prominent swordsmiths often founded schools of disciples who might carry on the master's methods for several generations. The swordsmiths did, however, have a strong corporate sense. Like the samurai warriors whom they served, they were strongly influenced by Zen Buddhism; their work assumed a ceremonial and religious nature, and the most skilled among them became important figures at the imperial court. One of Japan's most famous swordsmiths was Masamune, founder of the so-called Soshu school of swordmaking.

Masamune lived during Japan's early feudal period in the late thirteenth and early fourteenth centuries. After growing up in the district of Soshu, he was apprenticed at 17 to the prominent swordsmith Shintogo Kunimutsu. Within a decade Masamune had established his own reputation as a superb craftsman. When the emperor Fushimi ascended the throne in 1287, he named Masamune *Mikawa no Kami* (Chief Swordsmith) at his court. Masamune held this post for 10 years and afterwards continued to make swords for the imperial court. He once boasted that, despite a court regulation requiring all swordsmiths to set their mark upon their work, his own swords did not have to be identified in this way, since they could not possibly be confused with the work of others. He paid close attention to the progress of his apprentices, going so far as to adopt one, Sadamune, as his son. The strong bonds which formed around Masamune were the basis of the Soshu school, whose *mukugitai* (all-steel) swords were highly prized both in Japan and in China, where they were imported during the fourteenth century.

Outstanding Engineering Achievements:

Japanese swordsmiths generally made their blades from multiple pieces of wrought iron and steel, repeatedly heated, folded over one another and forged together. In Masamune's time, the process of folding and forging was repeated two to eight times; after the fifteenth century even more steps were added. Once the blade was shaped and the various layers melded together, the sword edge *(yakiba)* was tempered, or heated and suddenly cooled by dousing with water; this increased its hardness without making it brittle, and produced the sword's curvature. To preserve its toughness, the rest of the blade was covered with a clay sheath during the tempering process, so that it remained untempered.

Masamune and the Soshu school distinguished themselves from other swordsmiths mainly by making their swords entirely of steel. To preserve the blade's toughness, pieces of steel with varying carbon content (and thus different degrees of hardness) were forged together and tempered. The result was an "all-*yakiba*" blade, so called because it was hardened throughout rather than just along the edge. The swords of Masamune and his pupils were harder but no more brittle than those of swordsmiths who combined iron and steel. The technique required great skill, however, for careless forging or improper variation in the grades of steel used would produce a blade that was either too soft or too brittle. Thus *mukugitai* swords remained rare, made only by a small circle of swordsmiths. ■

Further Reading:

Frank Brinkley, *A History of the Japanese People.* New York, 1915.

James A. Murdoch, *A History of Japan.* New York, 1964.

Mikoso Hane, *Japan: A Historical Survey.* New York, 1972.

CHIA KU SHAN SHOU
fl. 1315
Chinese Civil Engineer

Life and Times:

Though the central government was officially responsible for road construction in China, it tended to let this task slip during periods of domestic unrest or dynastic decline. Even in the best of times, construction and repair of local roads had to take second place to main arteries connecting the capital with outlying areas. Fortunately, Taoist and Buddhist religious associations had a long tradition of support for road and bridge building, which they viewed as a meritorious act; such works also contributed to their political influence, which they used either to secure favor with the ruling dynasty or (often the case with the Taoists) to lay plans for a revolt. Eventually, the total mileage of roads built in this way far exceeded the length of all government roads.

The names of many local engineers have survived in connection with particular projects. Little is known of most of them, but one who stands out is Chia Ku Shan Shou, a Taoist engineer who lived during the declining years of the Yüan dynasty. Her fame rests not only on her works but also on the fact that she was one of the few women active as engineers in China's rigidly patriarchal society. She is best known for constructing a mountain road in Fukien province, completed in 1315. ■

Further Reading:

Needham, *Science and Civilisation in China.* Vol. IV, pt. 2.

ASHIKAGA YOSHIMITSU
b. 1358, Japan
d. 1408, Japan

ASHIKAGA YOSHIMASA
b. 1436, Japan
d. 1490, Japan
Japanese Rulers

Life and Times:

Civil war flared almost continuously in Japan throughout the fourteenth and fifteenth centuries. But this was also a period of lively activity in art and architecture, which saw the development of styles that have persisted to the present day. In 1338 the Ashikaga family won control of the office of shogun, or military overlord, which was the central authority in the country. The third member of the family, Yoshimitsu, while still engaged in quelling rebellion, opened diplomatic relations and trade with China, and encouraged interest in the arts and letters. In 1395, Yoshimitsu abdicated as shogun but continued to run the affairs of state. He then built what became Japan's most loved building, the Golden Pavilion.

The eighth Ashikaga shogun, Yoshimasa, saw the state disintegrate under feudal factionalism. Nevertheless, the No drama was established during his lifetime as Japan's major dramatic art form; a new kind of poetry eventually led to the Haiku verse of 17 syllables; and the tea ceremony, which became popular at this time, required beautiful porcelain and silver equipment. Yoshimasa built the Silver Pavilion, a simpler version of the Golden Pavilion.

Outstanding Engineering Achievements:

The Golden Pavilion, or Kinkaku, is on the edge of a pool in the grounds of the Kitayama Palace, near Kyoto. Erected in 1397, it is a square structure three stories high. Each story is encircled by a balcony. The second-floor balcony is protected by wide eaves. Above it, the third is set back on all sides, and is also protected by wide eaves. Inside, the lowest floor follows the then current style of domestic layout; the middle floor is transitional, and the highest was designed in accordance with Zen principles of understatement and spareness of form. The interior of its single apartment is covered with pure gold leaf. After the death of Yoshimitsu, the building became a Zen temple. It was destroyed by fire in 1951 but was considered so important to Japanese culture that it was replaced with an exact copy.

The Silver Pavilion, or Ginkaku, was a three-story building similar in design to the Kinkaku but marked more strongly by the restrained Zen style. The division of space in its living quarters influenced succeeding centuries of domestic architecture. Another of Yoshimasu's buildings, the Togudo, contained a room, nine feet square, intended specifically for the tea ceremony. This too was incorporated in the design of Japanese dwellings. ■

Further Reading:

George B. Sansom, *Japan: A Short Cultural History*. New York, 1943.

J. J. Norwich, ed., *Great Architecture of the World*. New York, 1975.

YI CH'ON
b. 1376
d. 1451
Korean Official and Instrument Maker

Life and Times:

Of the peoples who inhabited the periphery of medieval China, the Koreans probably showed the greatest interest in science and technology. This was especially true in the early fifteenth century, when Korean men of learning enjoyed the patronage of King Sejong of the Yi dynasty. Under Sejong, the Hall of Assembled Scholars and the Bureau of Astronomy gave official support to the sciences and encouraged projects that would benefit the state. Among the most versatile of the scientists who flourished in these institutions was the government official Yi Ch'on.

Already one of Korea's leading craftsmen at the start of Sejong's reign, Yi Ch'on served as Minister of Works in the early 1420s. During the following decade he was associated with the Bureau of Astronomy, where he worked with such scholars as Chang Yongsil [q.v.]. Among the many astronomical instruments which Yi helped design at this time were large, bowl-shaped sundials known as scaphes, two of which were set up in Seoul as the first public clocks in Korea. Another of Yi's projects at the Bureau of Astronomy was the world's first rain-gauge, commissioned by the government as an aid to agriculture. He also served the state as a designer of firearms, including a multi-tubular rocket launcher used successfully against the Mongols.

Yi's activity as a military engineer interested him in metallurgy and metal-working, though in these fields he generally popularized and adapted existing techniques. These included a new method of iron-smelting which Yi borrowed from the Jürchen nomads and an improved set of metal type for use in printing. The state showed particular interest in this last invention, since King Sejong firmly believed that good government depended on widespread understanding of the Confucian classics. Hoping to increase the availability of these writings, he personally ordered Yi to devote his attention to printing technology.

Outstanding Engineering Achievements:

Yi's rain-gauge was a simple device, a graduated metal cylinder 17 inches (43 cm) deep and seven inches (17 cm) in diameter. Yet it was the first reliable instrument of its kind: previous efforts to measure rainfall involved field markers which failed to allow for the absorptive capacity of the soil. Distributed throughout the country, the rain-gauge made it possible for the government to undertake a nationwide survey of precipitation. Yi also measured variations in the level of rivers by suspending a graduated marker between two stone posts set in the river bed.

The most advanced printing technique used in Korea before Yi's time involved bronze type set in a metal tray lined with beeswax. Traditionally, metal type was cast with tapered ends that frequently shifted in the wax-lined tray; as paper was pressed against the inked type, the soft wax often yielded and individual letters were displaced. Since these had to be reset by hand, output was limited and many finished pages were marred by uneven or blurred letters. Yi improved the technique by casting type with a more regular shape and a broader base that provided greater stability in the tray. Though he still used a wax coating, his innovation served as the basis of further improvements that dispensed entirely with beeswax. The resulting technique, known as Kyongja printing, produced pages with greater regularity at a faster rate than the older process. By the 1430s, the output of a Korean printer had increased from several sheets a day up to 40. ■

Further Reading:

Sang-woon Jeon, *Science and Technology in Korea: Traditional Instruments and Techniques.* Cambridge, 1974.

W. A. Henthorn, *A History of Korea.* 1971.

THAN-STON-RGYAL-PO
b. 1385
d. 1464
Tibetan Engineer

Life and Times:

Religion permeated the hierarchical society of Tibet, and so it is not surprising that a Tibetan religious figure, the lama Than-ston-rgyal-po, has been credited with designing one of the first flat-deck, iron-chain suspension bridges in the world.

Than-ston-rgyal-po's life has been the subject of legendary embellishments, many of them contained in a biography written a century after his death. According to tradition, he lived from 1361 to 1485; some commentators suggest that the dates 1385 to 1464 are more likely. Than-ston-rgyal-po was apparently an ascetic, associated with the Tantric wing of Tibetan Buddhism. In the main, he lived as a wanderer, perhaps a mendicant. But he also devoted himself to the design of bridges, in which activity he received the support of Tibet's ruling families. He was thus able to construct—among others—the suspension bridge across the Brahmaputra River at Chak-sam-ch'ö-ri. His patrons supplied him with the requisite materials, including iron, and a large number of forced laborers, enabling him to complete the project in 1420.

Outstanding Engineering Achievement:

Chinese engineers had built suspension bridges before the time of Than-ston-rgyal-po. But their design was less advanced, with a curved deck only partly supported by chains or cables. The bridge designed by Than-ston-rgyal-po, on the other hand, had a flat deck that depended entirely for its support on iron chains fastened to towers at either end of the chasm. The chains formed two cables, which ran from each tower to the bridge deck. The pathway, wide enough only for pedestrians, was 450 feet (135 meters) long. Western observers discovered the bridge only in 1903, by which time the wooden deck had been removed. ■

Further Reading:

Needham, *Science and Civilisation in China.* Vol. IV, pt. 3.

CHANG YONGSIL
fl. 1432, Seoul, Korea
Korean Horological Engineer

Life and Times:

The Ming dynasty in China began with the destruction of many clocks and other precision instruments built during the preceding Yüan dynasty. The imperial workshop of the Yüan at Peking was dispersed and many of its artisans driven into exile. Some sought refuge in the nearby kingdom of Choson (Korea), where they contributed to a scientific revival under the newly-founded Yi dynasty. The fourth Yi king, Sejong, was an enlightened monarch who introduced the Korean alphabet and himself designed a water clock. His court at Seoul was a center of astronomical studies and clock-making, supporting many experts in the field. Foremost among them was Chang Yongsil.

The early years of Chang's life are obscure. Originally a government slave, he rose rapidly at the Korean court to become Lord Protector of the Army and the king's chief engineer. From 1432 to 1439 he helped equip the royal astronomical observatory in Seoul with new instruments, many of them designed by Korean astronomers. But his most notable work was a monumental striking water clock, the "puppet clock," installed in the Chiming Clepsydra Pavilion of the royal court. Completed in 1434, the device bore a close resemblance to many palace clocks constructed by Islamic engineers in the tenth through twelfth centuries. It is possible that Chang Yongsil was influenced by the work of Arabs or Persian artisans, benefitting from the relative ease of communication across Central Asia during the era of Mongol domination.

Outstanding Engineering Achievement:

Chang's "puppet clock" made ingenious use of levers and rolling balls to activate jack-figures which sounded drums and gongs at various intervals. The device consisted basically of two tanks with floating rods, which rose as the tanks filled with water. At certain points the rods tripped levers, releasing balls which rolled down one of several conduits to strike a jack-figure and set it in motion. One rod governed the action of 12 placard-bearing jacks and one gong-sounding jack which signalled the passage of double-hours. The other rod regulated one drum-beating jack and a gong that sounded the varying intervals of the night watch. The spent balls were collected in a chamber and replaced daily at their starting positions by attendants, who also emptied the tanks of water. ∎

Further Reading:

Needham, *Science and Civilisation in China.* Vol. IV, pt. 2.

P'AN CHI-HSÜN
b. 1521
d. 1595
Chinese Hydraulic Engineer

Life and Times:

Chinese hydraulic engineers began to write treatises on water control in the third century A.D., and by the start of the Ming dynasty a millennium later a large technical literature had developed in the field. But all of these works were specialized in some way, dealing either with a particular region or with a particular branch of water control (canals, irrigation, river works, etc.). Many of them also represented a particular school of hydraulic engineering, whether the Confucianist with its emphasis on large-scale projects or the Taoist with its preference for minimal intervention in the course of nature. The first general compendium on water control, attempting to bring together all information and viewpoints in the field, was the work of P'an Chi-Hsün.

One of the most prominent engineers of the Ming dynasty, P'an served four terms as director of the Yellow River Works and Grand Canal during the sixteenth century. His compendium, entitled *Ho Fang Ch'uan Shu (General View of Water Control),* was completed in 1590. It soon became a standard source of information for Chinese hydraulic engineers and remained so for over 200 years. In the mid-eighteenth century P'an's work was supplemented by another general compendium, the *Method of River Control* by Chin Fu. But, though his information had to be adjusted to changing circumstances, P'an continued to be consulted by hydraulic engineers in China for the rest of the dynastic period.

Outstanding Engineering Achievement:

P'an's *General View of Water Control* provided general principles, case studies and a history of its subject area. Of special interest to modern scholars are copies of earlier edicts, memorials and maps which P'an included in his work. A strong partisan of extensive hydraulic engineering works, P'an took the Confucianist side in the centuries-old debate over flood control. Among the measures he advocated was the so-called self-scouring method, forcing a river to clear its own bed of sediment by building dikes and dams in towards the center of the channel.

But P'an took care to present opposing viewpoints in the form of debates with an imaginary opponent. ■

Further Reading:

Needham, *Science and Civilisation in China.* Vol. IV, pt. 3.

TAKEDA SHINGEN
b. 1521
d. 1573
Japanese Ruler and Military Leader

Life and Times:

Takeda Shingen is best known as a powerful warlord of the so-called Warring States period that preceded the unification of Japan under the Tokugawa shogunate. Head of the Takeda clan, he ruled the domain of Kai on the eastern shore of Honshu Island; he spent most of his career struggling for mastery of the Kanto plain in central Honshu. Like most rulers of the time, Shingen also sought to increase the prosperity and productivity of his lands. But in this respect he was more innovative than others, for his name is associated with an important Japanese method of water control, known as the koshu system. Whether Shingen himself had a hand in developing this technique or simply sponsored the work of skilled engineers is uncertain. In any case, a series of dikes still in use in the present-day Yamanashi prefecture of eastern Japan, the Shingen-zutsumi, is named for him.

Outstanding Engineering Achievement:

The koshu system of water control was basically a method of constructing embankments along rivers and irrigation canals to minimize erosion and flooding. Barriers were constructed in several layers or levels, beginning along the waterway with a terraced bank made of earth and bamboo stakes. Behind this, on higher ground, was a stone retaining wall reinforced by an earthen embankment. At points of rapid water flow, stone breakwaters were constructed at an angle into the current to reduce stress on the bank. The same purpose was served by *jakago* and *hijiriushi,* bamboo or iron containers filled with stones and placed in the current near the bank.

Like so much of Japanese culture and technology, the koshu system drew on Chinese example. The *jakago* and *hijiriushi* closely resembled gabions, stone-filled bamboo crates used since ancient times by Chinese hydraulic engineers. More generally, Shingen's waterworks can be viewed in the context of the long-standing Chinese debate between the so-called Confucianist and Taoist schools of water control. Hydraulic engineers with a Confucianist (or interventionist) orientation advocated costlier and more extensive waterworks than their Taoist rivals, who maintained that anything exceeding minimal interference in the flow of water would prove futile. The koshu system, with its multiple walls and embankments, followed the ambitious Confucianist course. But an alternate technique that developed in Japan during the seventeenth century, known as the Kanto system, prescribed low embankments that would permit periodic flooding. In its belief that the natural course of a waterway was safest, this method reflected the claims of Taoist hydraulic engineers.

The koshu system outlived Shingen and was applied extensively in Japan during the Tokugawa period. Some of the country's largest rivers, including the Tone, the Kiso and the Tenryu, were provided with waterworks of the koshu type. The resulting improvement in flood control contributed to the sharp rise in cultivated acreage that followed the end of civil strife. ■

Further Reading:

Frank Brinkley, *A History of the Japanese People.* New York, 1915.
Mikiso Hane, *Japan: A Historical Survey.* New York, 1972.
James A. Murdoch, *A History of Japan.* New York, 1904.

YAITA KIMBEI
fl. 1550
Japanese Swordsmith and Gunsmith

Life and Times:

The Japanese first came into contact with Western firearms in the mid-sixteenth century. It was a time of intense civil strife in Japan as contending warlords sought to unify the country under their rule. These leaders could scarcely afford to ignore an important innovation, and guns were quickly integrated into Japanese military organization and strategy. Demand almost immediately exceeded the meager supply from the West, and so firearms became the first Western implements to be manufactured in Japan. Fortunately for the soldiers, Japanese metal-working techniques were well-developed and easily adapted to the new weapon. This was true above all among swordsmiths, a highly-skilled and cohesive group of artisans with close ties to the samurai warrior class. Thus it is not surprising that swordsmiths became the first Japanese gunsmiths. The pioneer of this development was Yaita Kimbei.

Yaita had the good fortune to be a swordsmith on the small island of Tanegashima, located off the southern tip of Kyushu, the southernmost of Japan's main islands. In 1543 a ship that included among its passengers three Portuguese landed on the island. The Portuguese possessed several firearms, two of which they sold to Tokitaka, the local lord. Tokitaka immediately ordered Yaita to produce a firearm based on the European model. Yaita completed the task before the year was out; by the end of 1544, he had made 10 firearms.

Whether Yaita managed to parlay his unique knowledge into wealth or high position is uncertain. His monopoly was brief, however, for the manufacture of guns spread rapidly across Japan. Within a decade, firearms production was established in two major centers, Kunitomo and Sakai, and several minor ones. Japanese traders embarked on a vigorous program of exporting guns to other parts of Asia, especially Southeast Asia. Firearms may have contributed substantially to the success of the Oda and Tokugawa clans in consolidating power in Japan during the last decades of the sixteenth century. But the ban on guns imposed in the seventeenth century by the Tokugawa rulers who finally unified the country set back the design of Japanese firearms for over 200 years.

Outstanding Engineering Achievement:

Yaita's workshop reproduced the European arquebus, a musket with matchlock mounted for firing on a hook-shaped support. This type of gun became standard equipment in Japanese armies until the banning of firearms. Manufacture of the gun stock and barrel was apparently well within the capabilities of Japanese metal-working. But the trigger-and-spring firing mechanism was new to Japan, and required considerable skill on Yaita's part to duplicate. ■

Further Reading:

Sugimoto and Swain, eds., *Science and Culture in Traditional Japan.* Cambridge, Mass., 1978.

Noel Perrin, *Giving Up the Gun.* Boston, 1979.

WANG CHÊNG
fl. 1627, China
Chinese Horological Engineer

Life and Times:

In the waning decades of the Ming dynasty, China began to experience continuous and significant contact with Western culture. The agent of transmission was the Jesuit order, which operated missions in the Chinese countryside and at the imperial court for some 150 years from the late sixteenth century. The ultimate purpose of the Jesuits was religious, but they brought with them knowledge of scientific techniques then current in Western Europe. One result was the introduction of European astronomical and engineering instruments to a substantial audience of Chinese scholars. This was a period of stagnation in Chinese science, and the confidence of the Jesuits, who held their own work as scientists in high regard, produced a marked contrast between the two groups.

Scientific influence was not entirely one-way, however. One area in which China had much to teach the West was clock-making. Indeed, contact between the horological techniques of the two cultures produced one notable hybrid. This was a clock constructed in 1627 that combined a Western-style verge-and-foliot escapement with a Chinese-style waterwheel linkwork escapement. The device was the product of collaboration between the Jesuit priest Johannes Schreck and the Chinese horological engineer Wang Chêng, an official at the imperial court.

Wang Chêng described the joint creation, which he called a "wheel clepsydra," in the text of a larger work he wrote about machinery. Though little is known of Wang's life, his writings suggest that, like the court engineers of the Western and Muslim world, he sought to combine craftsmanship with mechanical ingenuity, if not theoretical insight. The "wheel clepsydra" drew on nearly a millennium of Chinese experimentation with water-driven clocks, beginning with I-Hsing's [q.v.] clock of 725 and continuing through the sand-clocks of the Ming period. But Wang's clock had no important successor. The initial effect of Chinese contact with the West was thus not to open new lines of development but to culminate and end a long engineering tradition.

Outstanding Engineering Achievement:

The "wheel clepsydra" was actually two mechanisms housed in a single cabinet 2½ feet (0.75 meter) high. The central compartment of the cabinet contained a Western-style clock powered by a falling weight, whose action was slowed and regulated by a verge-and-foliot escapement. Below the escapement was a gear-train which operated a jack-figure, whose function was to indicate each double-hour by pointing to one of 12 tablets fixed to the clock face.

The back of the clock measured the hours of the night-watch, which varied with the seasons. Here Wang Cheng relied on the traditional Chinese device of a rotating wheel that both powered the mechanism and controlled its rate of speed. Although this part of the clock is incompletely described in Wang Cheng's account, it appears that the wheel was turned by

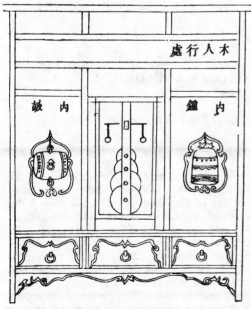

Wang Cheng's illustration of his wheel clepsydra; center, the verge-and-foliot escapement with a gear train below.

small leadshot which were dropped at a carefully measured rate into scoops fixed to the wheel's edge. This was a variation on the water-powered clocks of I Hsing and Su Sung [q.v.], the mercury-driven clock of Cheng Ssu-Hsün [q.v.] and the sand-operated clocks of the earlier Ming period. Like its predecessors, Wang's clock probably had a weighbridge mechanism, a set of levers and weights that permitted movement of the wheel only when each scoop had been filled with a certain amount of leadshot. The precise appearance of the gear train and figures that indicated the hours of the night watch cannot be reconstructed from Wang Cheng's description. ■

Further Reading:

Needham, *Science and Civilisation in China.* Vol. IV, pt. 2.

LI FANG-HSIEN
fl. 1630
Chinese Civil and Military Engineer

Life and Times:

The flat-deck suspension bridge originated in Tibet, where the monk Than-ston-rgyal-po [q.v.] built the first such structure in 1420. Some 200 years later an improved version of the design appeared in China. This was the Kuan-ling bridge in the southwestern province of Kwei-chow, built in 1629 by the military engineer Li Fang-Hsien.

Mountainous southwestern China had been the site of important bridgebuilding activity since the fourteenth century, when armies of the newly-established Ming dynasty invaded the area to suppress rebellious warlords. Li Fang-Hsien, an army major, was ordered to bridge the turbulent P'an Chiang river, in which many travellers had drowned. With several overhauls, the bridge lasted until 1939. Whether Li derived his techniques directly from Tibet or through some intermediary is uncertain. But the bridge itself was noteworthy enough to have an entire book devoted to it. This was the *T'ieh Ch'iao Chih Shu (Record of the Iron Suspension Bridge)*, written in 1665 by Chu Hsieh-Yuan, son of the prefect under whose jurisdiction the bridge was built.

Outstanding Engineering Achievement:

The Kuan-ling bridge spanned a chasm some 300 feet (90 meters) deep and 150 feet (45 meters) wide. Though shorter than some earlier suspension bridges, it was one of the first that could support not only pedestrians but also heavily-laden pack animals. The deck, made of double-layered wooden planking eight inches (20 cm) thick, was supported by iron chains slung between two towers on either side of the chasm. Additional support was provided by chains attached to two iron railings, which hung from the mouths of ornamental stone lions erected on both sides of the two towers. ■

Further Reading:

Needham, *Science and Civilisation in China*. Vol. IV, pt. 3.

SONG IYONG
fl. 1664, Seoul, Korea
Korean Horological Engineer

Life and Times:

During the mid-seventeenth century, Western technological influences began to spread through China and its border areas from the court of the Ming emperors, where Jesuit missionaries had established an embassy. The process of diffusion was of course very slow, limited at first to a few scholars in special fields. One of these fields was clock-making, whose close relationship to astrology and astronomy made it among the most highly valued of the mechanical arts. Chinese horological engineers were interested in any innovation which might improve the accuracy of their devices, even if it came from as strange a place as the West. The first Chinese clock incorporating elements of Western design was built by Wang Cheng [q.v.] not long after the arrival of the Jesuits. Within a generation knowledge of the new technique had spread to one of China's cultural satellites, Korea, where the engineer Song Iyong built a Western-style clock for King Hyojong.

Song Iyong worked at a time of intense interest in clock-making at the Korean court in Seoul. Most Korean clocks closely followed Chinese

models, particularly the water-powered type with a linkwork escapement first designed by I Hsing [q.v.]. Indeed, one such device was built in Seoul at the same time that Song Iyong constructed his own clock. Completed in 1664, Song's clock was of more than local importance, for it was apparently the first built in the Far East to rely entirely on "the gear-wheels of Western clock-work." It thus went beyond Wang Cheng's clock, a hybrid that included elements of both Chinese and Western design. In fact, Song's work marked a new era in oriental clock-making, for Western-style clocks became increasingly common in China and Korea as the native tradition slowly died out.

Outstanding Engineering Achievement:

Song Iyong's device was an armillary clock which both told time and permitted the movements of celestial objects to be traced. The court records were vague in their description of the clock; but the reference to "Western clockwork" undoubtedly indicates a verge-and-foliot escapement regulating the action of a falling weight or spring. ■

Further Reading:

Needham, *Science and Civilisation in China*. Vol. IV, pt. 2.

TOKUGAWA YOSHIMUNE
b. 1684
d. 1751
Japanese Ruler and Instrument Maker

Life and Times:

The eighteenth century in Japan was a time of reviving interest in Western culture and artifacts. The fear of Christianity which had caused the near-total suppression of European influence in 1640 had begun to fade, and many Japanese scholars now took up the study of "Dutch learning" (so called because most of the traders from whom the Japanese gained their knowledge of the West were Dutch). The trend received official sanction in 1720, when Yoshimune, eighth ruler of the Tokugawa shogunate, permitted the importation of European books. By this action he hoped to encourage scientific study, especially in astronomy and agronomy. But Yoshimune was important not only as a patron of science but as an instrument-maker in his own right. Among his works was the first Japanese telescope equipped with a set of coordinates on the eyepiece to permit the accurate location of celestial objects.

A distant figure in the line of succession, Yoshimune was unexpectedly elevated to the shogunate in 1716. He came from the remote province of Kishu, where he had served as provincial governor since 1705. Once in power, Yoshimune proved an active ruler who reversed some of the policies of previous shoguns. He sought to reform the financial and administrative structure of the government and to restore the martial vigor of the samurai warrior class. Yoshimune also devoted much attention to Japanese agriculture, working to expand the area under cultivation through extensive land reclamation projects and the introduction of new crops brought to Japan by the Europeans. Among the latter were the sweet potato and the silk worm.

Yoshimune sought to concentrate scientific activity at the capital city of Edo (present-day Tokyo). He established an astronomical observatory on the grounds of the palace and worked closely with his chief astronomer, Katahiro Tatebe, in its operation. Later, Yoshimune established the royal astronomical observatory in the Kanda district of the city.

Outstanding Engineering Achievement:

Yoshimune did most of his work as an astronomical instrument-maker in cooperation with Katahiro Tatebe at the palace observatory. It has been suggested that Yoshimune developed the idea of a telescope eyepiece with coordinates independently, though he probably had opportunity to see European telescopes that were similarly equipped. We also do not know whether he superimposed the coordinates on the surface of the eyepiece lens or set them in its focal plane, as European lensmakers had been doing since the mid-seventeenth century. In any event, it seems that the telescope for which Yoshimune made his eyepiece was part of a surveying instrument similar to the European transit. The coordinates were designed so that, at a certain setting of the telescope, the sun would pass through the center of the cross-hairs at high

noon. The telescope was apparently a refracting type then known in Europe. This was the first use of a telescope for surveying purposes in Japan.

Yoshimune was also known for the unusual dome which he constructed to protect his instruments in the palace observatory. Covered with thickly lacquered leather to keep out moisture, it was one of the first structures in Japan to have an iron framework. ∎

Further Reading:

Yasuaki Iba, "Fragmentary Notes on Japanese Astronomy," *Popular Astronomy* (1937).

James Murdock, *A History of Japan.* New York, 1964.

Shigeru Nakayama, *A History of Japanese Astronomy.* Cambridge, 1969.

KUROSAWA MOTOSHIGE
fl. 1690
Japanese Metallurgist and Author of Treatise on Mining

Life and Times:

The mining and processing of metal ores became increasingly important in Japan during the seventeenth century. In part, the growth of metallurgy resulted from the great demand for arms and armor brought about by the constant warfare that preceded creation of the Tokugawa state. After reunification was achieved, metals were needed for other purposes. In 1596 the Japanese court began to mint copper-based coins, after a hiatus of six hundred years, as part of its program of reestablishing the primacy of the central government. Japan's booming trade in precious metals also played a part in the development; by 1600 silver exports from Japan alone amounted to roughly one-third of world silver production.

The expansion of the mining industry focused attention on the techniques used to extract and purify metals. Moreover, new techniques often

Model of a Japanese metal-ore mine such as is described in Kurosawa's handbook.

brought new problems. By the end of the six-teenth century, for example, Japanese engineers had exhausted surface deposits and turned to digging deeper underground shafts; as a result, they now faced severe drainage difficulties. The rapid development of metallurgy made some sort of handbook for the field increasingly neces-sary, and in 1691 such a work was published. Compiled by the metallurgist Kurosawa Moto-shige, it was the first book of its kind in Japan.

Little is known of Kurosawa's previous work as a metallurgist, so it remains unclear whether his handbook grew out of his own experiences or was the product of observation and compilation. Entitled *Kozan Shiho Yoroku* (Handbook of Mining Techniques), it played an important role in popularizing information about Japanese mines and smelting techniques. Kurosawa de-scribed not only current practices but also the areas in which mines were worked, providing details on the possibilities afforded by different veins in various regions. Thus he pioneered the comprehensive study and evaluation of Japanese mining.

A second work on mining, which appeared in 1695, may also have been written by Kurosawa. It described the operation of Japan's most im-portant gold mine, located on the island of Sado off the western coast of the main Japanese island of Honshu.

Kurosawa's role in Japanese metallurgy re-sembles that of Georgius Agricola [q.v.] in Renaissance Europe. Both compiled informa-tion on past and present techniques of mining and preparation of metals, helping to standard-ize practices and opening the field to a much wider audience.

Outstanding Engineering Achievement:

Kurosawa's handbook is an important record of the progress made by Japanese mining engi-neers in the seventeenth century. Among the major subjects covered are: new techniques in the refining of copper and silver, the con-struction of shafts, tunnels and underground waterways as the primary means of obtaining ores for extraction, problems posed by flooding and the development of new devices to ensure proper drainage and improve the processing of impure and low-grade ores.

From the evidence provided by Kurosawa, most of the metals and many of the techniques common in contemporary Europe were also known to the Japanese. Gold, silver, copper, bronze, iron, tin, lead and mercury were among the metals commonly mined and used in imple-ments. Refining of silver ore by the technique of cupellation, or heating in a porous vessel, had been adopted from the Chinese by way of Korea in the early sixteenth century. New processes for smelting copper ore were also introduced in the sixteenth and seventeenth centuries. But Japan's remoteness, aggravated after 1639 by the gov-ernment's isolation policy, had its effect on the metallurgical trades. Water pumps, for instance, were known to the Japanese but not widely used in mine drainage; and new European developments in the area, culminating in the steam pump, were not appreciated. Drainage problems thus limited the growth of Japanese mines as shafts went deeper, creating a bottleneck which affected all branches of metallurgy. ■

Further Reading:

Tuge Hideomi, ed., *Historical Development of Science and Technology in Japan.*

Sugimoto and Swain, eds., *Science and Culture in Traditional Japan.* Cambridge, Mass., 1978.

ASADA GŌRYŪ
b. March 10, 1734, Kizuki, Japan
d. June 25, 1799, Osaka, Japan
Japanese Astronomer and Instrument Maker

Life and Times:

Great changes in Japanese astronomy began to occur in the second half of the eighteenth century, when a new school of astronomers and instrument-makers emerged in the commercial city of Osaka. Before this time the Japanese had generally relied on Chinese astronomical theories and observational techniques, which for centuries were the most sophisticated they had encountered. The ban on significant contact with Europeans, which kept Western books out of Japan from 1640 to 1720, retarded the development of new ideas in astronomy and other sciences. But between 1760 and the end of the century Japanese astronomers became interested in Western astronomical instruments and data. This trend received great impetus from the physician-turned-astronomer Asada Gōryū, who founded a school of astronomy that often bears his name.

Asada Gōryū was born Ayabe Yasuaki, the son of a Confucian scholar and government official in the fief of Kizuki. Though he practiced medicine for a living, he was drawn increasingly to the study of astronomy as he discovered discrepancies between official calculations and the actual occurrence of various phenomena, including a solar eclipse in 1763. From 1767 to 1772 he served as court physician to the lord of Kizuki, a task that prevented him from pursuing his interest in astronomy. When his lord refused to release him from service, he fled to Osaka,

changed his name to Asada, and began to promote new astronomical ideas and techniques.

The growing city of Osaka provided a favorable environment for Asada's activities. Many of Osaka's prosperous merchants had some contact with Western traders and were interested in foreign ideas; they were also wealthy enough to support scholarly work. One of Asada's ablest pupils, Hazama Shigetomi [q.v.], was a successful merchant. Much of Asada's effort in Osaka was devoted to reconciling Western astronomical observations with traditional Chinese astronomy, an undertaking that soon became obsolete as Japanese astronomers relied increasingly on European ideas. He did, however, insist on reliable data, and to obtain these he turned to Western instruments. In this way, and through his influence as a teacher, Asada helped introduce telescopes, transits and other devices into general use in Japan. By the 1790s he had attracted attention at the shogunal court in Edo. In 1795 Asada influenced the decision to appoint Hazama and Takahashi Yoshitoki, another of his pupils, as court astronomer and assistant charged with preparing tables upon which a revision of the calendar would be made.

Outstanding Engineering Achievements:

Asada contributed in two ways to Japanese engineering. He encouraged Japanese astronomers, who had earlier relied on Chinese instruments such as the sun-dial to use a new range of Western devices. In addition, he himself constructed a number of astronomical instruments, including a telescope with which he viewed the moons of Jupiter. Asada's level of technical expertise is not clear. He did grind lenses for his telescope, though he may have assembled the rest of the instrument from European parts. Iwahashi Zenbei [q.v.] is generally viewed as the first Japanese instrument-maker to build all the parts of a telescope; Asada at least prepared the way for this accomplishment.

Other Achievements:

In his theoretical work, Asada was credited by his pupils with the independent discovery of Kepler's third law, establishing the relationship between a planet's distance from the sun and the period of its revolution. He also proposed that the precession of the earth—the variation of its spin about its own axis—led to changes in the tropical year, a significant concern in calendrical computation. Though later disproved, Asada's theory was the first Japanese theoretical contribution to astronomy. ■

Further Reading:

Dictionary of Scientific Biography, s.v. "Asada Gōryū."
Shigeru Nakayama, *A History of Japanese Astronomy.* Cambridge, 1969.

IWAHASHI ZENBEI
fl. 1790
Japanese Astronomical Instrument Maker

Life and Times:

As Western scientific ideas gained influence in Japan during the late eighteenth century, Japanese instrument-makers gradually acquainted themselves with Western scientific instruments. This was not their first exposure to European techniques; as early as the start of the seventeenth century, before the ban on contact with Europeans, Japanese artisans had become familiar with Western methods of grinding glass for eyeglass lenses. Yet for some years, more complicated instruments of European design were made by assembling parts imported from the West. The first Japanese instrument-maker to gain full mastery of European techniques in his field was Iwahashi Zenbei, who produced the earliest refracting telescope made completely in Japan.

Little is known of Iwahashi Zenbei's life and career. A contemporary of the famous astronomer Asada Gōryū [q.v.], he shared in the rapid growth of interest in Western astronomy stimulated by Asada's work in Osaka. Unlike Asada, however, Iwahashi approached his work from the viewpoint of a craftsman rather than a scholar. By training he was an optician, well acquainted with the techniques of grinding glass to produce lenses of varying focal lengths. Iwahashi taught himself astronomy and in the 1790s turned to the construction of refracting telescopes. His first successful refractor, completed in 1793, was soon used to demonstrate the operation of a telescope to a group of skeptical Japanese scholars. Except for an instrument installed at the Government Observatory in Edo, Iwahashi's telescope was apparently the only one then in use in Japan.

Outstanding Engineering Achievement:

Iwahashi's first telescope was an octagonal tube about 2½ yards (2.3 meters) long with a circumference of about 10½ inches (27 cm). The refracting lens was apparently designed on the European pattern, one convex surface of crown glass set against another of flint glass. Using the telescope, Iwahashi was able to see sunspots, details of the lunar surface and the cloud covering of Jupiter and Saturn. In 1795 Iwahashi built a larger and more powerful telescope through which he could differentiate some of Saturn's rings and view the bands of Jupiter in greater detail. ■

Further Reading:

Dictionary of Scientific Biography, s.v., "Asada Gōryū."
Yasuaki Iba, "Fragmentary Notes on Astronomy in Japan," *Popular Astronomy* (1938).
Shigeru Nakayama, *A History of Japanese Astronomy.* Cambridge, 1969.

Engineering in the Renaissance

by Alex G. Keller

In the Middle Ages, an "ingenarius" was first and foremost a maker of siege engines; the name, like the weapons these engineers built, links the profession with a past reaching back to the civilizations of Antiquity. So, as the invention of the steam engine ushers in the Industrial Revolution for engineers, the Renaissance period begins with the invention of a new siege engine, more effective and terrible than any known before—the cannon.

Evidence for the early history of firearms is sparse—merely references in accounts or chronicles—but it is safe to say that artillery was first introduced into European warfare about 1325, following on the diffusion of gunpowder from China. The first cannon were slow to fire, tricky to work and cumbersome to move. They could only be used in sieges, and grew steadily larger until some real giants were cast for the siege of Constantinople in 1453. But the future lay with relatively small but highly mobile artillery pieces, transported on two-wheel carriages; the first appearance of such an artillery train, accompanying the French invasion of Italy in 1494, overwhelmed all opposition. Cannon demanded a different technique of manufacture than the old wooden catapults, trebuchets and battering rams. They could not be constructed on the spot from local timber by the engineers of a besieging army. Indeed, the casting of bronze cannon had to be adapted from the casting of bells; a peaceful industry took on the uniform of war. Nor was the use of the firearm similar to that of earlier siege engines. The preparation of gunpowder, wadding, match, aiming the gun and lighting the fuse all demanded care and skill. So a new type of bombardier replaced the old engineer in handling, as the gunfounder replaced him in manufacturing this new device.

The development of lighter, more mobile field artillery did not prevent the re-emergence of the cavalry as an effective military arm; the horseman's expensive and complex wheel-lock piston proved as good at breaking an infantry line as the lance of his predecessor, the knight. Cannon and match- or flint-lock muskets were still slow-firing, and had to be supported by pikes. Only when in the latter years of the seventeenth century the bayonet was attached, enabling the musket to be turned into a spear, did the pike finally disappear, and firearms become the soldier's standard equipment.

The old ingenarius had also designed castles to withstand siege engines; revising this design was an important task of the new engineer. The old fortress walls were relatively thin, height being the main consideration. But that was no longer practical. Prominent and projecting towers were

Early cannon depicted without its recoil, which would usually knock over gun and gunner.

for cannon an easy target. Instead a new style of fortification evolved over two centuries, roughly from 1480 to 1680. Its main feature was the bastion, in essence a low gun-platform, protected by a simple parapet. The walls were immensely thick, made of earth, kept low in order to offer the minimum target and faced with a sloping glacis of stone to deflect the besiegers' cannon balls. In the solid mass of earth, any ball which did penetrate the facing would bury itself harmlessly. Since the raw material was so cheap and abundant, walls could be made thick enough to stop anything; driving a breach through such a wall was a slow and costly business. One way was to blow up part of the wall with a sizable charge of gunpowder. But the charge had first to be brought up to and under the wall. Responding to this problem, engineers of opposing armies developed techniques of advancing trenches and counter-trenches, mines and counter-mines.

The bastions of a fortress were more exposed to hostile gunfire than the curtain walls between, and so had to be planned to give a maximum field of fire, to cover their own flanks, and to protect the curtain walls. The first bastions were quasi-circular, as appears from the sketches of Francesco di Giorgio [q.v.] and others, and retained the old battlements. Some of these early styles survive—notably in England, which had less need of fortifications except at a few southern ports and on the Scottish border. Elsewhere, the semi-circular bastions gave way to triangles and pentagons, and to a lobed and projecting triangle, a little like the spades in a pack of cards; and this in turn to something like an arrowhead. These new fortifications might be less romantic than the old, but they were effective enough to survive until the development of high explosives in the late nineteenth century.

Castles were nearly always too small for the new warfare. Fortified cities became the keys to provinces and kingdoms, and campaigning often meant a series of sieges; indeed, in the sixteenth century there were relatively few pitched open battles. The new fortification was much more geometrical than the old. Calculations of a potential field of fire became prerequisite, as bastions were protected by outworks and covered by further gun-platforms higher up. No less geometrical was the art of siegecraft, the laying out of trenches and mines, and the positioning of batteries. Courage and skill at tactics were no longer all that an army officer needed; he had to know mathematics as well. From about 1480 onward, a new type of professional military engineer made his appearance. He designed fortifications and was highly trained in geome-

try—at first by private tuition, from the later sixteenth century often in academies where sons of the gentry were given the technical skills which the warrior now had to know. Shakespeare pokes fun at the new professional in the character of Captain Fluellen in *Henry V;* but he knew that the future of war lay with such men.

In addition to attacking and defending the walls of fortifications, the engineer was also responsible for breaking down doors and gates with smaller explosive devices like petards and for using wrenches to force open lattice windows and barred doors. If he was besieging a port, he might attack the enemy with fireships and bomb ships. The time bomb employed at Antwerp in 1585 by Federigo Giambelli [q.v.] to explode a bomb ship against the Spanish besiegers' pontoon bridge caused the biggest explosion that had ever been heard to that time; chroniclers marvelled at the distance the blast was felt. If the Gunpowder Plot (1605) had succeeded, however, it might well have outdone the Antwerp explosion.

The military engineer had many other tasks and techniques. As warfare became more mobile, he might be expected to ferry his army across rivers, design mobile mills to grind their flour or construct pontoon bridges, either to close off the river which supplied a besieged town or to get his own troops across a river or moat. Pontoons might be built during the winter and carried with the army on the march. The principle of quick assembly of complex artefacts from light, transportable elements makes its appearance with such military bridges. Various designs for wooden bridges suitable for hasty construction were also studied, especially for use in mountainous regions.

Sometimes engineers were responsible for

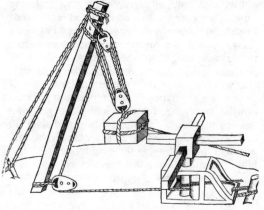

Pulley system for moving loads horizontally; Alberti, 1452.

constructing permanent bridges too. The more centralized kingdoms, like France, encouraged bridge-building as a means of connecting the nation and moving armies across potential obstacles. But most of the important bridges of the time were erected at cities and major crossings; such was the Pont Neuf in Paris, the first to attempt to span the Seine there at one reach, using the point of the Ile de la Cité. There were few real novelties in these stone bridges; almost all still derived from the old Roman form of the semi-circular stone arch, with piers protected by cutwaters. The most original concept was the quasi-elliptical arch, with a slightly better span-to-rise ratio; the first of note was the Ponte Santa Trinitá at Florence (1566-1569), designed by Bartolomeo Ammannati, and constructed of two parabolic curves. It is interesting to see that the ellipse and other non-circular conics and quasi-ellipses appear at the same time in architecture. The baroque style found beauty in irregularity, not just in the pure circle and the simple hemispheric dome of Greco-Roman tradition.

In practice, the new engineer was a kind of architect, and in times of peace he might well practice as a civil architect. Giambattista Aleotti (1546-1636) was equally famous in his own time for his work on the fortification of Ferrara and for his pioneering theater building in Parma. The first great masterpiece of Renaissance architecture, the cathedral of Florence, was surmounted by Filippo Brunelleschi [q.v.] by the famous cupola, which tapers as if its architect wished to combine the classical structure of the dome with the upward aspiration of the Gothic arch. For this building Brunelleschi pioneered other structural features—its double shell, connected by ribs, with a circular chain of wooden beams to serve as tie rods. To construct the dome he invented a three-speed, reversible hoist and a crane with lateral and vertical motion controlled by screws; a turntable under the crane helped hoist the lantern, which was to crown the great edifice only after his death. Brunelleschi's imaginative structure had few later rivals. Only St. Peter's in Rome, and later St. Paul's in London, compare for structural boldness. But it could well be argued that from a structural and aesthetic point of view the last great Gothic buildings, such as King's College chapel at Cambridge (completed only in the early sixteenth century), were as ambitious as any "Renaissance" building, at least until the masterpieces of seventeenth century baroque.

The invention of machinery was not yet really the province of the engineer, unless his architectural purposes demanded it. Perhaps because of

Sixteenth-century clock with a single hand to mark the hours and a bell to chime them.

their associations with Antiquity and the great Archimedes, screws became more popular. Brunelleschi made increased use of traversing screws in his lewises and other handling tools. The Archimedean water-screw became part of European drainage works and was even wind-driven in Holland. Traversing screws were frequently used in mathematical apparatus, and the fastening screw, that little invention which holds our civilization together, also appeared, evidently for the first time. Significantly, it was first used in clocks and hand-guns, the most complex artefacts then in use.

The invention and development of clocks with solid parts spans the Renaissance. Gradually such clocks superseded the water clock, which had been growing ever more elaborate in its use of jackwork since Antiquity. Gears, shafts and levers had replaced pulleys and cords, so that only power source and regulation remained to be converted from dripping water to the fall of a solid weight attached to an escapement like the foliot and the balance wheel. The first such solid clocks, like those of Richard of Wallingford [q.v.] at St. Albans in England (about 1320) or of Jacopo de' Dondi [q.v.] at Pavia a little later, were planetaria like the great water clocks of the past. All were grand public affairs, which dem-

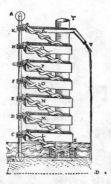

Series of Archimedean screws suggested by Cardano for raising water, 1560.

onstrated the movements of the sun and moon throughout the year, and sometimes those of the lesser planets too. The passage of the hours could be indicated on a dial, adapted perhaps from the face of the astrolabe, and by the ringing of bells, which could serve as an alarm or announce the opening of some activity, whether prayers in a monastery or public business in a town's market place. But once clockmakers had grasped the principle of escapement—the control of moving parts so as to make them pass through given equal time intervals in a regular manner—they could adapt this idea to domestic alarms, which might even strike a flint to light a candle.

For over a century all European clocks were powered by falling weights, but in the middle years of the fifteenth century a new type, whose power was stored in a spring, was introduced. Such clocks made the telling of time portable and depended on new techniques to regulate their motion, the fusee and the stackfreed. Watches grew more compact in the course of the sixteenth century; in the seventeenth, Galileo's [q.v.] discovery of the isochronism of the pendulum was soon adopted by Christiaan Huygens [q.v.] for a far superior method of control. His first pendulum clock, built in 1657, was confronted with priority claims from Galileo's pupils. His use of a spring regulator for watches in 1675 was similarly challenged by Robert Hooke [q.v.], who claimed that he had first demonstrated the device in 1659. From Hooke's work on spring driven and controlled clocks came the law that bears his name, equating stress and strain. He also laid claim to the anchor escapement, which certainly first appears in English clocks at this time.

The clock was for the late Renaissance the machine par excellence. It became the model for all possible improvements in technology, and indeed the model for theory too—for the "clockwork universe," for a cosmology which envisaged the operation of solar systems, tides, motions of air and living creatures, in terms of a chain of bodies impacting upon one another as arbor and pinion might mesh in some enormously complicated clock.

Warfare was revolutionized by gunpowder, mental life by the clock. The question of cultural diffusion is interesting here, for gunpowder weapons and clocks with escapements had been used in the Far East for several centuries before the Renaissance. In both cases, the devices that appeared in Europe were markedly different from their Oriental counterparts: Chinese clocks, for instance, used a regulated water wheel as an escapement rather than the verge-and-foliot mechanism developed in Europe. But if direct borrowing did not take place, ideas may well have passed westward from China along the trade routes or through intermediate cultures such as the Mongols. This was almost certainly true with gunpowder, and may also have occurred in time-keeping and other technologies, including printing. By the seventeenth century the process had reversed itself; European clocks and firearms were taken by Jesuit missionaries to China, where they were eagerly studied by scholars and officials.

Another great area of change during the Renaissance was water-use technology, the key to European economic development. Sixteenth century engineers were well aware of what the ancient Romans had done in this field. If anything, they exaggerated the achievements of their ancient predecessors and seldom dared to emulate them before the 1590s. Water was not only needed for man and beast to drink; it was the major source of power, driving mills and entering into manufacture in fulling cloth, making paper and soap, brewing, dyeing and refining. And water was needed for irrigation, to turn poor arable into rich pasture. Over long distances, water could be led by gravity to where the engineer wished it to go. But at some point he might have to lift it, a short distance at least, *against* gravity. What methods would then be available to him? Most were inherited from Antiquity: hauling up buckets, mechanized in the chain of pots; the noria, in which the pots were replaced by compartments on a turning waterwheel; the Archimedean waterscrew; and the force-pump.

The scoop wheel, first tried in Holland, soon spread to England and elsewhere. It was a kind of reversed waterwheel: instead of the water pushing the wheel to drive a machine, a machine

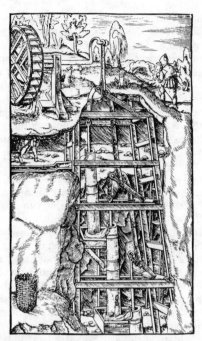

Triple-lift suction pump powered by an undershot waterwheel, recommended by Agricola for draining mines, 1556.

turned the wheel to push water up to a higher level. Another innovation was the rag-and-chain-pump, possibly adapted from the Chinese ladder-pump; the earliest European illustration attributed it to the Tatars. Much more important was the development of the ancient force-pump into a suction pump motivated by atmospheric pressure (or, as was universally supposed until the days of Galileo, nature's abhorrence of a vacuum). The use of a single cylinder might have made it cheaper to build and less likely to burst than a force-pump, although force-pumps certainly continued in use; the first powered apparatus installed to supply the city of London with water (in 1582) was a force-pump. But suction pumps were frequently used in confined spaces, to clear water from the bilges of ships or from mines.

Georgius Agricola's [q.v.] classic work on metallurgy (1556) shows a wide range of pumps used to clear mines, but the rag-and-chain and suction pump are the only two not based closely on ancient precedent. The suction pump's limits were soon observed, although scientists of the time failed to explain why it could only raise water about thirty feet (9 meters). The problem could be solved by mounting pumps in tiers, three or even four linked together. To Agricola this was an innovation newly invented or intro-

duced to Saxony, so the necessary linkage of bell-cranks and connecting-rods probably goes back to about 1540. Later chains of linked field-rods were used extensively to drive mine pumps up to a mile distant from their power source, while pump rods enabled miners to work tiers of pumps sometimes several hundred feet down. In a similar way several Archimedean screws might be arrayed one upon another, as at the early sixteenth century Augsburg waterworks. The Italian engineer Juanelo Turriano [q.v.] erected a train of rocking-troughs, motivated by rod-work, to supply water to the Spanish city of Toledo and its palace, the Alcazar. This device worked well at first, but maintenance difficulties proved its undoing in a few years.

The military engineer was frequently called upon to give advice on these civil problems, which resembled those of fortification. As the cities of Europe recovered from the ravages of the Black Death and expanded beyond their medieval limits during the sixteenth century, problems of urban water supply became increasingly pressing. First pumps drawing directly from rivers replaced buckets; then new springs had to be tapped to supplement the springs and wells within the city boundaries. Some towns were obviously under greater pressure than others, though few needed a channel capable of carrying as much water as London's "New River," completed in 1613. But by the end of the seventeenth century most of the larger towns had constructed a system of aqueducts and pipes to supply public fountains from springs beyond the walls, often some miles off; their exuberant decoration still enlivens many market places across Europe. Only the grandest houses had their own taps to public water.

Water was needed in the countryside no less than in town. Irrigation was carried out by diverting some stream over a water meadow, or connecting stream to meadow by a leat, just like those used to bring water to mills. In northern Italy, such irrigation might be motivated by the desire to plant rice, a crop introduced there only in the fifteenth century and soon popular, or even for maize, which also came into Italy and Mediterranean Europe within a few decades of Spanish settlement in the New World. But the usual motive was to increase and improve pasture land, for the rearing of cattle and sheep was more profitable than cereals. The only dairy product which travelled in those days before refrigeration was cheese—the harder the better. So in the Lombard plain the end-product of irrigation was Parmigiano or Gorgonzola, just as the product of Dutch drainage schemes might

Belidor's map of Menin on the French-Belgian border showing the use of dams for selectively flooding the area around a fortress. Note the arrowhead bastions.

finish up on the cheese markets of Edam or Gouda.

While many irrigation techniques spread from northern Italy to other parts of Europe, the acknowledged masters of drainage were the Dutch. Throughout the Middle Ages the peasants of Holland had been slowly encroaching on the sea marshes of the Rhine-Maas-Scheldt delta. Dikes, originally built to keep out the sea, could also be used to form polders, shutting the sea out from swampland which could then be gradually drained and reclaimed. In the sixteenth century Dutch engineers began to drain flooded peat diggings of the Middle Ages. By the middle of the seventeenth century no less than 27 lakes had been converted to farmland, most important among them the Beemstermeer (1608-12). Engineers like Jan Leeghwater [q.v.] and Cornelius Vermuyden [q.v.] were called abroad as experts with an international reputation, just as Italian fortification specialists like Giambelli and Agostino Ramelli [q.v.] found better fortune across the Alps than at home. Some Dutch masters left accounts of their techniques; best known of these was Simon Stevin [q.v.], who wrote on all branches of engineering and on mathematics. Perhaps the greatest project masterminded by Dutch engineers was the draining of the Great Level of the English Fens, an area of some 300,000 acres (121,405 hectares), completed in 1653. Vermuyden's success there has permanently altered the landscape of a considerable region.

The flat land and slow-moving streams which facilitated land drainage in Holland also contributed to another notable feature of Dutch engineering: the large-scale application of wind power. Indeed, for the Low Countries this was the Golden Age of the windmill. Tower-mills, in which only the cap rather than the whole build-

ing needs to be turned into the wind, date probably from the late fourteenth century; by the seventeenth century they had become the elegant structures which grace the landscape of Holland, performing all the tasks which in most parts of Europe were performed by water power. They served as sawmills, oilmills, powdermills, stamp-mills and pumping engines, but above all as corn-mills, supplying the growing towns of northern Europe. The industrial and agricultural wealth of the Netherlands was based upon her famous windmills. They were indirectly a force which enabled those marshland provinces to frustrate the empire of Spain and become the most progressive country in Europe, the first nation to enter the modern age.

If Italian engineers distinguished themselves in fortifications and the Dutch in land drainage, the Germans were most advanced in mining techniques. Mine captains of Saxony and the Harz mountains ventured wherever they could persuade local lords or financiers that a treasure in gold and silver lay under their feet. Their methods and equipment were encapsulated in Agricola's *De re metallica,* which advertised their skill everywhere, although it must be said that in some branches of metallurgy the *Pirotechnia* of the Sienese engineer Vanoccio Biringuccio [q.v.] has priority; and it is in Italy that we first learn of the application of the crank to work the bellows of the forge, making possible far higher temperatures and the eventual development of the blast furnace. The most remarkable mining engine was the stamp, described by Agricola, whereby ore was crushed, stirred, roasted and agitated in a laver by the action of a single wheel.

Spain had already begun to lag in many respects behind the lands to the north, its commerce weakened by the expulsion of the Jews and its most advanced agriculture by the expulsion of the Moslems (and subsequently even of those who had converted from Islam to Christianity). But Moslem irrigation techniques largely survived on the plains of Valencia, which were fertile but suffered from a very poor rainfall by the standards of Western Europe. A manuscript of hydrotechnics, composed by an Italian immigrant in Spain (possibly Turriano) about 1560, tries to combine the irrigation and drainage methods of the Po basin with those of eastern Spain; it includes a valuable section on weirs and dams, something the Italian tradition, less concerned with conservation of water, had relatively neglected. It is interesting to compare the drawings of Tuscan engineers like Peruzzi and Leonardo da Vinci [q.v.] with the dams which went up in Spain in the last years of the sixteenth century, especially the Tibi dam, the first high arched dam, on which Turriano worked briefly before his death in 1585.

There is no hard and fast line where irrigation channels become navigation canals. As late medieval Lombard canals grew larger, they could be used for either purpose. By 1500, the duchy of Milan had its Naviglio Grande, whose origins go back to the twelfth century. Fresh schemes now sought to link the city of Milan with the Po and with its main northern tributaries, the Adda and the Ticino. A parallel network was to link the river's southern tributaries, while the Brenta was canalized so that it could be used as a highway from Venice into the hinterland. This development involved some of the earliest miter-gated pound locks and a slipway over which goods were hauled by a horse-whim in little trolleys, to be transhipped to waiting barges.

Navigable canals in Europe were largely confined at this time to Italy, the Low Countries and parts of Germany. England and France had only a few stretches of improved river. On his arrival in France in 1516, Leonardo seems to have formed some idea of a canal to link a tributary of the Loire with one of the Saône; certainly the king who brought him, Francis I, became increasingly interested in such schemes after the failure of his Italian campaigns. In reality it was to take a century and a half to achieve even the more modest Briare canal, from the Loire via the Loing to the Saône. This was Europe's first summit level canal; begun in 1604, it took nearly forty years to finish. A much more ambitious "Canal des Deux Mers," to join the Atlantic to the Mediterranean via the Garonne and the Aude, was projected about the same time. But work was not really begun for many years, and then frequently interrupted until as the Canal du Midi it was completed in 1681.

These large-scale movements of water flow demanded a precise appreciation of the lie of the land. An error of even a few feet could easily mean the difference between success and failure, with disastrous flooding, or the laying out of great expense for a modest trickle of water. The art of surveying therefore became a necessary branch of engineering. It had a military side too, as was pointed out by writers who noted how often the soldier had to measure heights and distances at long range, when enemy gunfire prevented him from approaching an objective. Surveying was also required to measure and evaluate new lands. In the Protestant North, the dissolution of monasteries and secularization of church lands threw considerable areas on the market. In England the first two printed books

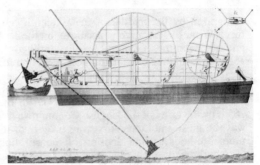

Dredging scow with treadmills for rotating the coordinated scoop arms; from Belidor.

on surveying coincided with the Reformation—the second was written by a former monastery steward who profited by his knowledge of its possessions. But elsewhere too, increasingly profit-minded landlords, eager to enjoy the comforts of bourgeois life, were less ready to accept their lands in the same condition in which they had inherited them. The monasteries which survived in the Catholic world were also affected by the need to rationalize and improve their possessions. Merchants in Italy and France no less than in Protestant countries bought estates, in part for greater security and in part for the prestige of landed wealth. In all these cases, new owners brought to their estates the attitudes of commerce; land was capital, to be improved and made more profitable like a stock of goods. For this the estate had to be exactly measured, bogs inspected for possible drainage and underused meadows prepared for irrigation. The surveyor became a common figure in the countryside—more than a little suspect in the eyes of peasants who feared the changes he would bring, such as enclosure of common land, felling of woods and increased rent from farms where the landowner had not been drawing enough grain.

The surveyor brought the regularity of mathematics to the land. His instruments were derived from those already used in ancient Rome, but he developed them further. The astronomer's quadrant was adapted for measuring heights and the astrolabe for measuring angles on the ground. Both functions were combined in the "polymetrum" of the German mathematician Martin Waldseemueller, invented about 1510. This device in turn gave birth to a host of ingenious and compendious angle-measuring instruments, of which the modern theodolite is the product. The employment of an inset compass in the early 1500s made it possible to find the meridian without complex observations of the sun, although the variation of "Compass North" from the true north of the diurnal revolution was recognized by the middle of the sixteenth century. With this relatively accurate method of finding azimuths, Gemma Frisius outlined in 1529 the technique of triangulation, used first for local maps, then for the mapping of provinces, and by the end of the period for whole countries. The Great Survey of Ireland carried out in the 1650s by the army of the English Commonwealth was the most ambitious surveying project of its time. Methods of fine division of mensuration also multiplied, including such devices as the vernier, named for Pierre Vernier, the military engineer who invented it in 1631. In the early 1660s M. Thévenot designed a bubble-level, which gradually superseded the water-level known to the ancients. At about this time Jean Picard first applied the telescope in survey in order to measure degree of meridian, the foundation of an estimate of the earth's magnitude. Picard later used telescopic sights to begin triangulations for an intended new map of France. Without these techniques, it would hardly have been possible to survey the vast regions occupied and settled by European explorers and colonists in the eighteenth and nineteenth centuries.

The Renaissance was not an era of radical inventions, to compare with the medieval applications of water-power to machinery or the Industrial Revolution of the eighteenth century. But new devices helped lay the foundation of future developments. The adaptation of the crank to the forge bellows and timber saw gave true mechanical control over reciprocating movement, which had previously been attained only by awkward expedients. No doubt the greater efficiency of the bellows promoted the diffusion of blast furnaces. But as yet the engineer worked far more commonly with wood and stone than with iron. The construction of bridges and harbors required wood for caissons, and

Shipyard in the Port of Lisbon with ships under construction, floating and fixed cranes; 16th century.

Printer operating a screw-press; V, a completed form of type; from Zonca, 1607.

canals and quays were often lined with wooden planks. Wood piles provided a foundation for many waterside structures, and all heavy-duty machinery still used wooden gears and shafts. The increased output of planks and boards made possible by the crank-driven saw was thus a prerequisite of Europe's economic expansion. And the sawmills must also have contributed to the enormous expansion of shipping, in both number and size of ships, during these centuries.

Perhaps the most sudden and important change in European life during the Renaissance resulted from introduction of the screw-press, a combination of lever and driving screw. This was the largest component of the printing press, which spread with amazing rapidity across Europe in the second half of the fifteenth century. Typographical printing began with Bibles and proclamations; by 1500 pocket book series of popular classics and cheap "how to do it" books were on sale in every market. Development of a roller-press to print engravings did for pictures what the printing press did for the written word. An ordinary middle-class family could easily acquire prints of great paintings in far-off palaces and cathedrals, so that at least in a simplified form it shared in this high culture. Woodprints and engravings ensured that medical students across Europe could view the same illustrations in their textbooks of human anatomy, just as a wider public could see the same representation in a herbal of some medicinal plant like the tomato or potato, lately discovered in the Americas. The roller-press was also combined with stamps and cutters to roll out and slit lead strips for windows. This was invaluable at a time when glass-makers could produce panes of only modest size and a large house might require hundreds of meters of lead strip to hold them in place. Machines operating on a similar principle were used to roll and impress images on gold ingots for coinage; and others rolled out the copper plates used for printing maps and pictures, or for engraving mathematical instruments. Harder iron could only be rolled and slit in units of small size, but nail-making mills were in use at Nuremberg by about 1520.

The beginnings of the Industrial Revolution in textile manufacure can be seen in the development of the silk-spinning machine of Lucca, which spread to many parts of northern Italy and from there to France. In 1589 the clergyman William Lee invented the knitting-loom, the basis of the machine-knitting industry. But Lee found little support in his native England and left to seek royal patronage for his device in France. The resistance of well-organized artisans made mechanization a slow and halting process until well into the eighteenth century.

Although in reality, then, the Renaissance produced only limited engineering innovation, it was an age of great expectation. The tradition of

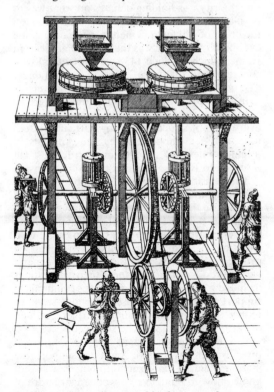

Double grinding mill powered by four men; from Besson's book of machines, 1582.

compiling manuscripts of real or imagined mechanisms was renewed in Western Europe with the strange war-engines of Guido da Vigevano [q.v.], followed by the more imaginative and comprehensive books of early fifteenth century figures like Konrad Kyeser [q.v.] and Domenico Fontana [q.v.]. In the middle years of the century, Taccola [q.v.] became the first inventor who tried to win fame and honor on the strength of his imagined future machines alone. He and Brunelleschi marked the start of a stream of such paper inventors, of whom the greatest in scope and vision (but not really in practical achievement) was Leonardo da Vinci. From the 1570s on these semi-secret manuscripts found their way into print; the first book of machines to be published was that of Jacques Besson [q.v.], granted copyright in 1569. A number of theaters (i.e. picture-books) of machines were published over the next century.

Like some of the treatises which described the actual technologies of the time—works of Agricola or Biringuccio or Lazarus Ercker [q.v.]—these books must have helped to propagate the idea that modern civilization had progressed over its predecessors, at least in the arts and crafts. Therefore civilization might attain far greater heights if a rational, experimental, mathematical approach were adopted. These hopes found their most articulate and outspoken mouthpiece in Francis Bacon, who dreamt of a new applied science to relieve human suffering and achieve increasing control over nature. By about 1660, such views were widely accepted and helped to inspire new scientific organizations like the Royal Society of London and the French Académie des Sciences. But no doubt even more of this confidence in the possibilities of technology came from the feats of Western explorers and conquistadores, which, ironically, would have been impossible without inventions that began in China—printing, gunpowder and the compass.

In the early fourteenth century, the peoples of Western Europe had been properly aware of only two other civilizations: Orthodox Christendom to the east, crumbling under the blows of Turks and Tatars; and Islam, which still enjoyed material superiority in goods, techniques and war. By the end of the seventeenth century, the guns and great galleons of Western European mariners had brought them to every continental coast and laid the foundations for a future world economy. Turks and Tatars had been checked or driven back, and European aggression had overthrown the new-found cultures of Mesoamerica. Certainly Ottoman Turkey, Safavid Persia,

Mogul India and Ming China still commanded much greater wealth and population than any of the Christian empires, even Spain. And of course, engineering activity continued at traditional levels in these territories, for everywhere the grandeur of monarchy was expressed in public works and public architecture. The mosques of Istanbul, the fortifications and water-works of Sultan Suleiman the Magnificent, the royal buildings of Isfahan, the Taj Mahal at Agra, should remind Europeans that ambitious and innovative architecture—ambitious structurally as well as aesthetically—was still going up in lands which nineteenth-century Westerners despised as decadent and unchanging. The invention of military devices like those of Fathullah Shirazi at the Mogul court shows that mechanical novelty as well was not confined to the West. Nevertheless, only in Western Europe had the pace of change increased past any precedent, to a point where it would soon transform not only science, technology and economic life, but all aspects of society. ■

Filippo Brunelleschi, the architect who achieved fame by solving the engineering problem of a 140-foot dome.

FILIPPO BRUNELLESCHI

b. 1377, Florence, Italy
d. April 16, 1446, Florence, Italy
Italian Civil Engineer and Architect

Life and Times:

Before the Renaissance, the prevalent architectural style in Europe was Gothic, with its spires and tapered arches that pointed to the heavens. Just as the Renaissance in philosophy meant a revival of interest in classical studies, so too the Renaissance in architecture meant a return to classical style, with Roman forms and decorations, the Greek use of blank spaces as elements of composition, and the inclusion of Doric, Ionic and Corinthian columns. The creator of the new style was Brunelleschi, who first achieved fame not for his architectural designs but for his technical achievement in constructing the enormous dome of the cathedral of Santa Maria del Fiore in Florence.

The cathedral was begun in 1294, the plan being cruciform with the crossing opened out into an octagon that was to be domed. Slowed by the ravages of the Black Death, the nave and aisles took about eighty years to build, and the walls of the octagon were not finished until 1400. Meanwhile Filippo had displayed more interest in art and mechanics than in books, so his father,

a notary on the cathedral committee, made him learn arithmetic, and placed him in the goldsmith's guild. Throughout the period when he was learning his craft as a goldsmith and sculptor, the city was holding debates on what was to be placed on the octagon. Its diameter was on the order of 140 feet (43 meters). The only dome ever built of this size was that of the Pantheon in Rome, which spanned 143 feet (44 meters) with concrete walls that were 23 feet (7 meters) thick. The octagon could never support such a weight.

In 1401, Brunelleschi went to Rome, where he spent three years studying architecture. He drew every kind of structure, paying particular attention to the methods used by the Ancients in joining stones and strengthening structures. He returned to Rome on several other occasions.

The decision was made to build up the walls of the octagon into a tambour, or drum, which would raise the base of the cupola above the roof of the rest of the cathedral. As the building progressed, the engineering problem of the construction of the dome could no longer be avoided. Architects and the public in general were asked for their opinions; their suggestions included a variety of arrangements of columns to support the cupola, the use of sponge-stone to reduce the weight, and building it over a mound of earth that would later be removed.

It was generally assumed that wooden armatures would have to be built to support the masonry during construction, but it was not known how to build even a wooden structure of such a size with the required rigidity. Brunelleschi alone maintained that a self-supporting dome could be built of double-thick masonry, without any armature. After four masons had constructed a twelve-foot-diameter (3.6 meters) model of his design, Brunelleschi was awarded the contract. Construction began in 1420 and continued to 1434, for the cupola; the lantern, designed by the architect, was not placed atop the dome until after his death.

To enable the work to progress, Brunelleschi invented the hoisting and positioning equipment that was set up inside the cupola. These mechanisms were the most complex known before the Industrial Revolution. Drawings of them later appeared in the notebooks of Taccola [q.v.], Francesco de Giorgio [q.v.] and Leonardo [q.v.], but they were never made again.

In 1421 Brunelleschi was granted the first patent on record. It was for a cargo ship to bring marble along the Arno from Pisa, and gave the inventor exclusive rights for three years to use the newly designed boat on the river. The venture was not a success, however.

As an architect, Brunelleschi designed churches, other public buildings such as the Foundling Hospital, and private mansions in Florence. His aim was to blend the forms of classical architecture into modern buildings, harmoniously and with beauty. He succeeded so well that European and American architects followed his lead for the next five hundred years, adding columns, pediments, and classical trimmings to their buildings.

Outstanding Engineering Achievement:

Rising to a height of 300 feet (91.4 meters) above the ground, spanning 138 feet (42 meters), and weighing some 25,000 tons the cupola of the Florence cathedral is constructed of two shells of masonry, four feet (1.2 meters) apart: the inner one is seven feet (2 meters) thick at the base and five feet (1.5 meters) thick at the top; the outer one, which provides weather protection and a more aesthetic shape, is thirty inches (76 cm) tapering to fifteen (38 cm). The weight of the cupola produces an outward stress on its own walls. The Gothic solution to this stress had been the inward push of buttresses, but Brunelleschi went back to the Roman solution by circling the internal space between the vaults with seven rings, or chains, of sandstone blocks connected by metal clamps and attached to the walls with metal rods. There is also a chain of massive timber beams. Unlike the stone chains, which are completely hidden, the joints of the wood chain are exposed and may have been intended as a testing device that would immediately reveal

The 25,000-ton dome of the Florence cathedral, built by Brunelleschi, with Roman rings of stone and Gothic buttressing ribs.

any unbalanced outward thrust. Since the cupola is mounted on an octagonal drum, it has eight sections joined by reinforcing ribs that project outside. There are two more hidden ribs in each section, the 24 ribs being connected by rungs to form a framework of stone. The combination of inner chains and buttressing ribs thus unites Roman and Gothic architectural practice.

One of Brunelleschi's positioning devices was essentially in the shape of a T, mounted on a base so that it could be rotated about the vertical. The load and pulleys were on one arm of the T, a counterweight on the other; both could be winched along the arm. One of the hoists was worked by men or a draft animal turning a winch that was geared to a horizontal axle. The rope from the load went up through a pulley at the top of the scaffold then down to the axle. The winch included a reversing clutch that enabled it to raise or lower the load, or to stop it, while the horse continued to circle in the same direction.

Other Achievements:

Brunelleschi was the first artist to have complete control of perspective, including central perspective in which receding horizontals are drawn as oblique lines that meet in a vanishing point. There are accounts of two panels he painted to demonstrate the true depiction of a three-dimensional scene on a flat surface; unfortunately neither has survived. One was of a certain palace, painted with the roof running along the top of the panel. If it was held up, at the spot where it had been painted, so that the top of the panel matched up with the actual palace roof, then the painting completed the scene that was hidden from view by the panel itself.

The second panel was of the Baptistry, painted from a doorway across the courtyard. Bored through the panel was a peephole. If the panel was held in the doorway with its back to the viewer, and the viewer looked through the peephole at a mirror held at arm's length, then the scene in the mirror and the actual scene across the courtyard would be identical. The reported success of these panels is taken as an indication of Brunelleschi's knowledge of geometry, which in its turn was to be the cornerstone of the Renaissance mastery of perspective drawing. ■

Further Reading:

H.J. Cowan, *The Master Builders*. New York, 1977.

G. Holmes, *The Florentine Enlightenment 1400-1450*. New York, 1969.

W.B. Parsons, *Engineers and Engineering in the Renaissance*. Baltimore, 1939.

F.D. Prager and G. Scaglia, *Brunelleschi: Studies of His Technology and Inventions*. Cambridge, 1970.

JACOPO MARIANO TACCOLA (or MARIANO DI JACOMO)
b. Feb. 4, 1381, Siena, Italy
d. Between 1453 and 1458, Siena, Italy
Italian Military Engineer

Life and Times:

Living at the threshold of the Renaissance, Taccola was the first of the famous engineers of the central Italian city of Siena. In his own time, Taccola was known as "the Sienese Archimedes," which suggests that he had a considerable reputation as a scientist and investigator. He is now known for his treatises and drawings on military technology and for the influence they exerted on later engineers. Francesco di Georgio [q.v.], a generation later, wrote a manuscript on hydraulics and mechanics that shows the influence of Taccola. Robert Valturio [q.v.] often quotes him, and even Leonardo da Vinci [q.v.] read Taccola's works and adapted several drawings from them.

Jacopo Mariano was the son of a grape grower, and received no formal education. He is said to have been given the nickname Taccola, which means "little crow," because of his ability at woodcarving, which he learned from his father. Taccola started his career as a sculptor but became interested in technology; his earliest sketches of mechanisms date from 1427. In those days of sovereign states ruled by despots, it was usual for a scholar, artist, or inventor to have a patron. Taccola found his in 1432, when Siena was visited by Sigismund, the Holy Roman Emperor. To Sigismund was dedicated Taccola's first manuscript, filled with drawings of machinery and unusual animals. It also contained an offer to join Sigismund's army to fight the Turks, but Taccola seems to have spent his entire life in Siena.

Outstanding Engineering Achievements:

Many innovations have been attributed to Taccola, although it is not clear whether he invented them or was the first to record them. They include the chain transmission system and the compound crankshaft by which rotary motion is converted to the reciprocal motion of a connecting rod. He wrote about the suction pump, the box-caisson method of building bridges, windmills, watermills and other hydraulic problems, and he drew an undersea diver wearing a helmet connected to an air pipe. In a treatise of about 1440, he showed mines being used to breach the high walls of fortresses. Mines already existed at that time, but there is no record of their being used in war until 1495, at Naples. Whether Taccola originated these ideas or not, he certainly played a significant role in their transmission and in the subsequent development of Italian engineering. ■

Further Reading

Maurice Daumas, *A History of Technology and Invention*, Vol. II. New York, 1964.

Bertrand Gille, *Engineers of the Renaissance*. Cambridge, 1966.

Dictionary of Scientific Biography, s.v. "Taccola."

JOHANNES GUTENBERG
b. 1394-1398, Mainz, Germany
d. Feb. 3, 1468, Mainz, Germany
German Printer and Inventor

Life and Times:

The development of printing was an idea very much "in the air" during the early fifteenth century. The intellectual ferment of the Renaissance created pressure for a more efficient means of disseminating information than the laborious hand-copying of manuscripts. The earliest typographic process appears to have been invented in the mid-11th century by Chinese alchemist Pi Sheng, who made a set of movable type from a baked mixture of clay and glue. The pieces of type were stuck onto a plate from which an impression could be taken by pressing paper onto the inked characters. The type could then be removed from the plate by heating. Nearly 300 years later, Wang Chen, a Chinese magistrate apparently commissioned a craftsman to carve many thousands of characters on individual wooden cubes in order to print copies of a treatise. However, these and other Oriental printing developments seem not to have reached Europe. During the late 1300s craftsmen in southern Germany and northern Italy began to print inexpensive playing cards and religious pictures using carved wooden blocks. Though not suitable for printing texts, this technique must have stimulated efforts to find a more versatile method with wider application.

It is thus not surprising that the European development of movable type occurred almost simultaneously in several parts of the Continent. The Dutchman Laurens Coster of Haarlem may have developed a crude version of the printing press around 1440. Others were at work on similar devices in Germany and southern France. The first printing shop to make large-scale use of movable type, however, was established in Mainz, Germany by Johannes Gutenberg (born Johannes Gensfleisch zur Laden).

Born into an aristocratic family, Gutenberg was apparently trained as a goldsmith. He was forced to leave Mainz in 1430, when the city's trade guilds succeeded in exiling a number of patricians. Settling in Strassburg (Strasbourg), he began experimenting with the various components of the printing press. To finance his work he went into partnership with two other craftsmen, to whom he promised to teach the secrets of his invention. This arrangement, indeed the very fact that Gutenberg was experimenting with printing equipment, is known to us only as the

result of a lawsuit brought by the heirs of one of the partners, who demanded admission into the partnership following the craftsman's death. Gutenberg won the suit and preserved the secrecy of his work, but found that financial support was no longer forthcoming in Strassburg. In 1444 he left the city and returned to Mainz, where the political situation had changed in his favor.

Gutenberg now entered into partnership with Johannes Fust, a goldsmith who may himself have experimented with movable type. Within several years Gutenberg's equipment was ready for use, and the first known products of his printing shop—part of a poem and an astronomical table—appeared around 1448. In 1455 Gutenberg printed 300 copies of his famous 42-line Bible, so called because each page contained 42 lines. Of the 47 surviving copies, a number are now held by various U.S. libraries, including the Library of Congress.

The printing shop established by Gutenberg and Fust grew rapidly, employing some 25 workers and producing over 50 known works. Shortly after printing the 42-line Bible, however, the two partners had a falling out. Gutenberg wanted to improve his equipment and work for higher quality, while Fust preferred to realize his investment quickly by putting the shop's full capacity to immediate use. Fust successfully sued Gutenberg for possession of the shop, taking on Peter Schoeffer as new co-owner. However Gutenberg managed to continue printing books for some ten years. Among his later efforts was a

Johannes Gutenberg, the first Western printer to make major use of movable type.

second edition of the Bible, printed at Bamberg with 36 lines to the page. Gutenberg gained such fame as a printer that upon retiring he was appointed to the court of the archbishop of Mainz and received an annual allowance until his death.

Though printing encountered initial resistance on aesthetic grounds, many writers and craftsmen fully appreciated its potential. By the time of Gutenberg's death, printing shops had been established in most major German and Italian cities, spreading within two decades to England and the rest of Europe. By 1500 some 30,000 works had been printed in editions totalling nine million copies. The effects of the new technique were incalculable. By vastly increasing the amount of information in circulation, printing laid the groundwork of the Scientific Revolution. It also increased the difficulties faced by religious and secular authorities in guarding against the spread of subversive ideas. The Reformation, for instance, would probably have been impossible without the flood of tracts and broadsides that issued from Protestant presses. Little wonder that Luther called printing "God's highest act of grace"—though later Protestant leaders, themselves besieged by heretics, may have rued his remark.

Outstanding Engineering Achievement:

The process developed by Gutenberg and his contemporaries, known as relief or letterpress printing, uses a raised surface to transfer ink under pressure onto paper. Though the details of Gutenberg's equipment were closely-guarded trade secrets, they can be divided into three components:

(1) The type: probably an alloy of tin and lead that melted at low temperature and solidified without distortion. Nothing is known of the molds within which the type was cast. Type was placed within a frame, inked, and the letters impressed on paper.

(2) The ink: charcoal or lampblack pigment mixed into linseed oil varnish. This differed from the water-based ink used by scribes, which did not adhere well to metal. Printer's ink was probably derived from a linseed oil varnish developed by Flemish painters in the early fifteenth century. It was applied thinly to the type with a leather pad.

(3) The press: probably based on the common linen press, consisting of a movable plate within a frame which could be screwed down onto a baseboard. Eventually, improvements were made to adapt the device to printing; a sliding

board was placed over the baseboard to facilitate the insertion and removal of paper, and the speed of the screw action was increased. Nevertheless, the presses of Gutenberg's time exerted relatively little force compared to later models. Since the paper used had a fairly hard surface, it had to be moistened to receive the impression of the type. This wetting and the subsequent drying added another step to printing; sheets also shrank while drying, resulting in pages of differing sizes within the same book. ∎

Further Reading:

D.S.L. Cardwell, *Turning Points in Western Technology*. New York, 1972.

Elizabeth L. Eisenstein, *The Printing Press as an Agent of Change*. New York, 1978.

Victor Scholderer, *The Invention of Printing*. London, 1940.

Singer et al., *History of Technology*. Vol. III.

LEON BATTISTA ALBERTI
b. 1404, Genoa, Italy
d. 1472, Rome, Italy
Italian Architect

Life and Times:

As the Renaissance flowered in fifteenth-century Italy, the universal man appeared: the scholar-merchant, artist-philosopher, gentleman-engineer. Great among these giants was Alberti, whose intellectual development may have been spurred by his having received an expensive education followed by a reversal of fortune which required him to earn his living. He was, essentially, a member of the new middle class.

Leon Battista was the second illegitimate son of a merchant-banker in exile from Florence as a result of the political disputes that were a feature of life in Italy. Leon was brought up by his father, sent to a fine boarding school in Padua, and in 1421 entered the University of Bologna. A few months later, the father died, followed soon after by the boy's guardian uncle. The rest of the family, claiming that illegitimate sons could not inherit, annexed the estate. Alberti managed to continue his studies, taking a master's degree in philosophy and a doctorate in canon law, and turning to geometry for recreation.

Self-portrait of Leon Battista Alberti, architect, surveyor, engineer, cryptographer, linguist, artist, musician, and athlete.

As secretary to a cardinal, he travelled about Europe. He then took holy orders to provide himself with a living, obtained a post in the papal chancery, and settled in Rome in 1432. Alberti's first practical work was in cartography, with the publication of a treatise on surveying and mapping cities. He also conducted experiments with the camera obscura, studying the formation of images with light rays. This laid the foundation for his writings on perspective, which formed the first part of his book *On Painting*, completed in 1435 (but not printed until 1540). Leonardo [q.v.] copied a number of its passages into his notebook. Asked to judge some artists' studies for an equestrian statue, he chose the horse from one, the rider from another, and completed the assignment with a treatise on the appearance and habits of horses.

In 1447, a friend from student days became Pope Nicholas V and appointed Alberti as his architectural adviser. Commissions followed. During the next twenty-five years, Alberti designed the Church of San Francesco for the Malatesta Temple in Rimini, the façade of S. Maria Novella and the Rucellai Palace in Florence, in the churches of San Sebastiano and Sant' Andrea in Mantua. Meanwhile he wrote

his most important book, *On Building,* completed about 1452, some three years before Gutenberg printed his Bible. *On Building* was published posthumously in 1485.

The astonishing range of Alberti's talents can be shown by a listing of some of his other publications: the first grammar of the Italian language, in which he demonstrated that the Tuscan vernacular was as valid as Latin for serious writing; a study of cryptography, including the first known frequency table of letters and the first known cipher wheel for coding and decoding messages; the book *On Sculpture* which, like *On Painting,* laid the technical foundations of Renaissance art while discussing cultural ideas that were to have a considerable influence for centuries; a new translation into Latin of Ptolemy's classical Greek work on astronomy, the *Almagest;* two lost treatises, one on ships and the other on lifting weights, which were the result of Alberti's attempt to raise a sunken Roman galley from Lake Nemi; a book *On the Family;* and a funeral oration on his dog.

To these can be added Alberti's artistic ability (he painted several pictures), his musical talent (he wrote, played and sang), and his athletic ability (he is reputed to have been able to leap over a standing man and ride the wildest horse). His greatest work, however, is generally agreed to have been in architecture.

Outstanding Engineering Achievement:

The book *De re aedificatoria* (which is translated either "On Edifices" or "On Building") concerns more than architecture: it is, in fact, the earliest printed treatise on town planning. It discusses the choice of site of a city, the overall plan, the placement of a square at the center, the disposition of dwellings and the location of crafts. On the importance of a good water supply and sewage system, he writes: "Among all the wonderful buildings in the city of Rome, the drains are accounted the noblest." Alberti recommends that city streets be straight and broad, and that highways between cities be open, without hiding places for rogues. The shortest way, he says, is that which is safest.

Before Alberti there was no distinction between master mason, architect and engineer. He stressed the need for beauty in buildings and distinguished between the artisan, who is the instrument of the architect, and the architect, whom he described as one who produces useful works of art through the movement of weights and massing of bodies. This introduced the

Illustration from Alberti's On Building, *showing many kinds of waterworks, including dams, aqueducts, and fountains.*

concept of the artist-architect and gradually led to the present-day dichotomy between designer-architect and architectural engineer.

On Building includes sections on timber and stone bridges, water channels and pumps, and the first description of the pound lock, the canal lock in which there are two gates that trap water between them. The first such lock in Italy was built by Bertola da Novate [q.v.] a few years later. The definitive source for the theory and practice of classical architecture, *On Building* retained its significance into the nineteenth century. ■

Further Reading:

J. Gadol, *Leon Battista Alberti: Universal Man of the Early Renaissance.* Chicago, 1969.

Bertrand Gille, *Engineers of the Renaissance.* Cambridge, 1966.

Neal FitzSimons, ed., *Engineering Classics of James Kip Finch.* Kensington, Maryland, 1978.

W.B. Parsons, *Engineers and Engineering in the Renaissance.* Baltimore, 1939.

ROBERTO VALTURIO
b. Feb. 1405, or 1413, Rimini, Italy
d. Aug. 1475, Rimini, Italy
Italian Technologist

Life and Times:

Rimini in the mid-fifteenth century was ruled by Sigismondo Pandolfo Malatesta, the most famous member of the dynasty that had dominated the area since 1239. A patron of the arts, Malatesta surrounded himself with architects and scientists, but, like other Italian lords of the Renaissance, he was involved in military affairs, both as a defensive measure and in battle. In addition to being a general, he was a military engineer who probably supervised the building of his own fortifications.

One of his court was Roberto Valturio, the well-educated descendent of an ancient Rimini family which held some hereditary administrative posts at the Vatican. Roberto had occupied these positions before returning to Rimini, where he was commissioned by Malatesta to write a treatise on military engineering. There is no evidence that he had any technical knowledge or experience, and he may simply have been the secretary who penned what was really Malatesta's book. On the other hand, since the book was a survey, not advancing new ideas, it could have been written by Valturio from manuscript books in the court library. Valturio was in any event highly esteemed in Rimini. Nine years

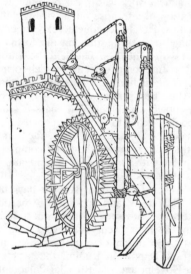

Scaling platform raised by a rack and geared wheel, for attacking towers; Valturio.

after his death, his burial place was moved to the Malatesta Temple, a church which Leon Battista Alberti [q.v.] had been commissioned to renovate.

Outstanding Engineering Achievement:

Valturio's book *On Military Matters* was completed by about 1460, and a number of manuscript copies were widely circulated. In 1472 it was printed, only the second book to be printed in Verona. It was also the first European printed book to contain technical illustrations. These were eighty-two woodcuts showing military and naval engineering equipment, including revolving gun turrets, bridges, paddlewheels, a submarine propelled by paddlewheels (certainly never built), and a diver's suit probably taken from Taccola [q.v.]. The text described military techniques from Roman times to the Renaissance. Reprinted a number of times, the book became the military handbook of the Italian Renaissance; Leonardo da Vinci [q.v.] owned a copy and adapted some of its ideas. ■

Further Reading:

Maurice Daumas, *A History of Technology and Invention*. New York, 1964.
Dictionary of Scientific Biography, s.v. "Valturio."
Carter and Muir, eds., *Printing and the Mind of Man*. New York, 1967.

FRANCESCO DI GEORGIO MARTINI
b. 1439, Siena, Italy
d. Nov. 1501, Siena, Italy
Italian Military Engineer and Architect

Life and Times:

The advent of gunpowder in Western Europe altered not only the form of attack used by an army, but also the appearance of fortresses and even of entire cities. Fortifications before the fifteenth century included high, thin walls that protected against arrows and the stones thrown by catapults, and were difficult to scale by ladder or with the siege engines equipped with wooden elevators that raised many men at a time. Running along the top of these walls were crenellations (battlements), and jutting out were machicolations—structures from which stones or boiling oil could be ejected onto the enemy.

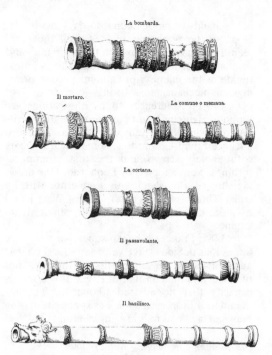

Various sizes of cannon from the treatise of Francesco di Giorgio.

Cannons could easily penetrate the thin walls; crenellations and machicolations were knocked down onto the heads of the defenders within. Furthermore, at the foot of each round tower or turret was a triangle of ground that could not be seen from any part of the fort. With gunpowder, miners could use these spaces for digging tunnels to lay their mines under the walls. Francesco di Georgio is the first engineer on record as using gunpowder and mines successfully in battle; he also changed the design of fortifications so that they could provide a good defense against the new methods of warfare.

Born of a humble family, Francesco was first trained in painting and sculpture, and then studied under Lorenzo di Pietro, a celebrated architect and engineer who had constructed fortifications in two cities. Francesco started his career as a sculptor, but by the age of thirty he was in charge of the water supply, aqueducts and fountains of Siena.

In 1477 he joined the service of Federico di Montefeltro, duke of Urbino, constructing fortresses and probably completing the ducal palace. At the duke's request, Francesco wrote a treatise on architecture, city planning, fortifications, hydraulics and mechanics. Manuscript copies were widely circulated and highly regarded; one copy exists that contains notations in the handwriting of Leonardo da Vinci [q.v.]. None of the book was printed until the nineteenth century, and even then the hydraulics and mechanics sections were omitted. This is unfortunate as the manuscript contains precise drawings of mechanisms, showing good control of perspective. References to its illustrations are found in eighteenth and nineteenth century writings on technology. Many of its devices are more advanced than Leonardo's; some, such as gears with endless screws and the first attempt at turbines, were adopted by Leonardo. One drawing showed a flywheel with a governor with fly balls. Three centuries later, James Watt [q.v.] used this device as part of his atmospheric steam engine.

In 1485, Francesco began supervising military operations in Siena. Five years later he served as an architectural consultant, first on the cathedral of Milan and then on that of Pavia. It was in this capacity that he advised Leonardo. The remainder of Francesco's life was spent alternating between civil and military engineering.

Outstanding Engineering Achievement:

In 1495, Francesco was employed by Ferdinand, king of Naples, to destroy the fortress of Castel Nuovo, which was occupied by the army of the French King Charles VIII. The use of mines in this successful operation is the earliest on record. Francesco had already written on the military use of gunpowder, and had designed and constructed fortresses that could best defend against cannon. Completely dispensing with the crenellations and machicolations, he made the walls lower so as not to offer an easy target, and much thicker, to withstand cannon balls. To eliminate the unsighted area near the towers, he built his towers on a star-shaped base. Every part of each wall could now be seen by someone in the fortress, and there were no invisible areas around the outside. Walls built at angles had the additional advantage of being more likely than flat walls to bounce the cannon shot away. One such tower, built in 1492, still stands in Mondavio. Francesco's influence is seen throughout the fortification design of the sixteenth century. ∎

Further Reading:

James Burke, *Connections.* Boston, 1978.

Maurice Daumas, *A History of Technology and Invention.* New York, 1964.

J. R. Hale, *Renaissance Fortification.* New York, 1977.

LEONARDO DA VINCI
b. April 15, 1452, Vinci, Italy
d. May 2, 1519, Amboise, France
Italian Inventor, Engineer, Painter, Anatomist, et al.

Life and Times:

Leonardo da Vinci has come to be regarded as the epitome of the Renaissance man, one who knew almost everything there was to be known in his time. He did, indeed, bring his genius to bear on an enormously wide range of subjects, but very little of his work had any relationship to that of his contemporaries whose writings he could read only with the greatest difficulty. Science in Renaissance Italy often meant studying the scientific works of Aristotle and other Greek texts, comparing them with the Bible, and trying thereby to draw conclusions about the universe. Leonardo, on the other hand, looked not in books but at the world around him. His desire to improve the lot of the craftsman and worker owed nothing to the revival of interest in ancient thought. And at a time when academicians hated to wear spectacles because they distorted light and therefore were not to be trusted, da Vinci wrote, "Make glasses in order to see the moon large."

Leonardo da Vinci, the acknowledged genius of the Renaissance, was employed as a military and hydraulic engineer; self-portrait.

Leonardo was a painter of frescoes that slid off the wall, a sculptor whose statues were never cast, an architect whose designs were not accepted, an engineer most of whose projects were rejected, an inventor of hundreds of devices, most of which were never made, a testator whose will was ignored. Yet in his lifetime, he was admired and respected, employed by dukes and kings. Even more enigmatic is the extent of his impact on Western civilization. Was there none, as some historians say, or was his influence felt for a full century after his death, as others insist? In particular, for our present purposes, what was his impact on the history of engineering?

Leonardo received only an elementary education—the three Rs, but no Latin, which was the universal language of scholarly writing and discussion. In his forties, he tried to make up this deficiency by studying Latin, but he never achieved proficiency in it. Even his Italian was that of a Florentine shopkeeper, easily distinguished from literary Italian, and his spelling was even more aberrant than usual for the time. What he showed as a child was considerable artistic talent, and so, at the age of fourteen, he was apprenticed to the distinguished artist Verrocchio, whose studio in Florence was frequented by leading painters, sculptors, architects and mathematicians. Leonardo spent thirteen years with Verrocchio, as apprentice, helper and co-worker.

In 1482, Leonardo left unfinished his first major commissioned painting and went to Milan, taking with him a silver lute he had designed and made to present to Ludovico Sforza, Milan's despotic ruler. Seeking a court position, Leonardo wrote a letter claiming that he could: construct movable bridges; remove water from the moats of fortresses under siege; destroy any fortification not built of stone; make mortars, dart-throwers, flame-throwers and cannon capable of firing stones and making smoke; design ships and weapons for war at sea; dig tunnels without making any noise; make armored wagons to break up the enemy in advance of the infantry; design buildings; sculpt in any medium; and paint. He got the job. Until Ludovico was overthrown in 1499, Leonardo held the title of Painter and Engineer to the Duke.

His engineering work mainly concerned the canal system around Milan, and he is credited with having been the first to use lock gates which swing open instead of sliding vertically. His gates for the Martesana canal have recently been described as exactly like modern lock gates. In architecture, he worked with Bramante on the dome of a Milan cathedral, and with Francesco di Georgio [q.v.] in Pavia. During the plague of 1484, he designed an ideal new town consisting of a spacious inner city, with plenty of plumbing, surrounded by separated suburbs. Sforza's interest in the plan diminished, however, as the plague abated.

Leonardo's chief court function was to be a producer of the spectacular displays, elaborately staged entertainments and costumed processions that were favorite diversions of the Italian aristocracy. For these, Leonardo designed costumes and floats, wrote music, and constantly delighted the court with ingenious devices—flying cupids on pulleys, a huge hemisphere containing lighted planets and stars which revolved on hidden gears, a cow's gut blown up by unseen bellows until it pressed courtiers against the wall. Meanwhile, he worked on the research and invention which eventually filled 5,000 leaves of notebooks, much of it done during the Milan period. The notebooks are crammed with drawings, in no particular order, with an accompanying text in mirror-writing, probably done for ease and speed because Leonardo was left-handed. (The mirror-writing has also been attributed to a desire for secrecy. His letters to others and the place-names on his maps are written in the usual left-to-right manner.)

When Sforza was overthrown by the French, Leonardo found employment as a military engineer to Cesare Borgia, for whom he made an inspection tour of cities and fortifications in Romagna, planned harbor improvements and advised on swamp reclamation. His scientific investigations moved into the fields of geology and botany in addition to hydraulics and mechanics, and he studied anatomy by performing dissections and making superb drawings on the spot. A collection of these drawings would have been the best anatomy textbook for centuries, if they had been published.

When Borgia in his turn was overthrown, Leonardo returned to Milan, then occupied by the French King Louis XII. Appointed Royal Architect and Engineer, he was able to continue his own research in anatomy and flight. In 1512 the Sforza family took back Milan, and Leonardo moved to Rome, planning architectural and engineering projects in the Vatican for Cardinal Giuliano de' Medici, brother of the pope. His last move was in 1515, when Francis I of France gave him a house on the banks of the Loire, near the French court at Amboise. Francis believed that Leonardo knew more than any man ever born, and delighted in showing him

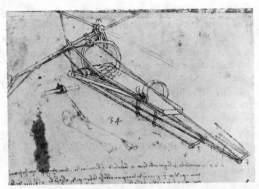

One of Leonardo's flying machines; the pilot lies face down and flaps the wings through the foot controls.

off. He encouraged Leonardo's project of connecting the Loire and the Saône for navigation and irrigation, and promised to publish an atlas of anatomy containing Leonardo's diagrams. He never did.

Leonardo's will left all his books, instruments, and portraits to his friend and pupil Francesco Melzi, adding: "In order that this advantage which I am giving to men shall not be lost, I am setting out a way of proper printing and I beg you, my successors, not to allow avarice to induce you to leave the printing un . . . ."

Melzi treasured Leonardo's legacy so much that he kept everything locked away for fifty years, and then left them to his son, a professor, who tossed them into an attic. A few were given away, and they soon became a highly prized collectible. From 1600 on, the entire collection was dispersed throughout Europe into the hands of private individuals, some of whom locked the books away, as Charles I of England did (for 120 years). Some notebooks were taken apart—carefully—and the leaves rebound in a different order. Miscatalogued in the Royal Library at Madrid, two volumes lay hidden for two centuries until accidentally found in 1967. By the time the notebooks were printed the inventions described in them had been rediscovered or superseded, and their impact was thus minimized.

Yet there was some impact. Although few of Leonardo's inventions were put to use, one of them—the gig mill—was a harbinger of the Industrial Revolution, a producer of technological unemployment. Designed to mechanize a previously manual cloth-finishing process, the mill was immediately successful when introduced in Italy during the early sixteenth century. In 1551 it was prohibited in England by Act of Parliament because it would cause hardship to the workers it replaced. A century later, however, it was being used there, and was indeed depriving piece workers of a source of income. Its widespread use at the beginning of the Industrial Revolution caused riots around the country, foreshadowing the desperate actions that were to come as mass production took over more functions.

Engineers who knew Leonardo were demonstrably influenced by his work. Their pupils and his own continued the tradition for a century. Copies of some of his drawings appeared in their published work. Girolamo Cardano [q.v.], regarded as a forerunner of Galileo [q.v.], included Leonardo's statics and hydraulics in his own writings. Agostino Ramelli [q.v.] included in his book some mechanisms which suggest that he had seen some of Leonardo's sketches; copies of Ramelli's machine drawings are reported to have been studied by James Watt [q.v.]. But the trail is faint, the genius scattered, and the history of engineering only lightly touched.

Outstanding Engineering Achievements:

One of Leonardo's inventions for the textile industry was the gig mill, a machine that replaced hand-workers in a finishing process called teaseling. After some fabrics are woven and dyed, they are brushed to bring up a nap on one side. The brush used was originally made of teasels—the prickly seed-cases of a plant. Though easily learned, the process was costly because it was slow and labor-intensive. In Leonardo's gig mill, a length of cloth to be napped was stretched over two horizontal rollers and the ends sewn together, looking like a modern factory conveyor belt. When one roller was turned by a horse circling a winch, the cloth moved in an endless band. Across the cloth, an adjustable beam held a row of teasels which raised the nap as the cloth passed under it. Leonardo's drawing shows very long rollers fitted with five belts of cloth, each with its own row of teasels.

Leonardo's main contribution to canal engineering was his invention of the miter-gate, or outward-swinging double gate, to replace the portcullis gate, which operated vertically, in canal locks. He used these gates in constructing locks for the Naviglio Interno and the Martesana canal, both connecting Milan with territories to the east. He also planned a canal between Florence and the River Arno, but the construction techniques of his time were inadequate to provide a satisfactory water supply at the canal's highest point. The same problem prevented construction of a canal linking the Mediterranean and Atlantic coasts of France, which Leonardo discussed with Francis I. It was not until the mid-seventeenth century that this plan was realized by Pierre-Paul Riquet [q.v.].

Leonardo's notebooks contain more inventions than Edison patented, covering every aspect of engineering. He continually concerned himself with power sources—water, weights, horse, or the more efficient use of human power. His machine tools included a lathe worked by a treadle and fitted with a flywheel for continuous action, and an automatic file cutter powered by a falling weight. His inventions ranged from large cranes to small gears; a pile-driver to a pair of pliers; a type of screw to a screw-cutting machine; lens grinders to a projector using lens and candle; from a flying machine to a diving suit. There were weapons—muzzle-loaders, steam-powered cannon, machine guns—and ammunition; all kinds of bridges and a revolving windmill; water pumps and dredgers; a treadle-operated paddle-boat and a spring-driven car with differential; furnaces and an air-conditioner; a camera obscura and a hurdy-gurdy.

His drawings of large machines were accompanied by detailed drawings of sub-assemblies within them, and sometimes with pictures of people using them. They were drawn to be constructed, and Leonardo conducted studies and tests of their feasibility. For instance, he tested the bearing strength of different fabrics to determine which would be best for his parachutes.

Some of Leonardo's ideas could not be realized with the available materials, while some were jotted down but never seriously suggested to anyone. Some, however, were thoroughly worked out, even down to their cost and probable return on investment, yet they were ignored. The eighteenth century would have welcomed them.

Other Achievements:

Until his notebooks began to be published, Leonardo was known as a painter, but even in art he was an experimenter. The non-traditional technique he used for *The Last Supper* in 1495-8 led to its disintegration, which began in 1517, and to its subsequent overpainting by many hands. In 1503, another fresco, the *Battle of Anghiari,* executed with yet another new technique, would not dry and the paint dripped down the wall.

The *Mona Lisa* was a portrait commissioned in 1503 by the sitter's husband, but Leonardo, under the pretext of its not being finished, kept it with him until he died. A painting that obviously was unfinished was *The Adoration of the Magi,* of which only the brown and gold groundwork had been applied when Leonardo left Florence for Milan. Yet of the small number of paintings that Leonardo did complete, he painted one, *The Madonna of the Rocks,* in two similar versions.

In his letter of application to Ludovico Sforza, Leonardo put painting at the bottom of his list of accomplishments. History has given him a name as one of the greatest painters of all time. His own treatment of his pictures seems to emphasize that he thought of himself primarily as an engineer. ■

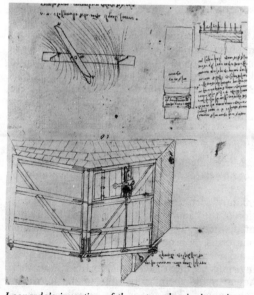

Leonardo's invention of the outward-swinging miter gate, a major contribution to canal engineering; from his notebook.

Further Reading:

R. Calder, *Leonardo and the Age of the Eye.* New York, 1970.

Bertrand Gille, *Engineers of the Renaissance,* Cambridge, 1966.

E. MacCurdy, ed., *The Notebooks of Leonardo da Vinci.* New York, 1956.

W. B. Parsons, *Engineers and Engineering in the Renaissance.* Baltimore, 1939.

M. Philipson, ed., *Leonardo da Vinci, Aspects of the Renaissance Genius.* New York, 1966.

Ladislao Reti, ed., *The Unknown Leonardo.* New York, 1974.

Vasari, *Lives of the Artists,* many editions.

BERTOLA DA NOVATE (or NAVATA)
fl. 1460
Italian Hydraulic Engineer

Life and Times:

Little is known of Bertola da Novate aside from his engineering work for Francesco Sforza, the military leader who seized power in Milan in 1450. A renowned general, Sforza also became a patron of the arts, concerned with beautifying and improving Milan. His plan for economic improvement called for building navigable waterways connecting the city to Lake Como and the Po River. For these projects, he employed Bertola da Novate and his brother Domenico.

Outstanding Engineering Achievements:

Bertola built two particularly notable canals, both constructed between 1457 and 1460. One, the Martesana canal, connected Milan to the Adda River, 24 miles (38.6 km) to the east. This river flows north-south from Lake Como to the Po. To reach it, the canal required two locks and also had to cross two smaller rivers, the Lambro and the Molgara. Since the Lambro was little more than a stream, it could be channelled through a culvert under the canal. To carry the canal over the Molgara, Bertola built an aqueduct in the form of a masonry arch.

The other canal, the Bereguardo, went north-south from Abbiate to Bereguardo, with an 80-foot (24 meters) drop in level, the largest that had been attempted to that time. Eighteen locks were needed to move boats along the route.

Until 1396, the only lock known in Europe was the flash lock, a gap in a weir closed by a single gate, through which boats could be winched slowly and with risk. Then the pound lock, which had been described by Leon Battista Alberti [q.v.], made its appearance in Belgium, four hundred years after its invention in China. This was essentially the modern lock in which two gates control the level of the water trapped between them, providing an elevator service for navigation. The gates at first were opened by sliding vertically, and these were the kind Bertola used. His locks were reputedly the first pound locks in Italy. The change to hinged and mitered gates was made subsequently by Leonardo da Vinci [q.v.]. ∎

Further Reading:

De Bono, ed., *Eureka! An Illustrated History* of Inventions from the Wheel to the Computer. New York, 1974.

W.B. Parsons, *Engineers and Engineering in the Renaissance.* Baltimore, 1939.

Singer et al., *A History of Technology,* Vol. III.

MICHELANGELO BUONARROTI
b. March 6, 1475, Caprese, Italy
d. February 18, 1564, Rome, Italy
Italian Sculptor, Painter, Architect, and Military Engineer

Life and Times:

Michelangelo was a towering figure whose genius left its mark on all the arts that he practiced. If his achievements in engineering do not match the standard he established in other fields, they nevertheless deserve mention.

One of five sons of a banker, Michelangelo studied sculpture in Florence, and then moved to Rome in 1496. He carved masterpieces in both cities until 1534, when he finally settled at Rome. In 1505, he obtained his first architectural commission, for the tomb of Pope Julius II. Three years later, his painting career began with his work on the ceiling of the Sistine Chapel. During the following decades he continued working in architecture, sculpture, and painting, and also composed poetry. By 1546 the aged Michelangelo had turned almost exclusively to architecture. That year Pope Paul III charged him with rebuilding the Capitol. He was also to direct the work already in progress on St. Peter's Basilica, and start the dome. This he did not live to complete, although he continued to work until a few days before his death.

Major Engineering Achievements:

Michelangelo's foremost contribution to engineering dates from 1529, with fortifications for the city of Florence. At the time the art of military fortification was in flux. The introduction of the cannon less than a century before had made medieval walls, with battlements and high platforms, obsolete. The towers were too cramped to hold artillery; parts of them were invisible to the rest of the fortress; and their height made them vulnerable to the impact of cannonballs. The tower was already being replaced by the thick, squat, pointed bastion when Michelangelo accepted his commission. But his

Michaelagelo Buonarroti, best known as a sculptor and painter, was also an architect and a military engineer.

designs were innovative, for he envisioned the offensive as well as the defensive role of fortifications, and built bastions that thrust out boldly from the wall behind, opening up a clear line of fire for the occupants. Their surfaces, made of packed earth to deflect or absorb enemy fire, were later replaced by masonry in which form they impressed the French engineer Vauban [q.v.].

Michelangelo's plan for the Capitol in Rome was a landmark in urban design. Three palaces stand on three sides of an oval piazza, surrounding the equestrian statue of Marcus Aurelius. On the fourth side, opposite the largest palace, that of the Senate, a majestic staircase leads to the city below. With great success, Michelangelo here initiated the method of working with units of architecture.

Further reading:

James S. Ackerman, *The Architecture of Michelangelo.* 1961.

Roberto di Stefano, *La Cupola di San Pietro.* Napoli, 1963.

Charles de Tolnay, *Michelangelo: Sculptor, Painter, Architect.* 1975.

VANNOCCIO VINCENZIO AUSTINO LUCA BIRINGUCCIO
b. Oct. 1480, Siena, Italy
d. April 1539, Rome, Italy
Italian Metallurgical and Military Engineer

Life and Times:

After the Roman author Pliny, we know of nothing written about metallurgy in Europe until about 1100. Then, a monk named Theophilus [q.v.] happened to be interested in metalworking and so combined the two separate traditions of literacy and craftsmanship into a treatise on the casting and working of metals. Following this there were still only occasional chapters in works on crafts that gave any account of metal techniques. Early in the sixteenth century, books on metallurgy started to appear, the first ones being confined to one aspect (for example, assaying). Georgius Agricola [q.v.] wrote one of these on mining in 1530. Biringuccio's *Pirotechnia* (1540) was the earliest printed work that dealt with the entire field of metallurgy. Even after Agricola's well-known second book on mining, *De Re Metallica,* was published in 1556, *Pirotechnia* remained a standard textbook for nearly two centuries.

Vannoccio's father was an architect and Superintendent of Streets for Pandolfo Petrucci, the dictator of Siena. As a young man Vannoccio traveled in Germany and northern Italy, visiting mines and metalworks. On his return he was appointed director of Pandolfo's iron mines. In 1513, Borghese Petrucci, who had succeeded his father as dictator, gave Biringuccio a post in the armory. Two years later a popular uprising forced the Petrucci party to flee the city. Biringuccio was accused of debasing the coinage and declared a traitor. He spent the next years traveling in southern Italy; but in 1523, Siena, at the insistence of the Pope, reinstated Fabio Petrucci, Borghese's younger brother, and Biringuccio was recalled, his property and armory post restored. It did not last. Three years later the Petruccis were again expelled, and Biringuccio's property again confiscated. Biringuccio now became a military engineer in the attempt to take back Siena, but though Florentine and Papal troops assisted, the effort was unsuccessful.

For the next few years Biringuccio again travelled to Germany, and performed various tasks for Italian nobles, including the casting of the nine-ton breech of a double cannon in Florence. In 1530 a general peace in Siena

To draw heavy wire, Biringuccio shows the worker clamping the wire with tongs pulled by the crankshaft of the undershot wheel. When the rope slackens, he swings forward moving the tongs along the wire.

brought him back to his native city for the third time, but now in the employ of the Republic, as a senator and as architect of the Opera. He also built fortresses and cast arms for the Venetian Republic and private aristocrats. His final position, taken in 1538, was as head of the Papal foundry and director of Papal munitions in Rome.

Outstanding Engineering Achievement:

Pirotechnia was published in Italian the year after its author's death. It is described on the title page as "Ten books in which are fully treated not only every kind and sort of mineral but also all that is necessary for the practice of those things belonging to the art of smelting or casting metals and all related subjects." Filled with practical information, the book covers prospecting and mining metals and other minerals (such as sulphur, salt and gemstones), assaying and smelting, casting statues, guns and bells, fine metalwork, fireworks and gunfire, the first account of the casting of printing type, and finally a short chapter on the fire of love. Long-winded and repetitive, the book reads like a first draft, which it might be considering its posthumous publication. But Biringuccio knew his subject well and was very careful to make it clear when

The use of paper cartridges (foreground) and gunner's sights and level (background); Biringuccio.

he was quoting earlier writers or hearsay rather than his own experience. Nor did he hesitate to ridicule alchemy or any other absurd views. In the sixteenth and seventeenth centuries, the book had five Italian editions, three French and two English. There have also been five in recent times, for their historical interest. ■

Further Reading:

V. Biringuccio, *The Pirotechnia*. New York, 1959 and 1966.
C.S. Smith and M.T. Gnud; Introduction to the above editions.

PETER HENLEIN (or HELE)
b. c. 1480, Nuremberg, Germany
d. 1542, Nuremberg, Germany
German Watchmaker and Locksmith

Life and Times:

Before clocks could be made portable, a power source had to be found to replace that of a falling weight. In the first quarter of the fifteenth century, spring-driven clocks began to appear. By the end of the century, they had been made small enough to accompany kings to and from summer residences, bankers and merchants on business trips, and scholars from one university town to another. Usually cylindrical, these carriage clocks were three or four inches (7.6 or 10 cm) in diameter, about three inches (7.6 cm) high, set in brass cases, sometimes with a hinged lid, and supplied with a leather carrying case. Some of them chimed.

By about 1510, the timepiece had been so miniaturized that it could be carried in a pocket or, for someone who wished to show off a rare watch in spite of its weight, worn on a chain round the neck. Peter Henlein has been credited with producing the first watches, although none of them have survived. He was a locksmith who was accepted as master in 1509; in his obituary he was described as a clockmaker. It was the practice of the city council of Nuremberg to send expensive gifts to significant people outside the city. In the 1520s seven such gifts were "self-acting horologia," which is understood to mean that they were spring-driven timepieces. Statements of payment to Peter Henlein still exist for three of these, and they were probably all his watches. After 1525 watches were no longer included in municipal gift-giving; they were no longer such rarities in Nuremberg, and were also being made in France.

The name "Nuremberg eggs" is now used for the early watches of that city, from Henlein's on, but they were cylindrical, like the carriage clocks, and not round or egg-shaped. The confusion dates from 1730 when a Nuremberg historian referred to a mention of the Nuremberg *eyerlein* (little egg) by Rabelais. In fact, the 1590 and later German editions of Rabelais' *Gargantua and Pantagruel* mention the Nuremberg *uerlein*, which means "little clock." What has helped popularize the misnomer is the fact that some oval watches were made in Nuremburg, but not until close to 1600, and certainly not by Peter Henlein.

Outstanding Engineering Achievement:

Henlein's achievement lay in making a complex mechanism in which all the parts were smaller than ever before. His power source was that of the first spring-driven clocks; a ribbon of tempered steel that was rolled by alternate heating and cooling around a drum. When the drum was turned, the spring tightened, storing the imparted energy to be released as the spring uncoiled. As the spring wound down, its tension weakened, diminishing the force transmitted to the gear train. The earliest device used to counteract this—the one Henlein may have used—was the stackfreed. This was a spiral cam attached to a toothed wheel that was geared to one end of the mainspring's drum. A semicircular spring pressed against the cam, braking it. As the cam turned, it presented a smaller diameter to the spring, lessening the braking action and compensating for the weakening of the mainspring.

Regulation of the watch was by a tiny version of the foliot and crown-wheel escapement used in the earliest clocks such as that of de' Dondi [q.v.]. Like them, the Henlein watch had only one hand, the hour hand. Since the screw was not recognized as a means of attachment until about 1550, its iron or steel parts were held together by pins and wedges. Henlein's watches were reported to have indicated and struck forty hours on one winding; how accurate they were is not recorded. ∎

Further Reading:

G. H. Baillie, *Watches; Their History, Decoration and Mechanism*. London, 1929.

GEORGIUS AGRICOLA (GEORG BAUER)
b. March 24, 1494, Glauchau, Saxony
d. Nov. 21, 1555, Chemnitz (now Karl-Marx-Stadt), Saxony
German Physician and Mining Expert

Life and Times:

Though the sixteenth century was not a time of major technological advance, economic growth and the development of printing encouraged the spread of improved methods in many areas of production. Techniques which had formerly been local customs could now be gathered, set down in manuals and made available to a mass audience. The role of compiler and descriptive analyst thus became an important one in this period. This was especially true in mining and metallurgy, where mechanization and increased investment of capital had already brought about many improvements. The most important compiler of manuals in these fields, who made great contributions to the systematization of technical knowledge, was the physician Georgius Agricola.

Son of a dyer, Agricola grew up in the Erzgebirge region of east-central Germany. At 20 he entered the University of Leipzig, where he studied the usual classical curriculum and gained a reputation as a learned humanist. It was presumably at this point that he latinized his family name Bauer (meaning "farmer" in German). After graduation he taught Latin and Greek and became rector of a newly-founded academy at Zwickau. In 1523 he travelled to Italy to study medicine. During a stay in Venice he served on the editorial staff preparing the famous Aldine Press edition of the Greek physician Galen's writings. He also met and became friendly with the humanist philosopher Erasmus, who predicted that he would some day "stand at the head of the princes of scholarship."

After returning to Central Europe Agricola became a physician in the Bohemian town of Joachimsthal (modern Jachymov), center of an important mining and smelting area. In 1535 he moved to Chemnitz, where he prospered despite his precarious position as a Catholic in a Protestant town. He made profitable investments in local mines and served several terms as mayor of the city. Nevertheless, religious differences asserted themselves, and by the time of his death Agricola was shunned by many of his fellow citizens.

Agricola became interested in mining and

Agricola's fan for ventilating mines moves air along the vent-pipe, E, and out through the blow-hole, C.

Bellows, tongs, and hammer in a finery forge in De Re Metallica; *E, stream of water for quenching.*

One worker fills a basket with iron ore to be smelted in the blast furnace; lower right, the charcoal; Agricola.

metallurgy while serving as physician in Joachimsthal. His practice made him familiar with ailments peculiar to miners, which he realized were occupational diseases. He paid frequent visits to the mines, at first in the hope of finding minerals for use in medications, later from interest in the mining process itself. Encouraged by Erasmus, he began writing a series of treatises on subjects connected with the mining of metal ores. In 1546 he published a book of four essays dealing with physical geography, sub-surface waters and gases, classification of minerals and the history of mining and metallurgy. The most famous of these was the third, *De natura fossilium* (On the Nature of Minerals), the first systematic treatment of mineralogy.

At the same time Agricola was occupied with his *magnum opus,* the *De re metallica* (On Metals). Twenty years in preparation, it was published one year after his death. Agricola wrote this comprehensive description of mining and metallurgy in Latin to ensure its international distribution. In 1557 the first German edition appeared, illustrated with 273 detailed woodcuts by Hans Manuel. Agricola had read Vannoccio Biringuccio's [q.v.] *Pirotechnia,* and had drawn from it, especially on iron metallurgy, sometimes without citation. But *De re metallica* was better written and better illustrated. Soon recognized as a work of exceptional scholarship, Agricola's treatise remained the standard text on mining for 200 years.

Outstanding Engineering Achievement:

The 12 books of *De re metallica* provide an exhaustive survey of mining and metallurgical techniques of the Renaissance, from surveying mineral deposits through the removal and smelting of metal ores. Book VI, perhaps the best-known section of the work, describes all types of mining tools, including devices for hoisting and hauling ore and for draining and ventilating mine shafts. Another book discusses methods of smelting all metal ores commonly mined at the time, including ores of gold, silver, copper, iron, lead, tin, antimony and bismuth. *De re metallica* was the first work to deal systematically (in Books VII and VIII) with assaying, or determining the metallic content of various ores. Agricola also discusses mine administration, patterns of employment and other economic aspects of the industry.

De re metallica is particularly impressive considering the strict criteria of evidence which Agricola for the most part maintained. He generally included only information which he had verified personally or drawn from reliable sources. Alchemy, popular during the Renaissance, and magical instruments such as the divining rod drew his scorn, although he accepted traditional stories of gnomes and other underground creatures encountered by miners. Agricola went to considerable personal expense to illustrate the work, realizing that words would often fail to convey a full impression of a complicated device or process. ∎

Further Reading:

Agricola, *De re metallica,* trans. by Herbert and Hoover. 1912 and New York, 1950.

Bern Dibner, *Agricola on Metals.* Norwalk, Ct., 1958.

Dictionary of Scientific Biography, s.v. "Agricola."

W.B. Parsons, *Engineers and Engineering in the Renaissance.* Baltimore, 1939.

Singer et al., *A History of Science and Technology.* Vol. III.

JUANELO TURRIANO
b. 1500, Cremona, Italy
d. June 13, 1585, Toledo, Spain
Italian Mechanical and Hydraulic Engineer, Clockmaker

Life and Times:

Leonardo da Vinci [q.v.] was famous and well-respected in his own lifetime, particularly as an ingenious inventor. Although no clearly recognizable school followed him, and his notebooks were not published, craftsmen and mechanicians in the area round Milan must have been aware of his work. One of these was Giovanni Torriano (or Della Torre) Gianello, who was born of poor parents and probably apprenticed to a clockmaker at about the time Leonardo died.

Gianello is first heard of in 1530, when Charles V was consecrated Holy Roman Emperor. Since Charles was very interested in horology, clockmakers were asked if they could repair the astronomical clock of Giovanni de' Dondi [q.v.], which had been in the library of the palace at Pavia since 1381 but no longer ran. Gianello agreed with other clockmakers that it was beyond repair, but undertook to make a replica. It took him fifteen years, and some time after 1545 he left Italy with it to join Charles' court, which was now in Toledo. Here, taking the Spanish form of his name, he made a second astronomical clock and a variety of clockwork mechanisms and automata.

When Charles died, Juanelo continued as Watchmaker and Chief Mathematician to Charles' son, Philip II of Spain. Juanelo displayed a multiplicity of skills. He was an architect, silversmith, ironsmith and woodcarver, his inventions including a gimbal chair to provide the king with jolt-free travel. But his masterwork lay in providing Toledo with water.

The Romans had built an aqueduct that brought water down by gravity from the hills surrounding the city. By the sixteenth century the aqueduct was in ruins, and water was brought up by pack animal from the Tijo River. A German engineer was brought in to help modernize the Alcazar Palace in 1526. His solution was to use a waterwheel as the power source and force-pump the water through a pipeline that extended a distance of 2000 feet (600 meters) and rose through a height of 250 feet (75 meters). Unfortunately, the pipes could not withstand the pressure and burst.

Juanelo set to work to supply the city by making a model of his proposal. This was accepted, and by 1573 the system was bringing water to the Alcazar, but could not provide enough for the whole town. A second machine was finished in 1581, by which time the first was in bad repair. Juanelo's works were kept going into the next century, but by 1639 the water was again being donkey-toted.

The king asked Juanelo to write manuals on the astronomical clocks that he had made, which he did. He was also a consultant on the Gregorian calendar reform, for which he sent tables and instruments to the Vatican, and published recommendations and explanations in Spanish and Italian. He also wrote an illustrated book of machines, such as was popular in his day. It was never published, however, possibly because the king considered it to have strategic importance and therefore "classified" it.

In spite of working for the royal family and the city of Toledo for forty years, Juanelo died in poverty. His daughter then wrote a letter to the king begging for help for herself, a widow, and her four orphans. Philip sent her 6,000 ducats, and kept the six chests full of manuscripts, papers, and instruments that Juanelo left.

Outstanding Engineering Achievements:

The waterworks of Toledo were a tourist attraction, but none of Juanelo's notes or drawings of them survive. From a contemporary description, together with drawings in the notebooks of Agostino Ramelli [q.v.] and Leonardo, the mechanism is believed to have been built on a timber framework resembling that of a scissors extension linkage but with the crossings pinned to a beam fixed to a masonry wall. At every other crossing, a horizontal brass water trough was fixed across the top of the two arms. The first pair of arms at the river end were attached to two wheels which rotated vertically in opposite direction, opening and closing the arms. This caused all the troughs to rock. Troughs A and B formed a V, as did troughs C and D, and troughs E and F, and so on. As the rocking motion tilted them the other way, it was troughs B and C that formed the V, and troughs D and E, and so on up the incline.

A chain and bucket system filled the first trough with water that poured down the V into trough B. When the framework rocked, and the V formed between troughs B and C, the water flowed down B and poured into C. The next rocking moved the water from C into D, and at the same time trough A, filled from the river, spilled into trough B. The system lifted the water through 250 feet (75 meters), the highest recorded at that time.

Juanelo's unpublished treatise, *Twenty-One Books on Inventions and Machines,* fills 900 pages with descriptions and drawings of every engineering project connected with water. Like the works of Vannoccio Biringuccio [q.v.], and Georgius Agricola [q.v.], Juanelo's book shows the actual technological practice of the day. There are industrial processes requiring water, such as the washing and dyeing of wool, preparation of saltpeter and the manufacture of starch from wheat. There are waterwheels and other types of mills in which water or cement or glue must be piped along. And, of course, there are harbors, aqueducts, and bridges. These include a drawing with construction details of a truss bridge, conceived independently of Andrea Palladio [q.v.]. ∎

Further Reading:

L. Reti, "The Codex of Juanelo Turriano," *Technology and Culture.* Vol. VIII (1967).

Conjectural drawing of Juanelo Turriano's rocking troughs, but without the scissors linkage.

GIROLAMO CARDANO (JEROME CARDAN)

b. Sept. 24, 1501, Pavia, Italy
d. Sept. 21, 1576, Rome, Italy
Italian Mechanical Engineer, Physician, and Mathematician

Life and Times:

The Renaissance in Italy was an age of unbridled individualism. The archetypal Renaissance man wished for success and fame in many fields, but he was not overscrupulous as to how he achieved them. The aspiring ruler of a city might poison his way to power. An intellectual like Girolamo Cardano, however, had to be content with misrepresentation, perjury, and the theft of others' ideas. Cardano felt no shame at the methods he used to speed his rise to eminence. On the contrary, his vain autobiography—in true Renaissance style—openly glories in these and other bizarre details of his troubled life. Whether or not he was insane, as some contemporaries charged, Cardano made several solid contributions to mechanical engineering and the theory of mechanics.

Cardano's illegitimate birth followed his mother's unsuccessful attempt to procure an abortion. His father, Fazio Cardano, was a jurist and a friend of Leonardo da Vinci [q.v.]. The father encouraged Cardano to study the classics, mathematics, and astrology. In 1520 Cardano entered the University of Pavia, going on to Venice to receive an M.A. in 1524, and obtaining his doctorate in medicine from Padua in 1526. Cardano repeatedly tried to gain admission to Milan's medical association, but was refused until 1539 on grounds of illegitimacy. He continued to practice medicine anyway, engaging in polemics with his colleagues and acquiring a good reputation in Europe as a result of his medical writings. Cardano's most famous cure was that of the archbishop of Edinburgh, whom the leading doctors of the time were unable to cure of his asthma. Less successful was the horoscope Cardano cast for King Edward VI of England on his way back to Milan from Edinburgh. Cardano predicted a long and happy life for the king, who died the following year.

Cardano's mathematical writings were as much admired as his treatises on medicine. His *Ars Magna* (1545) contained the solution for third-degree equations that still bears Cardano's name. He obtained this procedure from his rival Nicolò Tartaglia after promising never to publish it. It must be said that Cardano's own contributions to the theory of algebraic equations were considerable; his original work in probability theory arose from his addiction to gambling.

Three of Cardano's hundreds of treatises—*De Subtilitate* (1550), *De Rerum Varietate* (1557), and *Opus Novum* (1570)—contributed to the theory of mechanics and described useful inventions. Cardano owed more than he acknowledged to his predecessors, especially da Vinci. Though he improved on the work of Archimedes [q.v.] in some respects, he perpetuated a number of Aristotle's errors. Still, for a century his work stimulated scientists and engineers to investigate the possible practical applications of such phenomena as the pressure of gases and the flow of streams.

Outstanding Engineering Achievements:

Cardano did not claim to have invented "Cardano's suspension," the suspension in gimbals known to Philon of Byzantium [q.v.] and Ting Huan [q.v.]. But his description of it was widely circulated and encouraged its use in compasses and gyroscopes. Cardano was responsible, however, for developing the universal joint that also bears his name. Its ability to transmit rotation between two shafts in the same plane soon found wide application, especially in watchmaking.

Cardano improved the process of sifting flour by fitting the sieves then used into a bolter. Though his bolter was not mechanized, it permitted four successively finer separations of flour. Another innovation was the addition of optical equipment to the already-known *camera obscura*. Cardano placed a concave speculum in front of a pinhole in a shutter to collect the rays going through it. Cardano's investigations of pulley blocks, screws, screw-jacks, and irregular gear wheels also led to many subsequent improvements and mechanical applications. ■

Further Reading:

Rene Dugas, *La mécanique au dix-huitième siècle*. Neuchâtel, 1954.

George Sarton, *Introduction to the History of Science*. Baltimore, 1927-48.

Singer et al., *A History of Technology*. Vol. III.

Abbott P. Usher, *A History of Mechanical Inventions*. New York, 1929.

PALLADIO, ANDREA DI PIETRO DELLA GONDOLA

b. Nov. 30, 1518, Padua, Italy
d. Aug. 19, 1580, Venice, Italy
Italian Architect and Civil Engineer

Life and Times:

The nobles of sixteenth-century Venice were concerned with making better use of their mainland properties both to protect Venice from attack by land and to provide grain and other

Palladio, bridge-builder and architect, possibly the one who had the greatest influence on design in Europe and America.

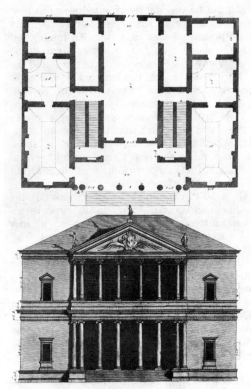

A page from the Four Books of Architecture *with the plan and elevation of a typically palladian villa.*

goods. Efficient drainage, land reclamation and farming required the personal attention of the property owners. Throughout the middle years of the century, wealthy Venetians were building mansions which gave them living quarters suitable to their rank and the necessary farm buildings. The architect to whom they often turned was Palladio. He provided them with villas suited to their needs and to the terrain. The classical harmony of his style in these villas, as well as in town houses, churches and other public buildings, have made Palladio one of the most influential architects of all time. In addition he built bridges, reviving and extending the truss bridge which later became a prominent feature of the American railroad.

Andrea di Pietro was the son of a hatmaker (who later became a miller), and was apprenticed at age 13 to a stonemason in Padua. The next year, his father, Pietro, took him to Vicenza where he was enrolled in the guild of stonemasons and apprenticed to the leading architectural sculptor of that city. After his apprenticeship he continued to work for the same masters, married a servant girl and fathered at least four sons and a daughter.

While in his mid-twenties, Andrea was hired to work on the masonry of a new loggia of the villa of Count Giangiorgio Trissano (1478-1550), a poet, antiquarian and amateur architect. At that time Trissano was forming a resident study group of young nobles, and although Andrea

had had little previous education, he so impressed Trissano that the Count invited him to join the group. Here Andrea studied the engineering, architecture, topography and military science of ancient Rome, and was taken to Rome three times. In 1540, Trissano gave Andrea the name Palladio, referring both to the wisdom of Pallas Athena and to Palladius, the fourth-century Roman who wrote on life in country villas.

The loggias of Vicenza's most prominent building, the Basilica, had been collapsing for 50 years without any architect being able to find an acceptable solution. In 1549, Palladio's design for the renovation was adopted, immediately establishing his reputation. Commissions started arriving from nobles in Vicenza, other towns of Veneto (the area ruled by Venice), and eventually from Venice itself. Palladio's most conspicuous work is, perhaps, the church of San Giorgio Maggiore, one of the sights of Venice.

In 1570, Palladio's *Four Books of Architecture* was published. This fully illustrated treatise is still unsurpassed as a textbook on classical and

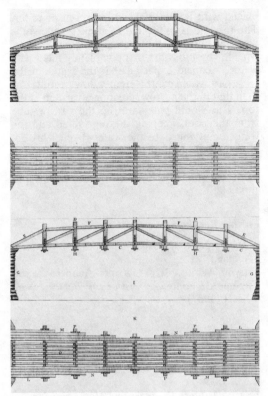

Palladio's versions of the Roman truss bridge that he revived and popularized.

early Palladian design, and has been translated and reprinted repeatedly. The first Polish translation appeared in 1955.

Outstanding Engineering Achievement:

The Cismone is a very rapid river that was used to transport timber from the mountains. Palladio was contracted to build a bridge without fixing any posts in the water, thus avoiding the violence of the current and the shock of the tree trunks. To do this, he went back to Roman truss construction in which the horizontal and vertical girders were anchored by diagonally crossing ties, but with an additional concept. Whereas Trajan's bridge over the Danube, built in 104 A.D., had masonry piers in the river supporting timber-truss arches and superstructures, Palladio's bridge spanned the river without any supports in the water. The distance from bank to bank was 100 feet (30 meters).

The bridge, together with several other truss and stone ones, is fully described and illustrated in Palladio's treatise. ∎

Further Reading:

A. Palladio, *The Four Books of Architecture,* trans. by I. Ware. New York, 1964.

W. M. Whitehill, *Palladio in America.* Milan, 1976.

JACOPO ACONCIO
b. ca. 1520, Trent, Italy
d. 1566 or 1567, London, England
Anglo-Italian Military and Mechanical Engineer

Life and Times:

The first patent in which an inventor was rewarded by being given exclusive rights to make and market his invention for a certain time was awarded to Filippo Brunelleschi [q.v.] in 1421. Previously, exclusive rights had been given to confer favors, to stimulate a particular industry, or to foster the introduction of skills from another country. They continued to be used for these purposes outside of Italy for a century longer. The first statement in England of the use of a patent as a reward for invention was in the petition of Jacopo Aconcio in 1559, covering a variety of machines. The patent was granted in 1565.

Aconcio had arrived in England only months before applying for his patent. In 1549 he left Trent, where he had been a notary, and joined the Viennese court of Emperor Charles V. There he associated with military engineers and set himself to learn the art of fortification, then rapidly changing due to the introduction of cannon. He also accompanied the emperor's army into northern Italy, working at fortifying towns.

There was a particular reason for Aconcio's military studies. He later wrote: "My mind was long vexed with plans to flee whither I might freely profess the Gospel, and I thought it possible that I might learn this art it would thereafter give me a living." He fled Catholic Europe in 1557, first to Switzerland, then, after the accession of Queen Elizabeth, to England.

Perhaps as a result of the promise of his patent application, Aconcio was awarded a pension of sixty pounds a year, and in 1561 he became an English subject. He then formed a company to reclaim flooded lands in Kent. Parliament granted him the right to half of the land reclaimed. His company drained 600 acres (243 hectares), which then flooded again, and again were drained. The considerable number of land reclamation projects begun in England during the next decade may have been encouraged by Aconcio's start.

The refortification of the town of Berwick upon Tweed, on the Scottish border, was considered an essential part of England's defense against possible invasion by France. In 1564 Aconcio was named to the advisory commission for this project. He sent reports of his own to the Queen, recommending a number of improvements, including building bastions, lowering the walls to no more than seventeen feet (5 meters), constructing a thick wall on one side of the town and a thinner wall resting on an earthen backing on the other side, and enlarging casements to allow the maneuvering of cannon. The defenses of Berwick were indeed carried out in the "new" Italian manner.

Meanwhile Aconcio was securing himself a permanent place in the history of theology with his writings. In 1558 he published his *Method,* a discourse "on the correct investigation and propounding of knowledge by reason." This small book was reprinted three times and was well known in Europe at the time that Descartes wrote his *Discourse on Method.* There were a number of shorter treatises in the form of letters, but Aconcio's major work was *The Stratagems of Satan,* in which he gave a systematic account of the Christian justification of religious toleration. The book had a great effect on Protestant thought and, between 1558 and 1674, it went into eleven editions in Latin, two in English, and one each in French, German, and Dutch. It was placed on the Catholic Index of Prohibited Books in 1569.

Outstanding Engineering Achievement:

Aconcio's patent application asked for the exclusive right to manufacture "new systems of all kinds of machines that use wheels [water wheels], a new system of furnace for dyers and brewers, and others with a great saving of fuel." It also suggested that those who take the trouble and expense of producing inventions should be compensated by being granted a monopoly of production and sale of their invention for a few years.

A variety of machines are specified in the patent grant, using water power (probably the vertical waterwheels which had become popular in Italy) and wind power for cutting wood, grinding and crushing.

Also included in the patent is a perpetual motion machine. A narrow vertical tube is placed with its bottom end in a pool of water. The top end is connected to a much wider tube with its bottom end over a horizontal waterwheel. The tubes are first completely filled with water. Aconcio expected that the water in the wide part would exert a greater downward thrust than that in the narrow, creating a vacuum at the top. This would pull water up the narrow tube from the pool, keeping the tube filled and the water emptying onto the waterwheel. This device, the only perpetual motion machine covered by a patent, was drawn and described (but evidently not tried) by Vittorio Zonca [q.v.] in 1607. ∎

Further Reading:

Dictionary of National Biography, s.v. "Aconcio."

Lynn White, Jr., "Jacopo Aconcio as an Engineer," *American Historical Review.* Vol. VXXII (1967).

LEONARD DIGGES
b. ca. 1520, Barham, Kent, England
d. ca. 1559
English Military Engineer and Mathematician

THOMAS DIGGES
b. 1546 (?), Wotten, Kent, England
d. August 1595, London, England
English Military Engineer, Mathematician and Astronomer

Life and Times:

The dissolution of the English monasteries by Henry VIII placed considerable tracts of church land on the market, requiring it to be surveyed and subdivided. This was reflected in the passing of a statute that finally fixed the size of an acre as forty rods by four rods, or its equivalent in any other shape. (A rod is 5½ yards, or about 5 meters.) There were, however, no surveying instruments for measuring areas other than rectangles. At the same time the cannon had arrived in warfare, but, without sights on elevation control, gunnery was totally a hit-or-miss affair. Leonard Digges and his son Thomas addressed themselves to both problems, although in the century before Newton expounded his laws of motion there could not yet be a science of ballistics.

All that is sure about Leonard Digges' education is that he entered Lincoln's Inn of Court in 1537. He was acquainted with the cartographers Peter Apian and Gerhard Mercator, but he is also reported by Thomas to have taken part in "conferences with the rarest soldiers of his time."

In 1555 Leonard wrote a popular sailor's almanac called *Prognostication*. The next year he completed a textbook of elementary mathematics and surveying which ran to eight editions by the end of the century. It described the three surveying instruments of the day: the carpenter's square; the geometrical square derived from the astrolabe, which contained a plumb-line and showed the tangent and cotangents of any angle it was turned through; and the cross staff or Jacob's ladder, in which a cross-piece could be moved along a stick and aligned with the top and bottom of a building to determine its height when its distance was known.

Meanwhile, Leonard had become involved in politics. In January 1554, when the proposed marriage between Queen Mary and Philip of Spain was announced, Sir Thomas Wyatt formed an army in Kent which marched on London, intending to dethrone the queen. The rebellion failed and Digges, who had joined Wyatt's forces, was condemned to death. But he was later pardoned, having only to pay for the redemption of his property. When he died soon after, he left most of the manuscript of a surveying book, along with notes on military organization and the results of his own experiments in ballistics.

Thomas, who is generally known as the most important English mathematician and astronomer of the Elizabethan period, built on the work of his father. Ten years after the latter's death, he completed the manuscript of *Pantometria*, which described two surveying instruments of Leonard's design. Thomas continued to study ballistics, and in 1579 he completed *Stratioticos*, a military treatise based on his father's notes and the gunnery experiments of both men. Although unable to produce a theory of his own, he did correct many common errors.

The heliocentric theory of Copernicus had been published in 1543. At first it was accepted, in accordance with the preface added by the publisher, simply as a mathematical device to make astronomical calculations easier. Thomas was one of the first to maintain that it gave a true description of our system in which the earth is but one of the planets orbiting the sun. In 1576 he included a translation of parts of Copernicus in the latest edition of Leonard's *Prognostication*. To this Thomas added his own theory

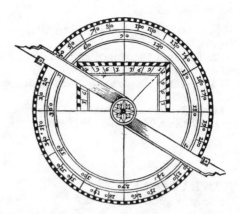

The theodelitus of Leonard Digges, an early device for measuring angles, gave its name to the modern surveying instrument.

that the solar system is surrounded by an infinite universe in which the fixed stars are placed at various distances. He called upon astronomers to cooperate in making observations to substantiate or modify the Copernican theory. (He had himself made very accurate observations of the nova of 1572, called Tycho's star.)

Thomas was elected to parliament in 1572 and 1584, served as inspector of the fortress in Dover and was involved in planning the harbor repairs of that port. He also served as the muster-master general of the army sent to help the Low Countries in their revolt against Spain.

Outstanding Engineering Achievements:

The two instruments described in *Pantometria* were significant for different reasons. One was a horizontal circle graduated in degrees for which Digges coined the name *theodelitus*, the original form of "theodolite," now the name of an important surveying instrument. The other of Thomas' inventions, called the topographical, was more advanced and was the direct forerunner of the modern theodolite.

The base of the instrument was a circle graduated in degrees. In the center of this circle a vertical axis was free to turn. Mounted to rotate in a vertical plane on the axis was a graduated semicircle, its diameter being fitted with sights. To measure elevations, the sights on the semicircle are rotated from the bottom to the top of a building. To measure azimuths, the sights are turned about the vertical axis, the angles being shown on the base circle. Versions of this "topographical" theodolite have survived from as early as 1586. ∎

Further Reading:

Dictionary of Scientific Biography, s.v. "Digges."

Olaf Pedersen and Mogen Pihl, *Early Physics and Astronomy*. New York, 1974.

H.J. Webb, *Elizabethan Military Science*. Madison, 1965.

Harriet Wynter and Anthony Turner, *Scientific Instruments*. New York, 1975.

HUMFRAY COLE

b. c. 1520, Yorkshire, England
d. 1591
British Instrument Maker

Life and Times:

Scientific instrument making was brought to England in the early sixteenth century by craftsmen from Germany and the Low Countries. At a time of growing interest in sea travel and exploration, their wares found a ready market. Humfray Cole, Sinker of the Stamps at the Mint during the reign of Queen Elizabeth I, built on this base to become the first native-born instrument maker in Britain. As such, he can be viewed as the founder of a tradition that flourished during the next century to meet the demand for nautical, astronomical, surveying and other instruments.

Little is known of Cole's background and early life. He first appears in history as assistant to Eloy Mestrell, the royal coiner. He took over Mestrell's position in 1577, supplementing his annual salary of 20 pounds by making scientific instruments. Cole also earned additional income by assaying samples of ore brought back from the New World. These activities notwithstanding, he was apparently in frequent financial distress and died poor.

Outstanding Engineering Achievements:

Cole's instruments were remarkable for their wide variety, their finely-wrought engravings and their ingenious attachments and aids, features that in later times would have been worthy of a patent. Many are now held in the British Museum.

One of Cole's most elegant instruments was a portable dial made around 1570 for Richard Jugge, Master of the Stationers' Company. Jugge's heraldic nightingale, executed by Cole

on the cover, is an early example of the literary use of "jug" for the nightingale's song. In 1574 Cole made a miniature astrolabe, three-and-one-half inches (9 cm) in diameter and weighing six ounces (170 g). The back features a horizontal projection of the heavenly sphere, a form attributed to al-Zarqali [q.v.]. One year later Cole made a giant astrolabe, two feet (60 cm) in diameter with a weight of 33 pounds (15 kg). Many of its features were similar to those of the miniature version. These were, of course, special devices, probably intended for collectors. The usual nautical astrolabe had its parts cut from a disc so that it would not swing in the breeze. ∎

Further Reading:

Dictionary of National Biography, s.v. "Cole."

R. J. Gunther, "The Great Astrolabe and Other Scientific Instruments of Humphrey Cole," *Archeologica*. Vol. VIIVI (1927).

TAQĪ AD-DĪN

b. 1526, Damascus, Syria
d. 1585, Istanbul
Islamic Horologist

Life and Times:

The Ottoman Empire in the reign of Suleiman I (1520 to 1566) extended from central Europe to Persia, and the cultural life of the empire reflected both European—especially Venetian—and eastern Islamic influences. During Suleiman's reign a major program of construction took place in Istanbul, and the court became a center of literary and scientific activity. Suleiman especially admired the art of clockmaking; he collected examples of clocks from the Venetians and distributed clocks as gifts. The best-known horologist of his reign was Taqī ad-dīn.

Taqī ad-dīn (full name Taqī ad-dīn Muhammad ibn Ma'rūf ibn Ahmad) was born to a family that had come from Nablus in the Jordan Valley. He left Damascus by his late teens, and by the mid-1540s had attached himself to a circle of scholars supported by the grand vezir, the leading administrative figure at the court. Under the tutelage of one of the vezirs, Alī Pasha, Taqī ad-dīn wrote at least several treatises on philosophy, mathematics and clockmaking, and most likely designed clocks as well. His best-known work is a treatise on the science of clockmaking, *Fi 'ilm al-binkāmāt,* which classifies different types of clocks and comments on the state of clockmaking.

The period between 1545 and 1565 was the most productive one for Taqī ad-dīn. He wrote treatises on algebra, arithmetic and conic sections. His interest in clocks was fundamentally religious; in a work entitled "The Unstrung Pearls and the Role of Thought" he sought to determine, with mathematical precision, the exact times for prayer each day and the exact direction in which one should pray. In the same treatise he introduced for the first time tables of sines and tangents based on decimal fractions rather than sixtieths.

Outstanding Engineering Achievement:

In *Fi 'ilm al-binkāmāt* Taqī ad-dīn identified three different kinds of clocks: sand clocks, water clocks, and mechanical clocks. He gave short shrift to the first two, but carefully described the third, many of which had come to his attention via Venetian traders. He noted the interrelation of the design of the various parts of mechanical clocks: the balance between the weight and position of the wheels—large and small—that provided the driving mechanism of the clock. He also noted that, once set in motion, the clocks ran continuously. Taqī ad-dīn was perhaps the first scholar in the Islamic world, and certainly in the Ottoman world, to devote detailed attention to the operation of mechanical clocks. ∎

Further Reading:

Heinrich Suter, *Die Mathematiker und Astronomen der Araber und ihre Werke.* Leipzig, 1900.

Eilhard Wiedemann, *Über die Uhren im Bereich der islamischen Kultur.* Halle, 1915.

ADAM DE CRAPONNE
b. 1526, Salon, France
d. 1575, Nantes, France
French Hydraulic and Military Engineer

Life and Times:

During the Renaissance, a network of navigational canals were constructed in Italy. By the sixteenth century, Holland had begun its canal

Adam de Crappone, engineer of France's first large-scale irrigation project.

construction, principally for the purpose of drainage. The only canal built in France during this period was for yet a third purpose—irrigation. Conceived and constructed by Adam de Craponne, the canal began the transformation of a section of southeastern France from a barren stony steppe into a significant agricultural area.

Craponne was born to an Italian family (originally named Crapone) that had emigrated from Pisa to Salon, a small town between Marseille and Avignon. After studying mathematics and hydraulic engineering in a military school, he began his career by constructing fortifications at Nice and draining marshes at Frejus near Cannes.

Throughout Craponne's lifetime, France was beset by external and internal strife. In 1552-53, the Holy Roman Emperor Charles V laid siege to the French town of Metz. Craponne helped devise military operations to raise the siege. War against other European powers was followed by war between the French Protestants (Huguenots) and the Catholics. In 1575, Craponne was sent to inspect the foundations of a fortification under construction in Nantes. The assignment, however, became entangled in court intrigue. King Henry III, who romped through the streets at night dressed as a woman, was emptying the treasury with lavish gifts for his favorites. Most Italians in France, including Craponne, remained loyal to Catherine de' Medici, the Queen Mother and former Regent, who longed for peace. Craponne may have been lured to Nantes as part of a plot. Or he may have refused to accept bribes from the contractors whose work he was inspecting. For whatever reason, he died by poison. Centuries later, a medal was struck in his honor, and a fountain and statue were erected at Salon.

Outstanding Engineering Achievement:

Just north of Salon flow the silt-laden waters of the Durance river. The area from Salon southwest to the Rhône delta is the Crau, an arid Pliocene alluvial cone which originally was of no agricultural value. Craponne realized that the silt in the Durance was eroded topsoil and that the combination of water and topsoil was what the Crau needed. Accordingly, he proposed to build a system of canals to irrigate the Crau. The largest part of the system, still known as the Craponne canal, runs west from the Durance above Salon to the Rhône at Arles. Forty miles long, it has no locks, but keeps a well-regulated gradient to ensure the even flow of both water and silt. Subsidiary canals, completed after Craponne's death, carry the flow throughout the Crau.

Although denigrated by some as merely a large ditch, the Craponne canal was France's first successful irrigation project. Over the centuries it has continued to change the character of the Crau, which now supports flocks of some 250,000 sheep. ■

Further Reading:

W.B. Parsons, *Engineers and Engineering in the Renaissance*. Baltimore, 1939.

Philippe Pinchemel, *France: a Geographical Survey*. New York, 1969.

JACQUES BESSON
b. ca. 1530, Briançon (Grenoble?), France
d. ca. 1573, Geneva, Switzerland
French or Swiss Engineer and Inventor

Life and Times:

During the middle of the sixteenth century, itinerant mathematicians moved about Europe, offering lessons and selling mathematical instruments of their own invention. In particular demand were surveying and navigational instruments and the manuals that described them. Jacques Besson invented one of these instru-

Wind-powered water pump by Besson; the chain of pots fill and empty no matter which way the sails revolve.

ments and published a book on it. He then followed with another book, the *Théâtre des Instruments Mathematiques et Méchaniques* (also called the *Theatrum Instrumentorum et Machinarum)*, a collection of drawings of various machines and engines. This was the first of the books of machines that became popular towards the end of the century, other notable ones being written by Agostino Ramelli [q.v.] and Vittorio Zonca [q.v.].

Besson's fame was posthumous, and little is known of his life. It is fairly certain that he was born in the southeast of France, probably around 1530. He entered the King's service as a mathematician and engineer, and before 1570 became a professor of mathematics at Orleans. Besson was first published in 1559. This early work on chemical analysis was followed by practical guides to stargazing, dowsing, and the use of the compass in geometry. Shortly after publication of his machine book in 1571-72, Besson, a Protestant, was forced to flee France because of religious persecutions. Various dates and places have been given for his death. An old claim that he found shelter in England and died there in 1571 is no longer tenable, since documents list him as one of the notables of Geneva before 1576.

The principle of the hammock made one of its first appearances in Europe in this coach of Besson's.

Besson is said to have traveled widely in various countries gathering material for his book. In it he claims to depict the different kinds of machine tools, pumping plants, ploughs, military engines, and other machines he had observed in use. In reality, it is doubtful that many of these machines were ever in operation, since they are not mechanically viable. Some make excessive demands on the strength of their wooden parts. Those using screws or worm-wheels require greater accuracy of construction than was then obtainable. Nevertheless, Besson shows great ingenuity in his designs, especially in that of a screw-cutting lathe. Here Besson reveals his familiarity with the notebooks of Leonardo da Vinci [q.v.].

Besson's work is interesting insofar as it shows the technological visions of the day. It also points the way to future developments, once lathes were made from metal rather than wood, for the screw-cutting lathe would develop into the industrial lathe that made the machine age possible.

Outstanding Engineering Achievement:

Besson's *Théâtre des Instruments Mathématiques et Méchaniques* had seven editions in four languages between 1578 and 1626. The first seems to have been produced in a hurry: its contents are listed in French but the captions to the sixty plates are in Latin; the printer's name is missing; apart from the captions there is no text. One plate shows a coach for a pageant in which the compartment is slung between two hooks on an ornate frame. The hammock is said to have been introduced to France about this time by a Protestant mercenary returning from Brazil. Besson seems to have used the hammock principle to provide jostle-free travel.

The other plates run the gamut from common usage to fantasy. Of the former, there is a dredging vessel in which a long lever arm has pulleys at the end in the boat and a shovel at the

end in the water. Of the latter there is a ship whose hull has a waterline in the shape of a Y. Described in the caption as "an invention scarcely credible," the ship is supposed to slow down in a high wind and accelerate when the wind drops.

Between these extremes Besson shows an early practical fire-engine. A hand-operated plunger squirts a jet of water from a funnel-shaped tank. The tank is filled by hand from the top and can be aimed at a blazing window. By the next century variations of this type of fire-engine had become quite common.

Also important was Besson's screw-cutting lathe, which incorporated an improved drive mechanism. Earlier lathes had been powered by springy poles; Besson's was driven by a cord, with an attached weight, that passed over a central pulley; the motion was then transmitted by other weighted cords to the work and a tool below. As depicted, the machine could cut left- or right-hand screws of any pitch.

Besson further designed guides which would permit a lathe operator to turn ovals and other irregular shapes. A tool holder was inserted through a guide slot mounted above the work. Following the shape of the slot, the cutting tool would produce the desired shape. Parts of Besson's design were incorporated in the rose engine later used by goldsmiths for ornamental turning. ∎

Further Reading:

A. G. Keller, *A Theatre of Machines*. New York, 1964.

———, "The Missing Years of Jacques Besson," *Tech. and Culture*, 14 (1973).

Kranzberg and Pursell, *Technology in Western Civilization*, Vol. I. New York, 1967.

François Russo, "Deux Ingénieurs de la Renaissance: Besson et Ramelli," *Thales*. 1948.

FEDERIGO GIAMBELLI (or GIANIBELLI)

b. c. 1530, Mantua, Italy
d. c. 1590, England
Italian Military Engineer

Life and Times:

The war in which the Spanish Armada was launched against England was the result of long-standing commercial rivalry, hatred between

Catholics and Protestants, and English support of the Low Countries' rebellion against Spanish rule. Since the use of gunpowder in warfare had been developed in Italy, Italian military engineers were in demand by all sides. Federigo Giambelli served the Dutch in their rebellion, and his reputation served the English in their naval battle with Spain.

Giambelli is believed to have first offered his services to King Philip of Spain. Offended at receiving no answer, he went to work instead for the other side. He may have entered the service of Queen Elizabeth of England and gone to Flanders with the English force sent to aid the revolt against Spain. In 1585 Spanish troops under the Duke of Parma besieged Antwerp. To supply his forces, Parma had a heavily fortified pontoon bridge built across the River Scheldt, between Antwerp and the sea. The city's Flemish defenders tried unsuccessfully to destroy the bridge with fireships, surplus boats coated with pitch and set ablaze. Giambelli, the defenders' military engineer, then suggested a new device: a ship loaded with an explosive device set to go off at a certain time. Jacob Jacobsen, commander of the city garrison, approved the construction of the world's first time bomb.

Two boats, the *Fortune* and the *Hope,* were equipped with bombs built according to Giambelli's specifications. Disguised as fireships, they were launched against the Spanish bridge on April 4, 1585. Spanish patrols turned aside the *Fortune,* but the *Hope* struck the bridge and exploded with devastating effect: the bridge was demolished, the river flooded and some 800 Spanish soldiers were killed. Many more were injured, including Parma himself, who was knocked unconscious by a falling timber.

Despite this setback, the Spanish took Antwerp in August 1585. But they did not forget Giambelli's floating bombs, which they called "devil-ships" and "hell-burners." Giambelli himself, who had escaped to England, was put to work designing the river defense of London. In 1588 the formidable Spanish Armada sailed up the French coast and anchored at Calais preparatory to invading England. The English naval commander, Sir John Hawkins, sent eight normal fireships into Calais harbor on the night of August 7-8 (New Style, Gregorian calendar) to harass the Spanish fleet. But the Spanish, fearing that they again confronted "hell-burners," precipitately pulled up anchor and scattered. They never succeeded in regrouping; worn down by English attacks and storms, the Armada disintegrated.

Giambelli's fame thus proved as important to England as his works. In 1590 Queen Elizabeth awarded him a life pension of 100 pounds a year.

Outstanding Engineering Achievement:

The *Fortune* and *Hope* were small ships, weighing 80 and 70 tons respectively. In the hold of each, Giambelli built a stone chamber filled with 600 pounds (272 kg) of priming powder of his own composition. He placed a heavy weight of stone slabs and millstones above that and crammed the deck with bricks, chains, knives, nails and anything else that could serve as a missile. Several small apertures were left in the chamber for slow fuses, which were lit by a mechanism that struck sparks after the lapse of a certain time. Finally, Giambelli camouflaged the vessels as fireships by heaping their decks with burning brimstone and pitch. The bridge which the *Hope* destroyed spanned 450 feet (137 meters). ■

Further Reading:

Michael Lewis, *The Spanish Armada.* London, 1960.

Conyers Read, *Mr. Secretary Walsingham and the Policy of Queen Elizabeth.* New York, 1978.

Henri Pirenne, *Histoire de Belgique.* Bruxelles, 1949.

LAZARUS ERCKER
b. c. 1530, Annaberg, Saxony
d. c. 1593, Prague, Bohemia
German Metallurgist and Chemist

Life and Times:

Not only modern chemistry, but also much of metallurgy and mining technology have their roots in alchemy. The preoccupation with transmuting metals into gold and silver had stimulated notable advances in these fields by the sixteenth century. Along with Agricola [q.v.] and Biringuccio [q.v.], Lazarus Ercker wrote one of the key treatises on mining and metallurgy to appear at this time, clearly demonstrating the advanced state of the technical arts in the early modern period.

Little is known of Ercker's life. The son of Asmus Ercker, he attended school in Annaberg. After studying at the University of Wittenberg, the Saxon elector Augustus appointed him assayer of ores at Dresden. Ercker quickly became one of the chief consultants in all matters relating to metallurgy and mining. In 1556, he

Gold being washed on a sloping table with many traps to catch the gold while the earth flows away with the water; Ercker.

wrote an early work on assaying, the *Probier-büchlein*. In 1567, he moved to Prague, where he was appointed court tester at the Kutna Hora mine. While at Prague, he wrote his famous *Beschreibung allerfürnemistern mineralischen Ertzt-und Berckwercksarten* (which was a work that was translated into English in 1683 as *Treatise describing the foremost kinds of Metallic Ores and Minerals*), dedicating it to the Habsburg emperor Maximilian II. The next emperor, Rudolf II, a patron of the arts and sciences, appointed Ercker his chief inspector of mines. Ercker's skills and knowledge earned him the respect of the emperor, and in 1586 he was knighted.

Ercker's *Beschreibung*, replete with 41 woodcuts, was the first manual of analytical and metallurgical chemistry. Eschewing alchemical symbols, Ercker systematically reviewed the methods of testing alloys and ores of silver, gold, copper, antimony, mercury, bismuth and lead. His work also described the procedures and equipment for these tasks. Less concerned with mining and smelting than Agricola, Ercker supplemented Agricola's work with precise instructions for assaying.

Outstanding Engineering Achievement:

Although four centuries have elapsed since Ercker's opus was published, many of the principles underlying the methods he outlined are still recognized as valid. His treatise is divided into five books. The first describes the processes and apparatus used in the assaying of silver. The procedure outlined in the book calls for the reduction of metal in the raw ore to a silver-lead alloy, followed by cupellation (or refinement in a porous vessel) to isolate the silver. The other books describe the recognition and assaying of gold, copper, and other ores. Ercker observed that precipitating copper from solution by dissolving iron does not mean that the transmutation of matter takes place, that iron becomes copper. Rather, iron replaces copper in solution. He also noted that a cupel containing copper and lead weighs more after roasting in a furnace than before.

Ercker also turned his attention to improving the apparatus used in metallurgical processes. For medieval metallurgists, operations which involved prolonged heating were very tedious, requiring frequent refueling. Ercker developed a gravity-stoked brazier which required refilling with charcoal only once daily. It was suitable for low temperature operations, such as cementation, distillation and evaporation. ■

Further Reading:

Eva Armstrong and Hiram Lukens, "Lazarus Ercker and his *Probierbuch*," *Journal of Chemical Education.* Vol. XVI (1939).

Lazarus Ercker, *Treatise on Ores and Assaying,* trans. and ed. by A. G. Sisco and Cyril S. Smith. Chicago, 1951.

J. R. Partington, *A History of Chemistry,* Vol. II. New York, 1961.

AGOSTINO RAMELLI
b. 1531, Ponte Tresa, Italy
d. in or after Aug. 1608
Italian Military Engineer

Life and Times:

Medieval and Renaissance engineers kept notebooks in which they recorded the instruments and mechanisms that they saw, heard of, invented, or just imagined. After the development of printing in Europe, illustrated collections of mechanisms began to be published, in many cases by engineers whose works are known to us only through their machine books. One of the earliest, and most popular of these books was written by Agostino Ramelli, who was a successful military engineer at a time when

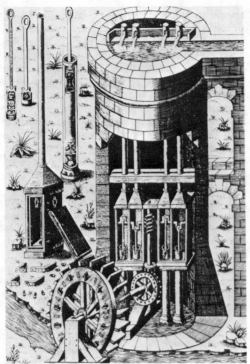

Quadruple suction pump by Ramelli in which the crankshaft is turned by a worm gear; details of the top left, valves.

Italian engineers were in great demand throughout Europe.

Ramelli, who came from a small village on Lake Lugano, north of Milan, was a professional soldier, first heard of as a military engineer in the army of Emperor Charles V. He became a captain under the Marquis de Marignon, who may have been a student of Leonardo da Vinci [q.v.]. When the marquis died, Ramelli moved to France as engineer in the Catholic army of the Duke of Anjou fighting against the Protestant Huguenots. In 1572, thousands of French Protestants were massacred, and those that occupied the port of La Rochelle closed its gates in siege. As engineer, Ramelli was sent in a boat to examine the fortifications of the city and take soundings of the depths of the water. The boat was seen and attacked; Ramelli and the crew were captured and spent some months in a Huguenot prison.

The Duke became King Henri III, enabling Ramelli to style himself, on the title page of his book, "Engineer to the most Christian king of France and Poland." The next January, Henri was driven out of Paris, with the people declaring their sovereignty; in August he was assassi-nated. Ramelli joined the extremist Catholic League and was listed as one of its officers during the subsequent siege of Paris. In 1593, Henri of Navarre, the former Protestant leader, turned Catholic and after a few more months of sporadic fighting he entered Paris as Henri IV. In 1604, Ramelli was referred to as the "grand architect of the King." The last record of Ramelli is from August 1608, when he signed some papers relating to property. He was then living in St. Germain.

Outstanding Engineering Achievement:

Ramelli's book *Le Diverse et Artificiose Machine* is a large, leather-bound volume containing 195 full-page engravings, each of which is fully described in both Italian and French. Published in 1588, it was unusual, perhaps unique, in having its text in two vernacular languages. A German edition was brought out in 1620. The first illustration shows a rooftop cistern being filled by a pump that is powered by a waterwheel. Succeeding illustrations explore varia-

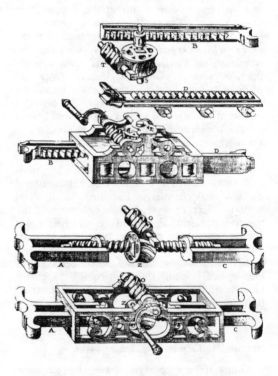

Machines in which the turning of a crank moves bars apart or together so that "one man alone can easily bend the iron gratings of a portcullis and make very little noise." Ramelli, 1588.

Water-driven grinding mill from Ramelli, 1588. Rotation of the waterwheel is transmitted via the horizontal wheel to lantern, L; a vertical shaft from L turns the grindstone, A.

tions on this theme—undershot and overshot vertical waterwheels, and horizontal ones with curved radiating vanes, horsepower, foot- and hand-power and a variety of single and double pumping arrangements. There are also piston pumps in which the rotary action of a turned shaft is converted into reciprocating action. (The rotary pump is an important device that was apparently one of Ramelli's own inventions.) After the pumps come the mills: a horse-powered mill grinds marble and stone, a hand-mill grinds spices, a grain mill is powered by a man walking in place on an inclined disc, a clockwork mill is powered by a falling weight which is frequently cranked up by a boy.

Ramelli's involvement in military affairs is displayed by a variety of portable bridges—telescoping, scissors-expanding and wheeled; by an armed amphibian vehicle with man-powered paddle wheels; and by many other engines of war.

Many of the machines are clearly under-powered. As one example, a large grain mill is worked by a man who sits at the top of the mill with his bare feet resting on the spokes of a horizontal wheel. By running his feet he turns the wheel, gears, pinions, and the heavy mill itself. A number of other machines contain a reversing device which would at least put an enormous strain on a system. In this device, there are two crown wheels on the same shaft, each one toothed on only half its circumference. Between them is a pinion. For half of one revolution of the shaft, one wheel engages the pinion, turning it to the right; for the remaining half the other wheel engages, turning the pinion to the left. The pinion and the pump to which it is connected are thus thrown from full ahead to full reverse, without slowing down or passing through neutral. If the device did not strip the teeth from the crown wheels, it would require far more power than could be provided by one man at a crank handle. Yet so it is shown, leaving the reader wondering which of these machines actually existed (and worked) and which were merely untried designs. However, most of the machines would have worked, being combinations of mechanisms in use at the time. The fine plates, Ramelli's explanatory text, and the details given of the smaller mechanisms such as gears and tools, all contributed to make this machine book widely read and influential for two hundred years. Copies of its plates appeared in a number of books in Europe and also in China. ∎

Further Reading:

M. T. Gnudi and E. Ferguson, eds., *The Various and Ingenious Machines of Agostino Ramelli (1588)*. Baltimore, 1976.

A. G. Keller, *A Theatre of Machines*. New York, 1964.

Abraham Wolf, *A History of Science, Technology and Philosophy in the Sixteenth and Seventeenth Centuries*. London, 1950.

GIAMBATTISTA DELLA PORTA
b. 1535, Naples, Italy
d. 1615, Naples, Italy
Italian Natural Philosopher

Life and Times:

In the intellectual ferment of the Renaissance, scientific inquiry was broad and unsystematic. It encompassed bizarre speculation as well as experiment, magic and alchemy as well as technology. The field of natural philosophy had not yet been divided into smaller disciplines, and scholars ranged freely over its entire scope. Among

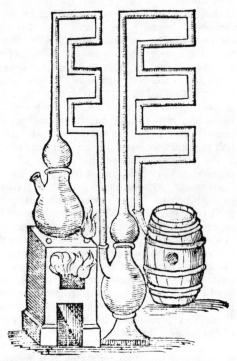

In Porta's steam pump, the escape of steam from the heated vessel causes a syphoning of water from the lower vessel and then from the water supply.

the most famous and eclectic of Renaissance scientists was Giambattista della Porta.

An active promoter of science, Porta traveled widely in Italy, France and Spain and founded several scientific academies. He is known to us mainly through his numerous writings, including *Magiae naturalis* (1588), *De refractione opices parte* (1593) and *Tre libri de spiritali* (1601). These books deal with everything from magnetism to palmistry, crystallography, the science of fortifications and the classification of plants. *Magiae naturalis* contains a valuable survey of metallurgical technology during the Renaissance. Most of Porta's original work, however, dealt with optics and the mechanical application of steam.

Outstanding Engineering Achievements:

Porta conducted several experiments to determine the basic properties of steam, an understanding of which was necessary to the later development of steam-powered devices. Among his discoveries was the fact that steam occupies a greater volume than water, and that condensation of steam leaves an empty space (most

Renaissance scientists did not yet think in terms of a vacuum) which can be filled by another substance. He determined this by filling a wine flask with steam and immersing the neck of the bottle in cold water; as the steam condensed, water rose into the neck until it reached the surrounding surface level.

Whether Porta understood the role of atmospheric pressure in forcing water into the bottle is uncertain. In any case, he put his knowledge to practical use by designing a rudimentary steam pump that could supply water to a fountain. Porta's device, described in *Tre libri de spiritali*, consisted of a vessel partly filled with water and connected by pipe to a well. When the vessel was heated, it filled completely with steam, which was allowed to escape through a vent. This created a partial vacuum which drew water from the well into the vessel, where it was diverted by another pipe to the fountain. This pump is the direct ancestor of the one developed a century later by Thomas Savery [q.v.], and stands less directly in the line of development of the steam engine.

Like many other Italian scientists of the Renaissance, Porta also devoted much attention to the properties and uses of lenses. His *Magiae naturalis* describes various ways of combining concave and convex lenses to improve vision at a distance. Porta has also been credited with invention of the compound microscope, though application of this device to the study of small objects began with Galileo [q.v.]. Porta's work with lenses interested him in the camera obscura, a dark box with a small hole in one side which projected an inverted image of an exterior object onto the opposite side. Though the device had aroused curiosity since the Middle Ages, Porta was among the first to study it seriously, believing that its function resembled that of the human eye. He noticed that placing a lens across the hole in the side sharpened the image on the opposite side. Porta's observation, reported in *Magiae naturalis*, places him among the remote ancestors of photography. ∎

Further Reading:

Dictionary of Scientific Biography, s.v. "Della Porta

Singer et al., *A History of Technology*. Vol. III.

Abraham Wolf, *A History of Science, Technology and Philosophy in the Sixteenth and Seventeenth Centuries*. London, 1950.

Abbott P. Usher, *A History of Mechanical Inventions*. New York, 1929.

DOMENICO FONTANA
b. 1543, Mili, Italy (or Melide, Switzerland)
d. 1607, Naples, Italy
Italian Architect and Civil Engineer

Life and Times:

There was no distinction in early times between the professions of architect and engineer. An architect was expected to know the strength of his materials, calculate the amounts required and their costs, and supervise the construction. To these requirements, the Italian Renaissance added the need to cultivate a political faction in order to obtain a position, and the preparedness to accept losing that position when another faction took over. So it was with Domenico Fontana, who rose to be chief architect to one pope but was ignominiously removed from office by another.

As a youth, Fontana excelled as a student of mathematics. At the age of 20 he joined his

Domenico Fontana, who laid out the present-day street pattern of Rome.

brother Giovanni, who was an architect in Rome. From Cardinal Montalto, Domenico obtained commissions to design and build a chapel attached to a church, and an imposing palace in the church grounds. The work attracted the attention of Pope Gregory XIII, who disapproved of conspicuous consumption by his cardinals and suspended Montalto's pension. This cut off funds for the project, but Fontana completed it by paying for the remainder himself. In 1585, Montalto became Pope Sixtus V, in whose grossly corrupt reign the treasury was filled by the sale of favors and church positions. Thus financed, he controlled Rome and its surrounding area. His architect was therefore the chief architect of Rome, and this is what Fontana became.

His first task was to complete work on the dome of St. Peter's Cathedral, which had been left unfinished when Michelangelo died. As an architect he designed the Vatican Library, a palace, and other buildings. As a hydraulic engineer, he increased Rome's water supply and erected fountains in the city. And as a city planner, he laid out the street pattern that survives in present-day Rome. He was also in charge of setting up three obelisks in Rome and moving one from the back of St. Peter's to the Piazza in front. This was considered to be a stupendous task and established Fontana as a skilled engineer. Fontana's own account of it, published in Rome in 1590, gives a detailed picture of the engineering practices of his time.

When Sixtus died, Fontana lost his mentor. He was accused of diverting public funds to his own use, and in 1592 was removed from office without trial by the new pope. Offered the post of architect and senior engineer in Naples, Fontana moved there, married and settled there for the remaining fifteen years of his life. His Neopolitan projects included a coast road, a drainage canal, the planning of an improved port and the design for a palace.

Outstanding Engineering Achievement:

The 79-foot (24 meter) obelisk, which dates from the tenth century B.C., was taken from Egypt to Rome in 41 A.D., by orders of the Emperor Caligula. Although Rome was sacked a number of times, the obelisk survived, its pedestal gradually being buried in eroded earth and dumped garbage. Before moving it, Fontana determined its weight. He first measured it and calculated its volume. Then he weighed and measured a piece of a similar kind of stone. His final calculation yielded a weight for the obelisk equivalent to 681,221 pounds (308,996 kg). He

Contemporary drawing of Fontana's force of 800 men and 150 horses raising the obelisk in Rome.

then estimated that he could raise most of this weight with forty windlasses, and the remainder with five 50-foot (15 meters) levers. He ordered hemp cables, three inches (7.6 cm) thick, and tested them to see if they could take the strain of a four-horse windlass.

The plan was to build a tower around the obelisk to hold the pulley blocks, raise the obelisk some two feet (0.6 meter) off its pedestal, run a carriage on rollers under it, and lay it down flat. Fontana actually used 907 men and 75 horses for this, coordinating the hoisting with a trumpet. A raised level fairway of earth and timber was built to take the carriage and monolith the 780 feet (237 meters) to the new location, and the tower was taken down and reerected at the new site to help raise the obelisk again. Fontana's meticulous planning included providing food for the men, metal hard-hats for those who worked under the tower, and police to control the onlookers and enforce silence. ∎

Further Reading:

Bern Dibner, *Moving the Obelisks,* Cambridge, Mass., 1970.

James Kip Finch, *The Story of Engineering.* Garden City, New York, 1960.

J.P.M. Pannell, *Man the Builder.* New York, 1977.

W. B. Parsons, *Engineers and Engineering in the Renaissance.* Baltimore, 1939.

Hans Straub, *History of Civil Engineering.* London, 1952.

GUIDOBALDO (or GUIDO UBALDI) DEL MONTE

b. Jan. 11, 1545, Pesaro, Italy
d. Jan. 6, 1607, Montebaroccio, Italy
Italian Mathematician and Mechanical Engineer

Life and Times:

In the late Middle Ages, European scholars rediscovered the scientific work of Aristotle, mainly discussing the logic of his statements without testing them experimentally. In its turn, the Renaissance revived the philosophy of Plato and the mathematical mechanics of Archimedes [q.v.], whose works were first printed in 1543. Guidobaldo was among the Renaissance scholars who advocated the rejection of medieval thought and the complete return to the science of antiquity. In doing so, he ignored the very great differences between the Aristotelian and the Archimedean approaches, claiming that Archimedes followed Aristotle's physical principles but with mathematical proofs. Drawing on both Greeks in his treatment of statics, he considered mechanics to be the most noble of all the arts, formed from the union of physics with geometry.

After leaving the University of Padua, which he had entered in 1564, Guidobaldo studied with Commandino, who produced accurate and scholarly translations into Latin of the works of Archimedes, Pappus, and Hero [q.v.]. In 1588, Galileo [q.v.] wrote a paper on the center of gravity of various solids, and sent it to Guidobaldo for comment or help in securing a university post. Guidobaldo was impressed. He was, furthermore, a nobleman—a marchese— whose standing as an engineer was shown by his appointment, that same year, as visiting inspector of the fortifications of Tuscany. His influence persuaded the authorities to appoint Galileo to be professor of mathematics at the University of Pisa. Continuing as Galileo's patron for twenty years, Guidobaldo encouraged him to study Archimedes and Pappus, thus serving to acquaint Galileo with a tradition which he was about to overthrow.

Outstanding Engineering Achievement:

Guidobaldo wrote books on mechanics, mathematics, astronomy and perspective, and contributed to the development of drafting instruments such as proportional and elliptical compasses and a mechanism for dividing a circle into degrees. His first book, *Mechanics,* was the first systematic treatise on statics since ancient times. It gave a detailed analysis of the balance, and improved the theory of the simple machines, that is, the lever, pulley, wheel and axle, wedge and screw. He completely separated statics from dynamics, explaining that the force that holds a weight in balance must be less than the one that moves it. Therefore, the rules for one do not apply to the other. Throughout his work,

Guidobaldo considered that mechanics, which was of such use in driving the plow, moving loads, raising water, throwing up walls, and working metal, nevertheless behaved "sometimes even in opposition to the law of Nature." Apparently he accepted that opposition without questioning his understanding of physical principles. Originally written in scholastic Latin, his books were translated into the languages of the day and widely read. ■

Further Reading:

S. Drake and I. E. Drabkin, *Mechanics in Sixteenth Century Italy*. Madison, Wisconsin, 1969.

F. Klemm, *A History of Western Technology*. Cambridge, 1964.

SIMON STEVIN
b. 1548, Bruges, Belgium
d. March, 1620, The Hague, Holland
Flemish Hydraulic Engineer, Mathematician and Physicist

Life and Times:

Late sixteenth-century Holland was occupied in two major projects: draining its inland lakes and freeing itself from the colonization of Spain. At the same time, mathematicians and physicists throughout Europe were freeing themselves from the ancient concepts, and beginning to make the advances that were to lead to Newton's laws of motion. Simon Stevin was closely involved in all of these activities as an engineer, as a researcher in the theory of statics and hydrostatics, and as a writer of books that helped bring about the widespread use of decimal fractions.

Little is known of Stevin's early life, apart from his birth in what was then Flanders, and a job as a merchant's clerk or bookkeeper in Antwerp. He travelled as an engineer through northern Europe, returning to Bruges in 1577, and moving to Leyden four years later. His published work began in 1582, with a set of tables of interest. He then joined the University of Leyden, one of the first European universities to institute formal training in engineering. Stevin's next four years were extremely productive. He wrote several books on arithmetic, one on geometry, and four on statics and hydrostatics. These latter included the first proof of the law of the inclined plane, the parallelogram of forces, and an analysis of the pressure a fluid exerts on its container.

The drainage of the inland lakes of Holland had begun in the sixteenth century, resulting in the reclamation of valuable agricultural land and consequent economic expansion. While still at Leyden, Stevin attacked the technical problem of water raising, and the needed improvement of the drainage mill. By 1588 he had considerably improved the scoop wheel. In partnership with Jan Cornets de Groot, a friend who was the mayor of Delft, he constructed a number of mills with the new wheels, raising water at four times the rate of the old mills. Later Stevin published his influential work *On Mills,* in which he gave the mathematical theory of his technical developments. This was the first book on the science of hydraulics, which previously had been regarded only as a craft.

Stevin enjoyed a long and close relationship with Prince Maurice of Orange, the head of state, serving as the prince's mathematics tutor and scientific adviser, writing books on technical subjects of interest to the state, and displaying his inventiveness in each one. In 1592 he was placed in charge of the waterways of Delft. Throughout his life there was intermittent warfare as the Low Countries revolted against the domination of Spain. Stevin served in the army for some years with the simple title of Engineer. His particular concern was water defense, and he introduced the practice of flooding foreign armies in lowland areas by opening the sluices of dikes. His 1617 treatise *New Manner of Fortification by Sluices* was the first such study published in Europe. His military inventions included an entrenching tool which was a combined shovel, pick, and axe.

In 1603 Stevin was appointed Quartermaster of the States Army, a position he held to the end of his life. He married late, and spent his last years with his family in The Hague.

Outstanding Engineering Achievements:

To increase the capacity of the drainage mill, Stevin concentrated on its gearing and the scoop wheel. Anticipating the development of bevel gearing, Stevin redesigned the scoop wheel so that the gears that turned it engaged on the face instead of on the rim. A further departure was his use of six blades on the scoop wheel instead of the standard twenty or twenty-four. Each blade was fitted with leather strips to slide over the floor and sides of the wheel-race.

Stevin received a number of patents relating to dredging and moving ships across shallow water or dams, including a special type of winch. He also invented a pivoted sluice-gate for canals and harbors. A patent which he took in 1589 describes the transportation of mud, clay and sand from a dredger to land through tubes. This remarkably early version of the mud-hopper, however, proved to be impractical for the technology of its time and was not perfected until the nineteenth century, when it could be operated with a steam pump.

In engineering theory, Stevin is particularly known for his proof of the law of the inclined plane. He postulated a closed chain draped over a right-triangular wedge and hanging below it. If it were not in equilibrium, the chain would move round into a position exactly like that at the start, and the motion would continue, perpetually. Since this is absurd, he stated, the system must be in equilibrium. Cutting off the part of the chain hanging below the wedge would have no effect on that state, and therefore the weight of chain on one side of the wedge must balance that on the other, and the weights are in proportion to the lengths of the sides. From this, he showed how the parallelogram of forces can be used to give the resultant of those forces. This method still underlies the study of forces. Centuries later, demonstrating that a system would lead to perpetual motion became a recognized way of disproving the existence of such a system. Stevin was the first to use perpetual motion in this type of proof. In so doing, he showed that he totally rejected the notion that perpetual motion was possible.

In hydrostatics, Stevin showed that the pressure exerted by a fluid on the bottom of its container is a function of the area covered, the height of the fluid, and its specific gravity, but is unaffected by the shape that the fluid fills or by its total weight.

Other Achievements:

Galileo [q.v.] is popularly credited with dropping balls from a height in order to refute Aristotle's proposition that a ten-pound ball falls ten times as fast as a one-pound ball. Contrary to legend, however, Galileo never published a word about this experiment and probably never performed it. Stevin did. He and Jan de Groot dropped two balls, one ten times the weight of the other, from a height of 30 feet (9 meters) onto a board. They could not distinguish separate thuds. If one ball did take longer than the other to fall, the difference was far smaller than Aristotle maintained. This experiment, published in 1586, was part of the final overthrow of Aristotelian physics.

In his 1585 book entitled *The Tenth,* Stevin showed how decimal fractions can be handled as easily as whole numbers if one observes a few rules, such as lining up the decimal points to add or subtract. Until then, the decimal system had been used only for whole numbers, fractions being handled by the ancient system of sixtieths, as we still divide hours into minutes, seconds and (lost) trices. The book, like all his work, was written in Flemish to reach the common people; translated into French the same year and into English and scholar's Latin in 1608, it was responsible for the widespread adoption of decimal fractions. It also recommended that the ell, instead of being divided into three feet of 12 inches, be divided into tenths and hundredths, and so for each other unit, such as the rod (for land measure) and the ame (which is 100 pots Antwerp). ■

Further Reading:

R.J. Forbes and E.J. Dijksterhuis, *A History of Science and Technology.* Baltimore, 1963.

S. Stevin, "The Tenth," in H. O. Midonick, ed., *The Treasury of Mathematics.* New York, 1965.

FAUSTUS VERANTIUS
b. *1551, Dalmatia*
d. *Rome, Italy*
Italian Amateur Engineer

Life and Times:

The late-sixteenth-century interest in mechanisms was so great that even amateur engineers published books of machines comparable with those of Jacques Besson [q.v.] and Agostino Ramelli [q.v.]. One by Faustus Verantius, *Machinae Novae,* is notable for its illustrations of suspension bridges, including the earliest printed example of an iron suspension bridge. The first known use of iron chains in such a bridge was in India in 630 A.D., but while suspension bridges of bamboo and rope were built in China, this form of bridge did not exist in Europe.

Fausto Veranzio latinized his name when he entered the priesthood. He was employed as Secretary for Hungary by the Hapsburg Emperor Rudolf II, and rewarded by being made Bishop of Czanad in Hungary. He never visited the diocese, and by 1608 he had retired and entered the Barnabite monastery in Rome. One of his brother monks was Mazenta, the first biographer of Leonardo [q.v.], and it is possible

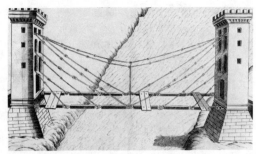

The earliest printed illustration of an iron suspension bridge, from Verantius' work of 1595.

that, through him, Verantius saw Leonardo's notebooks. One of the drawings in Verantius' book is of a parachute on a square frame, like a hang glider, that is reminiscent of one that Leonardo drew.

Outstanding Engineering Achievement:

Machinae Novae, or "New Machines," was published in 1595. Its full-page plates are explained in Latin, Italian, Spanish, French and German, and include the usual variety of machines to be found in similar books. There is a windmill with its sails rotating horizontally, a treadmill worked by a man on a gangplank on the outside of the mill, and a dredger with huge spoons that close like scissors.

Most interesting are the suspension bridges. In one, a heavy cable is held high between posts on each side of a river. Hanging on the cable by two pulleys is a box car. An endless cable is knotted to the pulleys and runs through a pulley on each post. By hauling on this cable, a rider in the box car can propel the monorail across the river.

The other suspension bridge is made of iron rods jointed to each other with eye-rings to make fourteen chains with a fair amount of flexibility. One end of each chain is mounted in one of the stone towers on either side of the river; the other end is attached to the roadway of the bridge. The roadway itself consists of planks laid across a pair of heavy chains made from iron bars linked with eyes. The longest pair of chains hangs from one tower to the other; a vertical rod attaches each to the center eye of the roadway, as in a modern suspension bridge. ■

Further Reading:

A.G. Keller, *A Theatre of Machines.* New York, 1964.

J.P.M. Pannell, *Man the Builder.* New York, 1977.

HUGH MYDDLETON
b. 1560
d. 1631
British Civil Engineer

Life and Times:

In the early seventeenth century, London's population grew rapidly. For Londoners plagued by unreliable water supplies, mainly from local wells easily contaminated by seepage from outhouses and street refuse, this abrupt expansion exacerbated an already critical problem. Parliament had frequently discussed the need for engineering works which would increase the supply of water to the northern part of London. In 1608 an Act was passed authorizing the construction of an aqueduct to carry water to London from springs in Hertfordshire, 21 miles (33.7 km) to the north as the crow flies. For five years, however, no one could be found to undertake such a formidable venture. Hugh Myddleton, a wealthy "merchant adventurer" and member of Parliament, finally agreed to finance and supervise construction of the waterway which became known as the New River.

Born into a large Welsh family, Myddleton came to London as a goldsmith's apprentice. He

Hugh Myddleton, engineer of Britain's largest water-supply project up to his time.

amassed his fortune by various means, including money-lending, marriage and mercantile investments. He needed all his wealth and ingenuity for the project, beset by repeated cost revisions and vehement opposition from landowners whose property lay along the proposed route. Finally King James I was forced to intervene, advancing half the project's cost in return for a half interest in the eventual profits. Even so, Myddleton virtually exhausted his resources on the New River, whose final cost was estimated at the equivalent of $2.5 million, an unheard-of-sum in those days.

The New River was completed and began delivering water to London in 1613, an event celebrated by public festivities. But the hoped-for profits did not begin to appear until 1640, by which time they did neither Myddleton nor King James any good. Nevertheless, Myddleton went on to other commercial ventures, including silver mines in Wales and a drainage project on the Isle of Wight. In 1622 he was knighted for his contributions to the public welfare. It was not until 1902 that London's municipal government formed a Metropolitan Water Board to take over management of the New River and other parts of the city's water supply, until then privately operated.

Outstanding Engineering Achievement:

When completed, the New River flowed 40 miles (64 km) from Chadwell Spring in Hertfordshire to Islington, where the water was stored in a reservoir. Sixty culverts and 160 bridges carried the waterway over the intervening countryside. From the reservoir, 58 wooden water pipes distributed water to London. At one time 400 miles (64 km) of wood piping ran through the city's streets. Due to constant leakage, they were later replaced by cast iron pipes. The New River was notable not for technological innovation but rather for its magnitude—it was the largest work of its kind attempted in England up to that time. Enlarged and improved, the New River supply remains part of London's water system today. ∎

Further Reading:

James Kip Finch, *The Story of Engineering.* Garden City, New York, 1960.

James Kip Finch, "Pioneer British Engineers: Makers of Civilization and History," *Engineering History,* (1963).

Rhys Jenkins, *The Collected Papers of Rhys Jenkins,* Vol. IX. Cambridge, 1936.

PETER PETT of Deptford
fl. 1560, London, England
PHINEAS PETT of Chatham
b. Nov. 1, 1570, Deptford, England
d. Aug. 21, 1647
PETER PETT of Chatham
b. Aug. 6, 1610, Deptford, England
d. 1670
British Shipbuilders

Life and Times:

British shipbuilders often passed their trade through their families for many generations. One such line was the Petts of Deptford, who held important positions in the royal shipyards from the reign of Henry VIII through the Restoration. These were important years in maritime history, as English seapower expanded and struggled with Spain and then with Holland for control of the sea lanes. It was a time when ships increased in size and armament and when the English fleet changed from partly foreign-built to mainly native-built vessels. In all these developments the Pett family played an important part.

The first Pett of prominence was Peter Pett of Deptford, the son of a shipwright also named Peter. He apparently became a shipbuilder during the reign of Henry VIII; he was master shipwright at Deptford under Edward VI and principally responsible for building most of the ships of the English Navy until his death. Pett's ships included the *Elizabeth Jonas,* one of the largest vessels to sail against the Spanish Armada. Among his apprentices and later associates was Matthew Baker, a master shipwright under Elizabeth I who left behind a valuable set of technical drawings and ship illustrations.

Peter Pett had 14 children by two marriages. Among them was Phineas Pett of Chatham, who carried on the family tradition and rose to high office under the first two Stuart kings. Though he received no training from his father, Phineas studied at Emmanuel College in Cambridge and later worked for Matthew Baker, who helped him continue his education in mathematics, drawing and the theory of shipbuilding. Baker performed an even more valuable service for Pett by introducing him to Lord Charles Howard, Earl of Nottingham, who had commanded English naval forces in the battle against the Spanish Armada. Through Howard, Pett became acquainted with other high officials, including John Trevor, surveyor of the Navy, and Robert Mansell, the royal treasurer. In 1598 Pett entered Howard's service; three years later

The 1500-ton warship Sovereign of the Seas, *designed by Phineas Pett and built by his son Peter.*

he became assistant master shipwright at Chatham, and in 1605 he succeeded his half-brother Joseph as master shipwright at Deptford. Increasingly influential at the royal court, he was named one of the Principal Officers of the Navy in 1630 and soon afterwards became a naval commissioner, responsible for supervising all construction work at the Chatham shipyard.

The first important ship built by Phineas Pett was the 1,200-ton *Royal Prince,* constructed at Deptford and launched in 1610. The trend of the time was towards more elaborate and costly ships, and the *Royal Prince* was a floating palace, suitable for royal entertainment as well as fighting. It was specially fitted out in 1613 to take the daughter of James I to her future husband, the Elector of Palatine, and again in 1623 to bring the Spanish Infanta to England as the king's bride. Charles I naturally wished to surpass the splendor of his father's principle ship, and in 1635 Pett designed a still larger vessel, the 1,500-ton *Sovereign of the Seas.* Far more heavily armed than the *Royal Prince,* the *Sovereign* saw service in three wars against Holland and the English Succession War of 1689-97. It was accidentally destroyed by fire at Chatham in 1696.

In addition to these first-rate ships, Pett constructed a number of smaller warships and re-built the *Ark Royal* and the *Merhonour,* important ships of the Elizabethan era. He also built many of the largest merchant ships of the time, including the East India Company's *Increase* and *Peppercorn* in 1609-10. Pett often exceeded the contract specifications in his private commissions, and in this way lost a good deal of money. His court connections, however, rescued him from these financial difficulties.

Phineas Pett married three times and fathered 11 children. Most of his eight sons became shipwrights; but the fifth oldest, Peter Pett of Chatham, soon emerged as his father's principal assistant and successor. As master shipwright at Woolwich he constructed the *Sovereign* after Phineas' design, and he rebuilt the *Royal Prince* in 1641. Seven years later he succeeded Phineas as naval commissioner at Chatham.

Despite his father's close royalist ties, Peter stayed at his post during the Commonwealth and helped prepare the English Navy for the first Dutch War of 1652-54. He remained in favor during the early part of the Restoration, perhaps because he was in the process of rebuilding the *Sovereign of the Seas.* His career ended abruptly during the second Dutch War, however, when Dutch naval forces surprised the laid-up English fleet in the Medway and did severe damage.

Ship	tons	keel	breadth	depth	guns	built	rebuilt
Ark Royal	828	107' (32.6 m)	37'10"	15'4" (11.5 m)	44 (4.7 m)	1587	1607–8, 1637
Merhonour	946	112' (34.1 m)	38'7" (11.8 m)	16'5" (5 m)	40	?	1613–14
Royal Prince	1187	115' (35 m)	43' (13.1 m)	18' (5.4 m)	55	1610	1641
Sovereign	1522	127' (38.7 m)	46'6" (14.2 m)	19'4" (5 m)	102	1637	1659–60, 1685

Tried by a special board of inquiry in 1667, Pett was acquitted on charges of failing to resist the Dutch but convicted on the lesser charge of using Navy ships to move his personal property. His appointment as naval commissioner was revoked, and he died soon afterwards.

Peter Pett had seven sons, but none followed their father into naval architecture. The family tradition was carried on by collateral branches of the Petts, though none attained the prominence of Phineas and Peter. Yet it is worth noting that the master shipwright Sir Phineas Pett, a cousin of Peter Pett of Chatham, built the first English warship larger than the *Sovereign:* the 1,740-ton *Britannia,* launched in 1682.

Outstanding Engineering Achievements:

The trend towards construction of larger and more heavily armed ships during the seventeenth century is evident in the details of the first-rate vessels built or rebuilt by Phineas and Peter Pett *(see chart).* These ships represent the transition from Elizabethan warships like the *Elizabeth Jonas* to the eighteenth-century ships of the line; Admiral Horatio Nelson's flagship, the *Victory,* weighed 2,000 tons.

The *Royal Prince* and the *Sovereign of the Seas* were respectively the first and second three-deck ships in the English Navy. The *Royal Prince* had four masts in the style of the previous century; by the time of the *Sovereign,* the number of masts had been reduced to three, with larger sails. Increasing size and ornamentation brought about an astounding increase in the cost of the Petts' ships: the *Royal Prince* cost 20,000 pounds to build, compared to 3,600 pounds for the *Merhonour.* This trend too continued into the next century; the H.M.S. *Victory* cost 65,586 pounds. ∎

Further Reading:

H. Farnham Burke and Oswald Barron, "The Builders of the Navy; A Genealogy of the Family of Pett," *Ancestor.* Vol. X (July 1904).

Geoffrey Callender, *The Portrait of Peter Pett and the Sovereign of the Seas.* Newport, Isle of Wight, 1930.

Dictionary of National Biography, s.v. "Pett."

W.G. Perrin, ed., *The Autobiography of Phineas Pett.* London, 1918.

E.W. Williams, "Phineas Pett, Naval Constructor," *Gentleman's Magazine.* (Sept.-Oct. 1902).

GALILEO GALILEI
b. Feb. 15, 1564, Pisa, near Florence, Italy
d. Jan. 8, 1642, Arcetri, near Florence
Italian Mathematician, Astronomer, and Physicist

Life and Times:

Galileo was a Florentine by birth and education, but he spent his most fruitful years at the University of Padua in the Venetian Republic. He was a teacher there from 1592 until 1610, and so was able to witness the last of the big land reclamation schemes in the hinterland of Venice. His interest in this work is shown by the patent he was granted for an unspecified "device for raising water and for most easily watering the land, at small expense and with great utility." This was a pump of some kind, driven by the power of a horse, and it apparently worked well when it was tested.

Later in life, when he had moved back to Florence, Galileo became involved in other land drainage schemes there. He was appointed "su-

Galileo Galilei, whose work played a vital role in the development of the principles of mechanics and the experimental method.

perintendent of the waters," and in 1630 drew up a report on the River Bisenzio with the assistance of two practicing engineers.

While he was still living in Padua, however, Galileo became involved in other practical projects. The hinterland of Venice was not only being developed for agriculture but was being made more secure from a military point of view. The Venetians were anxious to preserve their independence at a time when Austria, to the north, was growing in importance as part of the Habsburg Empire. In 1593 they began to construct the fortified town of Palmanova; its plan was a regular nine-sided polygon with bastions at the corners.

At times Galileo was called on to teach students about the design of fortifications of this kind. On one occasion also he was asked for advice about what mathematical knowledge should be required "of a perfect cavalier or soldier" in an academy or military school which was being set up to train the sons of Paduan gentlemen. Galileo's list of the subjects to be taught encompassed mechanics, navigation, drawing, military architecture and methods of calculating the range of a gun.

From the 1580s to 1610, Galileo accomplished vital work in the field of physics. He showed that, air resistance aside, objects fall at the same rate regardless of weight, and that objects moving under the influence of both horizontal and vertical forces follow a parabolic curve. This

knowledge could be used in estimating the range of artillery, and Galileo's work here reflects his interest in military engineering. Also related was the sector or "military compass," which Galileo designed for use in observation and calculation. He hired an artisan to make copies of it on a full-time basis, and the device did much to popularize instrumentation for scientific purposes.

In separate studies, in which he treated all machines as lever systems, Galileo established an approach which enabled later scientists to calculate the efficiency of machines. He also applied the theory of the lever in calculating the load which could be supported by a cantilevered beam. As a first step in establishing the science of strength of materials, this work had its limitations. But Galileo primarily intended the theory as an examination of the structural behavior of scale models. In this respect it was entirely successful, and as late as 1800, a version of the theory was being used by associates of Thomas Telford [q.v.] in analyzing tests on model components for iron bridges.

Galileo's best-known and arguably most important work was based on the astronomical discoveries he made with his telescope. In 1609, he heard about the invention of a telescope by a Dutch optician. He quickly reinvented the device and by the end of the year had enhanced the magnification sufficiently to use it for observing the heavens. His discovery of four satellites of Jupiter, the rotation of the sun, the irregularities of the moon's surface, and the phases of Venus all gave support to Copernicus' heliocentric conception of the solar system. His observations made Galileo famous throughout Europe, and established the central role of the telescope in astronomy.

In 1616, Pope Pius V declared Copernicanism a heresy. Galileo, who two years after returning to Florence in 1611 had openly spoken in favour of the Copernican view, was warned not to continue in his defense of the theory of heliocentrism. But in 1632, believing that Pope Urban VIII would permit him to speak out, he wrote a cogent defense of Copernicanism in the form of a debate. Called before the Inquisition in 1633, Galileo was convicted of heresy and forced to recant. For the remainder of his life, he was confined to his villa near Florence.

Outstanding Engineering Achievements:

About June 1609, Galileo learned of the invention by Dutch optician Hans Lippershey of a telescope of three-power linear enlargement. Lippershey invented his device by the accidental juxtaposition of a convex and concave lens. Galileo, using his knowledge of optics and geometry, reinvented the telescope in a few days. He inserted a plano-convex lens, which served as the objective, at one end of a lead tube 1.6 inches (4 cm) in diameter. At the other end, but anterior to the focus of the objective, he used a plano-concave lens as the eyepiece.

Not content merely to reproduce Lippershey's telescope, Galileo began working on improvements. His lenses, like others of his day, were sections of spherical surfaces. They were the easiest shape to make, since they required equal grinding at all points. But with his skill in grinding glass and checking the curvature of the lens, Galileo was able to improve the quality of his lenses. Furthermore, since Galileo knew that the power of his telescope was related to the ratio of the radii of the two lenses' spherical surfaces, he ground an exceptionally deep concave eyepiece. He also had to deal with the problem of spherical aberration, a phenomenon that caused fuzzy images. The problem was endemic to the spherical surface lens, since light near the center of the lens came to a different focus than light passing through near the edge. Although Galileo did not know the cause of the difficulty, he found that he could enhance image definition by covering the lens so that only the center was used. But this procedure had the disadvantage of reducing image brightness.

By the end of July 1609, Galileo had built a nine-power telescope with an improved tube made of a rolled sheet of tinned iron plate soldered at the edges and covered with crimson cotton. He displayed his work to the leaders of the Venetian Republic, presenting it as a military weapon for spotting ships before they became visible to the naked eye.

Before year's end, Galileo had constructed a 20-power telescope. With this third model, he began observing the heavens. By early January 1610, Galileo had built a fourth model, 1¾ inches (4.4 cm) in diameter and four feet (1.2 meters) long, with 33-power magnification. It was with this telescope that he was able to see four satellites of Jupiter and the moon's irregularities. This model offered the greatest magnification possible with Galileo's system of lenses.

Galileo's telescope had a short length and produced an erect image. Because of these advantages, his system of lenses still forms the basis of binoculars, or opera glasses. But because of its low magnification, its small field of vision (about one-half the apparent diameter of the moon), and its problems with spherical aberration and chromatic aberration (red rays

Model made from Galileo's design for the escapement of a pendulum clock.

have longer focal lengths than violet rays), his telescope was soon superseded as an astronomical instrument.

In 1610 Galileo transformed his telescope into a microscope by extending the distance between the two lenses. It probably gave a linear enlargement of about 36 times, but the details of its construction are not known. The Galilean microscope was soon superseded by the compound microscope, which featured two convex lenses. Some writers have claimed that Galileo invented the compound microscope, too, but the evidence is unclear.

About 1598 Galileo perfected what he called his geometrical and military compass, a pair of pivoted, movable arms to which a quadrant could be attached. Although similar instruments had existed before, Galileo added new features, including new radial scales along the arms, so that his compass became the first modern calculating instrument applicable to practical mathematical problems of all kinds. It was useful not only to mathematicians but also to engineers, navigators and others.

Between 1604 and 1606, Galileo invented a thermoscope, the antecedent of the thermometer. It was a glass bulb with a long, narrow neck inserted in a vessel of water. When the air in the bulb cooled and contracted, the water rose up the neck. When the air warmed and expanded, the water level receded. The thermoscope had no scale and could thus measure only qualitative change. In addition, since the water in the vessel was not enclosed, the thermoscope was affected by changes in the pressure of the atmosphere as well as by temperature. The device was not a practical instrument and had no effect on the engineering practice of Galileo's time. But it did stimulate further work on the problems of atmospheric pressure and the vacuum, the one unknown and the other rejected for philosophical reasons in the late sixteenth century. From Galileo the path of investigation led through the mercury barometers of Evangelista Torricelli, Galileo's assistant, and Blaise Pascal [q.v.] to the experiments of Otto von Guericke [q.v.], which definitively established the existence of a vacuum. This knowledge in turn was later important in the development of Thomas Savery's [q.v.] steam pump and the atmospheric steam engine of Thomas Newcomen [q.v.].

In 1641 Galileo, by then blind, transmitted to his son instructions for making a pendulum clock. Since the amplitude of the pendulum was small, it needed a small push during each swing to stay in motion. For this purpose and to keep the clock's mechanism functioning at a steady rate, Galileo designed an ingenious pinwheel escapement. This consisted of a wheel with twelve pins projecting from the side at right-angles and with twelve small teeth along the rim. As the pendulum swung towards the wheel, a hook-shaped pallet attached to the pendulum's axis lifted a locking mechanism from the wheel's rim; this allowed the wheel to rotate until one of the pins extending from its side struck a second hook-shaped pallet attached to the pendulum's axis. The motion of the pendulum was then reversed, and the locking mechanism was released to hook onto one of the teeth projecting from the wheel's rim, stopping its rotation until the next swing of the pendulum. Each fractional turn of the escapement wheel not only gave impetus to the pendulum but also, by means of a pinion attached to the wheel's axis, rotated the gearwork of the clock. Galileo's son never completed the mechanism. ∎

Further Reading:

Stillman Drake, *Galileo At Work: His Scientific Biography*. Chicago, 1978.

Elma Ehrlich Levinger, *Galileo: First Observer of Marvelous Things*. 1957.

Ernan McMullin, ed., *Galileo, Man of Science*. New York, 1967.

VITTORIO ZONCA

b. 1568, Padua, Italy
d. 1603, Padua, Italy
Italian Architect and Mechanical Engineer

Life and Times:

Before the tenth century the only known sources of energy were manpower, oxen and waterwheels. The development of an efficient harness then made horsepower practicable. The windmill was first mentioned in 1191 in England but was not fully developed until the sixteenth century. The falling weight of clockwork also appeared in the Middle Ages. Application of these power sources became crucial after the waves of bubonic plague in the fourteenth and fifteenth centuries, followed by other fatal diseases such as the English sweating sickness and the epidemic of virulent syphilis in 1495. All of these reduced the population to such an extent that Europe was short of workers. By the end of the sixteenth century the need for and interest in mechanization was shown in a number of books that pictured mechanisms. One was by Zonca, who is identified on the frontispiece as the "architect to the magnificent commune of Padua." Beyond that and his death date, we know nothing about him.

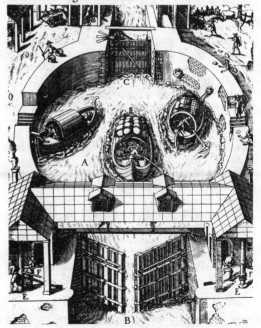

The pound lock (top), first mentioned in the West by Alberti, and the miter gate (bottom), invented by Leonardo; from Zonca's machine book.

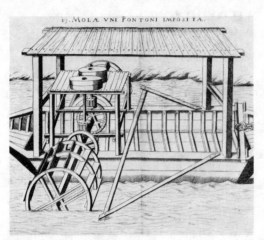

Zonca's design for a mill on board a boat, with waterwheels turned by the current.

Outstanding Engineering Achievement:

Zonca's book *New Theatre of Machines and Buildings* was posthumously published in 1607, in Italian. As in the machine book of Agostino Ramelli [q.v.], Zonca shows a wide variety of mechanisms. But whereas Ramelli's are often clearly unworkable, Zonca's (apart from a single perpetual motion machine in which a syphon pumps water onto a waterwheel) are taken to be close to the actual practice of his day. For instance, Zonca has a press with a reversing mechanism in which a pinion placed between crown wheels can be rocked from one to the other, causing the shaft through both crown wheels to reverse its direction of rotation. Meanwhile the horse that turns the pinion continues circling in the same direction. The pinion is moved by hand, and between engaging the crown wheels it can rest in neutral to allow the press to slow to a stop before being thrown into reverse.

A number of industrial processes are included. In textiles Zonca shows a watermill that simultaneously runs 240 silk spinners, and mills for finishing cloth and grinding dyestuffs. One of his devices, which is known to have been in use in Switzerland, is a barbecue spit turned by gears connected to a windmill; this is driven by the hot air forced upwards by the cooking fire itself. ■

Further Reading:

A. G. Keller, *A Theatre of Machines.* New York, 1964.

Singer et al., *A History of Technology,* Vol. III.

CORNELIS DREBBEL
b. c. 1572, Alkmaar, Holland
d. 1633, London, England
Dutch-English Inventor

Life and Times:

Cornelis Drebbel was known in his own time as an alchemist and designer of toys and curiosities that amused the royal courts on which he depended for patronage. But he was also a serious inventor who made important contributions to chemical technology, optics and pneumatics.

Born into a well-to-do Dutch family, Drebbel had already patented a water-supply system and written an alchemic treatise by the time he moved to England in 1604. He gained the attention of the English court through a "perpetual motion" device activated by changes in temperature and air pressure. King James I gave him an annuity and installed him at Eltham Palace, where he perfected his device and engaged in alchemic experiments. From these Drebbel eventually developed a new method of producing sulfuric acid, important in the manufacture of soda (see below). He also invented a brilliant red dye, known as bow-dye scarlet, which became popular throughout Europe and was used in the Gobelin tapestry works (see below).

Around 1610 Drebbel accepted an invitation by Rudolf II, Holy Roman Emperor, to visit Prague and display his inventions. He remained in Central Europe for the better part of a decade, serving as tutor to the son of Archduke Ferdinand of Bohemia, later Holy Roman Emperor. But Drebbel was imprisoned and his possessions were confiscated at the start of the Thirty Years' War when Prague was occupied by the Protestant forces of Ferdinand V, the Elector of Palatinate. Released at the request of King James, he returned to England to remake his fortune.

Despite his strict pacifism (probably the result of an Anabaptist upbringing), Drebbel agreed at this time to design weapons for the English Navy. Among these were a floating petard, or explosive-filled box, and a rudimentary submarine capable of carrying several people (see below). From 1626 to 1628 he advised English forces attempting to relieve French Huguenots besieged at La Rochelle. Failure of the effort led to criticism of Drebbel's weapons, and he fell from royal favor. Although his two sons-in-law attempted to market his inventions, Drebbel spent his last years in relative poverty and supported himself as an innkeeper.

Outstanding Engineering Achievements:

Drebbel's bow-dye scarlet was made by treating a naturally-occurring, mild red dye known as cochinal with tin or pewter dissolved in nitric acid. The process was first used in a dye works owned by Drebbel's son-in-law, Abraham Kuffler, and for many years the substance was known as "color Kufflerianus."

The process developed by Drebbel for manufacturing sulfuric acid consisted of heating sulfur and potassium nitrate, or saltpeter, in a glass or earthenware vessel. This method was simpler than others used at the time and produced a greater yield of sulfuric acid in proportion to the raw materials. Over a century later, it served as the basis for the industrial production of sulfuric acid as developed by John Roebuck [q.v.] in the lead chamber process.

Drebbel's submarine functioned like a diving bell, with an open bottom. The device was apparently steered and propelled by a rower above the surface of the water. Though tested several times, it was never used and did not anticipate the later designs of David Bushnell [q.v.] and Robert Fulton [q.v.].

Aside from alchemy, Drebbel seems to have been most interested in pneumatics. His most important invention in this area was a thermostat which could be used to regulate furnaces or ovens. The device consisted of a column of mercury attached to a bulb of enclosed air or alcohol and fastened to the side of a furnace. As the temperature rose, the expanding air or alcohol forced the mercury to rise until it pushed a lever which closed the furnace damper. A drop in temperature had the reverse effect.

Drebbel was also a skilled lens-grinder and maker of optical instruments. Although some sources credit him with inventing the compound microscope, it is more likely that he only introduced this device (along with the telescope) from the Continent to England. ∎

Further Reading:

Dictionary of National Biography, s.v. "Drebbel."

Dictionary of Scientific Biography, s.v. "Drebbel."

L.E. Harris, *The Two Netherlanders.* Cambridge, 1961.

J.R. Partington, *A History of Chemistry,* Vol. 2. London, 1961.

Gerrit Tiere, *Cornelius Drebbel (1572–1633).* Amsterdam, 1932.

INIGO JONES
b. July 15, 1573, London, England
d. June 21, 1652, London, England
British Architect

Life and Times:

The first major modern architect to emerge in England, Inigo Jones singlehandedly transformed English architecture by introducing to it Italian styles of building. Jones' carefully worked out classicism, spectacularly displayed in his masterpiece, the Whitehall banqueting house in London, eclipsed the sometimes crude classical detail of the Jacobean style which dominated English architecture at the beginning of the seventeenth century. Jones' architectural style bore the imprint of the Italian master, Andrea Palladio [q.v.], whose grand works at Vicenza Jones especially admired. Jones termed Pal-

P. 267

INIGO JONES.

Inigo Jones, the architect who introduced the Italian classical style to England.

ladio's style "masculine and unaffected," a couplet which has been frequently used to describe his own brand of Renaissance classicism.

The son of a clothworker, Jones in his youth apprenticed as a joiner in St. Paul's churchyard. Although he had some formal schooling, he was largely self-educated. Increasingly enthralled by what he called the "arts of design," he journeyed to Italy in 1603 and studied painting and perhaps the theater. He joined the court of King James I in 1605 as a designer of costumes and scenery for royal masques. In his collaboration with Ben Jonson on the production of these lavish pageants, Jones introduced Italian methods of staging. His costume designs were of a Renaissance style akin to Vasari's and heralded the fashion of the baroque theater.

It was as a royal architect that Jones gained prominence. Nevertheless, the court patronage which sustained him also meant that he had to spend much time on routine chores as Surveyor to kings James I and Charles I, or on designing costumes and sets for court masques. His best work was done for the royal family: the Queen's House at Greenwich in Kent, the Whitehall banqueting house, the Queen's chapel at St. James (now the Marlborough house chapel), and the repair of St. Paul's. In the 1630s, he designed a palace for King Charles which would clearly reflect the absolutist ideals of the king—to be funded in part by fines which the Crown levied on the City of London. The city, however, had some reason to be grateful to Jones, for he initiated the first attempts at town planning in London history. These were Lincoln's Inn Fields, laid out by Jones in 1618, and Covent Garden, which he undertook to plan in 1631.

Jones' close ties to the Stuart monarchy caused his influence to wane when England's political and social strife boiled over into civil war in the 1640s. As a supporter of the king's cause, Jones loaned Charles money, but was too old to join the Cavaliers. At the storming of the Basing House in 1645, the aging architect, apparently asleep during the battle, was captured by Cromwell's forces. He was soon released, and lived quietly until his death in 1652.

Outstanding Achievement:

Jones gave London several of its finest buildings. His architectural style, often described as "Palladian," emphasized the symmetry, monumentality, and classicism of Italian Renaissance design. The houses he designed for several wealthy nobles were centered on a cubical block dominated by the pavilion, often fronted with a single row of columns. His most celebrated buildings displayed such Italian features as coved ceilings; large, mullioned windows; rusticated masonry; stone cornices and balustrades; and low-pitched roofs. If his unexecuted plans for the royal palace reflected the absolutist ideals of the monarch, he remained rather too attached to the court, certainly the greatest but not the most influential architect in the England of his day. Quite independently of Jones, English architecture proceeded at its own pace, buffeted by the revolutionary decades and the rejection of court taste in architecture. ■

Further Reading:

Peter Cunningham, *Inigo Jones: A Life of the Architect.* London, 1849.

John Gotch, *Inigo Jones.* London, 1928.

Singer et al., *A History of Technology,* Vol. III.

John N. Summerson, *Architecture in Britain, 1530–1830.* Baltimore, 1969.

The Banqueting House on Whitehall, London, a classical building of Inigo Jones in the "Palladian" style; it is still in use.

JAN ADRIAASZ LEEGHWATER
b. 1575, De Rijp, Netherlands
d. 1650
Dutch Hydraulic Engineer

Life and Times:

By the end of the Middle Ages, the Dutch had constructed a network of dikes to protect the low-lying North Sea coastal region from inundation. They then turned their attention to reclaiming the low marshland along the seaboard for agricultural use by draining its many lakes and pools. Beginning in the mid-sixteenth century, drainage proceeded at a rapid pace. It was accomplished by drainage mills, windmill-driven scoop-wheels for raising water. At first smaller bodies of water were drained by individual entrepreneurs more interested in immediate profit than the long-term agricultural value of the reclaimed land. But early in the seventeenth century the Dutch East India Company, seeking to reinvest the capital gained in its Far Eastern enterprises, decided to finance the draining of the vast Beemster lake. About 25 miles (40 km) north of Amsterdam, this was the largest lake in the northern Netherlands. In April 1608 the Company contracted with Jan Adriaasz Leeghwater, a hydraulic engineer and millwright, to drain the lake.

The son of a poor carpenter, Leeghwater was born in De Rijp, a small village north of Amsterdam lying amidst the lakes and pools of the region. He was a self-educated man with skills in many fields, including mechanics, construction, linguistics, and sculpture. After four years of work, Leeghwater completed the Beemster project in May 1612.

Although he did not significantly improve the construction of drainage mills, Leeghwater's success at Beemster lake made him famous. One reason was the vastness and intricacy of the project, which employed 26 drainage mills. Another was his full development at Beemster of a system whereby a series of mills raised the water in stages from the lowest level of the lake to a drainage canal that surrounded it.

After completing his work at Beemster lake, the now highly-esteemed Leeghwater was called upon to supervise or consult on many drainage projects both in his native land and in the North Sea coastal areas of France, Germany, Denmark and Poland. In 1629 he helped subdue the Catholic fortress city of s'-Hertogenbosch in the southern Netherlands by draining the marshes that surrounded it. Later in life, Leeghwater gained great renown for a proposal he never implemented. It called for the draining of the 72-square-mile (186 square km) Haarlem Lake a few miles southwest of Amsterdam. In 1640 he wrote *Haarlemmermeerboek* (Book on Haarlem Lake), which proposed the use of 160 mills for draining the lake. The boldness of the plan caught the public imagination, and the book passed through seven editions within 70 years. But the project was too daunting and was not carried out until the nineteenth century, when steam engines became available to power drainage pumps.

Outstanding Engineering Achievement:

The sheer magnitude of Leeghwater's project at Beemster lake, where he reclaimed 17,000 acres of land, testified to his skill as a construction expert. A ring canal was built around the lake, its inner edge bordered by a dike. A number of drainage mills were placed around the lake near the dike, their scoop-wheels positioned to lift water into the ring canal. From there the water was channeled to one of the canal complexes built in the countryside to serve as reservoirs until the drained water could be released to the sea.

But Beemster lake was 10 feet (3 meters) deep, and the largest scoop-wheels then in use could not lift water more than four or five feet (1.2 or 1.5 meters). When the work had progressed to the point where the water level exceeded the reach of a single scoop-wheel, Leeghwater constructed a second set of mills in the deeper part of the lake. The mills at this level pumped water into intermediate storage basins, from which it was lifted by the first set of mills into the ring canal. Multi-stage water-lifting had been employed before, but it was with Leeghwater that the system received its most extensive application. He later applied the multi-stage system to other drainage projects.

Leeghwater also suggested a modification of the windmill sail, creating the type still used today. Previously, the sail-cloth had projected both in front of and behind the stock, or windmill arm, to which it was attached. When the wind suddenly changed direction, gusts began to blow on the back of the sails, which caused them to reverse their direction. Leeghwater solved the problem by replacing this sail with one attached entirely behind the stock. ■

Further Reading:

Frederick Stokhuyzen, *The Dutch Windmill*, trans. by Carry Dikshoon. London, 1962.

SALOMON DE CAUS (or DE CAUX)
b. 1576, Dieppe, France
d. 1626
French Engineer and Architect

Life and Times:

A prolific inventor and popular architect, de Caus served in several European royal courts. He tutored the Prince of Wales in London, landscaped the gardens of Heidelberg Castle in

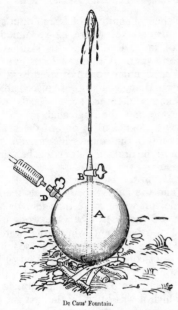

De Caus' Fountain.

De Caus' fountain, in which water is forced upward by the pressure of steam.

Germany and served as an engineer to the Elector of the Palatine before returning to France in 1623. His engineering fame results from his use of a steam-powered device to raise water in ornamental fountains. At a time when steam pressure and air pressure were considered identical, de Caus was the first to distinguish between the two and to realize the mechanical possibilities of steam. His work was an early contribution to the development of the steam engine, foreshadowing the later discoveries of Denis Papin [q.v.] and Thomas Savery [q.v.]. Though de Caus did not understand the nature or characteristics of a vacuum, he helped prepare the way for Otto von Guericke's [q.v.] work in this area.

Interested in a wide variety of mechanical devices, de Caus also improved the design of a turning lathe invented by Jacques Besson [q.v.]. The lathe turned out wooden ornaments cut to pattern, and became a predecessor of various machines that made mass production possible during the Industrial Revolution.

Outstanding Engineering Achievement:

De Caus' steam fountain was a simple device based on a steam-driven pump designed by Giambattista della Porta [q.v.]. A fire was lit beneath a partly empty water vessel connected

by pipes to a well. As the water boiled, the pressure of the steam in the top of the vessel forced water up the tube in a jet, creating a vacuum which drew water from the well. ■

Further Reading:

John D. Bernal, *Science in History,* Vol. II. London, 1965.

Arthur Fleming, *A History of Engineering.* London, 1925.

CORNELIUS VERMUYDEN
b. 1590, St. Maartenskiik, Isle of Tholen, Zeeland, Netherlands
d. 1677, England
English Hydraulic Engineer

Life and Times:

Drainage of the Great Level of the English Fens was the greatest land reclamation project ever undertaken in England, and one of the largest in the world. Covering 700,000 acres (283,000 hectares), the Fens extended inland some 35 miles (56.3 km) from the Wash, an inlet of the North Sea in eastern England. The Great Level (known today as the Bedford Level) comprised 302,000 (122,000 hectares) of these acres. Attempts to drain parts of the Great Level had been made since Roman times, but they failed for lack of the necessary resources and technology. Only in the sixteenth century did engineers and land speculators seriously consider draining the entire Great Level, and only in the seventeenth century did the project become a practical possibility. The engineer who finally accomplished the task was the Dutch-born Cornelius Vermuyden.

Vermuyden's great accomplishment was the planning and coordination of a drainage scheme which cleared the Great Level's marshes and prevented flooding by four rivers—the Nene, the Ouse, the Withan and the Welland—that flowed through the Fenland into the Wash. A survey conducted in 1589 by Humphrey Bradley a hydraulic engineer from Holland, showed that the land descended steadily in the direction of the Wash. Bradley concluded that the use of expensive drainage-mills to reclaim the Fens was unnecessary, and instead proposed a gravitational system by which "canals [would] serve to make the waters run to the sea." But political wrangling between financial interests in England and Holland delayed reclamation of the Great Level until 1630, when Vermuyden undertook the project.

Although little is known of Vermuyden's early years, some historians suggest that he may have learned the techniques of land reclamation from the Dutch hydraulic engineer Jan Leeghwater [q.v.]. When war between Holland and Spain restricted reclamation work, Vermuyden became a tax collector on the Isle of Tholen. He emigrated to England in 1621, evidently to resume his career in hydraulic engineering. Vermuyden's transition to England was eased by influential relatives—representatives of Dutch financiers—who introduced him to prominent British authorities. He soon entered into a business partnership with Sir Robert Heath, attorney general and chief justice of the common pleas during the reign of Charles I. This alliance proved beneficial to Vermuyden throughout his career as court influence was often exercised in his favor.

In 1624 Vermuyden became a British subject and, two years later, obtained permission to drain 70,000 acres (28,000 hectares) of the Royal Level of the Hatfield Chase, near the border of Yorkshire and Lincolnshire. Such a large area had never been drained in England, and Vermuyden was able to experiment with reclamation techniques he would use later at the Great Level. Meanwhile, various groups at the court of Charles I and in English and Dutch financial circles were competing to obtain the concession to drain the Great Level. Ever since Bradley's survey made drainage appear simply a matter of digging adequate canals, a handsome profit had seemed assured. Bids for the project came under review by the Commissioner of Sewers in 1630, when reclamation of the Great Level was authorized by the Lynne Law. The law allotted six years for completion of the project and required that the reclaimed land be made winter arable, or suitable for year-round cultivation.

The opportunity to drain the Level was first extended to a group of investors headed by Vermuyden, but the offer was withdrawn when he refused to accept less than 95,000 acres (38,500 hectares) as compensation for his work. A consortium represented by Francis, the fourth earl of Bedford, subsequently won the concession. In return for financing the project the group was guaranteed 95,000 acres of reclaimed land. Then the Earl announced Vermuyden's appointment as director of the works. It became apparent that all along the principal investors had been the Earl of Bedford and two anonymous partners: Vermuyden and Heath.

By 1638 the Great Level had been substantially drained. But additional reclamation work was necessary because the Level was plagued by periodic flooding, especially during the winter months, and crops could be grown only in the spring and summer. Rival land speculators attempted to nullify the Bedford group's claim to success. They contended that Vermuyden had not fulfilled stipulations set forth in the Lynne Law—work had exceeded six years and failed to render the land winter arable. As the controversy intensified, Vermuyden was attacked as an unscrupulous fortune hunter and "foreigner" who wielded undue influence in the royal court. Charles I, however, regarded Vermuyden as the only engineer in England capable of completing the project, and quashed efforts to have him dismissed as director of the works.

This dispute prompted Vermuyden to write "Discourse Touching the Drayning of the Great Fennes" (published in 1642). Intended to win the King's favor, the tract reviewed and defended Vermuyden's work at the Great Level. Despite the outbreak of the English Civil War in 1642, the Great Level was successfully drained in 1653, and Vermuyden retired two years later.

Outstanding Engineering Achievement:

The principle upon which Vermuyden based the drainage of the Great Level of the English Fens was gravitational discharge. The fall of the land in a gradual slope to the Wash caused the water to drain through a series of canals and feeder channels constructed across the Level. To prevent flooding by the Level's main rivers, he built canals extending from the point at which the rivers entered the Level to their outfalls in the Wash. Water from the Fenland's marshy surface was carried off through feeder channels which emptied into the larger canals. Vermuyden also constructed several sluices to guide water through swamps where the river courses become lost.

The success of the drainage scheme, however, depended upon one large canal that is known today as the Bedford River. This canal diverted excess flow from the river Ouse which wound thirty miles (48 km) through the Level's southern section, where it joined with three tributaries. Large enough to drain the Ouse and receive water from subsidiary channels, the canal was seventy feet (21 meters) wide and twenty-one miles (34 km) long.

Vermuyden's drainage system continued to work for a number of years after its completion in 1653. But shrinkage of the dry silt and peatlands, owing to contact with an aerobic bacteria, eventually caused the lowering of the land's surface and the Great Level flooded again. Vermuyden's successors failed to understand the actual reasons for the land's shrinkage. Believing the system of gravitational flow to be at fault, they recommended that all subsequent drainage efforts be conducted with mechanical water-raising devices. ■

Further Reading:

L. Harris, *Vermuyden and the Fens*. London, 1953.

Singer et al., *A History of Technology*. Vol. III.

Samuel Smiles, *Early Engineering*. London, 1974.

DUD DUDLEY
b. 1599
d. 1684
British Inventor

Life and Times:

Dudley is important as the first forgemaster known to have experimented with coal as a fuel for smelting iron. Charcoal, customarily used to fire blast furnaces, was becoming increasingly expensive with the depletion of England's forests. Coal was cheaper but contained sulfur and other mineral impurities which produced iron of poor quality. Though Dudley's claim to success in resolving this problem is disputed, he began a series of experimental efforts which culminated in the coke-fired blast furnace constructed by Abraham Darby I [q.v.] in 1709.

Son of the Earl of Dudley, Dud left his studies at Oxford in 1619 to manage a family-owned iron works in Staffordshire. After lengthy experiments, he was awarded a patent for smelting iron ore in a coal-fired furnace. Dudley's foundry, however, produced only pig iron, an unrefined form which had to be worked further to yield usable iron. Lacking facilities to process the metal, Dudley depended on other forgemasters to purchase his product and convert it into structural forms. Since these same forgemasters also smelted their own iron in traditional charcoal-fired furnaces, they were unlikely to form a sympathetic or receptive market. Dudley's iron was dismissed as an inferior product with a far higher content of sulfur and other impurities than charcoal-smelted iron. Despite efforts to disprove these charges in public tests, Dudley failed to prosper with his innovation. He rebuilt his furnace after it was damaged by flooding, but suffered further setbacks during England's Civil War. Eventually he was imprisoned for bad debts and his patent was revoked, leaving charcoal to dominate smelting for the rest of the seventeenth century.

Outstanding Engineering Achievement:

Dudley's furnace was a rather crude first attempt at coal-fired smelting, and claims that it produced inferior iron were probably true. The furnace used pit coal taken straight from the ground, with no attempt to remove some of the impurities through charking or coking. Sulfur, phosphorus and other substances thus passed into the iron, which made it much more brittle and difficult to refine than charcoal-smelted iron. Nevertheless, Dudley deserves credit merely for taking on the task; the problems which he confronted still plagued forgemasters using more advanced techniques a century later.

In addition to his work in iron smelting, Dudley developed a new method of tinplating, or coating iron with tin for the manufacture of domestic utensils. Though Britain was then seeking a means of curbing its tinware imports from Germany, the method did not prove commercially successful. ■

Further Reading:

Arthur Fleming, *A History of Engineering*. London, 1925.

Singer et al., *A History of Technology*. Vol. IV.

EDWARD SOMERSET, MARQUIS OF WORCESTER
b. 1601
d. 1667
British Inventor

Life and Times:

The path to invention of the steam engine begins in England with Edward Somerset, the second Marquis of Worcester. Of the many would-be inventors who tried to develop an effective mechanical water pump, Worcester is the first whose name is known to history. He apparently began his engineering work from necessity. A partisan of Charles I in Britain's civil war, he had lost his wealth by 1660 and faced imprisonment. Indeed, legend has it that he conceived the idea of a steam-operated "water commanding engine" while confined in the Tower of London. Whether Worcester knew of Salomon de Caus [q.v.], a Frenchman who proposed a device that would raise water by the suction effect of a vacuum, is uncertain. In any case, he built and demonstrated his water pump in 1663. Though Parliament granted him the right to exploit the device for a period of 99 years, he failed to improve or market it, and died in poverty. It is not known if Worcester's device had any influence on Thomas Savery [q.v.], who developed a similar steam-operated water pump 35 years later.

Outstanding Engineering Achievement:

The Marquis of Worcester's "water commanding engine" raised water to a height of 40 feet (12 meters) in its first public demonstration at Vauxhall. Exactly how it operated is uncertain, since Worcester's published description is unclear and lacks an accompanying diagram. One drawing made in conformity with his account depicts a boiler and two vessels connected by pipes to a water source. Steam from the boiler was presumably injected into the vessels and

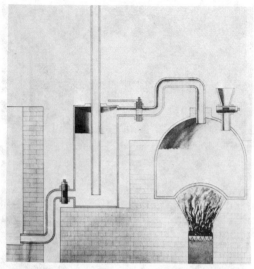

In Worcester's water pump, steam from the boiler enters the top of the other vessel and presses on the water in it, forcing water to rise up the tube.

allowed to condense, creating a partial vacuum which raised water through the pipes by the force of atmospheric pressure. The device resembled that of Savery but probably lacked some of the latter's refinements, such as a water jet for condensing steam in the vessels or a steam injection valve that drove water higher in the pipes. ■

Further Reading:

Arthur Fleming, *A History of Engineering*. London, 1925.
Rhys Jenkins, *The Collected Papers of Rhys Jenkins*. Cambridge, 1936.
Abraham Wolf, *A History of Science, Technology and Philosophy in the Sixteenth and Seventeenth Centuries*. London, 1950.

Edward Somerset, Marquis of Worcester, who built the first effective steam-operated water pump, 1663.

OTTO VON GUERICKE
b. Nov. 20, 1602, Magdeburg, Germany
d. May 11, 1686, Hamburg, Germany
German Physicist and Engineer

Life and Times:

Scientists and engineers of the Renaissance became increasingly interested in the effects of air pressure from their experience with various pumps. Galileo Galilei [q.v.] speculated as to

*Otto von Guericke who demonstrated very
dramatically that a vacuum can exist.*

why a normal suction pump could raise water no
more than 32 feet (9.7 meters), and the physicist
Evangelista Torricelli conducted experiments indicating that this limitation resulted from the
restricted force of air pressure. One unresolved
dispute in the study of pressure concerned the
existence of a vacuum and its effect on objects
exposed to it. Traditionalists accepted the ancient notion of *horror vacui,* claiming that a
vacuum cannot exist. Torricelli and others did
believe in the existence of a vacuum, but could
produce no convincing experimental evidence
for it. This achievement was the work of an
amateur German scientist named Otto von
Guericke.

Von Guericke was a lawyer by training and
public administrator by profession, serving for
most of his career in the central German city of
Magdeburg. He began as alderman in 1626 but
fled the city five years later when it was destroyed in the Thirty Years' War. After serving
as official engineer in several German states he
returned to Magdeburg, where he became
mayor in 1646. Von Guericke remained mayor
of Magdeburg for 30 years, was raised to the
nobility (an honor entitling him to preface his
name with "von") and retired to Hamburg in
1681 to escape the plague.

Parallel to his official career, von Guericke
engaged in equally important work as a scientist.
His interests encompassed the nature of electricity and magnetism as well as the existence
and properties of a vacuum. Von Guericke

began his experiments on the latter subject while
serving as mayor of Magdeburg, first developing
an air suction pump that could create a near
vacuum within a metal sphere. He performed his
first public experiment demonstrating the effects
of a vacuum at Ratisbon in 1654, followed by
another at Magdeburg in 1657 (see below).
These demonstrations effectively laid to rest the
horror vacui theory. Although von Guericke
never put his experiments to practical use, he did
show that work could be done by creating and
dispersing a vacuum (see below). This discovery
was vital to the later efforts of inventors such as
Thomas Savery [q.v.] and Thomas Newcomen
[q.v.], whose steam-powered devices depended
on the suction effect of a vacuum to perform
their tasks.

Outstanding Engineering Achievement:

Von Guericke's public experiment of 1654,
perhaps the most important of his vacuum demonstrations, involved a fixed cylinder with a 20-
inch (50 cm) diameter enclosing a piston. When
air was pumped out of the cylinder beneath the
piston, the force of air pressure above the piston
caused it to descend; even 50 men pulling on a
rope fastened to the top end of the piston could
not hold it up. Substitution of a large object for
the straining men would have resulted in the
accomplishment of work, though von Guericke
did not follow up this line of inquiry. In 1657 von
Guericke performed his famous "Magdeburg
hemisphere" experiment, fitting two large, hollow copper hemispheres together and removing
the air within them. To the astonishment of
observers, two teams of horses pulling in opposite directions could not overcome the force of
air pressure which sealed the two hemispheres
together.

*A re-enactment of von Guericke's demonstration: the
horses were unable to separate two hollow hemispheres
after the air between them had been pumped out.*

Other Achievements:

Seeking some explanation for planetary motion, von Guericke became interested in electricity and magnetism. He constructed a device for producing electric charges and became one of the first modern scientists to notice the attractive force of static electricity. Von Guericke failed, however, to distinguish clearly between magnetic and electrical phenomena. ■

Further Reading:

John D. Bernal, *Science in History.* Vol. II. London, 1954.

Dictionary of Scientific Biography, s.v. "von Guericke."

Lewis Mumford, *Technics and Civilization.* New York, 1934.

R. Taton, *The Beginnings of Modern Science.* New York, 1964.

Abraham Wolf, *A History of Science, Technology and Philosophy in the Sixteenth and Seventeenth Centuries.* London, 1950.

PIERRE PAUL RIQUET DE BONROPOS
b. 1604
d. 1680
French Civil Engineer

Life and Times:

As early as 1516, King Francis I of France consulted with Leonardo da Vinci [q.v.] on the possibility of constructing a canal to link his country's Atlantic and Mediterranean coasts. Though it was beyond the resources of the sixteenth century, French leaders did not forget the advantages to national wealth and prestige that would result from such a massive project. Only in the mid-seventeenth century did the personalities come together who made the plan a reality: Louis XIV, a king with a taste for grand public works; Jean Baptiste Colbert, an able administrator who built up the royal treasury to support the king's ambitions; and Pierre Paul Riquet de Bonropos, an ingenious civil engineer capable of planning on an almost unheard-of scale. The result was the great Canal du Midi, or Languedoc Canal.

Riquet had two qualifications for the project: engineering ability and personal wealth. Born into a noble family, he could devote ample private means to his interests. Even with the administrative skills of Colbert, the seventeenth-century state was not wealthy enough to support the entire cost of large-scale public works. Important civil engineers thus commonly invested in their own projects, hoping to profit later from tolls or other income. In the case of the Languedoc Canal, Louis XIV deputized Riquet as tax collector for the area along the waterway's route. Riquet thus financed the canal largely with his own money plus what he could raise in the countryside.

In November 1662 Riquet submitted his plan for the canal to Colbert, who promptly brought it to the king's attention. Like earlier engineers who had surveyed the route, Riquet envisioned a waterway linking the River Garonne, which flows north to the Atlantic, and the River Aude, which flows southeast into the Mediterranean. A royal commission appointed to investigate the project recommended an even more ambitious undertaking, extending from Toulouse on the Garonne to the Mediterranean, where a new port would be constructed at Sete. This was the plan eventually adopted when full-scale work began in early 1667. Riquet was named contractor with overall responsibility for the project. At its height, work on the canal involved 8,000 men divided into 12 geographical sections, each supervised by an inspector-general. Riquet died only seven months before completion of his project in May 1681. Though the canal was open to traffic from this time, further improvements were undertaken during the rest of the decade by Riquet's son, Jean Mathias.

The canal that "joined the two seas" was the wonder of Europe, by far the largest engineering work of its kind in the Western world. Voltaire called it the "most glorious monument" to the reign of Louis XIV. Riquet's work solved important problems in canal construction, and the Languedoc became a model for later canals that served the expanding economy of eighteenth-century Europe. For Riquet himself, however, the project was a mixed blessing. At a final cost of some $6 million, it absorbed most of his personal fortune. His heirs had to sell a large part of his share in the canal to pay off his debts, and waited 40 years before receiving any return on the original investment.

Outstanding Engineering Achievement:

The Languedoc Canal extends 150 miles (240 km) from Toulouse to Sete on the Mediterranean. When in use the waterway was 64 feet (19.5 meters) wide at the top and 32 feet (9.75

Pierre Paul Riquet de Bonropos, builder of the 150-mile (240 km) Languedoc Canal, the greatest French project of the century.

meters) wide at the base, with a depth of 6½ feet (2 meters). Twenty-six locks were constructed to lift vessels 206 feet (62.7 meters) from Toulouse to the summit at Naurouze, and an additional 74 locks spanned the 620-foot (190 meters) descent to Sete. Three major aqueducts, two designed by the famous military engineer Sebastian Vauban [q.v.] carried the canal across large rivers; lesser streams were diverted beneath the canal in culverts. Work on the project also included construction of road bridges, port facilities at Sete and a 180-foot (55 meters) tunnel at Malpas.

The most technically difficult part of the undertaking was ensuring an adequate water supply along the three-mile (5 km) course at the canal's summit. Riquet solved this problem by constructing two feeder channels which carried water from streams north of the canal to the summit at Naurouze. The larger of these channels, the Rigole de la Plaine, extends 27 miles (43 km) in a conduit 20 feet (6 meters) wide and nine feet (2.7 meters) deep. Riquet also built a 105-foot-high (32 meters) dam across the River Laudot, creating a reservoir with a 250 million cubic foot (7 million cubic meters) capacity which supplied the Rigole de la Plaine during the dry summer months. ∎

Further Reading:

Kranzberg and Pursell, *Technology in Western Civilization.*
Singer et al., *A History of Technology,* Vol. III.

ANDREW YARRANTON
b. 1616
d. 1684
English Civil Engineer

Life and Times:

Canal-building in England did not assume the proportions of French efforts until the industrial revolution. Still, investment from both private and public sources in the development and extension of Britain's river system began to grow after the middle of the eighteenth century. By the close of the century there were nearly 2,000 miles (3,000 km) of navigable streams in Britain, one-third of which were undertaken between 1600 and 1750.

Andrew Yarranton was the only British canal-builder whose technical command and popular influence were comparable to those of the great French civil engineers of the seventeenth century. Yarranton had vision: in his published writings he proselytized for opening up arteries of transport in England's economically expanding North. He grasped the relation between internal water transport, manufacturing and the growth of trade.

In 1677 Yarranton authored *England's Improvement by Sea and Land, to Outdo the Dutch without Fighting,* a work that was considered a classic text on river-works at the time. Yarranton regarded iron manufacture and linen production as England's most vital industries and, to hasten trade and transportation, he urged the opening up of the waterways of northwestern England.

Outstanding Engineering Achievement:

The Severn is the principal river of western Britain, and it was apparent that advantages existed in making its larger tributaries navigable. Between 1675 and 1677 Yarranton worked on a project to make the Avon navigable from Stratford to Tewkesbury, where it joins the Severn. Yarranton's efforts in this period involved the construction of flood-gates, weirs, bridges, wharves and locks. ∎

Further Reading:

Arthur Fleming, *A History of Engineering.* London, 1925.
Singer et al., *A History of Technology.* Vol. III.

FRANÇOIS BLONDEL

b. July 15, 1618, Ribemont, France
d. Jan. 21, 1686, Paris, France
French Military Engineer, Architect, Diplomat,
Educator

Life and Times:

In 1618 the Thirty Years' War broke out in central Europe. That conflict left Germany devastated and cleared the way for France's later attempt at European domination under Louis XIV; it also shaped the career of François Blondel, who was born in the year the war began. Until 1635, the French government prudently avoided direct military involvement, preferring to channel funds to the enemies of the Holy Roman Empire. Even thereafter, the French did not neglect intrigue and diplomacy, the extension of war by other means. Blondel studied the various arts of war from the very beginning of his adult life and practiced them with few interruptions throughout his career.

Blondel was the eldest son of François Guillaume Blondel, a lawyer and functionary in the Queen Mother's court. At the outbreak of hostilities with Austria, Blondel was 17. As an infantry cadet, Blondel served at the siege of Landrecies in 1637; he later began training as a naval engineer. Blondel gained the confidence of the French minister Mazarin, who sent him on a secret mission to sketch the coastal defenses of the Iberian peninsula. In 1640 Blondel played a role in the revolt by which Portugal regained its independence from Spain. But he also saw active service commanding a galley and distinguished himself in Sicily in 1647.

For several years after the war ended, Blondel built forts on the Mediterranean coast of France. His career took a new turn in 1651, when he became private tutor to the son of the French secretary of state. Blondel and his charge traveled throughout Europe for 3½ years. After this trip, Blondel was entrusted with several diplomatic missions, but by 1662 he had resumed work as an engineer. After fortifying strongpoints on the Channel and Atlantic coasts, he spent several years in the Caribbean planning the defenses of France's island possessions.

Blondel's career was reaching its zenith. In recognition of his achievements, he was admitted to the French Academy of Sciences in 1669. Two years later he was appointed professor of mathematics at the Collège Royale and was also named to head the newly created Academy of Architecture, where he lectured for eight years.

His active work continued, for Louis XIV chose Blondel in 1672 to superintend all public works in the city of Paris. Further honors followed before Blondel's death at age 68.

Outstanding Engineering Achievements:

Although Blondel strongly fortified the Channel ports of Dunkirk and Le Havre, he did his most notable military engineering work at Rochefort, near the mouth of the Charente river. The French minister Jean Baptiste Colbert had ordered the construction of a major naval base on the Atlantic coast. Blondel chose the site, planned the city and port, and in 1666 constructed the rope factory, the forges and the powder magazines of its arsenal. The famous Sebastian Le Prestre Vauban [q.v.] was responsible for the city's defenses.

At Saintes, upriver from Rochefort, Blondel devised an innovative though costly technique for founding bridges: in effect, he constructed a false river bottom. Blondel was assigned to restore the Roman bridge there, which had been severely undermined. Test borings revealed that the only firm natural foundation, a layer of clay, lay 66 feet (20 meters) below the bed of the river, far too deep for use. Blondel therefore dammed the Charente upstream of the bridge. When the waters had ebbed he dug a trench underneath the ruined bridge. There, seven feet below the natural river bed, he laid down oak beams in a checkerboard pattern the width of the river and filled the interstices with stones set in mortar. To the beams he bolted a platform of oak, and on the platform set up piers of masonry five feet (1.5 meters) in height. Rebuilt on this sturdy foundation, the bridge stood until 1845, when it was torn down.

In Paris, Blondel's principal surviving work is the Porte St. Denis, built in 1674 to celebrate French victories on the Rhine. Twenty-four meters (79 ft) high, this triumphal arch was the tallest such structure in Paris until the building of the more famous arch on the Etoile (now Place Charles de Gaulle), begun in 1806.

Blondel's theoretical work varied in quality. In 1657 he made an ill-considered attempt to correct a proposition of Galileo's on the strength of beams. But several empirical rules he formulated became canons of French architecture. Among these were his rules for designing a well-balanced staircase and for determining the dimensions of vault abutments for arches of any size. Blondel's published lectures were the principal textbook for French architects through the end of the eighteenth century. ■

Further Reading:

Dictionary of Scientific Biography, s.v. "Blondel."
Dictionnaire de Biographie Française, s.v. "Blondel."
Richard S. Kirby et al., *Engineering in History*. New York, 1956.
Hans Straub, *A History of Civil Engineering*. London, 1952.

BLAISE PASCAL

b. June 19, 1623, Clermont-Ferrand, France
d. Aug. 19, 1662, Paris, France
French Mathematician, Scientist, Inventor and Religious Thinker

Life and Times:

The seventeenth century was not an age of specialization. It was not surprising then that one person should pursue mathematical theory as well as experimental physics, create practical devices and also produce deeply religious writings. Yet Blaise Pascal was unique in the outstanding talent he displayed in these disparate fields. As a mathematician he devised new solutions to problems raised in the classical subject of conic sections; he also helped found the

Blaise Pascal, a many-sided genius who invented the first calculating machine.

mathematical theory of probability. As a scientist he elaborated the principles which formed the basis of hydrostatics and hydrodynamics, the sciences concerned with the behavior of fluids at rest and in motion. Pascal's advocacy of the importance of intuition and inner belief has deeply affected French religion and philosophy. For all that, his contributions to engineering were substantial in their own right.

The son of a mathematician and provincial administrator, Pascal received most of his education at home. He revealed his prodigious talents as a mathematician when he began studying geometry at age 12; four years later he published an innovative treatise on conic sections. A practical problem then claimed his attention. While working in his father's tax office in Rouen during the early 1640s, he conceived of a device to count the tax figures. In 1645, after three years of effort, Pascal completed construction of the first calculating machine whose movements were determined by the meshing of a train of gears. All told, mechanics hired by Pascal built 70 such machines. Pascal's device, which could add and subtract, began a line of development which led through the "calculating engine" of Charles Babbage [q.v.] to the modern science of cybernetics.

In 1646 Pascal supervised an experiment in hydrostatics confirming the assertion by Evangelista Torricelli that the atmosphere exerts pressure. Pascal's discovery dispelled the common belief that nature abhors a vacuum. It also pointed the way to long-term practical applications, since the development of the steam engine depended upon recognizing that atmospheric pressure could move a piston beneath which a vacuum had been created. The next year Pascal began writing a treatise on the behavior of fluids in which he related hydrostatics to general mechanics. An exchange of letters in 1654 with the mathematician Pierre Fermat marks the establishment of the theory of probability.

During these extremely productive years Pascal was becoming involved in Jansenism, a movement within Catholicism that practiced a rigorous morality. After a conversion experience in 1654 he abandoned science and mathematics. Instead, he applied himself to two major religious works: the *Provincial Letters*, in which he jousted with the Jesuits, and the *Pensées*, a collection of meditations. Although largely absorbed by religious problems, Pascal did at one point advocate the creation of a public transport system using omnibuses. This was his last practical interest, for prolonged ill-health led to his untimely death in 1662 at the age of 39.

Outstanding Engineering Achievements:

Pascal's mechanical calculator was analogous to the odometer first sketched by Heron of Alexandria [q.v.]. A rectangular box measuring 14 by five by three inches, the calculator contained eight windows, through each of which could be seen a number. The numbers, located on the cylindrical surfaces of drums, ranged from 0 to 9 and represented decimal places. (The last two columns, representing the subdivisions of the *livre* or pound, were not in the decimal system.) The drums were rotated by a train of gears that connected to turnstyle wheels on the box's upper face; the operator turned these wheels to rotate the corresponding drums. What made addition and subtraction possible was the ability of the machine to transfer tens, that is, to carry over from one column to another by mechanical means. This was done by the operation of a one-step ratchet: when the right-hand wheel passed 0, completing a full rotation, the gearing of the right-hand drum forced a lever to advance the next drum one step. The activation of the drum of the next higher order by the manipulation of the wheel of the next lower order drum established the technical basis for the design of digital computers.

The hydraulic press, with its multiplication of force, is predicated on Pascal's principle of hydrodynamics. Pascal observed that the pressure in an enclosed fluid is transmitted equally in all directions and that it acts with equal force on equal surfaces. He envisioned a machine comprising two cylinders of unequal diameter linked by a tube, the whole being filled with water. A small force pressing down on the narrow column of water would then cause the wider column of water to exert a crushing upwards force. It was more than a century before Joseph Bramah [q.v.] developed a practical hydraulic press. Even so, Pascal's work did have immediate practical consequences: he improved Torricelli's barometer and invented the syringe. ■

Further Reading:

Dictionary of Scientific Biography, s.v. "Pascal."

Morris Bishop, *Pascal, the Life of Genius.* New York, 1936.

Jean Mesnard, *Pascal, His Life and Works.* London, 1952.

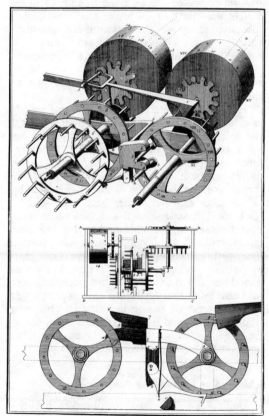

The gearing of Pascal's calculating machine, showing the mechanism for carrying 'one' over to the tens wheel whenever the unit wheel passes the zero.

CHRISTIAAN HUYGENS
b. April 14, 1629, The Hague, Netherlands
d. June 8, 1695, The Hague, Netherlands
Dutch Physicist, Astronomer, Mathematician and Optician

Life and Times:

The great Dutch scientist Christiaan Huygens, like his seventeenth-century colleague Galileo [q.v.], applied mathematics and theoretical physics with brilliant results to the solution of technical problems in engineering, particularly with regard to the production of accurate timepieces and telescopic observations. Acquainted with René Descartes since his childhood, Huygens was much influenced by Cartesian mechanistic philosophy, whose conception of a universe composed of interacting particles enabled him to construct an early version of the wave theory of light.

Christiaan Huygens, inventor of a telescope eyepiece, the micrometer, the pendulum clock, and the balance wheel.

Huygens was born into a cultured Dutch family (his father and grandfather were in the diplomatic service of the House of Orange) and began his education at home. He then attended the University of Leiden and the Collegium Arausicum at Breda, where he studied law and mathematics. From 1650 to 1666 he lived at home, where he continued his mathematical and scientific studies with the aid of his father's financial support. During this period Huygens made several journeys to Paris and London to meet with the leading thinkers and scholars of the day, including Blaise Pascal [q.v.] and Robert Boyle. He became a member of England's Royal Society in 1663. Between 1666 and 1681 he lived mostly in Paris as a member of the Académie Royale des Sciences and as the recipient of a stipend from Louis XIV; but the opposition of French Catholics to his Protestantism compelled his return to Holland, where he died in 1695.

Huygens did his early work in mathematics; his 1657 *Tractatus de ratiociniis in aleae ludo* was the first book on theories of probability. He took up the study of lens-grinding, aided by the philosopher and lens-grinder Baruch Spinoza. Improved lenses which he produced in 1655 enabled him to build a telescope of high resolving power, with which he discovered the Great

Nebula in Orion, the rings of Saturn, the surface markings of Mars, and a moon of Saturn, which he named Titan. A micrometer invented by Huygens in 1658 allowed him to measure minute angular separations between celestial objects. Modern telescopes still use his compound eyepiece, the "Huygens ocular," designed to minimize chromatic aberration.

In 1673 Huygens published his multi-volume *Horologium oscillatorium,* in which he presented his studies of pendulum and compound pendulum motion, including the isochronism of cycloidal arcs, the determination of centers of oscillations, his theory of evolutes (the curve described by a cord attached to an object moving along a cycloidal arc), the effect of centrifugal force, and the free fall of bodies along curved and inclined paths. He also studied gravitational forces, the motion of bodies in resisting media, and the possibility of intelligent life elsewhere in the universe. In the last decade of his life he developed a wave (or pulse) theory of light which postulated a serial transference of motion, like shock waves, through the minute particles which, according to Cartesian mechanistic philosophy, comprise the atmospheric medium called ether. The theory was temporarily eclipsed by Isaac Newton's [q.v.] corpuscular theory of light, but was revived a century later; both, in modified form, are now standard elements of modern physics.

Huygens' main contribution to engineering was his invention of the first accurate mechanical timepieces, which proved indispensable for his own astronomical observations, for the determination of longitude at sea, and for the general development of experimental science. In 1656 he began work on the design of a clock regulated by a pendulum, as had earlier been suggested by Galileo. The success of this device made accurate timekeeping possible and widely available and stimulated the development of more precise gear-cutting techniques. Huygens also designed a balance spring to regulate timepieces that could be used at sea. Less immediately practical but also important for future developments was a gunpowder-fired engine invented by Huygens; though never used (it was far too dangerous), it inspired his assistant, Denis Papin [q.v.], to experiment with his own engines.

Outstanding Engineering Achievements:

Galileo was the first to observe that the regular periodicity of an oscillating pendulum can be employed to keep time. He left behind a design for a pendulum-controlled clock in his

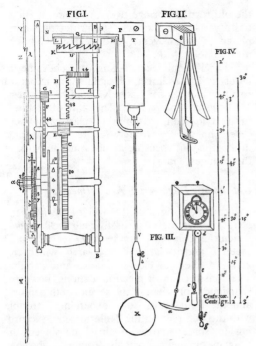

The mechanism of Huygens' pendulum clock: K, Fig. I, the crown wheel; Fig. II, the device that produced a more regular swing of the pendulum.

papers, but the device was never completed. Huygens was the first to perfect such a clock, in which the pendulum's oscillation drives the clock-hand mechanism.

All of Huygens' clocks, built to his design by the Amsterdam clockmaker Salomon da Coster, utilized the crown-wheel (verge) escapement, which transmitted motion from the pendulum to the gears by means of an oscillating weighted bar. Huygens' first clock, patented in 1657, was regulated by a freely suspended pendulum moving in a circular arc. But a pendulum describing such an arc, as Huygens soon realized, does not display regular periodicity (isochronism); rather, its period depends to a small extent on its amplitude (the distance it travels from the center to the endpoint of its oscillation). To eliminate this dependency, Huygens suspended the pendulum between two bent metal cheeks, which served to alter its path from a circular one to one which was more nearly isochronous.

Huygens' mathematical studies of 1659 proved that isochronism results when a pendulum moves on a cycloidal arc and that such an arc is produced when the pendulum's swing is defined by metal cheeks curved in a cycloidal shape and scaled to the pendulum's length. His solution proved too complex for use in the majority of pendulum clocks; instead, the general practice is to use pendulums on circular arcs with amplitudes so small that they approach isochronism. The invention of the anchor and deadbeat escapements made smaller amplitudes easier to achieve.

In the mid-1670s, realizing that pendulum clocks were ill-adapted to marine use, Huygens developed an alternative mechanism in the form of a balance spring. This consisted of a spiral spring of thin steel fixed at the outer end to a flat base and at the center to a pinion turned by a balance wheel with a heavy rim. The approximately isochronous oscillations of the self-reversing spring performed the same function as did the gravity-driven pendulum. Motion was transmitted from the turning pinion to the clock hands by means of a toothed contrate wheel. Huygens' claim to priority of invention, however, was disputed by the English physician and inventor Robert Hooke [q.v.].

Huygens' practical and theoretical studies of geometric optics and lens grinding, in which he was assisted by his brother Constantijn, resulted in the production of powerful refracting telescopes with focal lengths as long as 210 feet (64 meters). In the mid-1680s he investigated chromatic aberration and invented a compound eyepiece which utilized a second lens to compensate for aberrations in the main lens. ∎

Further Reading:

A.E. Bell, *Christiaan Huygens*. 1947.
Dictionary of Scientific Biography, s.v. "Huygens."
Singer et al., *A History of Technology*, Vol. III.

JACQUES GABRIEL
b. 1630
d. 1686
JACQUES GABRIEL II
b. 1667
d. 1742
French Architects and Engineers

Life and Times:

The ubiquitous Gabriel family played an important part in the building and architecture of France's Ancien Régime. Three generations of Gabriels left their mark on more than a century

Jacques Gabriel, the son, builder of the 1000-foot, (300 m) Bridge of Blois.

of French building design, from the later years of Louis XIV through the reign of Louis XV.

The first Jacques Gabriel and his cousin, François Mansart, established the principal French architectural firm of the seventeenth century. Their business flourished at a time when the close connection between architecture and engineering fused the roles of builder, artist and designer. Profiting from the lavish support granted by Louis XIV to building projects of all sorts, Gabriel and Mansart employed some of the most talented craftsmen of their time and set the pace for Europe's leading architects. The firm's most notable project was the Pont Royal, commissioned by the king to make the Tuileries palace more accessible to the south bank of the Seine. Begun in 1685, it became known as one of Paris's most elegant bridges.

Jacques Gabriel II began his career as an architect in the family firm, but went on to still better things. In 1716 he was named first engineer of the newly-created *Corps des Ponts et Chaussées*, an organization responsible for all civil engineering projects undertaken by the government. Though trained as an architect, Gabriel served effectively as France's chief civil engineer by appointing capable subordinates to technical posts. Shortly after his appointment his fledgling organization was called upon to rebuild

the old fortified bridge over the Loire at Blois, destroyed by floodwaters. The project was completed in seven years, and became Gabriel's most famous work.

Gabriel's son, Jacques-Ange, also became famous as an architect, designing a number of royal residences for Louis XV and his mistress, Madame de Pompadour. The shift of architectural style from baroque to classical, whose severe lines were strongly favored by Madame de Pompadour, became manifest in the work of the youngest Gabriel.

Outstanding Engineering Achievements:

Jacques Gabriel's Pont Royal is known for the attractive symmetry of its five elliptical arches, which range in span from 68 to 77 feet [21 to 23 meters], and its larger central arch, which creates the effect of elegant repose and stability. The construction of pier foundations, however, remained a problem in the seventeenth century, and the Pont Royal soon experienced trouble with the first pier on the Tuileries side. According to some sources, Gabriel employed the Belgian engineer François Romain, who had constructed notable bridges in the Low Countries, to strengthen the pier foundations with caissons. These were large, water-tight timber boxes in which repair work could proceed without danger of erosion. If this account is true, the Pont Royal was the first project to use this underwater construction technique. Gabriel was also the first bridge engineer to use pozzolana, an Italian volcanic earth, as cement. This substance facilitated pier construction because, when mixed with lime and water, it formed a natural mortar capable of setting under water without air contact.

The Bridge of Blois undertaken by Jacques Gabriel II resembled the Pont Royal in design, though built on a larger scale. Nearly 1,000 feet (305 meters) long, the bridge is supported by eleven elliptical arches, with a central span of 87 feet (26.5 meters). In order to allow adequate passage for floodwaters, Gabriel provided for slender piers, most of them only one-fifth the width of the arch span. His design ensured the stability of the bridge, which still stands today. ∎

Further Reading:

Kranzberg and Pursell, *Technology in Western Civilization*. Vol. I.

Singer et al., *A History of Technology*. Vol. III.

CHRISTOPHER WREN
b. Oct. 20, 1632, East Knoyle, Wiltshire, England
d. Feb. 23, 1723, London, England.
English Architect

Life and Times:

The architectural style of the Italian Renaissance spread to England during the seventeenth century, somewhat later than to other parts of Europe. Inigo Jones [q.v.] designed a number of neo-classical buildings in the early part of the century, but he remained an isolated figure in his own time. Only under the influence of Robert Hooke [q.v.] and Christopher Wren, the country's most famous architect, did the so-called Roman revival come fully to its own in Britain.

A clergyman's son, Wren attended Westminster School in the early 1640s and then served as assistant to a London surgeon-physician from 1646 to 1649. He received his B.A. at Waldham College, Oxford, after only two years of study. In 1653, Wren obtained his M.A. at Oxford and was elected a fellow of All Souls College, where he remained four years, engaged mainly in scientific study and experiment. He obtained the chair of astronomy at Gresham College, London, in 1657, and in 1661 was named Savilian professor of astronomy at Oxford. There and in London Wren associated with a circle of distinguished men of science, including Hooke and the chemist Robert Boyle. In 1661 he joined them in forming the Royal Society, which he served as president from 1680 to 1682.

Christopher Wren, who replaced many of London's buildings after the Great Fire of 1666.

From his teenage years, Wren was adept at designing mechanical devices, most of which stemmed from his interest in astronomy, meteorology, geometry and physics. He also made significant theoretical contributions in mathematics and physics. An inveterate experimenter, he contributed during the 1660s to the development of the laws of motion—a contribution later acknowledged by Isaac Newton [q.v.] in his *Principia*—by observing the collision of suspended balls.

In 1661 King Charles II appointed Wren assistant surveyor-general of public works, promoting him to surveyor-general in 1668. Although Wren remained at his Oxford post until 1673, these royal appointments marked his transformation from scientist to architect. He began devoting his full efforts to architecture after London's Great Fire of September 2–6, 1666, which destroyed three-fifths of the city. Just a few days later, Wren offered a reconstruction plan. His new London would have been a rational, functionally organized city with focal piazzas, broad vistas and wide streets. The plan was rejected in the interest of speedy reconstruction and because landowners did not want to be dispossessed. But Wren found ample work in reconstructing many of London's buildings.

Though Wren was near the top rank of British scientists of his time, as an architect he may be the best England has ever produced. Employing such classical features as the semi-circular arch, Roman stone pillars, ornamentation of the ancient Greek and Roman kind and the dome, Wren created a vogue in England for Renaissance architecture. Never a slavish imitator, however, Wren adapted the classical style to contemporary needs. Wren designed some 80 buildings in London and 20 in the provinces, most of them churches and other public buildings. His most famous work was St. Paul's Cathedral in London, which he rebuilt after the Great Fire. Construction began in 1675 and was completed in 1710.

Knighted in 1673, Wren retained royal favor through the reign of Queen Anne but lost his surveyor's post under King George I in 1718.

Outstanding Engineering Achievements:

The crowning achievement of Wren's architectural career was the dome of St. Paul's Cathedral, the first dome built in England. He gave many years of thought to the project, studying the domes of great French and Italian churches. He finally decided on a double dome similar to that of St. Peter's in Rome, combining the

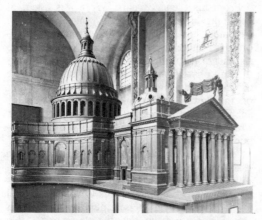

The model Wren made to demonstrate his design for St. Paul's; now on display in the cathedral.

The Sheldonian Theatre built by Wren for Oxford University, with a 70 ft. by 80 ft. wooden beam-and-truss roof.

The interior of St. Paul's, drawn soon after the cathedral was opened.

soaring appearance of a steeply curved external dome with the more intimate effect of a hemispheric internal dome. The inner dome was made of brick 18 inches (45 cm) thick, while the outer dome consisted of lead-covered timber. Wren also followed the design of St. Peter's in constructing a masonry lantern surmounted by a cross atop the outer dome. To support the 700-ton weight of the stone lantern, Wren hit upon the ingenious device of constructing an unseen brick cone, 18 inches (45 cm) thick, between the domes. Around the structure where the bases of the cone and inner dome met, he inserted a reinforcing iron band to prevent them from spreading apart. Wren added a fine aesthetic touch by allowing light to stream through an

open "eye" at the center of the inner dome. He achieved this effect by making eight openings at the top of the cone, through which light passed from invisible windows immediately below the lantern.

Another of Wren's works, the Sheldonian Theatre at Oxford, won fame for its innovative roofing. Designed in 1663, the Theatre was modeled on an open-air classical design but required a roof because of the English climate. Since the building was some 80 by 70 feet (24 by 21 meters), it could not be bridged by single pieces of timber. Taking advantage of the work on loaded beams done by Oxford mathematician John Wallis, Wren created a truss made of timbe dovetailed and tenoned into each other and bound by heavy iron bolts, straps and plates.

Other Achievements:

Wren's innovations were hardly limited to architecture. By 1654 he had invented a deaf and dumb language using hands and fingers, an instrument for writing in the dark, and a device for automatically measuring the distance travelled by a revolving coach wheel. Another early invention was a weather clock, with components for measuring wind, humidity, rainfall, temperature, and pressure over time. From the mid-1650s to the mid-1660s, Wren invented a self-emptying rain gauge; a pair of telescopes hinged and calibrated like a sextant for measuring distances between heavenly objects to half minutes; and a bowl level, mounted on a ball-and-socket joint, that lay level in all directions when a drop of quicksilver was placed at the center. In 1656, he became the first to inject a liquid directly into the bloodstream of an animal, a step that laid the foundation of modern blood transfusion. ■

Further Reading:

Harold Dorn and Robert Marli, "The Architecture of Christopher Wren," *Scientific American,* July 1981.

Harold Hutchinson, *Sir Christopher Wren.* 1976.

John Summerson, *Sir Christopher Wren.* New York, 1953.

SEBASTIAN LE PRESTRE DE VAUBAN
b. May 1633, Saint Leger de Foucheret, France
d. March 30, 1707, Paris, France
French Military Engineer

Life and Times:

The growth of urban areas and the development of gunpowder weapons after the Middle Ages drastically altered European techniques of fortification. Castles became less important as guardians of strategic geographical points, and the efforts of military engineers focused on the attack and defense of cities. The growing firepower of cannon, moreover, made the high, straight walls of medieval fortifications worse than useless. New city walls had to be built with angles that maximized the opportunity for bringing fire to bear on the enemy. A start in this direction had been made during the Renaissance by such engineers as Francesco di Georgio Martini [q.v.]. The science of fortification, however, reached its peak in the seventeenth century with the Frenchman Sebastian de Vauban.

The son of a minor nobleman, Vauban grew up in Burgundy. He began his military career at 17 during the second Fronde, or revolt against the royal government, joining the forces of the rebellious Louis II, prince de Conde. Pardoned with the rest of Conde's troops at the end of the revolt, he joined the royal army. He had already established a budding reputation for skill in the construction of fortifications, and in 1655 became a military engineer. Three years later, during a brief Franco-Spanish conflict, he added to his reputation by successfully besieging several cities in the Low Countries. Following the War of Devolution in 1667–68, he was promoted over his immediate superior to become chief military engineer of the French army.

Vauban's 56-year military career roughly coincided with the reign of Louis XIV. The skills of a military engineer were much in demand as Louis sought relentlessly to expand his kingdom; it was a period of frequent wars, punctuated by truces that served as little more than opportunities to prepare for the next conflict. Vauban spent nearly all his time on the move in France's northern and eastern border areas, constructing fortifications in peace and supervising siege operations in war. By the end of his career he had commanded at least 50 successful sieges and either designed or improved 160 fortresses. Among the cities fortified by Vauban were Lille, Tournai, Maubeuge and Neuf Brisach, the latter a new town laid out in an octagonal shape to maximize its defensibility. Perhaps his most famous success was the capture of the fortress of Namur in 1692, a struggle that pitted him against the formidable Dutch engineer M. Coehoorn.

In addition to his technical accomplishments, Vauban was known for his strong support of administrative reform, both in the army and in broader areas of government. He constantly urged creation of a unified corps of military engineers to replace the haphazard system of selection then in force. His proposals resulted in

Sebastian Le Prestre de Vauban, military engineer of at least 50 successful sieges.

1671 in creation of the *Corps du Genie,* which brought together some of the functions of military engineering in a single organization. Less successful were Vauban's suggestions for reform of the country's tax system, with replacement of onerous consumption taxes and labor levies by a single direct tax, or *dime royale.* Most of the tax abuses that Vauban complained of were not eliminated until the French Revolution.

Vauban's work was important in the development not only of military engineering, but also of civil engineering and related fields. His skills in surveying, excavation, the movement of construction materials and the management of labor gangs could readily be studied and adapted by builders of canals and other public works. Indeed, Vauban himself took time from his military duties in 1686 to design two aqueducts for the Languedoc Canal. The exigencies of fortification also influenced city planning in the late seventeenth century, not only in new towns like Neuf Brisach but also in many cities of northeastern France whose dimensions were set by Vauban's walls.

Vauban's achievements brought him ample recognition towards the end of his career. He was elected to honorary membership in the French Academy of Sciences in 1699 and named marshall of France in 1703. Two years later Louis XIV bestowed on him the highest royal honor, the Ordre du Saint Esprit. His last years were clouded by frustration, however, as the king kept him from important campaigns to make way for younger men.

Outstanding Engineering Achievements:

By the mid-seventeenth century, the design of fortifications had become an elaborate and highly mathematical science. Vauban's accomplishment was to take the individual elements of this science—the proper dimensions of walls, the angles of bastions, the placement of ditches and covered ways—and adapt them to local circumstances. Unlike many military engineers of the time, he did not have an ideal system to be applied in all situations. His work relied instead on subtlety and skill in choosing which aspects of traditional fortification technique to emphasize in a particular project. The result, according to Lazare Carnot [q.v.], another military engineer, was a series of "brilliant combinations." In his mature works, such as the fortifications of Neuf Brisach, Vauban sought to extend the defense perimeter by constructing outworks, such as

detached bastions and hornworks, beyond the main wall. He also favored backing up the outer defenses with a second wall protected by low gun chambers capable of covering any breach in the fortification. In offensive operations, Vauban was apparently the first to use a system of parallel trenches by which attackers could approach the walls of a fortress without exposing themselves to fire. He also originated the *tir à ricochet,* a method of firing a low-velocity mortar shell into a fortress so that it rebounded off interior walls, cutting down the defenders who manned them. ■

Further Reading:

Dictionary of Scientific Biography, s.v. "Vauban."

Lewis Mumford, *Technics and Civilization.* New York, 1934.

Singer et al., *A History of Technology.* Vol. III.

GIUSEPPE CAMPANI
b. 1635, Castel San Felice, Umbria, Italy
d. July 28, 1715, Rome, Italy
Italian optician and horological engineer

Life and Times:

During the seventeenth century technological advancement in western and central Europe proceeded along two fronts. Societies of scientists and engineers formed in Italy, France, and England discussed the technical possibilities of new scientific theories and discoveries. At the same time, the invention of devices such as the telescope and microscope and the increasing use of spectacles, posed practical problems of design and construction whose solutions engaged the efforts of skilled craftsmen. Among the craftsmen of the seventeenth century who fashioned these new instruments of precision, Giuseppe Campani was one of the most prodigious and inventive. At his workshop in Rome, Campani built the first lathe used to grind lenses.

Giuseppe Campani left his home in the Umbrian foothills to learn lens-grinding in Rome. He collaborated with his two brothers, one a priest, the other a Vatican clockmaker, on the construction of a silent night clock, which was completed in 1656 and presented to Pope Alexander VII. The workmanship in the clock drew attention to the Campanis' skill as craftsmen and launched Giuseppe's career.

In the early 1660s Giuseppe Campani established his workshop in Rome, and remained there until his death in 1715. After experimenting with combinations of lenses, he designed a triple ocular—an eyepiece with three lenses. Previous eyepieces had contained only two lenses. (Campani was helped by having available Venetian glass.) For the objective lens of a telescope, a large diameter is required, to gather as much light as possible. Single lenses were used, but suffered from spherical aberration (blurring of the image) and chromatic aberration (colored fringes). The greater the curvature of the lens, the more blurring it produced, so astronomers turned to less curved lenses, which had very long focal lengths. Telescopes made with them were too long for a tube; the objective was mounted with pulleys on a pole and the eyepiece was placed on a stand on the ground.

Glass lenses were generally cast in molds but Campani ground his own on an open-faced lathe of his own construction. Campani developed a reputation as a superior craftsman among the courts and scientific societies of Italy and western Europe. For a time he worked closely with Giovanni Dominique Cassini, who discovered the division in Saturn's rings that bears his name, and for whom Campani built telescopes with objective focal lengths of over 100 feet (30 m).

Outstanding Engineering Achievement:

Campani's lathe was perhaps the first face lathe, a machine that was perfected in the eighteenth century. With it, Campani could shape the face of a glass blank held in place by a horizontal rod that extended from the housing of the tool to the center of the blank. Campani fixed the glass in place in the lathe. While he adjusted the movement of the cutting and shaping tool over the glass, an assistant turned a wheel, causing the glass to rotate rapidly around the horizontal axis formed by the rod. In this way the surface of the glass was contoured. In addition to his work on telescopes Campani explored ways of improving microscopes. He was the first to use the turning of a screw to adjust the length of the tube between objective and eyepiece, which produced greater control in focusing. ■

ROBERT HOOKE

b. July 17, 1635, Freshwater, Isle of Wight, England
d. March 3, 1703, London, England
British Scientist and Inventor

Life and Times:

One of a brilliant gathering of scientists at the time when modern science had just been born, Hooke made contributions to physics, chemistry, paleogeology, mineralogy, crystallography, meteorology, microscopy, telescopy, horology, entomology and other forms of biology. He was an instrument maker, a mechanical engineer, and an architect. His drawings showed great artistic ability; and he could play the organ.

A sickly child, Hooke was fascinated by mechanical toys and models. When he was thirteen, his father, a minister, died, leaving him one hundred pounds. With this Robert was sent to London to study painting. Instead he was befriended by the master of Westminster School and received a classical education, to which Hooke added his own study of Euclid and mechanics. At Oxford he found others interested in science, including Robert Boyle and Christopher Wren [q.v.], the group that called itself the Invisible College. Working as Boyle's assistant, Hooke improved Otto von Guericke's [q.v.] air pump. Hooke's role in the experiments conducted with the pump is uncertain, but they led to a series of important publications by Boyle.

In 1660, with the restoration of the British monarchy, most of Hooke's scientific acquaintances moved to London and began regular meetings there. In 1662 the Royal Society was chartered and appointed Hooke to be its curator of experiments. He was required to demonstrate several experiments, on a great diversity of topics, at each meeting. He was well suited for the position; all his life his fertile mind produced ideas, although he rarely developed them. In 1665 he also became a lecturer at Gresham College, London. That same year, Hooke's most important publication, *Micrographia,* appeared.

After the Great Fire of London in 1666, Hooke presented a plan for laying out the streets of London in a rectangular grid. Since most of the land was subdivided into privately owned lots, the plan was not practical, but it earned Hooke a place as one of the three men responsible for resurveying the city. This was necessary because so many building lines had been obscured not only by the fire itself but also by the buildings that had been pulled down to make fire breaks. Hooke also designed several replacement buildings, including the Bedlam Hospital.

Hooke's famous feud with Isaac Newton [q.v.] began as soon as the two men had their first contact. In 1672 Newton sent his first paper to the Royal Society, describing his discovery that a prism breaks light into a spectrum, and suggesting that this showed white to be a composite of light of all colors. Even before the paper appeared in print Hooke presented a reply; he agreed with Newton's observations, which Hooke claimed to have performed "many hundreds" of times, but rejected Newton's theory in favor of the established idea that color was a modification of white light. Newton, frustrated by Hooke's failure to accept his theory, and convinced Hooke had not even tried to understand it, wrote an answer. Running for 20 pages of the Society's *Philosophical Transactions* (in contrast to the 12 of the original paper), it showed every detail of Hooke's misunderstanding. The tone of their relationship was set from then on.

Newton was not alone in having trouble with Hooke. After Christiaan Huygens [q.v.], in 1658, had used a pendulum as the regulator of the first truly accurate clock, Hooke had tried to develop an equally reliable mechanism that could be used on board ship. In 1660 he obtained backers for his invention of a timepiece regulated by the steady movement of a spring. For some reason, however, Hooke discontinued the negotiations. In 1674 Huygens produced a watch with a spiral spring as its regulator. Hooke claimed that his idea had been given to Huygens, and presented the king with a watch of his own design inscribed "Robert Hook inven. 1658." Then, continuing to work with springs, Hooke discovered the law which now bears his name, that the displacement of a spring from its equilibrium position is proportional to the force producing it. This was announced in 1678.

When Newton published the first volume of *Principia Mathematica* in 1686, Hooke again claimed that his own ideas had been adopted by others. Actually, the idea that the attraction of celestial objects is inversely proportional to the square of the distance between them was in the minds of leading scientists of the time, but none could derive the observed planetary orbits from it. Hooke did however anticipate Newton's first law of motion, for in 1679 Hooke wrote, "All bodies whatsoever that are put into a direct and simple motion will so continue to move forward in a straight line till they are by some effectual powers deflected . . ." Forms of this law had

however, already been stated by Galileo [q.v.] and René Descartes [q.v.].

Outstanding Engineering Achievements:

"For communicating a round motion through any irregular bent way," Hooke invented an early universal joint. This consists of two rods each ending in a U, and a piece in the shape of a plus sign. The vertical arm of the plus is fitted across one U and the horizontal is fitted across the other. The joint allows rotation between the plus and each U, so that the angle between the rods may vary. But any twist imparted to one rod will be carried through to the other. Hooke used this device in optical instruments, though the real need for it arose centuries later in self-propelled vehicles.

Hooke's contributions to clock-making, though often disputed, were undoubtedly significant. Whether or not Hooke is credited with invention of the spiral-spring escapement, his version of the balance spring, with a more restricted motion than Huygens', was generally adopted in the seventeenth century. Use of the balance spring permitted development of smaller timepieces, leading to the pocket watch; it also opened the way for a practical marine chronometer, since the spring, unlike the pendulum, was not affected by the roll of a ship. In addition, Hooke developed a version of the anchor escapement, a device for regulating the motion of a pendulum which greatly increased the accuracy of clocks.

Interested in meteorology, Hooke invented a wind gauge, a rain gauge, a hygrometer that used the tendency of oat fibers to curl when moistened, and versions of the barometer, trying to obtain one which reliably showed small changes of pressure. He also contributed to marine technology, designing a ship's log which measured the speed of a vessel by means of water flowing past a spinning vane; this moved a pointer on a dial to indicate the ship's speed. For taking soundings, Hooke designed a weighted, hollow cone with a small hole. As the cone was lowered, water flowed through the opening and compressed the air inside. The deeper it went, the greater the pressure, and therefore the more water would be trapped in the cone, where it would remain when brought up.

Few of Hooke's inventions were fully developed; many of his ideas were, as he admitted, just hints. Such was his prediction that a fiber could be drawn from a mucilagenous substance, much as a silkworm spins; and when working on the conduction of sound, he predicted the stethoscope.

Other Achievements:

Hooke's scientific interests included astronomy (he was among the first to observe a double star) and geology (he proposed that earthquakes were caused by the cooling and contraction of the earth's crust). But his most important contribution was in the field of biology, where he helped pioneer the art of microscopic observation. His *Micrographia* included descriptions of observations that Hooke had made with a compound microscope of his own design. Featuring his own illustrations, it was a masterpiece of insect anatomy, astounding its readers with a louse drawn 18 inches (45 cm) long, the compound eye of a fly, a bee sting, and stages in the metamorphosis of a gnat. The volume also described investigations of the colors of thin films, which Hooke obtained by peeling off layers of mica. He discovered that whether or not colors appeared depended on the thickness of the film, a relationship which he viewed as an indication that light travels in waves.

Among Hooke's posthumous works was a study of fossils which he believed to be the remains of living creatures. To explain fossils of creatures that were not known in the live state, he suggested that species change as a result of earthquakes. He also saw the possibility of dating strata by the fossils within them. ∎

Further Reading:

Frederick James Britten, *Old Clocks and Watches and Their Makers*. New York, 1969.
Dictionary of Scientific Biography, s.v. "Hooke."
Margaret Epinasse, *Robert Hooke*. 1962.

PHILIPPE DE LA HIRE
b. March 18, 1640, Paris, France
d. April 21, 1718, Paris, France
French Mechanical and Civil Engineer

Life and Times:

An engineer of widely varied interests, Philippe de La Hire was a pioneer in applying mathematical—and particularly geometrical—principles in his work. His father, a painter at the French court, was a disciple of the mathematician Gerard Desargues. As a youth, La Hire studied both art and geometry. After his father's death he continued this dual training in Venice, where he admired the masterpieces of painting and read Apollonius' work on conic sections. In 1672 he completed and published the second part of Desargues' *Traité sur la Coupe des Pierres*. La Hire solved a difficult problem of stonecutting in this work by applying his knowledge of conic sections. Several theoretical treatises followed, and in 1678 he was admitted to the Royal Academy of Sciences.

La Hire was soon assigned to a number of geodesic projects. Until 1685 he was largely occupied with surveying various points on the Atlantic and Mediterranean coasts of France, mapping the meridian of Paris and tracing the route for an aqueduct from the Eure river to Versailles. In 1682 he joined the faculty at the Collège Royal, where he taught mathematics; five years later he became professor at the Royal Academy of Architecture.

In the meantime La Hire had taken up residence at the Observatory in Paris, and in 1687 he published the first of a series of astronomical observations. These were purely empirical. Some of his continuing work in geometry was purely theoretical. But the bulk of his published work fell between these extremes. Most notable is the *Traité de Mécanique* (1695), in which La Hire applied statics to the solution of problems with arches. Also in this vein was a treatise setting forth the geometrical principles of the design of cycloidal gear teeth.

An avid experimenter, La Hire conducted the first studies of how much work a horse could accomplish. He collaborated with many leading scientists of the age and found time to edit some of their works. His only exercise was to walk from the Observatory to the Collège Royal or the Academy of Architecture, and most nights his sleep was interrupted by observations of the heavens. Nevertheless, La Hire outlived his first wife and worked until the month before he died, aged 78. He had five children, two of whom followed in his footsteps.

Outstanding Engineering Achievements:

La Hire's *Traité de Mécanique* contained descriptions and analyses of many of the machines then used in various trades. It also set forth his "smooth voussoir" theory of arches, so called because it disregarded the effect of friction between adjacent stone blocks. La Hire showed that loading should vary across the span of the arch. He based his exposition on force diagrams and link polygons which correctly showed the triangle of forces for particular points in the arch. This treatise marked the birth of graphic statics, an important tool of later civil engineers.

La Hire demonstrated that cycloid gear teeth provide continuous contact with a minimum of friction; since the toothed surfaces roll over each other, they wear out less quickly. He applied this principle to a large waterworks at Beaulieu, near Paris. For it La Hire designed a train of gears to transform the rotary motion of a windmill into the alternating motion of a piston rod in a water pump. His design was in general use until the nineteenth century.

La Hire was a fertile inventor. He improved the design of the astrolabe, the sundial, and the surveying level, adding a telescopic sight to the latter. La Hire made several planispheres six inches (15 cm) in diameter on the basis of his astronomical observations. He also invented a machine capable of showing past and future eclipses. Powered by a pendulum, it could be set to reproduce the conditions of any given year. A copy was taken to the Emperor of China, along with a number of other European curiosities; he liked La Hire's device best of all. ∎

Further Reading:

Biographie Universelle, s.v. "La Hire."

Aubrey F. Burstall, *A History of Mechanical Engineering*. London, 1968.

Maurice Daumas, *Histoire Générale des Techniques*, Vol. II. Paris, 1968.

Niels Nielsen, *Géomètres français du dix-huitième siècle*. Copenhagen, 1935.

Singer et al., *A History of Technology*. Vol. III.

ISAAC NEWTON
b. Dec. 25, 1642, Woolsthorpe, England
d. March 20, 1727, London, England
English Mathematician and Natural Philosopher

Life and Times:

Newton was not an engineer in any sense, but his three laws of motion and his concepts of mass, weight and momentum are fundamental to modern engineering theory. These concepts were developed by Newton as part of his explanation of how the planets moved in their orbits under the influence of gravity. So although the relevance of the laws of motion for engineering theory is now obvious, they were quite unconnected with it when first put forward; and only after Newton's ideas had been worked over by the great mathematicians of the eighteenth century were they applicable to engineering problems.

Newton thus stood at a pivotal point in a long process of development. He developed ideas about motion which had first been imperfectly expressed by Galileo [q.v.], Simon Stevin [q.v.] and others. He also used the discoveries made by Johannes Kepler, Galileo's contemporary, that the planets moved in elliptical orbits. But his work was in turn developed by members of the Bernoulli family, by Leonhard Euler [q.v.], and by many French mathematicians. Thus it is only in the work of Daniel Bernoulli [q.v.] that we begin to see some of Newton's ideas being applied in an engineering context. Later still, Lazare Carnot [q.v.] stands out as an engineer who developed the theory of his subject to the point where Newton's work could be assimilated.

Apart from these men, one engineer who made exceptional and unusual use of Newton's work was John Smeaton [q.v.]. He was an active astronomer as far as his engineering commitments allowed, and because of this read Newton's work on planetary motion with particular care. In it he found comments about the accuracy required in astronomical measurement which he was able to apply directly in developing his ideas about measurement in engineering.

Newton was born just about a year after Galileo died. He was sent to local schools but showed less interest in schoolwork than in building sundials and models, including a working model of a windmill that he saw under construction. He was taken out of high school to learn to manage the family farm, but now he showed more interest in books than farming, so he was sent back to school to prepare for university.

After taking his B.A. at Cambridge, he went on to his M.A., but the threat of plague closed the university for eighteen months from 1665 to 1666. During that time Newton worked out the calculus that he had started to invent before graduating, developed the generalized form of the binomial theorem, demonstrated that white light is made up of all other colors, and devised an instrument for grinding lenses into non-spherical curvatures. In considering the moon's motion as a continual fall towards the earth from straight-line motion in space, Newton surmised that it might be caused by the same force that pulls an apple down. He then worked out ele-

Isaac Newton whose laws of mechanics were the theoretical foundation of the industrial revolution, here shown demonstrating the formation of a spectrum.

ments of his theory of universal gravitation, but laid it aside for a number of years. In 1666, he returned to Cambridge, took his M.A., and in 1669 the professor of mathematics resigned in his favor.

Newton devoted much time to experiments in optics. The refracting telescope—the only type that existed—had the problem of producing colored fringes around the image. Likening this to the spectrum, Newton correctly attributed it to the fact that the different colors of light are bent through different angles as they pass through glass. Huygens had tried to minimize this effect by using three lenses of different sizes, with limited success. Newton saw no hope for improvement in refractors, and turned to a design for a reflecting telescope proposed by James Gregory of Scotland. In 1668 Newton totally altered Gregory's optical arrangement and made the first reflecting telescope. Three years later he made a second one, sent it to the nine-year-old Royal Society and was promptly elected a Fellow.

Always reluctant to publish, Newton now sent the Society his first paper. On optics, it included his theory of the composition of white light. The controversy produced by this revolutionary idea and the time Newton spent in answering tedious objections, particularly from Robert Hooke [q.v.], determined Newton not to publish again.

It was not difficult to calculate that if a planet moved in a circular orbit then the force on it would be inversely proportional to the square of its distance from the sun. Edmund Halley (of the comet), Hooke and Christopher Wren [q.v.] tried to prove that such a law could also result in elliptical orbits. All failed. In 1684 Halley consulted Newton, only to find that Newton had already completed the proof. Halley urged him to publish, even bearing some of the costs himself. For eighteen months Newton worked on his *Mathematical Principles of Natural Philosophy,* usually known by one word of the Latin title, *Principia.* He reworked every one of his proofs, which originally were in his calculus, into Euclidean geometry, in itself an extraordinarily difficult task. Written in scholar's Latin, *Principia* first appeared in 1687, and had two more Latin editions before being translated into English in 1729.

Meanwhile Gottfried Wilhelm von Leibnitz [q.v.] had published his differential and integral calculus. The general principles of Newton's form of calculus, which he called fluxions and fluents, were not published until a short reference to them was included in *Principia.* A few years later, a minor Swiss mathematician suggested in print that Leibnitz had taken his ideas from Newton. In 1704 Leibnitz protested to the Royal Society against the imputation of plagiarism, but followed this up by an anonymous hint that Newton had taken the idea from him. A bitter priority fight started between the followers of the two men. The general judgment now is that the discoveries were independent, with Newton developing calculus first but Leibnitz publishing first.

In 1692–93 Newton suffered a nervous breakdown, after which his friends obtained for him a post as Warden of the Mint. He was in charge of recoining the currency, which had become debased, and did so well at this unpopular (deflationary) task that in 1699 he was appointed Master of the Mint, at the very high salary of 1,500 pounds a year. He was knighted by Queen Anne in 1705, and when he died he received England's highest honor, never before afforded to a man of science—interment in Westminster Abbey.

Outstanding Engineering Achievements:

Principia, probably the single most important book in the history of science and technology, begins by distinguishing mass from weight, and defining momentum as mass times velocity. Newton then states his laws:

(1) Every body continues in its state of rest or uniform motion in a straight line unless it is compelled to change that state by forces impressed on it.

(2) The change of momentum is proportional to the impressed force and is in the direction in which the force acts.

(3) To every action there is always opposed an equal reaction; or, the mutual actions of two bodies upon each other are always equal, and opposite in direction.

From these laws Newton shows that Kepler's laws of planetary motion could be derived if, and only if, each planet was attracted to the sun by a force that was inversely proportional to the square of its distance from the sun. He extends this principle into his universal theory of gravitation: every particle of matter attracts every other with a force directly proportional to the product of their masses and inversely proportional to the distance between them.

The remainder of Book I covers planetary orbits, and the three-body problem of earth, sun and moon. Book II investigates the motion of

The first reflecting telescope, invented and constructed by Newton; the tube's diameter is one inch (25 mm).

bodies in a resisting medium, whether liquid or gas. This covers hydromechanics and wave motion in elastic fluids, and demonstrates that Descartes' vortex theory was inconsistent with Kepler's laws. Book III returns to problems of the solar system, proving that the earth, as was suggested from pendulum timings, was flattened at the poles; explaining the libration of the moon, and the precession of the equinoxes; and showing how the moon's gravitational pull raises tides on the waters directly below it and at the far side of the earth.

Even if Newton had not been the founder of modern mechanics, his work on optics would deserve a notable place in the history of science. His 1704 book *Opticks* is an account of his researches in this field, discussing reflection, refraction, dispersion through a prism, the rainbow, propagation, interference, permanent colors, colors in soap bubbles and the glow of flames and hot metals.

In the Newtonian telescope light enters at one end of the tube and is reflected at the other by a parabolic mirror which brings it to a focus. A small flat mirror set diagonally inside the tube diverts the reflected beam to a hole in the side of the tube, where it is magnified by the lens of the eyepiece. This arrangement is still used, particularly for small instruments.

Another optical device that Newton invented was intended for measuring the moon's position. The frame was part of a circle with a half-silvered mirror mounted at the center. The moon is viewed through a tube which can be rotated until the moon's reflection in the mirror appears to be on the horizon (visible through the unsilvered glass). The angle of rotation is then one half the altitude of the moon. This idea was incorporated by John Hadley [q.v.] in his development of the sextant.

Newton made his own glass lenses and metal mirrors. He polished them with pitch, a method that he seems to have initiated, and which is still used.

Other Achievements:

Newton's calculus enabled him to perform the mathematics required for his gravitational theory. It is fundamentally the same as is used today, but Newton's notation was not as flexible as Leibnitz's, which became standard. Had Newton done no work in mechanics or optics, his calculus, generalized binomial theorem, numerical solution of equations and other algebraic contributions would have guaranteed him a place in the history of mathematics. ■

Further Reading:

W.W. Rouse Ball, *A Short Account of the History of Mathematics*. New York, 1960.

Holmes Boynton, ed., *The Beginnings of Modern Science*. New York, 1948.

I. Bernard Cohen, *The Newtonian Revolution*. Cambridge, 1980.

Isaac Newton, *Opticks*. New York, 1952.

———, *Papers and Letters on Natural Philosophy*. Cambridge, 1958.

R.S. Westfall, *The Construction of Modern Science*. New York, 1971.

———, *Never at Rest: A Biography of Isaac Newton*. Cambridge, 1980.

DENIS PAPIN
b. Aug. 22, 1647, Blois, France
d. c. 1712, London, England
French Physicist and Inventor

Life and Times:

A French Protestant, Papin fled religious persecution in his native country when Louis XIV revoked the Edict of Nantes in 1685. Shortly before his emigration, however, he was able to serve briefly in Paris as research assistant to the celebrated Dutch scientist Christiaan Huygens [q.v.]. Papin travelled widely in England, Germany and Italy, holding the Chair of Mathematics at the University of Marburg. He became

Denis Papin, who constructed the first engine in which the condensation of steam was used to create a vacuum.

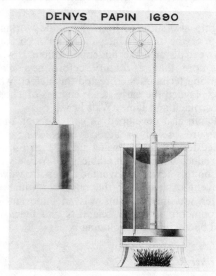

DENYS PAPIN 1690

In Papin's design for the first steam engine, steam would push up the piston; removing the fire would condense the steam, creating a vacuum and allowing atmospheric pressure to push the piston back.

interested in development of the steam engine after witnessing Huygens' experiments with a gunpowder-powered model. A member of Britain's Royal Society since 1680, Papin used the Society's resources to begin his own work on the mechanical applications of steam power.

Papin's initial efforts to create a steam pump followed Huygens in using a gunpowder explosion to create a vacuum in a cylinder. Luckily, he survived these experiments to construct the first atmospheric steam engine, in which the condensation of steam was used to produce a vacuum. On the basis of theoretical discovery alone, the steam engine should thus be credited to Papin. Papin was a man of original ideas but not, like Thomas Newcomen [q.v.], a mechanic. He thus never managed to develop anything more than a working model of his invention. The same fate befell Papin's effort to build an improved version of Thomas Savery's [q.v.] steam pump; though used once (in 1707) to power a model boat, it never proved practically successful.

Outstanding Engineering Achievement:

Papin's model steam engine had a cylinder with a 2½-inch (6.3 cm) bore and a piston capable of raising a 60-pound (27 kg) weight once a minute. Papin was on the right track, but his methods were impractical. He attempted, for instance, to use the cylinder as a boiler, and had to remove the fire from beneath it to condense the steam after each stroke of the piston. The engine also suffered from the crude workmanship of the time, which made an accurate fit between piston and cylinder impossible. It would be more than a century before new metal-working techniques corrected this defect, which also plagued the early steam engines of Thomas Newcomen and James Watt [q.v.].

Papin also developed an early version of the pressure cooker or autoclave. Known as the "digester," it heated water under high pressure to reduce bones to an edible jelly. While working on this device he invented a pressure valve to prevent explosion of the boiler in which the water was heated. This was an important development, for many scientists and mechanics had been killed by exploding boilers. ■

Further Reading:

Singer et al., *A History of Technology.* Vol. IV.

Abraham Wolf, *A History of Science, Technology and Philosophy in the Sixteenth and Seventeenth Centuries.* London, 1950.

THOMAS SAVERY
b. c. 1650, Shilston, Devon, England
d. 1715, London, England
British Mining Engineer and Inventor

Life and Times:

The steam engine owed its early development in Britain to the need of coal mines for reliable and inexpensive pumps. Indiscriminate clearing of the country's forests had resulted by the early seventeenth century in general reliance on coal for fuel. As coal seams near the surface became exhausted, shafts were sunk deeper; they often became flooded, however, by water from subterranean streams. Clearing the mines by horse-powered pumps was inefficient and expensive, and many would-be inventors sought a more economical way of doing the job. The first of these to achieve some sort of success was a mining engineer named Thomas Savery.

Born into a Puritan family with a history of military and political service, Savery held several public positions and enjoyed access to the British court. Most of his life, however, was spent devising and perfecting his many inventions. The one to which he devoted the most effort was a device called the "miner's friend," which he claimed would "raise water by the force of fire." Although there is some question about the relationship between Savery's machine and the earlier invention of the Marquis of Worcester [q.v.], Savery is generally regarded as the inventor of the first practical steam pump. In 1698 he patented the device, which he later demonstrated to King William and the fellows of the Royal Society.

But the "miner's friend" was not the commercial success which its inventor had hoped. Its capacity to raise water—about 50 feet (15 meters)—was exceeded by the depth of many mines. Though Savery established a workshop in London, he turned out few machines; most of them were used not for mine drainage but for the more manageable task of supplying water to the upper floors of large buildings. Savery later recognized the superiority of another type of steam engine invented by Thomas Newcomen [q.v.]. In 1712 he gave his consent (required by his patent on the steam pump) to construction of the first Newcomen engine at Dudley Castle. After Savery's death, the heirs to his patent rights invested in Newcomen's invention, and the "miner's friend" was superseded.

Outstanding Engineering Achievement:

Savery's engine worked on principles discovered by Otto von Guericke [q.v.] and Denis Papin [q.v.], raising water through the suction effect of a vacuum. The device had no moving parts, and consisted only of two vessels and a boiler. Steam injected from the boiler into each of the vessels was condensed by a douse of cold water on the surface of the vessel; water was drawn into the resulting vacuum and driven higher by a second injection of steam, which started the cycle again. Valves in the boiler were timed to inject steam alternately into the two vessels.

The "miner's friend" suffered from two drawbacks: its reliance on atmospheric pressure, limited to 15 pounds per square inch (a 35-foot, 10-meter water column), to force water into the vacuum; and the stress caused by the injection of high-pressure steam, which frequently ruptured the vessels and water pipes. These defects limited the pump's usefulness and reliability, making it unsuitable for use in most mines.

Savery patented a number of other inventions, most of them relating to water transport. These included a rowing machine (a pair of hand-operated paddlewheels) and a device for moving

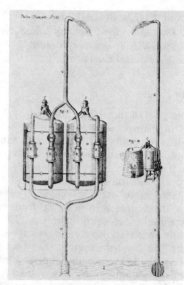

Savery's double-pumping steam engine, the first practical steam pump, condensed steam by dousing the vessel with cold water.

and placing cannons on shipboard. He also developed a double hand-bellows for foundries that provided a strong, continuous blast of air to facilitate the smelting of metal ores. ■

Further Reading:

D.S.L. Cardwell, *Steam Power in the Eighteenth Century*. New York, 1972.

Samuel Rapport and Helen Wright, *Engineering*. New York, 1963.

Hugh P. and Margaret Vowles, *The Quest for Power*. London, 1931.

Williams, *A Biographical Dictionary of Scientists*.

Abraham Wolf, *A History of Science, Technology and Philosophy in the Sixteenth and Seventeenth Centuries*. London, 1950.

HUBERT GAUTIER

b. 1660, Nîmes, France
d. 1737
French Civil Engineer

Life and Times:

The close relationship of engineering and science has not always been taken for granted, as it is in the industrialized world of the late twentieth century. Engineering was an outgrowth of the necessity of finding progressively more sophisticated solutions to practical problems of transport, communications, construction, warfare, and other elements of civilized life, while the sciences developed from the abstract study of mathematics and philosophy. Their integration was initiated by the more farsighted engineers of the eighteenth century, especially Hubert Gautier, who recognized the importance of applying scientific techniques to the planning, execution and testing of engineering projects.

Gautier spent nearly 30 years as chief government engineer of the Province of Languedoc before his appointment in 1716 as Inspector of the newly-created Corps des Ponts et Chaussées (Department of Bridges and Roads), the organization founded after the death of Louis XIV to supervise public works. Though not an innovative engineer himself, Gautier was the author of two classic handbooks, *Traité des Chemins (Treatise on Roads,* published in 1715) and *Traité des Ponts (Treatise on Bridges,* published in 1716), which summarized ancient and current engineering methods and were long regarded as standard texts in the Corps, going through several editions each.

Outstanding Engineering Achievements:

Gautier's *Traité des Ponts* (1716), a 436-page octavo volume with 30 engraved illustrations, was the first book devoted solely to the subject of bridges. It described a number of existing Roman and French structures and supplied specifications for three contemporary French bridges, including the bridge over the Loire River at Blois, then being reconstructed by the Corps after floodwaters had washed it out. These accounts included instructions on bridge design and construction, mortar composition, the quality and precision cutting of stone, and the necessity of supervising unscrupulous contractors. Gautier's advocacy of narrow piers (equal in width to one-fifth of the arch span) and reduced arch-ring thickness (equal to one-fifteenth of the arch span) was instrumental in rendering obsolete the massive piers then in use, which, by obstructing the river flow, created powerful and potentially destructive floodwaters.

A large part of *Traité des Ponts* was devoted to Gautier's views on the relationship of architecture and science to bridge-building and to engineering in general. Neither architects nor scientists, he wrote, were willing to address themselves to questions of structural mechanics, materials testing, and safety; architects, who dominated the field of bridge design, concerned themselves entirely with aesthetics, while scientists were occupied with mathematical and astronomical abstractions. Among the targets of Gautier's criticism was the mathematically-oriented civil engineer Philippe de la Hire [q.v.], whose work "is not comprehensible to those who are not savants as he is and who do not understand algebra." Gautier was particularly eager to find a scientific basis for the design of arches, which were modeled from existing examples without an adequate analysis of the stresses they were to bear. In his desire for more functional, scientifically designed bridges, Gautier was among the first engineers to reject the emphasis on aesthetic considerations in bridge design which had prevailed since the Renaissance.

In his 1715 book *Traité des chemins*, Gautier described the history of the outstanding French road system from the Roman era through the days of King Louis XIV, when increased troop movements, royal tours, internal commerce, and the establishment of a state coach service necessitated the organized maintenance of good roadways. Construction and repair of roads, according to Gautier's account, were carried out through the imposition of a poll tax and a forced-labor system (the *corvée*) on the local peasantry. The book reflected the emphasis of contemporary French engineers on surfacing rather than on laying a strong foundation; roads were built of earth, sand and gravel, compacted by the forced labor of women and girls, although Gautier noted that rain and road traffic would do the job of compacting more efficiently and economically. Royal routes were paved with stone setts laid horizontally. The methods described by Gautier remained in effect until 1764, when Pierre Tresaguet [q.v.] developed a method, later perfected by Thomas Telford of England [q.v.], of building a foundation of flat stones set vertically into the road-bed trench. ∎

Further Reading:

James Kip Finch, "Hubert Gautier's Roads and Bridges," in Neal FitzSimons, ed., *Engineering Classics of James Kip Finch*. Kensington, Maryland, 1978.

Kranzberg and Pursell, *Technology in Western Civilization*.

Abraham Wolf, *A History of Science, Technology and Philosophy in the Eighteenth Century*. London, 1952.

CHRISTOPHER POLHEM
b. Dec. 18, 1661, Visby, Gotland Island, Sweden
d. Aug. 30, 1751, Tingstaede, Sweden
Swedish Mechanical Engineer

Life and Times:

At the start of the eighteenth century, the use of iron in Europe was limited by its relatively high cost. Wrought iron, a malleable substance that could be worked into structural shapes, was formed from brittle, unrefined pig iron through a long process of repeated heating and cooling which separated out carbon and other impurities; these were then removed from the iron with repeated blows of tilt-hammers. The entire procedure was laborious and costly and left wrought iron bars of irregular shape which had to be reworked (again with hammers) into usable form. Beginning in the 1730s, British forgemasters devoted considerable effort to developing a faster and cheaper technique for producing wrought iron. The first important advance along this line, however, was the work of a Swedish factory owner, Christopher Polhem.

Born into a poor family, Polhem managed with great sacrifice to attend Uppsala University, and became a mining engineer in 1690. After

Christopher Polhem whose innovations in the manufacture of wrought iron made Sweden the world's leading producer for much of the 18th century.

several years as director of mines in Falun, he built a water-powered factory for the manufacture of tools. In 1704 he built another water-powered factory in Stjaernsund, devoted to iron and other metal products. The Stjaernsund factory was among the most advanced of its time, relying on extensive division of labor. Polhem also used such devices as hoists and conveyor belts to reduce heavy manual labor as much as possible.

Among Polhem's innovations at Stjaernsund was the large-scale use of rollers to refine and shape wrought iron bars. Rollers had been employed before in metal-working, but never so extensively or in so many ways. Heavy rollers operating at high speed could process up to 20 times more wrought iron than the traditional hammering technique. Moreover, rollers could be cut with various patterns to shape the iron as desired by the customer. In 1745 Polhem designed a rolling-mill which could refine and shape iron in a single process. Partly as a result of this advance in technique, Sweden became the world's leading producer of wrought iron for much of the eighteenth century. Some 40 years later the British inventor Henry Cort [q.v.] incorporated the rolling-mill into his puddling-and-rolling process, which further reduced the cost of producing wrought iron.

Though overshadowed by Cort and other metallurgical pioneers, Polhem was sufficiently prominent in his own time to be ennobled in 1714. In addition to his work as a mechanical engineer, he built several canals and other large public works. Polhem also used his prestige to promote such processes as mechanization and the division of labor, which later culminated in the Industrial Revolution.

Outstanding Engineering Achievement:

The rollers in Polhem's Stjaernsund factory were up to seven inches (17.7 cm) in diameter, made of wrought or cast iron with steel-hardened surfaces. Two high-speed rollers could be used to press the impurities out of an iron bar passed between them. Most rollers were also cut with grooves in various patterns to shape the metal. Operated by water wheels, the rolling mill constructed by Polhem processed up to 15 tons (13.6 metric tons) of wrought iron in 12 hours. Polhem naturally gave careful attention to the manufacture of his rollers, which were generally hand-made. He described the complicated process in his treatise *Political Testament*.

Polhem's work was important not only to metallurgical technology but also to tool-making

and factory design. As early as the 1720s he began to manufacture uniform clock gears, an early step in the mass production of standardized parts developed more fully by Eli Whitney [q.v.] and others at the turn of the century. ∎

Further Reading:

W.A. Johnson, tr., *Christopher Polhem.* Hartford, 1963.

Singer et al., *A History of Technology.* Vols. III and IV.

RENE ANTOINE FERCHAULT DE RÉAUMUR
b. Feb. 28, 1663, La Rochelle, France
d. Oct. 18, 1757, La Bermondière, France
French Mathematician, Natural Historian

Life and Times:

In 1675 the French finance minister Jean Baptiste Colbert charged the Royal Academy of Sciences with the task of describing all the crafts and industries of the kingdom. At that time most industrial processes were trade secrets; artisans jealously guarded their private recipes and passed on their knowledge only to a few apprentices. Colbert believed that if industrial techniques were made public they could more easily be examined and improved. But the Academy was slow to act, and the repeated wars of Louis XIV caused further delays. Soon after the Treaty of Utrecht in 1713, the Academy assigned René Antoine Ferchault de Réaumur to carry out Colbert's order. His subsequent investigation of the iron and steel industry marked the beginning of a new era in metallurgy.

Réaumur was born to a wealthy provincial family. His father, a judge, died when Réaumur was less than two years old. At sixteen Réaumur began to study law at Bourges, moving to Paris in 1703. There he developed an interest in mathematics and came to the attention of the mathematician Pierre Varignon, who in 1708 nominated him as a "student geometer" at the Academy of Sciences. In the following years Réaumur presented a number of papers on mathematics, experimental physics and natural history, gaining full admission to the group in 1711.

Réaumur's first and vast assignment led him to investigate the arts of working gold and precious stones, tin-plating and the manufacture of porcelain from soft paste. Réaumur was unable to identify the ingredients of the hard-paste, or true, porcelain produced in China, but his research laid the groundwork for the future triumph of the French porcelain industry. In contrast, Réaumur's impact on the ferrous metals industry was immediate, despite his lack of previous training in metallurgy or engineering.

Réaumur did not confine himself to the study of industries. He developed the thermometric scale named after him, which was much used for the rest of the century. Between 1734 and 1742 he published a six-volume study of insects and other animals, notable for the accuracy of its observations. Réaumur was quite active in the debates of the day over taxonomy, genetics, and regeneration of organs. In a series of simple but innovative experiments he clarified the nature of the digestive process in birds. A leading participant in the scientific life of his time, he served as director or subdirector of the Academy 19 times and was elected to scientific societies in five other countries as well. He never married and died two years after retiring to his country estate.

Outstanding Engineering Achievements:

In addition to observing metallurgical processes, Réaumur sought ways to improve them. He determined the best way to make steel by cementation, the laborious method of hammering and heating used in his day. He also discovered a method for removing the brittleness of cast iron. Although he did not realize its significance at the time, the nineteenth century was to see widespread exploitation of the "Réaumur process" for making malleable castings.

These advances were the result of purely empirical experimentation, yet Réaumur was also responsible for a theoretical breakthrough. He came to suspect that the greater amount of carbon present in steel was what made it harder and more brittle than wrought iron. Cast iron, in turn, had even more carbon, and showed these qualities to an even higher degree.

Finally, Réaumur introduced metallographic examination and process control to metallurgy, conducting the first scientific study of the hardness of steel. He took samples at regular intervals during manufacture. He designed an instrument for testing the hardness of metals and ranked them on a relative scale of seven substances. With another instrument, perhaps the first materials testing machine, he measured the flexibility of tempered steel wire. By fracturing

iron and steel rods and microscopically examining the structure of the exposed face, he was able to distinguish ten grades of ferrous metals. The same procedure is still used today. ∎

Further Reading:

Arthur Birembaut, "Réaumur et l'Elaboration des Produits Ferreux," *Revue d'Histoire des Sciences.* Vol. XI (1958).

A.G. Sisco, *Réaumur's Memoirs on Steel and Iron.* Chicago, 1956.

Jean Torlais, *Réaumur, un esprit encyclopédique en dehors de "L'Encyclopédie."* Paris, 1961.

FRANCIS HAUKSBEE
b. c. 1666
d. 1713
British Instrument Maker and Physicist

Life and Times:

Though not an original theoretician, Hauksbee was an ingenious experimenter who continued the work of such pioneering figures as Robert Hooke [q.v.] and Robert Boyle. He is also interesting as a transitional figure between the seventeenth and eighteenth centuries, active in areas of inquiry that attracted scientists of both periods. In part of his work Hauksbee built on discoveries of the 1600s concerning the nature and effects of a vacuum; but he also anticipated later work in electricity and magnetism.

In the early 1700s Hauksbee began to conduct experiments with electricity, an infant science then beginning to arouse public curiosity. Observing that a bluish light appeared when a barometer was shaken, Hauksbee surmised that this resulted from friction caused by the movement of mercury against the barometer's glass tube. To prove his point he constructed a rudimentary machine for producing static electricity, consisting of a piece of amber rotating against the wall of an evacuated glass vessel. He conducted many experiments, noticing the attraction and repulsion of threads by a charged sphere, and the production of light and snapping sounds. Hauksbee's work helped stimulate interest and further work in electricity.

Outstanding Achievements:

Aside from his work on the air pump, Hauksbee did not contribute directly to the

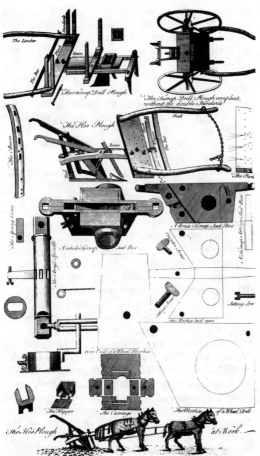

Tull's drill plough for sowing seed, with the turnipseed box; also Tull's hoe plough for cultivation between rows.

engineering of his time. His experiments, however, were of great interest to later scientists and engineers. Among his discoveries was the effect of water on the propagation of sound. When a bell sealed in an air-filled flask was lowered into water, Hauksbee found that the pitch and volume of sound produced by the bell changed appreciably. ■

Further Reading:

Dictionary of Scientific Biography, s.v. "Hauksbee."

Joseph Priestley, *The History and Present State of Electricity*. London, 1769.

Singer et al., *A History of Technology*, Vol. III.

Abraham Wolf, *A History of Science, Technology and Philosophy in the Eighteenth Century*. London, 1952.

JETHRO TULL
b. 1674
d. 1741
British Agricultural Engineer

Life and Times:

The early eighteenth century was a time of steady progress in British agricultural techniques and the development of mechanical implements. Although the Royal Society had earlier failed to improve agricultural methods, the experiments of individual farmers brought about a more scientific system of cultivation. One of the most important figures in this area was Jethro Tull.

Tull's most important invention was his seed-drill of 1701 for planting seed in rows. Previously, only two ways of sowing seed were known in Europe—broadcasting and dibbling. Smaller seeds like grain were generally thrown by hand onto plowed land, while larger seeds like potatoes were dibbled, i.e., dropped carefully into parallel series of prepared holes made in the soil. Broadcasting wasted much seed and obstructed the cultivation of the soil after the sowing process. Both systems required extensive labor and were uneconomical.

Tull's seed-drill was based on years of experimentation with seeds and sowing. He had observed that the best crops came from seeds planted thinly at a specific depth, but farm laborers resisted his attempts to sow seeds this way. Propelled to find some alternate means of planting, he developed a drill that combined the advantages of broadcasting and dibbling by sowing seeds continuously in parallel rows. The seed-drill was equipped with a bush harrow which covered over the seed after it had been deposited. In addition to saving seed and labor, the seed-drill made possible the cultivation of the soil between rows. To facilitate this, Tull drew upon French techniques and in 1714 invented the horse-hoe to take the place of the laborious hand-hoe.

Eighteenth century agriculture also saw the improvement of older traditional instruments such as the plow, which tended to be bulky and unwieldy. Around 1730 Tull invented a plow with four cutters capable of turning up weeds and burying them beneath the soil. Tull also

made the important observation that it is better
to pulverize the soil without manuring than
manuring it without pulverization. Pulverized
soil, he noted, permits rainwater, air and dew to
penetrate deeply to the roots of plants and
nourish their growth. To Tull, then, is owed the
straight, more productive lines of the modern
harvest field and the practice of keeping the soil
weeded and loose by tillage even after the crops
are sowed. He published his ideas in a book in
1731, but it was another thirty years before they
were generally adopted.

Outstanding Engineering Achievement:

Tull's seed-drill was horse drawn and deposited the seeds through notched barrels. The seed
was held in hoppers and passed through funnels
to the opened notches. Tull varied the design of
the drill for use with different seeds. ■

Further Reading:

Kranzberg and Pursell, *Technology in Western
Civilization*, Vol. I.
G.E. Fussell, *Jethro Tull*. Reading, 1973.
Abraham Wolf, *A History of Science, Tech-
nology and Philosophy in the Eighteenth Cen-
tury*. London, 1952.

SAWAI JAI SINGH II
b. 1686, Jaipur, India
d. 1743
Indian Ruler and Instrument Maker

Life and Times:

As the power of the Mughal dynasty waned in
the seventeenth and eighteenth centuries, India
experienced a major cultural efflorescence. Writers and scholars drew on native Indian, Islamic
and European ideas to create new developments
in both the arts and sciences. One of the most
interesting figures of this period was Sawai Jai
Singh II, a ruler in northwestern India who made
important contributions to astronomy and the
technology of astronomical instruments.

Jai Singh was born into the princely family
that ruled Jaipur in present-day Rajastan.
Though a member of the Sikh minority that
generally opposed the Islamic Mughals, he remained loyal for the most part to his Moslem
overlords and played a significant role in the
Mughal state. While still in his early twenties, he
helped subdue resistance to Mughal rule in

central and western India. From 1709 until his
death he served the Mughals as general and
governor in disputed territories in the area of
western India known as the Rajputana. He was
governor of Jaipur, his home state, and in 1722
became governor of Agra in northern India. In
1732 he attempted to secure control of the
province of Malwa for the Mughals, but two
years later the area was lost in the Maratha
rebellion.

As ruler of Jaipur, Jai Singh actively supported astronomers and other scientists in his
domain. He established astronomical observatories at Jaipur, Delhi, Ujjain, Benares and Mut-
tra. He also encouraged the study of Islamic and
European scientific texts, sponsoring the translation of Euclid's *Elements* and Ptolemy's *Almagest* from their Arabic versions into Sanskrit. Jai
Singh was aware of contemporary European
advances in astronomy and cultivated contacts
with Jesuit missionaries who knew of these
developments; one, the French astronomer Father Boudier, he invited to his court at Jaipur.

These actions would have been enough to
make Jai Singh famous as a patron of science.
But he pursued his astronomical interests still
further. Disturbed by discrepancies between the
predicted and actual motions of celestial bodies,
he worked with his chief court astronomer,
Jagannatha, to construct instruments that would
improve the accuracy of astronomical observations. Many of these were variations of the
gnomon, or sun-dial, a traditional device of
Hindu and Islamic astronomers. Installed in Jai
Singh's observatories, the new instruments were
used in measurements which served as the basis
for an astronomical table; named for the Mughal
ruler of the time, it was known as the *Zīj
Muhammad Shāhī*.

Outstanding Engineering Achievements:

The techniques and materials available to Jai
Singh dictated that the accuracy of an astronomical instrument increased with its size. Therefore
the devices which he designed and constructed
were enormous. One, a hollow hemispherical
dial known as the *jai prakāś*, had a diameter of
27 feet (8.2 meters); it was used to measure
declinations and azimuths. Another instrument
with the same function, a cylindrical protractor
called the *digamśa yantra*, consisted of a central
graduated pillar four feet (1.2 meters) tall and
surrounding walls eight feet (2.4 meters) in
height. Also important were the *samrāt yantra*, a
large equinoctial dial and quadrant; the *rāmyan-
tra*, a cylindrical astrolabe; and the *rāśi valaya*, a

set of 12 dials used for determining solar longitude by measuring the positions of signs of the zodiac.

One interesting feature of Jai Singh's instruments was their masonry construction. Bronze and other metals commonly used in astronomical instruments could not be cast accurately in the size and shapes which Jai Singh required; he also hoped to avoid the distortions which developed with use in metal devices. Since few of his instruments had important moving parts, they could be made primarily of mixed stone and lime. These devices can be viewed as a final extension of the gigantism that characterized measuring instruments during the Renaissance. But the future of instrument-making lay elsewhere, with clocks and new optical devices, and Jai Singh's masonry instruments remained unique. ■

Further Reading:

Cambridge History of India, Vol. IV: *The Mughal Empire.* 1922–68.

S.M. Ikram, *Muslim Civilization in India.*

PIETER VAN MUSSCHENBROEK
b. *March 14, 1692, Leiden, Holland*
d. *Sept. 19, 1761, Leiden, Holland*
Dutch Physicist

Life and Times:

In the middle of the eighteenth century, the science of electricity was still in its infancy. Although popular interest in the subject had been aroused by electricity produced artificially in the laboratory, experimenters proceeded largely by trial and error. Frictional machines could generate ample supplies of static electricity, but serious "electricians" needed a device capable of storing charges at high voltages to enable them to do more studies. The idea of storing an electrified fluid in a glass vessel had already been suggested when Professor Pieter van Musschenbroek of the University of Leiden accidentally discovered the effectiveness of what came to be known as the Leyden jar. Musschenbroek was aware of an earlier experiment by Georg Matthias Bose in 1744 which consisted of drawing a flame from electrified water in a glass, and he hoped to repeat the experiment. In 1745 J.G. von Kliest, a Pomeranian clergyman,

had received a shock while attempting to pass electricity into a glass tube through a nail, but those whom he told of it were unable to repeat his experiment. It was Musschenbroek who drew the attention of researchers and the public to this method of storing electricity.

Declining a position in his family's well-established instrument-making business, Pieter van Musschenbroek instead became one of the leading academics of his day. After receiving a doctorate in medicine from the University of Leiden in 1715, he attended lectures in London given by John Desaguliers, who was then an influential experimental physicist. In 1715 and 1719, Musschenbroek obtained doctorates in medicine and mathematics, both of which he taught, along with philosophy, at Duisburg; and, from 1723 to 1740, he taught experimental philosophy and astronomy at Utrecht. Publication of his lectures on experimental physics brought him fame and a teaching position at the University of Leiden in 1740. Following the philosophical trend of his time, Musschenbroek was a strict empiricist. He believed that scientific knowledge had to be induced from the results of practical experiments. Musschenbroek's views on the mechanics of inert bodies, heat, and electricity were widely influential. Jean-Antoine Nollet, the noted French physicist and popularizer of the Leyden jar, was his pupil at Leiden.

When Musschenbroek experimented with electrical storage in 1745 a laboratory assistant touched a conductor while also holding a charged jar that was partially filled with water, thus producing a severe electric jolt. Musschenbroek wrote a letter to the chemist R.A.F. de Réaumur [q.v.] describing the effects of the unintentional "experiment" but warned repeatedly of its potential dangers. Réaumur informed Nollet of the discovery, and Nollet wrote articles and conducted demonstrations which made it known. The Leyden jar was initially used as little more than a toy. It was fashionable for groups of people to form a circle and receive shocks together. It was, however, an essential tool for research in electricity, and was the forerunner of the modern capacitor.

Outstanding Achievement:

The Leyden jar was simply a glass container filled with water into which an electrical charge had been passed through a conductor. There was initially some doubt as to whether glass or water was the active material, until Benjamin Franklin [q.v.] demonstrated that it was indeed the glass which held the charge. ■

Further Reading:

Dictionary of Scientific Biography, s.v. "Mus-schenbroek."

R. Heilbron, *Electricity in the Seventeenth and Eighteenth Centuries.* Berkeley, 1979.

Joseph Priestley, *The History and Present State of Electricity.* London, 1767.

BERNARD FOREST DE BELIDOR
b. c. 1693, Catalonia, Spain
d. 1761, Paris, France
French Mechanical and Civil Engineer

Life and Times:

The later seventeenth and early eighteenth centuries were a time of rapid growth of state-supported engineering in France. By the mid-1700s both military and civil engineers had their own government organizations, which trained personnel and carried out important projects. The growth of a national engineering profession had the effect of standardizing practices, eliminating or restricting local variation. Under these circumstances, handbooks of practical information that provided rules, figures and diagrams were greatly appreciated by engineers. The compiler of the most heavily used engineer-

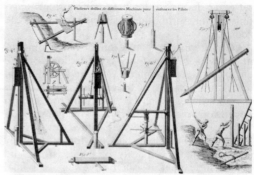

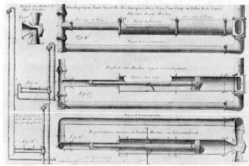

A variety of pile-driving machines from Belidor, including falling-weight hammers for use on land and over water.

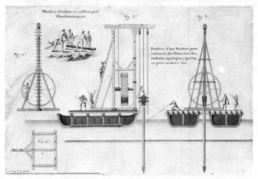

Bernard Forest de Belidor, compiler of pre-revolutionary France's most widely used engineering handbook.

Water-pressure pumping engine from Belidor; Fig. 3, general view; 4, elevation; 5, vertical cross-section; 6, horizontal cross-section.

ing handbooks in pre-Revolutionary France was Bernard Forest de Belidor.

The son of a French officer, Belidor was orphaned at an early age and grew up with a distant relative. He began his career as a mathematician but soon turned to the related science of ballistics, gaining an appointment as professor of artillery at the newly-founded La Fere military school. He eventually rose to inspector of artillery in the French army. While at La Fere he compiled a handbook for bombardiers and wrote several instruction manuals for military engineers.

Belidor also became interested at this time in the application of science to engineering problems. His researches in this area led to his first popular engineering handbook, *La Science des Ingenieurs* (1729), which discussed principles of statics relating to the strength of various building materials and the stability of architectural designs. Shortly afterwards he began compiling his magnum opus, a four-volume work on hydraulic engineering. Entitled *Architecture hydraulique,* it was published between 1737 and 1753. Both works gave Belidor an international reputation, exerting particular influence in England. Due to their great popularity, they went through so many reprintings that the copper plates originally used in the presses wore out and had to be replaced.

Outstanding Engineering Achievement:

Belidor's *Architecture hydraulique* is a thorough compendium of contemporary knowledge on marine structures, bridges, canals, pumping stations and the devices used to construct them. The work is about evenly divided between what we would today call mechanical and civil engineering. Volume I deals with engineering mechanics and the fundamental principles of hydraulics, including hydrostatics, capillarity and water flow from a vessel. Volume II describes water wheels and other machinery used to provide power from flowing water. Volume III discusses pumps and pumping stations, the design of ornamental fountains and the distribution of water in pipe systems. The final volume is devoted to the construction of shipping facilities such as harbors, lighthouses, canals and locks; it also deals with some of the agricultural applications of hydraulic engineering, including river control, land drainage and irrigation. Belidor provides ample theoretical discussion of these topics, but is careful, as ever, to derive his rules and recommendations from practical experience. The work's 200 illustrations are accurate in detail. According to modern engineering sources, *Architecture hydraulique* indicates a surprisingly high level of mechanical knowledge for a pre-industrial society. ∎

Further Reading:

Dictionary of Scientific Biography, s.v. "De Belidor."

James Kip Finch, *The Story of Engineering.* Garden City, New York, 1960.
Hans Straub, *A History of Civil Engineering.* London, 1956.

JOHN HARRISON
b. March, 1693, Foulby, Yorkshire, England
d. March 24, 1776, London, England
British Mechanical Engineer and Clockmaker

Life and Times:

The seventeenth and eighteenth centuries saw repeated attempts to solve the problem of longitude determination. Navigators could derive latitude from relatively simple astronomical observations, but the determination of longitude involved comparing local time with that of the Greenwich meridian, which is absolute solar, or standard, time. The only practical method for a ship at sea to determine Greenwich time was by a precise clock set at Greenwich time. Christiaan Huygens [q.v.] solved the problem theoretically by applying Galileo's laws of motion of the pendulum to the regulation of a clock mechanism, but this could not be used on board ship,

John Harrison, inventor of the marine chronometer that solved the problem of determining longitude at sea.

where the pitch and roll of the vessel disturbed the operation of a pendulum clock. A practical solution to this problem came only with the invention of John Harrison's marine chronometer in 1759 and its adoption by the British Admiralty in 1764.

Harrison's background was typical of the eighteenth century clockmaker. The son of a minor artisan (a carpenter and clock-repairer), he received almost no formal education. As a child, he moved with his family to Barrow-upon-Humber, Lincolnshire, where he was soon employed in his father's carpentry shop. Harrison eventually established a clockmaking business with his brother, and they acquired a reputation for the construction of excellent wooden clocks of ingenious design. Harrison was regarded as one of the most skilled precision mechanics of his day, and his numerous innovations (see below) significantly improved the accuracy and reliability of clocks and watches.

In 1713, the Board of Longitude of the British Parliament offered a £20,000 prize for the invention of a timepiece capable of determining longitude at sea within thirty minutes of arc, or one-half degree, maximum of error. The startlingly large sum indicated the critical need for precise determination of a ship's position at sea as England's economic and military growth became increasingly dependent upon overseas ventures. Between 1735 and 1759, Harrison constructed four chronometers that became more compact and more accurate with each successive design.

Unlike previous models, the fourth timepiece did not have to be mounted or firmly supported upon a ship's deck; it was the size of a pocket-watch and had hour-, minute-, and second-hands. Tested for accuracy in many voyages of great distance, this chronometer consistently calculated longitudes to within the limit of error set by the authorities. The Board of Longitude, however, withheld full payment of the prize until it had been established that Harrison's timepiece could be easily reproduced and that derivative models were equally accurate. King George III, an ardent supporter of scientific achievement, finally intervened on Harrison's behalf, securing the reward for him in 1773.

Outstanding Engineering Achievement:

Harrison's innovations in watch and clock design were incorporated into each of his chronometers. Changes of temperature tended to alter the length of a clock's pendulum, causing it to oscillate more slowly in the summer than in the winter. To ensure uniform motion, Harrison

Harrison's chronometer Number 4 never gained or lost more than two minutes on any of its long test voyages and so could determine longitude to within one-half a degree.

devised in 1725 a bi-metallic gridiron, a pendulum consisting of alternate brass and steel rods. These rods had different coefficients of thermal expansion, so that changes in size balanced one another. In Harrison's fourth chronometer, this function was performed by riveting together thin strips of brass and steel. The bi-metallic strip was connected to the ends of balance springs which provided the mechanism's motive power. The expansion and contraction of the strip moved the ends of the springs, automatically regulating their tension. As a result, internal friction was reduced and the chronometer needed infrequent oiling. As with all Harrison's watches, his chronometers had a secondary spring which kept the mechanism smoothly running while being wound. ■

Further Reading:

John D. Bernal, *Science in History*, Vol. II. London, 1965.

R.T. Gould, *The Marine Chronometer: Its History and Development*. London, 1960.

Humphrey Quill, *John Harrison, the Man Who Found Longitude*. London, 1966.

Singer et al., *A History of Technology*. Vol. IV.

Abraham Wolf, *A History of Science, Technology and Philosophy in the Eighteenth Century*. London, 1952.

HENRI PITOT

b. May 29, 1695, Aramon, France
d. Dec. 17, 1771, Aramon, France
French Hydraulic and Civil Engineer

Life and Times:

French engineers of the eighteenth century were accomplished builders not only of roads and bridges but also of canals, harbors and other waterworks. The growth of French cities at this time created a pressing need for supplemental water supplies. In order to maximize the efficiency of pumps and waterways, however, engineers needed an increased knowledge of liquid mechanics. Henri Pitot both provided the means for this development and corrected important misconceptions about water flow.

Trained as a mathematician and astronomer, Pitot was elected to the French Academy of Sciences in 1724. He subsequently became interested in hydraulics, an area where his background in the natural sciences could be applied to mechanical problems. In 1730 he invented a device later known as the Pitot tube (see below), which allowed him to measure the velocity of water. Using it, he refuted the accepted notion that the speed of flowing water increases with depth. Instead, Pitot demonstrated that water velocity is greatest at the surface of a channel, where least drag is exerted by the bottom and sides. The hydraulic engineer Bernard Forest de Belidor [q.v.] used Pitot's device to improve the efficiency of the pumps at the Notre Dame water station. Pitot himself applied his invention to studying the motion of ships; he published his findings in 1731 in his *Théorie de la manoeuvre des vasseaux.*

In addition to his work on hydraulics, Pitot became a prominent civil engineer, serving as chief engineer of the province of Languedoc. In this capacity he was responsible for repairing bridges, draining marshes and seeing to the upkeep of the Canal du Midi. He also designed a water supply system for Montpellier, a town near Marseilles.

Outstanding Engineering Achievements:

The Pitot tube was a simple device with an opening facing the direction of a water current.

Henri Pitot, hydraulic engineer, inventor of a device for comparing the speeds of water currents.

The current's velocity could be estimated by observing the height to which water was forced in the tube. This was not a means of determining the precise velocity of water, but rather for comparing the velocities of different currents. It was enough, however, for Pitot to make his important observations on the flow of water in a channel.

Pitot is also known for constructing an aqueduct as the main feature of Montpellier's water supply system. Regarded as his main engineering work, the aqueduct was built largely in the Roman style over a 33-year period. When completed, it brought water from St. Clement and Boulidon to a central distribution point in the town. ■

Further Reading:

Kranzberg and Pursell, *Technology in Western Civilization,* Vol. I.
Singer et al., *A History of Technology,* Vol. V.

The Industrial Revolution

by W. David Lewis

The term "Industrial Revolution" was first coined in France during the early nineteenth century and later popularized by a famous series of lectures delivered at Oxford University in the 1880s by the British historian Arnold Toynbee. Since then it has become part of our common parlance, an apparently indestructible feature of modern consciousness. No other combination of words seems to express quite so well the dynamic series of changes which swept aside deeply-ingrained habits of thought and custom that had flourished for many centuries and created the intensively mechanized economic and technological order in which we now live. In his book *Industry and Empire*, the distinguished historian E. J. Hobsbawm captures both our sense of what has happened and our conviction of its overwhelming importance by observing that "the Industrial Revolution marks the most fundamental transformation of human life in the history of the world recorded in written documents." It is a bold assertion, but nevertheless it carries the ring of truth.

Yet the term is also misleading, at least to the degree that the word "revolution" implies a sudden, cataclysmic change. Most historians no longer believe, as Toynbee's lectures seemed to suggest, that the Industrial Revolution was a phenomenon that burst upon the world in Great Britain during the last few decades of the eighteenth century and the first few decades of the nineteenth. In a series of books and articles commencing in 1932 with his massive study *The Rise of the British Coal Industry* and continuing through the early 1950s, John U. Nef argued persuasively that an earlier "industrial revolution" had occurred in Great Britain and France during the sixteenth and seventeenth centuries, citing as evidence the growth that took place then both in mining and in the manufacture of such products as alum, brass, bricks, glass, gunpowder, lead, lime, iron, pottery, salt, soap and sugar. More recently, such scholars as Jean Gimpel and Lynn White, Jr., have pushed the beginnings of the transformation that produced the modern industrial world even farther back into late medieval times. Gimpel's thesis is contained in the title of his recent work *The Medieval Machine: The Industrial Revolution of the Middle Ages,* in which he contends that "the Middle Ages was one of the great inventive eras of mankind. It should be known as the first industrial revolution in Europe."

Nef's conclusions have been searchingly criticized in a number of recent publications by such economic historians as L. A. Clarkson, D. C. Coleman, and Barry E. Supple, who have argued that the growth rates cited in his works are distorted by the low base figures with which they commence, that he ignored important products which continued to be made in traditional ways, and that he exaggerated evidence of a timber shortage in England which in his view prompted

Engineers occupy the center of the mid-19th century. English painting "Men of Science Living in 1807–8." Seated, far left: Brunel and Boulton; in front of table: Watt. Standing, right of Watt: Telford, Murdock, Rennie, Jessop, Mylne, Congreve. Seated, far right: Crompton.

the burgeoning use of coal. On the other hand, as A. E. Musson points out in his recent study *The Growth of British Industry,* the limitations inherent in Nef's quantitative evidence should not obscure the qualitative significance of changes that took place from 1540 to 1640 in a number of key industries which, regardless of their size or total output, were clearly in the vanguard of technological progress. Nor is it easy to dismiss the findings of Gimpel and White, among others, who have examined in great detail the efflorescence of mechanical ingenuity during the twelfth and thirteenth centuries which clearly foreshadowed the material achievements of the modern era. It is evident that the Industrial Revolution, however suddenly and dramatically it appeared in Great Britain some two centuries ago, was in fact deeply rooted in previous developments reaching far back in time. This is especially true if we accept the claim of Lewis Mumford that, like all great historical processes, the Industrial Revolution must be seen as a cultural phenomenon which was already taking place in the human mind before it assumed concrete expression in material forms. For this reason, it is worthwhile to examine at least briefly some early portents, stretching back into late medieval and early modern times, of the great transformation which ultimately took place.

Beginnings of the Industrial Revolution

In his widely influential work *Technics and Civilization,* published in 1934, Mumford identified the appearance of the mechanical clock in Europe during the late Middle Ages as a key event in the genesis of modern industrial civilization. "In its relationship to determinable quantities of energy, to standardization, to automatic action, and finally to its own special product, accurate timing," he asserted, "the clock has been the foremost machine in modern technics: and at each period it has remained in the lead: it marks a perfection toward which other machines aspire." Even more important to Mumford was the cultural significance of the way in which the mechanical clock ticked off a succession of uniform seconds and minutes, which he regarded as the first characteristic "product" of the industrial age: "by its essential nature it dissociated time from human events and helped create the belief in an independent world of mathematically measurable sequences: the special world of science."

Later scholarship has called into question Mumford's belief in the monastic origin of the escapement, which made the mechanical clock

possible by regulating the falling weight that provided the mechanism's motive force. But, as Gimpel points out, this in no way diminishes the significance of the device itself. Many aspects of industrial civilization are grounded in a distinctive view of time as a linear sequence of standardized, interchangeable units which can be manipulated, rationed, accounted for, and saved like any other commodity. The meticulousness with which successive generations of clockmakers fabricated the gear trains, stackfreeds, fusees, pendulums, and other components of their timepieces to meet increasingly strict standards of accuracy was an early portent of the passion for precision which became part of the marrow of industrialization. There was also, as Gimpel observes, a clear connection between late medieval accomplishments in clockmaking and the belief in progress—the possibility of an endless series of material achievements occurring incrementally as time marched forward into a boundless future—which was unknown in the pre-industrial world and became so important an ingredient of modern consciousness.

Both Gimpel and White have devoted much attention to the impressive series of technical innovations which took place during the late Middle Ages in agriculture, in the construction of cathedrals and other large public buildings and in the generation of power. As White points out in his massively documented study *Medieval Technology and Social Change,* the period commencing in approximately 1000 A. D. saw fundamental advances in the harnessing of water and wind power; in the utilization of cranks, flywheels, and connecting rods; and in the conceptualization of the universe itself as a potentially inexhaustible reservoir of energy for the satisfaction of man's material needs. In his sprightly volume *Machina ex Deo: Essays in the Dynamism of Western Culture,* White explains how Christian theology itself was interpreted to justify a frankly exploitative attitude toward nature and to promote the spread of labor-saving inventions in the monasteries and cathedral towns of medieval Europe. As the British scholar Arnold Pacey has emphasized in his recent work *The Maze of Ingenuity,* both idealistic and economic drives contributed during the closing centuries of the medieval era to what he calls "the spirit that brought modern technology to birth."

The Renaissance also played a major role in the early development of modern industrial consciousness. If the mechanical clock epitomizes the growing technological awareness of the late Middle Ages, the rise of printing with interchangeable type may be seen as the key innovation of the fifteenth century. It was significant not only for the role which it played in the dissemination and ultimate democratization of knowledge but also because it exhibited the same tendency to break down a process of fundamental importance—in this case the flow of information—into a linear sequence of standardized units, just as the mechanical clock had done with the flow of time. In his controversial work *The Gutenberg Galaxy*, Marshall McLuhan has made much of this aspect of print technology and its crucial bearing, as he sees it, upon the development of modern modes of visual perception. His methods have been cogently criticized in Elizabeth L. Eisenstein's study *The Printing Press as an Agent of Change*, and it seems clear that he has exaggerated the discontinuity between printing and script. As Lewis Mumford has pointed out in *The Pentagon of Power*, standardized styles of hand-lettering had already been worked out by monastic scribes prior to the appearance of the printing press. Furthermore, early printed works tended to resemble hand-lettered manuscripts, partly because this facilitated reader acceptance. It would therefore seem that the spread of printing merely intensified tendencies toward standardization, uniformity and interchangeability which had already appeared in late medieval times. But this is in itself an important role, and there is nothing implausible about the idea that the rapid multiplication of printed works, with their neatly regimented lines of standardized type marching toward scrupulously justified margins, promoted habits of disciplined thinking and visualization that were vital to the emergence of modern industrial society.

The basic technology of printing itself required the meticulous accuracy already noted in connection with the development of the mechanical clock. The rows of metal characters in the type-bed had to be of a precisely uniform height in order to avoid uneven impressions, while the press had to bring the paper down upon the upraised type with a minimum of wobble so as to avoid smudging. The elaborate proofreading that accompanied the process was part of the same pattern, as was printing's tendency, noted by James Burke in *Connections*, to promote uniformity of spelling, the consistency of texts, and the development of specialized expertise which went along with pride of authorship. Finally, as Burke has also noted, printing made it "easy to transmit information without personal contact," foreshadowing subsequent advances in communication which were crucial to industrial-

ization, particularly in the creation of complex systems of production and distribution.

Printing was accompanied by the growth of rationalism, an indispensable ingredient of industrial civilization which, as Gimpel points out, had already appeared during the late Middle Ages in the writings and works of such persons as Robert Grosseteste, Roger Bacon [q.v.], the clockmaker Giovanni de' Dondi [q.v.], and the architect-engineer Villard de Honnecourt [q.v.]. A reaction against reason and the experimental method emerged briefly amid the social and economic chaos that prevailed during the fourteenth century, but the fifteenth and sixteenth centuries saw the rapid development of the urge to understand the workings of the physical universe and to turn this knowledge to practical use in exploiting the material environment. Accompanying this trend was the appearance of nascent capitalist institutions as former prohibitions against usury were discarded and far-flung mercantile enterprises spread throughout Europe. The age of discovery and exploration got underway with the voyages of da Gama, Columbus, Cabot, Cabral, Magellan and other navigators; soon the gold and silver of the New World and profits from trade with distant lands contributed to an inflationary spiral that unsettled established interests and tended to redistribute wealth in favor of those who were sufficiently quick-witted to benefit from it. The previously unified facade of Christendom was shattered by the Protestant Reformation, and men began to "search for new structures," as Eugen Weber has aptly put it in his *Modern History of Europe*. Among these was the centralized nation-state.

It would be impossible, in dealing with such a crowded era, to mention, let alone analyze at any depth, all of the developments that were gradually preparing the way for modern industrialism. Certainly one of these was the growing conviction, epitomized by the writings of the fifteenth century humanist Pico della Mirandola, that man was ultimately constrained by no limits, circumscribed by no definitions of himself other than those of his own making. Yet another, accompanying the steady replacement of barter by commercial relationships based upon money, was the declining importance of personal considerations in most economic affairs and the creation of that vast and abstract, but nevertheless crucial, force known as "the market." Mercantile values, emphasizing the spirit of rational calculation enlisted in the relentless pursuit of profit, became assimilated by more and more elements of society—all the way "from the yeoman to the lord," as economic historian Eric

Lampard has put it. In the course of these developments, the institutional fabric of economic life became increasingly complex, and correspondingly less susceptible to control by all but the most powerful individuals.

At this stage of technological development, far more money could be made by gathering and distributing goods than by producing them. Nevertheless, in certain key industries a change was taking place that foreshadowed events to come: the appearance of relatively large enterprises which were carried on with the assistance of power-driven machinery, requiring substantial amounts of capital. The foremost of these was mining, which had already enjoyed a brief surge of development in the thirteenth century before falling into the doldrums in the fourteenth. From the mid-fifteenth century onward, particularly in Central Europe, the mining of metals began to take place on a previously unprecedented scale, stimulated in part by new techniques for extracting silver from argentiferous copper ores with the aid of lead. As it became profitable to mine at deeper levels, increasingly expensive equipment was required for pumping, ventilating, and hoisting; complex devices were used above the surface in washing and refining operations. Georgius Agricola's [q.v.] famous treatise *De re metallica*, published in the mid-sixteenth century, abounds in woodcuts depicting the way in which teams of animals or water wheels, some of the latter of considerable size, provided the motive power for a variety of machines which obviously required large outlays of capital from mine owners in the Saxon district where Agricola lived.

Similarly, the various arts associated with the assaying, smelting, alloying, casting, and fabrication of metals began to be practiced on a much larger scale than before, with equipment of correspondingly greater size and complexity. In the iron industry, for example, blast furnaces powered by water-driven bellows began gradually to replace small bloomeries. The resulting substitution of cast for wrought iron in turn created the need for fineries at which decarburization was accomplished with the aid of powerful bellows and massive tilt hammers. Here again, as in mining, greater investments of capital were required for the necessary facilities. Similar tendencies appeared in the manufacture of armaments, stimulated particularly by the development of artillery. As Nef has pointed out, such trends also produced the beginnings of a cleavage between capital and labor that was to become increasingly marked in the industrial society of the future. In mining, for example, wage-earning operatives, supervised by managers and foremen who reported to absentee owners, replaced the small groups of independent miners which had flourished when the working of relatively shallow surface deposits dominated the industry.

Britain and France

From the mid-sixteenth century onward two European nations, England and France, assumed special importance in the development of industrial enterprise. At the beginning of this period French manufacturing was far in the lead, but within three generations the situation changed. In Nef's words, "By the reign of Charles I, from 1625 to 1642, England was on the point of becoming, if she had not already become, the leading nation in Europe in mining and heavy manufacturing." British production of coal and metals had clearly outstripped that of France, while the same was true, at least on a per capita basis, of alum, bricks, glass, lime, soap, wool and many other products. British industrial enterprises tended to be significantly larger than their French counterparts with regard to capitalization, work force and the number of labor-saving machines used. Until almost the end of the eighteenth century, as Melvin Kranzberg has pointed out, "France was the greatest power in Europe politically, militarily, economically, and culturally," yet England is indisputably the country in which the Industrial Revolution first emerged in a relatively mature form.

Historians have identified a number of circumstances which help account for this development. In such works as *Industry and Government in France and England, 1540–1640*, Nef has explained that the degree of centralized power attained by the French monarchy actually proved a stumbling block to the development of modern capitalist enterprise because of a tendency toward over-regulation; British industry, by contrast, enjoyed a much greater degree of freedom. Nef has also pointed out that French tastes led to a concentration on the production of high-quality and luxury goods for discriminating clienteles, whereas British manufacturers showed a greater inclination to make relatively cheap goods for wider markets. French values discouraged, and in many cases actually prevented, members of the aristocracy from participating in industrial activities. Religious intolerance, manifested in revocation of the Edict of Nantes by Louis XIV, resulted in the emigration of many skilled Protestant workers

The mechanism of Joseph Marie Jacquard which used punched cards to program a loom to weave complex patterns (1810).

whose talents could ill be spared. During the same period members of the British aristocracy could and did take part in entrepreneurial activities, while the island kingdom attracted numerous artisans and merchants from various parts of the European continent, some for economic and others for religious reasons. Historians have also pointed to the superiority of British financial institutions for funneling capital into commercial and manufacturing ventures; the Bank of England, dating from 1694, antedated its French counterpart by more than a century.

Britain's transition to a mature industrial economy was also promoted by agricultural changes which did not take place in France. Beginning in the late seventeenth century, new legal procedures for the enclosure of open fields gradually resulted in the decline of inefficient manorial systems of cultivation. The consolidation of holdings facilitated the adoption of new crops and led to increased yields, new systems of crop rotation which maximized the productivity of available land, progress in the feeding and breeding of livestock, and a growing use of labor-saving agricultural machinery. The work of such historians as J. D. Chambers and Gordon

E. Mingay makes it more difficult to generalize about the degree to which the dispossession of yeoman farmers contributed to the formation of large pools of cheap industrial labor in cities, but it should be remembered that many of the factories and mills that appeared in England during the eighteenth and early nineteenth centuries were built in rural areas where such a supply certainly existed. In any case, making allowances for periodic cycles of bad weather and abnormal conditions in times of war, increased agricultural efficiency and productivity favored the growth of manufacturing by assuring a larger food supply for the growing population out of which the industrial work force was recruited. In France, where the peasantry tended to remain on the farm and where new methods of cultivation failed to secure widespread adoption, this important stimulus to industrial growth was missing.

England also benefited industrially from the relatively widespread dissemination of knowledge resulting from the Scientific Revolution that occurred throughout Western Europe from the sixteenth century onward. With its emphasis on the rational discovery of natural laws which could be expressed in mathematical terms and applied to yield predictable results, science promoted the belief that "knowledge is power" and opened up enormous vistas, eagerly scanned by such enthusiasts as Francis Bacon, of material improvement for mankind. Historians long assumed that science was of peripheral importance to technological and industrial development until a relatively late stage, supposedly at some point in the nineteenth century. But the untenability of this view has become increasingly clear in recent years, thanks in part to the diligence of A. E. Musson and Eric Robinson. Their *Science and Technology in the Industrial Revolution* massively documents the way in which scientific theory and technological practice interpenetrated in England throughout the seventeenth and eighteenth centuries and traces with lavish detail the proliferation of institutions which fostered this process.

Similarly, case studies like Robert Schofield's *The Lunar Society of Birmingham* have pointed out how science, entrepreneurship and technical innovation were brought together through the interaction of such figures as Matthew Boulton, Erasmus Darwin, Joseph Priestley, James Watt and Josiah Wedgwood. As Schofield indicates, Wedgwood attempted to establish in the potteries of Staffordshire what would today be called an industrial research laboratory. "Never before in history," as Archibald and Nan L.

Clow have stated in their pathbreaking work *The Chemical Revolution,* "was there such an advantageous syncretism of pure science and advancing industry as in the Lunar Society." Yet, as Musson and Robinson have shown, this was only one of many similar organizations that appeared in eighteenth-century Britain. Courses in science and its practical applications also became common throughout the realm, not only in formal educational institutions—particularly the academies established by dissenting religious sects—but also in the increasingly popular offerings of itinerant lecturers.

Certainly the country of Amontons, Ampère, Berthollet, Coulomb, Diderot, Lavoisier, Leblanc, Perronet and Vaucanson was lacking neither in scientific and engineering genius nor in the desire to promote the application of science to practical pursuits. Indeed, as far as formalized higher education in technical subjects was concerned, the French actually surpassed the British, who had no counterparts of the École des Ponts et Chaussées, the École des Mines or the École Polytechnique. Here again, however, the more highly structured French approach had unfortunate consequences, for it failed to disseminate scientific and technical knowledge as broadly as did the looser, more voluntarist path taken in Great Britain. Much of the French effort in organized technical education aimed at training military engineers; some of France's most distinguished scientists, including Sadi Carnot [q.v.] and Charles Augustin de Coulomb [q.v.], chose a military career. The more haphazard British process produced more individuals—some with only on-the-job training like James Brindley [q.v.], others with formal higher education like John Rennie [q.v.]—who turned their engineering talents to projects of a commercial or industrial nature.

Religious conflict also took its toll on French science. The same intolerance of Protestantism which cost France the services of many skilled Huguenots led to the emigration to England of such scientists and inventors as Denis Papin [q.v.] and John Theophile Desaguliers. Britain was by no means free of religious persecution, as the career of Joseph Priestley demonstrates; but dissenters whose beliefs barred them from government or professional careers actually found entrepreneurial and industrial activities a means of upward mobility.

But perhaps the most important circumstances which favored industrial growth in Britain over France had to do with geography and natural resources. Kranzberg, among other historians, has noted that England benefited from relatively

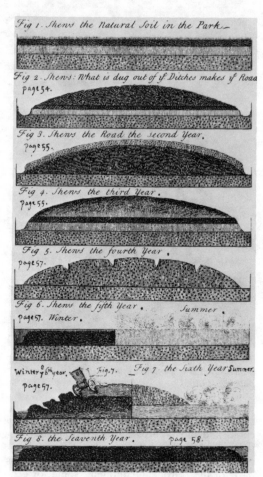

Drawings of the condition of English roads in 1737, before the improvements of Telford and McAdam.

short lines of transportation, which facilitated the development of canal and road systems. The island's exterior configuration also promoted the rise of an extremely active coasting trade between such points as Newcastle and London. France, a larger country, suffered from regional variations and geological barriers which impeded the creation of an adequate transportation system, while its exposure to invasion from the east dictated that its roads—which were actually the best in Europe—be laid out primarily with regard to considerations of military strategy. Relatively secure against invasion, Britain could concentrate on building a large navy, increasing its overseas trade and establishing a colonial empire. This gave a decided stimulus to industry, both by building up markets for exported goods such as wool and by developing sources of raw materials. British shipbuilding and its ancillary industries also benefited from the growth of foreign contacts.

The key natural resource which set Britain apart from France was its abundant supply of the crucial fuel that powered the Industrial Revolution—coal. Historians have debated vigorously in recent years about the extent and significance of a supposed timber shortage in England resulting from the country's relatively small size, the growing demand for wood in the shipbuilding industry, and the increasing consumption of charcoal in iron manufacturing. The claim by such scholars as Nef that this "energy crisis" provides a key to the entire process of industrial change in Britain is probably less widely accepted than it once was; but no one has refuted Nef's impressive evidence that from the sixteenth century onward there was a dramatically increasing tendency for coal to be substituted for wood throughout Britain in the manufacture of such products as alum, beer and ale, bricks and tiles, dyestuffs, glass, metals and metal wares, pottery, salt, soap, sugar, and so on. The trend was encouraged by the discovery of various ways to reduce the spread of sulfur and other contaminants contained in coal; these included the conversion of coal to coke and the introduction of reverberatory furnaces, in which the fuel did not come into actual physical contact with the material being heated.

Coal also became widely used for domestic heating in Britain. Nef's tables in *The Rise of the British Coal Industry* document substantial increases in the amounts of coal shipped via the coasting trade from the mining districts to urban markets, particularly London, which amazed foreign visitors with the vast amounts of soot and coal smoke which blackened its skies. British coal production between 1550 and 1700 was perhaps six times greater than that of the rest of the world put together, and the disparity grew even greater during the eighteenth century with advances in adapting coal to the requirements of such processes as the smelting and refining of iron. French coal production, by contrast, was limited by the country's relatively poor mineral resources and by an abundance of timber, which lessened the need for creative adaptation in the manner of the British.

The Developing Web of Change

As Nef and other historians have indicated, the British coal industry was closely connected with a number of key developments which heralded the dynamic phase of the Industrial Revolution that began in the late eighteenth century. One of these developments took place in transportation, beginning in the sixteenth century with the improvement of navigation on natural waterways and the start of the canal movement. Coal, an especially heavy and bulky product, could be moved overland only with great difficulty by pack animals using the miserable roads of the time. Colliery owners, particularly those with mines in areas lacking convenient access to the sea, frequently initiated or supported efforts to dredge rivers, dig canals, and install locks. In the face of strong opposition from vested interests—sometimes including rival mine operators favored by existing natural routes—canal and navigation schemes were pushed with increasing vigor during the 1600s.

The canal movement reached a climax in the following century with the creation of such waterways as the Duke of Bridgewater's Canal, which connected the Duke's coal mines at Worsley with Manchester and gave enormous impetus to the growth of that city. This project, which first demonstrated the engineering genius of James Brindley [q.v.], was quickly followed by such important works as the Manchester-Liverpool Canal, the Grand Trunk Canal connecting the Mersey and Trent rivers, the Wolverhampton Canal linking the Trent and the Severn, and the Birmingham Canal. By 1795 these and other ventures had produced some 2,600 miles (4160 km) of canals in England alone, not to mention smaller systems in Scotland and Ireland. The growing network of industries which used coal in one form or another, and thus stood to gain from reduced transportation costs, played a major role in lobbying for many of these improvements; the famed Staffordshire potter Josiah Wedgwood [q.v.] was a leading promoter of the Grand Trunk Canal, which brought cheaper coal and other raw materials to his Burslem works.

Nef has noted a striking coincidence between the use of coal and the development of modern methods of large-scale capitalist organization in a variety of key industries. Improved transport promoted this trend by enabling growing, technologically progressive enterprises to compete more effectively with small producers who had been able because of geographical isolation to cling to more traditional manufacturing techniques. Well before the canal movement had reached its peak, however, strong tendencies toward consolidation and combination had already appeared in the mining industry among entrepreneurs who supplied "sea coals" to expanding markets on coastal shipping routes. Just as earlier in the metal mining districts of Central

Europe, increasing production and deeper mines led to the formation of larger business units which could provide the capital needed for more elaborate pumping equipment and other materials. More frequently, powerful mine operators combined with one another for mutual advantage; in the Tyne Valley, pooling arrangements among colliery owners dating from the early seventeenth century anticipated the modern cartel. The growing scale of the industry also caused a deepening cleavage between capital and labor and stimulated wage-earning miners to attempt combinations of their own as pay scales decreased and working conditions deteriorated. Meanwhile, the expansion of the coal trade fostered the growth in such cities as London of merchant organizations bent on maximizing the rewards of distribution.

Perhaps the most important result of the expansion of British coal mining was the impetus it gave to development of the steam engine. A detailed history of this crucial device, from the discovery of atmospheric pressure by natural scientists in the mid-seventeenth century through Thomas Newcomen's [q.v.] construction of the first effective steam engine for Midlands collieries in 1712, lies beyond the scope of this essay. But, in view of the deep historical continuities emphasized here, it is important to note the evidence advanced by Milton Kerker, A. E. Musson and others against the traditional view that practical inventors, including both Newcomen and Thomas Savery [q.v.], owed little or nothing to the theoretical work of such scientists as Evangelista Torricelli, Blaise Pascal [q.v.], Otto von Guericke [q.v.], Robert Hooke [q.v.], Robert Boyle, and Denis Papin [q.v.]. It detracts nothing from Newcomen's stature or inventive genius to concede that his accomplishment took place in a scientific and technological ambience that had been well prepared for his atmospheric engine, which met the needs of mine operators for a better means of pumping water out of their ever-deeper shafts. Similarly, Musson has pointed out that such engineers as Henry Beighton and John Smeaton [q.v.], who played significant roles in improving the efficiency of the Newcomen engine, were well versed in the science of their day.

The same combination of industrial need, technical skill and scientific insight appeared in the dramatic series of inventions, beginning in 1765, by means of which James Watt [q.v.] transformed the Newcomen engine. In his aptly-titled book *Steam Power in the Eighteenth Century: A Case Study in the Application of Science,* D.S.L. Cardwell has shown how genuinely scientific Watt's methods were, and how carefully he brought theoretical insights to bear in his quest for ways to satisfy the stiff efficiency requirements of his likeliest customers, Cornish tin mine operators. These entrepreneurs had to obtain coal for their pumping equipment from other parts of Britain and were thus acutely affected by the Newcomen engine's lack of fuel economy. In their various essays on the role of science in the Industrial Revolution, Musson and Robinson have repeatedly stressed the degree to which Watt and his chief financial backer, Matthew Boulton, were on familiar terms with the most distinguished scientists of England and other countries, partly through their activities in such organizations as the Lunar Society and the Royal Society. Kerker makes the same point, emphasizing Watt's friendship with such academic "natural philosophers," to use the parlance of the day, as Joseph Black and John Robison. In this perspective, Watt's brilliant series of innovations in steam technology can be seen as an authentic precursor of the type of work that is carried on in industrial research laboratories today.

The interaction between coal, steam and the fabrication of metals in transforming British industry during the eighteenth and early nineteenth centuries has been so frequently analyzed by historians—T. S. Ashton, Eugene S. Ferguson, Paul Mantoux and H. R. Schubert, to name a few—that extended discussion is unnecessary. Significant milestones in the iron and steel industry include the achievements of the Darby family [q.v.] at Coalbrookdale in smelting iron with coke; progress in the manufacture of boilers and cylinders at such installations as the Carron Ironworks in Scotland and John Wilkinson's [q.v.] establishment at Broseley; the substitution of steam-powered blowing tubes for water-powered bellows in blast furnaces; and the invention by Henry Cort [q.v.] of the puddling process for refining iron, which utilized a reverberatory furnace and thus made it possible to burn relatively cheap grades of coal in the smelting process.

Manufacture of the steam engine raised problems in securing an accurate fit between pistons and cylinder walls, as well as in achieving close tolerances between other moving parts, and led to significant improvements in boring machines, lathes and other machine tools. By the start of the nineteenth century, the increased precision of these devices had made possible the emergence of the high-pressure steam engine which, through the work of such engineers as Richard Trevithick [q.v.], Oliver Evans [q.v.] and

The demonstration railroad of Richard Trevithick offered rides in a carriage drawn by his locomotive Catch-Me-Who-Can *(London, 1809).*

George Stephenson [q.v.], was applied to the steam locomotive and ushered in the railroad age. With this momentous development a long series of historical events came full circle, for the railroad itself had been born in the mine. Agricola's *De re metallica* contains a woodcut showing a cart laden with ore being drawn along a primitive railway, and British colliery operators had long used horse-drawn tram cars moving on rails to transport coal from the pithead to the nearest navigable waterway. Stephenson himself grew up among the collieries of the Newcastle area and advanced within the mines until he became engineer of the Stockton and Darlington Railway, which provided an outlet for the vast coal reserves of the Bishop Auckland Valley. His locomotive, the *Rocket*, which won the celebrated Rainhill Trials of 1829 on his newly-built Liverpool and Manchester Railway, is thus a fitting symbol of the connection between coal, iron, and steam through which the Industrial Revolution was beginning to feed upon itself, acquiring its own momentum.

The Industrial Revolution in Textiles

So far we have emphasized how a series of developments over several centuries involving coal and metals supplied much of the dynamics that brought the modern industrial world into being. Yet much of the historical literature dealing with the Industrial Revolution, beginning with Toynbee's classic lectures of the 1880s, stresses the innovations which transformed the British textile industry in the late eighteenth and early nineteenth centuries. This emphasis is almost inescapable if the Industrial Revolution is viewed as a primarily British phenomenon which

The entrance to the Liverpool station of the Liverpool and Manchester Railway, with Rocket *locomotives by the Stephensons (1831).*

occurred between approximately 1750 and 1840. During these years the production of textiles, especially cotton goods, was by all odds the most important industry in Britain in terms of employment, amount of capital invested, the value of manufactures produced, and the contribution to British foreign trade. But the perspective changes if one looks at the Industrial Revolution as a series of interconnected developments that occurred over a long period of time, beginning in the late Middle Ages at various points in Europe, reaching a particularly critical stage in Great Britain, and then spreading throughout the world.

Nevertheless, the importance of the textile industry in the development of modern industrialism was enormous, amply justifying the emphasis placed upon it in such studies as David S. Landes' *The Unbound Prometheus*. Much of its historical significance is institutional. Although large enterprises gradually appeared in a number of key European industries from late medieval times onward, as for example in mining and armaments production, most manufacturing was carried on in small shops with only a few workers. A master craftsman was typically assisted by a handful of journeymen and apprentices, as shown in plate after plate of Denis Diderot's late eighteenth century French *Encyclopédie*.

It was in the manufacture of textiles that time-honored methods of organizing work began to change drastically for many people. This appeared first with the so-called "putting-out" system, under which merchants by-passed restrictive town and city-based craft guilds by distributing raw materials to spinners and weavers to be worked up in their own dwellings, often scattered throughout the countryside. Later came the modern factory, where large numbers of unskilled or semi-skilled operatives were brought together under strict and impersonal discipline to tend power-driven machines. The social and psychological impact of this change, both on the many skilled craftsmen who lost their livelihood and on the masses of new factory workers, often women and children, was profound. Countless people now felt the overwhelming impact of changes which had previously been restricted to relatively small groups of workers in such industries as mining. This was especially true in the opening decades of the nineteenth century, when dislocations caused by the Napoleonic wars compounded the difficulties of workers. It was suddenly much more obvious that things were becoming different, a realization that brought with it a widespread sense of alienation and outrage. This perception seemed to justify applying the terminology of "revolution," stimulated by the recent memory of the French Revolution, to industrial developments which were in fact deeply rooted in centuries of gradual change.

Particularly after Karl Marx transmuted the outrage of the early nineteenth century into a powerful ideology in the guise of an economic theory, some scholars naturally began to think of two parallel revolutions, one French and political, the other British and industrial. Such inventions as the spinning jenny, the water frame, the mule and the power loom seemed more important to many historians than others that were at least equally significant in the overall process of industrialization. These were the only devices discussed by Toynbee in his chapter on "The Chief Features of the Revolution" except for Watt's steam engine, which seems to have come to mind only because it was applied to the manufacture of cotton 16 years after it was patented; presumably it did not seem important to explain who was buying it during the intervening period.

The point is not to dispute the importance of the various machines invented by James Hargreaves [q.v.], Richard Arkwright [q.v.], Samuel Crompton [q.v.], Richard Roberts [q.v.], and Edmund Cartwright [q.v.], but to reaffirm Abbott Payson Usher's statement that, "despite the importance of the textile industries for the consumer, and the conspicuous development of the

Replica of an early version of Samuel Crompton's spinning mule (ca. 1790).

factory system in the cotton industry, it is a mistake to think of textiles as the primary focus of industrialization." Certainly no one did more to promote a just understanding of textile technology than Usher, whose *History of Mechanical Inventions* remains a scholarly landmark. As he indicates there, the application of power-driven machinery to textile manufacture goes back to the late Middle Ages with the introduction of the fulling mill by the twelfth century, while water-powered spinning machines originated as early as the beginning of the seventeenth century in the silk industry. The physical properties of wool, flax and cotton barred the development of similar equipment for them until the late eighteenth century, but the intervening years saw the development of ingenious hand- or foot-operated devices such as the stocking frame and the knitting loom. Here, as in other areas already discussed, Usher's observation that "industrialization is an evolutionary process, not a revolutionary change," holds true.

Space permits only a brief glance at recent scholarship dealing with textile manufacture in the late eighteenth and early nineteenth centuries. A few points can be made based upon the work of such scholars as Musson, Robinson, G. N. von Tunzelmann, and Richard L. Hills, whose valuable book *Power in the Industrial Revolution* focuses, despite its sweeping title, entirely on the textile industry. In an important article on "The Origins of Engineering in Lancashire," Musson and Robinson have documented how completely textile manufacturers depended for the installation of new machinery on the skills of artisans whose crafts stretched back into late medieval times, particularly clockmakers. Indeed, the components of textile machinery were occasionally referred to at this time as "clockworks." Instrument-makers too, carrying on a centuries-old tradition, were greatly in demand among the manufacturers of Manchester, Salford and other centers. Because so much of the machinery of the era was still made of wood, traditional skills in carpentry and other aspects of woodworking were required on every hand. So were the talents of smiths and metalworkers of all kinds, similarly the product of long historical development.

In contrast to theories of radical and swift change, Usher has stressed that the initial impact of even a major invention on a particular industry was usually undramatic. A case in point is the relative slowness with which Watt's steam engine caught on in the textile industry. All of the writers mentioned above point out that the older Savery and Newcomen engines enjoyed much greater popularity among factory owners than historians once believed. Contrary to a longstanding impression, the roundabout way of converting reciprocating into rotary motion by using steam engines to pump water over a water wheel, clumsy as it seems to us, was widely adopted and made sense given the cost requirements of certain mills. Watt's engine was quite expensive and, as Hills has shown, frequently difficult to install and maintain. Furthermore, as von Tunzelmann has indicated, the cost savings which the Watt engine could provide over other power sources at this time may have been seriously overestimated by modern scholars.

A crucial point made by all four authors is that water wheels remained a viable source of energy for even relatively large textile mills well into the nineteenth century; indeed, Musson and Robinson have called water power "the basis of the early Industrial Revolution." Abundant evidence for the same contention, so far as America is concerned, appears in the recently-published first volume of Louis Hunter's impressive *History of Industrial Power in the United States.* Once more we can see the deep historical roots of technological development, for the extensive use of water wheels in England dates back to the late Middle Ages. In the long run, of course, events favored the predominance of coal and steam engines, or, looking into the more distant future, coal transmuted into electrical energy. This trend again illustrates the thesis of the present essay that it was the mining and heavy engineering industries, not textile production, which lay at the core of modern industrialization.

Despite the subordinate role of textiles in overall industrial developments, it is worth noting that they were indispensable to the emergence of the modern chemical industry. As Archibald and Nan Clow point out in their authoritative work *The Chemical Revolution,* and as Musson and Robinson have recently reiterated with fresh detail, the massive increase in British textile production during the late eighteenth and early nineteenth centuries created demands for bleaches, mordants and other chemical products which traditional methods of manufacture could not fulfill. The circumstances attending the development of such innovations as chlorine bleaching, the Leblanc process for the production of soda, and improved methods of making sulphuric acid in lead chambers are generally well known. Musson and Robinson have deepened our appreciation of the connections between theoretical science and industry that made these innovations possible, and enhanced our awareness of the degree to which James Watt, who was heavily involved in perfecting new ways of producing bleaches and dyes in large quantities, deserves to be ranked among the pioneers of chemical, as well as mechanical, engineering. It should be noted, however, that textile manufacturing was not alone in stimulating the development of both theoretical and applied chemistry. The production of glass, iron, pottery, soap and other commodities also played a role. The significance of coal must also be emphasized again, for heating is fundamental to many chemical processes which could not have been carried out on a large scale without abundant supplies of this crucial fuel.

Expansion and Diffusion

Throughout the first half of the nineteenth century the process of technological and industrial change intensified in Great Britain and

Fitch's Delaware River steamboat which dipped several sets of paddles in and out of the water.

began to affect other nations in Europe and the Western Hemisphere. The creation of complex transportation networks proceeded rapidly as roads, bridges, canals and railroad systems took shape through the projects of such great engineers as Thomas Telford [q.v.], John McAdam [q.v.], Isambard Kingdom Brunel, and the remarkable father-and-son team of George and Robert Stephenson [q.v.]. This was also a dramatic era on the high seas, as the coming of the ocean-going steamship substantially reduced the amount of time needed to reach the far corners of the world. The spirit of the age was epitomized by such triumphant structures as Telford's bridge across the Menai Straits, Robert Stephenson's high-level viaduct spanning the Tyne at Newcastle, and, shortly after mid-century, by Brunel's colossal vessel the *Great Eastern*. Popular fascination with the wielding of unprecedented power through the union of coal, iron and steam was aroused by such inventions as James Nasmyth's steam hammer, originally devised in 1839 to permit the massive screw-shaft of the steamship *Great Britain* to be successfully forged. Technology also began to promote public comfort, safety, and convenience. A case in point was the development of gas lighting, introduced in Paris by Philippe Lebon [q.v.] in 1801 but first used on a large scale in England; there William Murdock [q.v.] devised horizontal cast-iron retorts for the distillation of coal, thus opening up another use for this ubiquitous commodity.

Britain also retained, at least temporarily, its leadership in the production and use of machine tools. At the beginning of the century, Henry Maudslay [q.v.] successfully executed Marc Isambard Brunel's [q.v.] order for the celebrated machines which turned out pulley blocks in record numbers for the Royal Navy. The later accomplishments of engineers and instrument makers such as Richard Roberts [q.v.], Joseph Clement [q.v.], James Nasmyth and Sir Joseph Whitworth maintained the British reputation for unsurpassed excellence in lathes, planing machines, shapers, drilling machines, and other devices for the precise fabrication of industrial equipment.

But the process of industrialization was very broadly based, with roots reaching far backward in time, as this essay has attempted to demonstrate: and however dominant Britain's role in events of the late eighteenth and early nineteenth centuries, the forward thrust of scientific, technological and economic change was not, and could not be, confined within one nation. The impetus of this change was felt in many places,

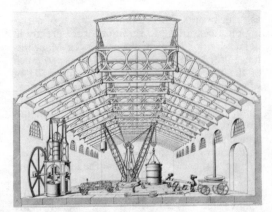

The interior of Henry Maudslay's steam-engine factory (1834).

foreshadowing the globalizing tendencies which are so clearly apparent today. If Belgium, France, Prussia, the United States and other countries relied heavily on British know-how during these years, we should remember that this was possible only because Britain itself had already borrowed much from the accumulated experience and resources of its neighbors in establishing an industrial supremacy which it could not indefinitely prolong.

Such scholars as Rondo E. Cameron, Herbert Heaton, W. O. Henderson and David Landes have analyzed in detail the process of industrial and technological transfer that took place in Western Europe as a number of nations tried to emulate or surpass the achievements which temporarily made Great Britain the "Workshop of the World." Case studies by Carrol W. Pursell, Nathan Rosenberg, Norman B. Wilkinson and others have enhanced our understanding of the same process in the United States. It is impossible to describe here in detail how two nations in particular, Germany and the United States, outstripped Britain industrially in the course of the nineteenth century. But one topic deserves special mention for the period before 1850, the date with which this essay ends. This was the growth in the United States of what came to be known as the "American System of Manufacture," characterized by the production and use of interchangeable parts. The researches of Robert O. Woodbury have effectively demolished the once-prevalent notion that Eli Whitney [q.v.] was primarily responsible for this crucial development; Rosenberg, Merrit Roe Smith, Paul Uselding and others have helped demonstrate how such inventors as John H. Hall, Roswell Lee and Elisha Root actually brought about the "American System." In his informative study

Harpers Ferry Armory and the New Technology, Smith has also shown how social values conditioned the reception of changes brought about by new manufacturing methods in two different parts of America, New England and northern Virginia. The circumstances that generally favored the adoption of mechanical devices in the United States are explored in a preliminary way in H. J. Habakkuk's pathbreaking work *American and British Technology in the Nineteenth Century: the Search for Labour-Saving Inventions.*

American displays at the famous Crystal Palace Exhibition of 1851 in Britain stunningly revealed the triumph of interchangeable parts, manufactured in quantity for such items as firearms, clocks and agricultural machinery. A new stage had been reached in an old story: The profusion of identical metal parts made in the machine shops and factories of the United States were characteristic products of the same forces in the human mind which had conceived the endless succession of uniform units of time ticked off by the mechanical clocks of the early modern era and the proliferating lines of standardized type turned out by the printing presses of Johannes Gutenberg [q.v.] and John Caxton in the Renaissance. And the same passion for rationality, quantification, careful measurement, impersonal calculation, and unceasing exploitation of the material environment that was stirring then continued in the late nineteenth and twentieth centuries to produce a succession of new scientific and technological wonders, as well as a tangled web of increasingly pressing and intractable problems. For the so-called "Industrial Revolution" is all of a piece and cannot be seen simply as something that happened in one country in one relatively short spasm of change, as the work of an earlier generation of analysts seemed to suggest. It is an ongoing process in which the entire world is now involved, and its final outcome remains yet to be seen. ■

THOMAS NEWCOMEN
b. Feb. 28, 1663, Dartmouth, England
d. Aug. 5, 1729, London, England
British Inventor

Life and Times:

By the start of the eighteenth century, scientists and inventors had devoted much effort to developing a practical method of pumping water by steam power. The ideas of the Marquis of Worcester [q.v.], Denis Papin [q.v.] and Thomas Savery [q.v.] brought the goal more and more within reach. Yet Thomas Newcomen, the man who finally developed the first economical steam engine, was a practical mechanic with uncertain knowledge of his predecessors in the field.

The son of a Baptist merchant, Newcomen had little formal education. After serving an apprenticeship with a dealer in iron tools, he set up his own business as ironmonger in Exeter. His trade put him in touch with mine operators in Cornwall and the Midlands, where he undoubtedly learned of the difficulties caused by the flooding of deep shafts. Horse-powered pumps, the only existing remedy, were of limited use and could not prevent many mines from closing when seams near the surface were exhausted. Assisted by his business partner, John Calley, Newcomen began to seek a mechanical means of removing water from mines.

In 1712, after a decade of experiment, the two constructed the first atmospheric steam engine at Dudley Castle in Worcestershire. The invention, far cheaper and more practical than any rival pumping system, caught on rapidly; by the time of Newcomen's death it had brought about a virtual rebirth of the mining industry in north-central England. Foreign mine and waterworks operators also became interested in the device, spreading its use to France, Belgium, Spain and Central Europe. The Newcomen engine, however, remained limited to pumping service. Only the improvements introduced some 50 years later by James Watt [q.v.] permitted more general industrial use of the steam engine.

Newcomen himself, as is the case of many inventors, derived little profit from his invention. Due to Thomas Savery's patent on all devices that raised water "by the impellant force of fire," Newcomen had to take him into partnership in construction of the first steam engine at Dudley Castle. The heirs to Savery's patent subsequently took over commercial exploitation of the Newcomen engine, which they manufactured and delivered to mine operators in return for an annual royalty. This state of affairs lasted until expiration of the patent in 1733. When Newcomen died during a trip to London, he was little known and certainly not wealthy.

Outstanding Engineering Achievement:

Newcomen's atmospheric steam engine consisted of a boiler and a cylinder enclosing a piston. A chain attached the piston to one end of a centrally-balanced wooden beam, the other end of which was connected by another chain to a pump rod. At rest the piston was held in a raised position by the heavier pump rod. When the boiler was fired, steam was injected into the cylinder beneath the piston at atmospheric pressure. A jet of cold water on the surface of the cylinder condensed the steam; the resulting vacuum sucked the piston down, pulling the cross-beam in a seesaw motion which raised the pump rod. Steam was then injected into the cylinder beneath the piston, and the cycle began again. The first Newcomen engine at Dudley Castle was capable of about 5.5 hp (4 kw) at 12 strokes per minute, raising 10 gallons (45 liters) of water 51 yards (45.9 meters). Subsequent engines were effective at up to 300 yards (275 meters).

The Newcomen engine could raise water from far greater depths than Savery's steam pump, the only other mechanical pumping device then in existence. The use of steam at atmospheric pressure also prevented the frequent blowouts to which Savery's device was prone. Nevertheless, the Newcomen engine suffered from several defects that limited its efficiency. Most importantly, the metal-working techniques of the time were simply too inaccurate to produce a cylinder that exactly fitted the piston. Although Newcomen tried to rub down irregularities on the inside of each cylinder, the piston still did not fit

perfectly. This limited the engine's ability to produce a vacuum and consequently the force of the piston stroke; air and other gases occasionally accumulated beneath the piston, bringing the machine to a stop.

Another problem was the practice of condensing the steam by injecting the cylinder with cold water. This meant that the entire cylinder had to be cooled and reheated with every piston stroke, a cumbersome procedure which limited the engine's speed and vastly increased its energy consumption. Finally, the engine was held to a relatively low horsepower by the fact that the piston was single-acting. Only the downstroke of the piston exerted force which moved the crossbeam and pump rod; the weight of the heavier pump rods accomplished the reverse motion. It was left to James Watt to develop a double-acting engine which exerted force in both directions, far surpassing Newcomen's model in speed and power. ∎

Further Reading:

Kranzberg and Pursell, *Technology in Western Civilization,* Vol. I.
Jenkins, *The Collected Papers of Rhys Jenkins.* Cambridge, 1936.
David Landes, *The Unbound Prometheus.* Cambridge, 1969.
L.I.C. Rolt and J. S. Allen, *The Steam Engine of Thomas Newcomen.* New York, 1977.

Newcomen's "atmospheric" engine. The cylinder, B, was filled with steam, then sprayed with water to condense the steam and create a vacuum; atmospheric pressure then forced back the piston, D.

ABRAHAM DARBY I
b. 1676
d. 1717

ABRAHAM DARBY II
b. 1711
d. 1763

ABRAHAM DARBY III
b. 1750
d. 1791

British Forgemasters and Engineers

Life and Times:

The Industrial Revolution owed much to the Darbys, a Quaker family of forgemasters who flourished for three generations in the Severn River valley of southwestern Britain. The elder Darby built the first blast furnace which smelted iron ore with a coke fire instead of the customary charcoal. The second Darby improved the new smelting process, while the youngest of the line developed new uses for coke-smelted iron. Their work laid the basis for the rapid growth of heavy industry in the nineteenth century.

Traditional charcoal-fired blast furnaces had two drawbacks. The amount of iron ore they could handle at once was strictly limited due to charcoal's propensity to collapse under a heavy load, smothering the fire. Of still greater immediate importance was the fact that wood, the source of charcoal, was scarce and expensive in eighteenth-century Britain. Coal, an alternative fuel, was available in abundance. But coal contained minerals such as sulfur and phosphorous which penetrated the iron during smelting and made it weak and brittle. Coke, which is produced by heating coal in insufficient oxygen to support combustion, also produced unsatisfactory results for similar reasons. The first Abraham Darby succeeded where earlier attempts to overcome these difficulties had failed.

Darby operated a copper-smelting furnace in Bristol before moving to Coalbrookdale in the Severn River valley, where he founded the Bristol Iron Company in 1708. His initial partners in the venture grew alarmed at what they regarded as his risky experiments in coal-fueled smelting, and Darby was soon left as sole proprietor. In 1709 he began producing iron of acceptable quality in a coke-fired blast furnace (see below). Since coke could withstand a greater load of ore and yielded a hotter blast than charcoal, Darby was soon able to manufacture larger quantities of iron at a lower price than rival forgemasters. But his iron still contained more impurities than the traditional charcoal-smelted product; for this reason it could not be refined into wrought iron, a malleable form with superior ability to withstand stress. Darby's son, the second Abraham, apparently managed to reduce impurities in coke-smelted iron to a point where wrought iron could be produced. He kept the technique such a closely guarded secret, however, that nothing is known of it. It was only the puddling-and-rolling process developed by Henry Cort [q.v.] in the 1780s that made possible the widespread production of wrought iron in coke-fired furnaces.

Meanwhile, the Darby foundry devoted most of its output to cast iron, a high-carbon alloy that was more brittle than wrought iron but suitable for most structural purposes. Coalbrookdale iron was initially used in pots and cooking utensils, but soon found more important functions. The Darby firm was commissioned to manufacture cast-iron cylinders for Thomas Newcomen's

Coalbrookdale by night in 1801, after the Darbys had made it a center of the iron industry.

[q.v.] atmospheric steam engine, and later built the first high-pressure steam boiler for Richard Trevithick [q.v.]. Another area of application opened up when civil engineers discovered that cheap cast iron could be used to ornament buildings and as a structural material in public works. The most dramatic advance in this area was the work of Abraham Darby III, who designed and constructed the world's first cast iron bridge in 1779. Spanning the Severn near Coalbrookdale, it still stands as a national monument.

The technique of coal-fired smelting spread slowly outside Coalbrookdale, due partly to continuing problems with impurities and partly to the unwillingness of the Darbys to disclose their trade secrets. Nevertheless, by the late eighteenth century well over half of Britain's iron production came from coke-fired blast furnaces. This development was vital in the removal of iron foundries from forested areas and the concentration of burgeoning heavy industry in coal fields. The area around Coalbrookdale in particular became the scene of intense manufacturing activity, sometimes called "the cradle of the Industrial Revolution."

Outstanding Engineering Achievements:

The success of the first Abraham Darby in constructing a coke-fired blast furnace rested partly on the high-quality, low-sulfur coal and iron ore found in the Coalbrookdale area. Earlier problems with impurities were thus reduced by Darby's astute choice of location. The Darby foundry, built from a converted charcoal-fired blast furnace, was charged with alternating layers of coke and iron ore, with limestone added to absorb impurities. A water wheel operated the bellows, which provided the hot blast that raised the fire to smelting temperature. In 1777 the furnace was rebuilt with a deeper hearth capable of handling a larger load of iron ore.

The iron bridge built by Abraham Darby III at Coalbrookdale spans the Severn in a single arch, 100 feet (30 meters) long with a 45-foot (13.7 meters) rise. Parts of the bridge were fitted together with wedges, eliminating the need for bolts and rivets. The bridge's original ironwork weighed 378 tons, by far the largest single cast iron structure then in existence. ∎

Further Reading:

Kranzberg and Pursell, *Technology in Western Civilization,* Vol 1.

Singer et al., *A History of Technology.* Vols. III and IV.

Abraham Wolf, *A History of Science, Technology and Philosophy in the Eighteenth Century.* London, 1952.

DANIEL BERNOULLI (or BERNOUILLI)
b. Feb. 8, 1700, Gröningen, Netherlands
d. March 17, 1782, Basel, Switzerland
Swiss Physicist and Mathematician

Life and Times:

The first decades of the eighteenth century were marred by the bitter dispute between the followers of Isaac Newton [q.v.] and those of Gottfried Wilhelm von Leibniz [q.v.] over whether or not Leibniz had taken the concepts of calculus from Newton. English scientists and mathematicians, out of a misplaced loyalty, felt themselves required to confine themselves to Newton's fluxional calculus, and few of them ventured to question or even develop his mathematical or physical ideas. As a result, the initiative passed to the supporters of Leibniz's differential calculus on the continent. The first to apply Leibniz's calculus to Newton's mechanics was Daniel Bernoulli, who is regarded as the founder of mathematical physics in general, and of hydrodynamics in particular.

The Bernoulli family produced a remarkable number of mathematicians. Daniel's father, two uncles, two brothers and nephew were all professors of mathematics or astronomy, mostly at Basel, although Daniel's father Johannes (or

Jean) was at Gröningen University when Daniel was born. Later the family moved back to Basel.

Like his father before him, Daniel started by studying medicine, taking his degree in 1721. His doctoral dissertation was on the mechanics of breathing. Three years later his first publication appeared—four papers on fluid flow, probability, calculus and geometry. These attracted the attention of the St. Petersburg Academy, and in 1725 Bernoulli took a position there. The same year he won the prize awarded by the Paris Academy of Sciences for a paper on the required subject of the shape of hourglasses. He was to win, or share, this prize ten times.

Bernoulli spent eight productive years in Russia, where he was joined in 1727 by his friend from student days, Leonhard Euler [q.v.]. His works published there included the book *Hydrodynamica,* as well as papers on friction, rotating bodies, movement in a resisting medium, and the curves and oscillations of flexible strings. At last, wearied by the rigors of climate and life in St. Petersburg, he returned to Basel as professor of botany, then of physiology, and finally, in 1750, of physics. He did not retire until 1776.

Outstanding Engineering Achievement:

The title of the book *Hydrodynamica* introduced the name of the new subject of hydrodynamics. First drafted in 1733, the work was published five years later. In it, Bernoulli formulated a principle of the conservation of *vis viva* ("live force"), a concept very close to the modern one of mechanical energy. He stated, in effect, that for a flowing fluid, the sum of the potential and kinetic energies remains constant. He also hypothesized that all particles of a fluid in a plane perpendicular to the flow have a velocity that is inversely proportional to the area of the cross section of that plane.

From these assumptions Bernoulli derived formulas for the flow of a liquid through an opening, leading to the Bernoulli equation for pressure in a horizontal tube. Although modified since, particularly by Euler, this equation has been fundamental to the study of fluid motion. ∎

Further Reading:

D. Bernoulli, *Hydrodynamica.* New York, 1968.

R. Taton, ed. *The Beginnings of Modern Science.* New York, 1964.

BENJAMIN HUNTSMAN
b. 1704, Holland
d. June 21, 1746, Sheffield, England
British Mechanical Engineer and Metallurgist

Life and Times:

In eighteenth century Britain, metal began to displace increasingly scarce wood in the manufacture of tools, machines and other articles. Cast and wrought iron were the most commonly used structural metals, but each had its defects. Steel, a form of iron with 0.5 to 1.7 percent carbon content, was far superior in strength and elasticity. Yet until the middle of the century, it could be produced only by a slow and uneconomical process known as cementation, which involved prolonged heating and hammering of the metal. As a result, steel was too costly and uneven in quality for large-scale use. The first important advance beyond this point was Benjamin Huntsman's development of the crucible, or cast, steel-making process between 1740 and 1742.

The son of Dutch emigrants, Huntsman grew up in England and began his career as an instrument-maker in Doncaster. He became interested in steel manufacture due to the high cost and uneven quality of steel which he imported from Germany and Sweden for use in his instruments. He experimented with various steel-making techniques, and by 1742 had developed a process that was cheaper than cementation, used less fuel and yielded a superior metal (see below).

At about this time, Huntsman moved to Handsworth near the cutlery-making center of Sheffield in the hope of marketing his steel. But English smiths resisted the new product, in part because it sharply reduced the amount of forge work necessary. Crucible steel also had a lower melting point than the types produced by cementation, which meant that it was more difficult to shape and weld. Despite these drawbacks, French cutlers readily accepted crucible steel and imported large quantities from Huntsman; their competition eventually forced English manufacturers to use the metal. Even so, production of cast steel grew slowly for several decades, due to Huntsman's insistence on preserving a monopoly on his process. The first crucible steel furnace outside England was built in 1802 by Johann Conrad Fischer of Switzerland, who developed the process independently.

Though it gradually spread throughout Europe, the crucible process was far from being the last word in steel-making technology. It sharply reduced the cost of steel, but iron remained far cheaper. Only the advent of the Bessemer and Siemens-Martin steel-making processes in the mid-nineteenth century made steel competitive in price with iron, allowing it to become the chief structural metal of industry.

Outstanding Engineering Achievement:

Like Henry Cort's [q.v.] puddling and rolling process, crucible steel-making relied on the relatively high temperatures made possible by the coke-fueled reverberatory furnace developed in the early eighteenth century. Huntsman's technique began with so-called blister steel, made by immersing red-hot wrought iron in a mixture of carboniferous matter. In order to remove impurities and ensure even distribution of carbon, this metal was traditionally hammered at red heat for several days. Huntsman's innovation consisted of melting the blister steel entirely in clay crucibles nine to ten inches high and six to seven inches in diameter. A typical Huntsman furnace held two crucibles on the floor of the melting chamber and heated the metal for five hours. Carbon spread evenly through the molten metal, and mineral impurities separated out. The result was a steel freer of impurities, more homogeneous and harder than any variety previously produced. Since the entire steel-making process was considerably shortened, less fuel was consumed and the costs of production were reduced. ■

Further Reading:

Samuel Smiles, *Industrial Biographies: Ironworkers and Tool-makers*. Boston, 1864.

David Landes, *The Unbound Prometheus*. Cambridge, 1965.

Singer et al., *A History of Technology*, Vol. IV.

BENJAMIN FRANKLIN
b. Jan. 17, 1706, Boston, Massachusetts
d. April 17, 1790, Philadelphia, Pennsylvania
American Scientist and Inventor

Life and Times:

Benjamin Franklin is one of the few prominent figures of the Western world who is known equally for his involvement in politics and sci-

Benjamin Franklin, printer and public figure, inventor of an effective heating stove and the lightning rod.

ence. Indeed, he has been called "the Bacon of the eighteenth century" after the celebrated British statesman who promoted science in the courts of Elizabeth I and James I. Franklin made important contributions to the infant sciences of electricity and oceanography while helping establish the infant government of the United States.

One of 17 children in the family of a poor Boston candlemaker, Franklin left school at 10 to serve as apprentice in a printing shop owned by his brother. At 17 he moved to Philadelphia to establish his own printing shop, which published among other books his famous collection of aphorisms known as *Poor Richard's Almanac*. He quickly became a successful businessman and community leader, cultivating an extensive correspondence with public figures and philosophers. By 1748 he had a fortune large enough to enable him to retire from publishing and devote himself to his political and scientific interests.

Franklin first served in public office as postmaster general of England's American colonies. Beginning in 1757 he represented Pennsylvania and other colonies in London, a task which gradually convinced him of the intractability of the British government and the need for American independence. When the break with England finally came he served in the Second Continental Congress, signed the Declaration of Independence and helped draft the U.S. Constitution. He was perhaps most valuable to the Revolution as American ambassador to France,

where he won enormous popularity and helped secure vital French support for the cause of independence.

Franklin's scientific work developed parallel to his public career. During his youth electrical phenomena had begun to arouse intense public curiosity due to their startling and seemingly magical effects. Franklin first became interested in electricity in 1746, when he witnessed a demonstration of static electricity in Philadelphia. Although he lacked any scientific training, his strongly practical bent enabled him to design experiments that considerably advanced knowledge in the field. Franklin first formulated the modern theory of electrical charge, demonstrated that lightning is a form of static electricity (in his famous kite experiment of 1752) and designed a series of glass panes that could be charged with electricity. His frequent trips across the Atlantic also interested him in oceanography, a science which he hoped would improve the speed and safety of sea transport. Franklin's work in electricity won him the Copley Medal of Britain's Royal Society, and he later became the first American member of the French Academy of Sciences.

Throughout his life, Franklin sought to encourage scientific and general education. As early as 1743 he founded the first American Philosophical Society and established one of the earliest public lending libraries in the colonies. He also founded an academy in Philadelphia which later became the University of Pennsylvania.

Outstanding Engineering Achievements:

Franklin's inventions were strictly practical and usually intended for a specific purpose. As early as 1740 he developed the famous Franklin stove, an improved heating device which facilitated circulation of warm air through the room. Twelve years later, while experimenting with electricity, he found that a kite flying in a thunderstorm diverted the electrical charge of a lightning bolt down its string into a metal key attached to the end. Though extremely dangerous (several scientists were killed trying to repeat the experiment), this discovery was the basis of the lightning rod, developed by Franklin to divert lightning from buildings.

Other Achievements:

Franklin was equally famous among his contemporaries for his theoretical work in electricity and other fields. In the early eighteenth century, electrical phenomena were attributed to two insubstantial "fluids" flowing in opposite directions. Franklin proposed that electricity was a single "fluid" saturating all objects. An electric current, in his view, resulted only when a surplus of this fluid collected in an object that was connected or in close proximity to another object. An object with a surplus of electrical fluid Franklin called positively charged; an object with less than its normal level of fluid would be negatively charged. With a reversal of signs and the substitution of electron flow for fluid, Franklin's theory stands today as the explanation of electrical charge.

In addition to his work in electricity, Franklin conducted experiments that helped establish the sciences of oceanography and meteorology. In 1775 he took water temperature measurements in the Atlantic that allowed him to map the Gulf Stream, whose strong counterclockwise currents frequently slowed eastbound ships. He also developed a theory of storm systems, proposing that hurricanes are formed from ascending warm air masses in the tropics, which then move northward. ∎

Further Reading:

John D. Bernal, *Science in History,* Vol. II. London, 1965.

I. Bernard Cohen, *Franklin and Newton.* Philadelphia, 1956.

Dictionary of Scientific Biography, s.v. "Franklin."

Feldman and Ford, *Scientists and Inventors.* New York, 1979.

Singer et al., *A History of Technology,* Vol. IV.

Abraham Wolf, *A History of Science, Technology and Philosophy in the Eighteenth Century.* London, 1952.

LEONHARD EULER

b. April 15, 1707, Basel, Switzerland
d. Sept. 18, 1783, St. Petersburg, Russia
Swiss Mathematician

Life and Times:

When Leonhard Euler was born, engineering was still predominantly a craft in which technological problems were tackled with experience and ingenuity. Following the lead of his friend

and colleague, Daniel Bernoulli [q.v.], Euler explored the mathematical theory of all aspects of mechanics. By the time he died, the theoretical foundation of modern engineering had been laid, and mathematics had become a necessary tool of every engineer.

Euler learned mathematics from Johannes Bernoulli, Daniel's father, and then followed Daniel to the St. Petersburg Academy. There he began the most prolific outpouring of scholarly work that the mathematical world has ever known. He wrote papers on every branch of mathematics then known, invented branches that did not exist before, and applied mathematics to problems of mechanics, fluid mechanics, optics, astronomy and probability theory. He also helped Russia to reform its weights and measures, and wrote textbooks for its schools.

Nevertheless, like Bernoulli, Euler found the regime oppressive, and in 1741 he accepted the invitation of Frederick the Great to join the Berlin Academy. He continued to publish some of his articles in St. Petersburg, and Russia continued to pay him part of his salary. For Frederick, Euler also worked on practical problems such as coinage, canals and pension plans. Extremely well educated in many fields, including philosophy and languages, Euler remained a simple man, not the gracious courtier that Frederick would have preferred. After 24 years in Berlin, he returned to St. Petersburg.

Years before, Euler had lost one eye to illness. Aware that he was losing the sight of the other, he had a desk made with a slate top. When blindness came, he dictated to his sons (he had 13 children) and chalked his formulas on the table. Since the sons now attended to such chores as proofreading, Euler's output actually increased. During his lifetime he published some 560 books and papers; another 296 appeared posthumously. A collection of his complete works has been under way since 1911. Now close to completion, it will fill nearly 80 large volumes.

Outstanding Engineering Achievements:

Problems in the theory of mechanics were originally treated by Euclidean geometry. Euler completely replaced this approach by systematically applying the method of analysis—the reduction of a problem to a set of equations. His first major work in mechanics concerned the equations of motion of a point-mass in resisting mediums; 30 years later he gave the differential equations of motion of heavy solid bodies.

Almost every branch of mechanics contains formulas that bear Euler's name. For example, in materials science Euler's formula for slender columns, which he derived in 1757, relates the maximum deflection of a column to the critical load, modulus of elasticity and moment of inertia. Fluid mechanics, the entire subject of which he placed on a rigorous basis, contains the Euler equations for the motion of an incompressible liquid or gas. In optics, his formulas for refraction and color dispersion showed that, contrary to Isaac Newton's [q.v.] belief, it could be possible to combine lenses to produce images with little or no colored fringes; this led to development of the achromatic telescope. Euler's differential equations express the general motion of a solid body about a fixed point; they involve the moment of inertia, a concept that Euler introduced.

Other Achievements:

Euler's contributions to mathematics can merely be hinted at here. It was Euler who introduced the symbol i for the square root of negative one, e for the base of natural logarithms, and he settled on π for the ratio of circumference to diameter of a circle. His formulas for sine and cosine in terms of complex powers of e led to the succinct and surprising relationships:

$$e^{i\pi} = -1 \text{ and } i^i = e^{-\pi/2}$$

Several of Euler's computational methods, including finding the numerical solution of differential equations, have been adapted to the computer. He originated the calculus of variations, which gives a general method of solving problems concerning the maxima and minima of integrals. In the theory of numbers, Euler's identity is part of the proof that the number of primes is infinite. And in topology, another subject that he pioneered, the Euler characteristic of a surface is the number of vertices plus the number of faces minus the number of edges; for a simple polyhedron he proved the characteristic to be 2. ∎

Further Reading:

Dictionary of Scientific Biography, s.v. "Euler."

E. E. Kramer, The Nature and Growth of Modern Mathematics. Hawthorn, New York, 1970.

R. Taton, ed. The Beginnings of Modern Science. New York, 1964.

BENJAMIN ROBINS
b. 1707, Bath, England
d. 1751, Madras, India
British Mathematician and Military Engineer

Life and Times:

The growth of engineering as an exact science was hastened in the eighteenth century by the rapidly diminishing distance between mathematics and practical mechanics. The gap between mathematical systems developed by René Descartes, Gottfried Wilhelm von Leibniz and Isaac Newton [q.v.] and the hit-or-miss methods employed by inventors like Thomas Savery [q.v.] and Thomas Newcomen [q.v.] began to close when engineering was undertaken by gifted mathematicians. In this respect Benjamin Robins might be viewed as the predecessor of the modern engineer, who is in equal measure empiricist and mathematician.

Robins became famous for his work in ballistics, a highly mathematical branch of engineering that increased dramatically in importance during the eighteenth century. Under Prussia's Frederick the Great and other military commanders of the time, the expanded use of artillery transformed military strategy; the proportion of cannons to combat troops doubled over what it had been in the smaller armies of the previous century. As the importance of heavy artillery grew, the variety of calibers was reduced and field pieces were redesigned. Scientific knowledge lagged behind practice, however, and retarded mechanical progress. Isaac Newton and Johannes Bernoulli had done important work in the previous century on missile trajectories and the effect of air resistance. But misapprehensions remained on how guns worked, perpetuating errors in design. Robins did much to correct this situation.

Outstanding Engineering Achievements:

Robins is best known as an engineer for inventing the ballistic pendulum, a device which could determine the velocity of a missile at any point in its trajectory. The pendulum consisted of a heavy weight suspended from a single point and allowed to swing freely; when a cannon or musket ball was fired at the pendulum, its velocity at the moment of impact could be determined by the weight of the ball and pendulum and the distance of the pendulum's deflection. In 1747 Robins demonstrated that firing a rifle caused the discharged musket ball to spin, allowing it to maintain a uniform direction in flight by countering the propensity to swerve produced by air resistance. Robins reported his early ballistics work in his book *New Principles of Artillery,* published in 1742.

Robins was also highly regarded as a military engineer, sought out by both the Dutch and British governments to redesign fortifications. He was a fellow of the Royal Society, Britain's most prestigious scientific institution, and received the Society's Copley medal in 1747 for his ballistics work. In addition to his gunnery book, he published a *Mathematical Tract* in 1751. He also authored political pamphlets and taught physical science and mathematics. ∎

Further Reading:

T. K. Derry and Trevor Williams, *A Short History of Technology.* New York, 1961.

Abraham Wolf, *A History of Science, Technology and Philosophy in the Eighteenth Century.* London, 1952.

JEAN-RODOLPHE PERRONET
b. 1708, Suresnes, France
d. 1794, Paris, France
French Civil Engineer

Life and Times:

In the eighteenth century civil engineering began to assume its modern character, and it was in France that advances in construction techniques were most pronounced. There had previously been little distinction between the roles of the military and civil engineer and the architect. But in the years of the absolute monarchy, French engineering flourished with full state support. In contrast to Britain, where engineering developed largely in the sphere of private enterprise, French construction works were primarily government undertakings. The career of Jean-Rodolphe Perronet, the first great bridge builder of the eighteenth century, reflects the growing specialization and scientific character of engineering, the European hegemony of French engineering and the first outlines of the role of the contemporary engineer.

Perronet began his career at 17 as an assistant in an architect's office, but entered government service in 1736 as an assistant engineer. Within four years he rose to become chief civil engineer of the province of Alençon. He was then pro-

Jean-Rodolphe Perronet, the great bridge builder who perfected the masonry arch.

moted to the Corps des Ponts et Chaussées, a national agency established in 1716 to plan and execute the most important works of French civil engineering. In 1747 Perronet was named first director of the newly-created Ecole des Ponts et Chaussées, a training institute for engineers of the Corps. Under Perronet, the Ecole, the first civil engineering school in the world, played an important role in furthering the exchange of knowledge and establishing engineering as a separate profession, distinct from architecture and theoretical science. In 1764 Perronet was appointed first engineer of the Corps, which by then had a well trained staff at all levels.

Perronet was known not only as an engineering administrator but also as a supremely skilled bridge designer. Breaking with tradition, he designed bridges with flatter arches, shallower arch-rings and thinner piers than earlier structures. This made his bridges more slender and aesthetically pleasing, yet as strong as the more cumbersome type of the seventeenth century, which had been modeled on the great Roman bridges. Perronet's rule of thumb was to make piers one-tenth the width of the corresponding span, compared to one-fifth in the most advanced earlier French bridges; as a result, obstruction of the natural waterway was reduced to one-third, compared with two-thirds for some

The elliptical arches of the Pont de Neuilly, Perronet's bridge over the Seine, near Paris. Engraving from 1783.

of the great Roman bridges. By leaving more room for the passage of flood waters, Perronet's arch and pier designs reduced the likelihood of storm damage, while the low gradient resulting from his flattened arches made bridges more accessible to wheeled vehicles. The best known of Perronet's bridges are the Pont de Sainte-Maxence over the Oise River, the Pont de Neuilly over the Seine below Paris and the Pont de la Concorde (originally the Pont Louis XVI) in Paris.

Outstanding Engineering Achievements:

Perronet's Pont de Sainte-Maxence set a new level of skill and innovation in stone arch design. The bridge revived, in modified form, the segmental arch style that flourished in the Italian Renaissance. Its three 72-foot (21.9 meters) segmental spans had a daringly low rise of just over six feet (1.8 meters), reducing both the dead weight of the arches and the downward component of their thrust. This made it possible to support the entire structure on four slender columns nine feet (2.7 m) in diameter instead of the massive piers which had traditionally burdened segmental arch bridges.

In designing the Pont de Neuilly, Perronet adroitly used several low-rise elliptical arches combined with circular face openings by means of the *corne de vache,* or cow's horn. This was a shorter, tapered form of pier that helped increase the free flow of water through arch openings. While this form did not originate with Perronet, he helped bring it to a state of near perfection. The Pont de Neuilly was Perronet's aesthetic masterpiece, supported by five arches of 120-foot (37 meters) span with a rise of 30 feet (9 meters). Considered by many to be the most beautiful stone arch bridge ever built, it was replaced in 1956 by a modern span.

Construction of Perronet's last bridge, the

Pont de la Concorde, was interrupted by the French Revolution; according to one account, it was completed with rubble from the Bastille. Perronet's original design for the bridge was regarded as too insecure by many engineers, who persuaded him to adopt rounder arches and a higher rise. Even so, the rise remained so slight that the bridge could be fed by a road running level from the quays. ■

Further Reading:

Kranzberg and Pursell, *Technology in Western Civilization,* Vol. I.
Singer et al., *A History of Technology,* Vol. III.

JACQUES GERMAIN SOUFFLOT
b. 1708 or 1709, Irancy, France
d. Aug. 29, 1780, Paris, France
French Architect

Life and Times:

The second half of the eighteenth century saw the birth of neoclassicism, a movement whose leading exponent in France was the architect Jacques Germain Soufflot. Neoclassicism was the Enlightenment's reaction against the excesses of the Baroque. Neoclassic builders drew their inspiration from the simple geometric forms of classical antiquity and called for rationality in architecture. No mere antiquarians, these architects of the Age of Reason led the way in applying the science of statistics to the planning and construction of buildings. Soufflot was typical of the times, both in his appreciation of the past and in his pioneering work in materials testing and construction technique.

Soufflot's father was a wealthy merchant who gave him the best education available. When the son showed an interest in the arts, the father encouraged him to study architecture, sending him to Lyon, to Rome and even to Asia Minor, where Soufflot sketched classical monuments. Soufflot was enrolled in the French Academy at Rome for three years. He then returned in 1737 to take up his first architectural commission, a domed church for the charterhouse at Lyon. While in Lyon he built a hospital, a concert hall and a theater, restored the archbishop's palace, and enlarged the commercial exchange building.

The hospital, with its classical facade and imposing dome, brought him fame; in 1749 he was enrolled in the Academy of Architecture, an official body to which few architects and engineers won admission. The following year Soufflot traveled to Italy with the Marquis de Marigny, the brother of Mme. Pompadour. Marigny was Louis XV's superintendent of buildings and used his influence to get Soufflot several government positions. From 1756 on Soufflot worked mainly in Paris, restoring old structures, building new ones, and serving as a consultant on others' projects.

Soufflot's admiration for the architecture of the past developed early. In a 1741 dissertation sent to the Academy he maintained that the builders of medieval times were more scientific and ingenious than contemporary architects. Soufflot admired Gothic buildings for their functional logic, not their emotional appeal. He hoped to build a structure that would combine the clarity of classical buildings with the lightness of Gothic. He got his chance when Marigny convinced the king to award Soufflot the commission for reconstruction of the church of Ste. Geneviève (later the Panthéon Français) in Paris.

After construction began in 1764 it became clear that Soufflot's design was unconventional. No massive piers were rising to support the weight of the dome. Instead, Soufflot planned clusters of a few fairly slender Corinthian columns. The effect would be one of great openness; however, rival architects condemned the design as unsound. Soufflot's friend Emiland Gauthey [q.v.], a noted civil engineer, tested samples of the stone used in the columns and found that they would bear the weight of the dome. Soufflot conducted similar tests and decided he could make the dome still larger.

Soufflot died before construction of the dome had begun. Once the dome was complete and the scaffolding had been removed, cracks in fact began to develop in some of the columns.

Although the fault appeared to be in the workmanship rather than the design, in 1796 the columns were reinforced with additional masonry. Despite other modifications in his plans made by later architects, the Panthéon stands as Soufflot's crowning achievement. The street leading up to it was named in his honor, and in 1829 his remains were placed in the Panthéon's crypt.

Outstanding Engineering Achievements:

Soufflot's design for the Panthéon involved two innovations. To strengthen the masonry that would be receiving the horizontal thrust of the dome, wrought iron bars were embedded in the mortar binding the stone blocks; grooves were cut in the stone to receive them. Although iron clamps had been used in the past to join stone blocks, Soufflot's systematic use of iron foreshadowed the reinforced concrete of the mid-nineteenth century.

After critics questioned the ability of his columns to withstand the dome's vertical thrust, Soufflot conducted extensive materials tests, modifying the device developed by Gauthey for this purpose. Soufflot's unpublished papers included a table of specific weights for hundreds of varieties of stone. It was on the basis of these tests that he modified his building plans, considerably increasing the height and mass of the projected dome. ■

Further Reading:

Charles Bauchal, *Nouveau Dictionnaire Biographique et Critique des Architectes Français.* Paris, 1887.

Singer et al., *A History of Technology.* Vol. IV.

Hans Straub, *A History of Civil Engineering.* London, 1952.

JACQUES DE VAUCANSON
b. Feb. 24, 1709, Grenoble, France
d. Nov. 21, 1782, Paris, France
French Mechanical Engineer

Life and Times:

By the early eighteenth century, the growing international importance of the French silk weaving industry brought repeated efforts to improve the draw-loom. Used for weaving silk threads into ornate and intricate patterns, the draw-loom was slow and subject to human error. A weaver's assistant, called the draw-boy, was used to pull the warp threads, or cords, in a sequence that produced the desired pattern. Manual arrangement of the cords for a particular pattern took two weeks, and the procedure had to be repeated each time a different pattern was needed. Mechanization of the loom and elimination of the draw-boy's function was not finally achieved until 1801, when Joseph-Marie Jacquard [q.v.] introduced fundamental improvements to a device invented by Jacques de Vaucanson in 1745.

Vaucanson came of a noble family and displayed an advanced mechanical aptitude as a child by making wooden clocks. After receiving his education at the Jesuit College of Grenoble, Vaucanson went to Paris, where he invented several mechanical toys which attracted wide attention; one particularly novel device was a duck which swam, quacked, flapped its wings and swallowed its food. Vaucanson's interest in improving industrial machinery began when he was appointed an inspector of silk factories in 1741. A powerful administrative figure in the French Academy of Sciences, Vaucanson donated a large collection of tools and weaving devices to the institution at the time of his death. The automatic loom was salvaged from neglect years later by Jacquard, who found the abandoned device in a museum.

The draw-loom constructed by Vaucanson never took hold in the French silk weaving industry. The loom depended upon the motion of a complex cylinder (see below) whose motion was erratic. Vaucanson's device also failed to achieve full automaticity because the threads snapped easily, making the presence of a machine attendant mandatory. Resistance to mechanization by the silk weavers' guilds, strengthened by support from the royal government, contributed to the neglect of the invention.

While working on the draw-loom, Vaucanson discovered that certain parts which he needed could not be produced by existing machines. For this reason he turned his attention to precision tool-making, a field in which he made several early contributions. Among these were a horizontal drill and the first all-metal lathe capable of turning large metal pieces. Certain features of Vaucanson's lathe anticipated innovations introduced some 50 years later by Henry Maudslay [q.v.], but the device was no more successful than the draw-loom in bringing Vaucanson an immediate return for his effort.

Outstanding Engineering Achievement:

Prior to Vaucanson's innovations, the draw-loom had been furnished with a mechanism for selecting and lifting the correct warp-threads which simplified but did not eliminate the work of the draw-boy. In 1725 Basile Bouchon used rolls of pierced paper attached to a perforated cylinder to govern the needle's selection of warp threads, thereby determining which needles would be used and which ones would be left idle. In this method, only those needles which would produce a pre-determined pattern were admitted through the holes to hook the proper cords. Three years later, Falcon introduced the use of perforated cards for this procedure. Vaucanson retained Falcon's card and Bouchon's perforated cylinder. He mounted an apparatus above the loom which connected the warp threads to the needles by means of hooks. The lower ends of the hooks were fastened to the cords and the upper segments were passed through the eyes of needles. The selection of the needles was governed by perforated cards revolving around a pierced cylinder; the cylinder was set upon a carriage capable of backward and forward motion which would engage and disengage the cylinder with the needles. The operative hooks were then raised by a metal bar controlled by a hand-treadle turned by the weaver. Vaucanson intended falling water or animals to supply the loom with power. ■

Further Reading:

Alfred Barlow, *The History and Principles of Weaving by Hand and by Power.* London, 1879.

Abbott P. Usher, *A History of Mechanical Inventions.* New York, 1929.

Singer et al., *A History of Technology,* Vols. III and IV.

PIERRE TRESAGUET
b. 1716
d. 1794
French Civil Engineer

Life and Times:

With the rapid growth of commerce and population during the eighteenth century, the sad state of Europe's roads became an acute problem. The old network of Roman roads had long since fallen into decay, and new road construction suffered from primitive and costly methods. Nevertheless, most European countries, responding to military as well as economic pressures, gradually improved their road systems. The process was quickest in France, where the absolute monarchy gave strong support to civil engineering projects of all sorts. French road builders of the early eighteenth century, however, did not stray far from ancient Roman methods. The first real improvement in road construction was the work of Pierre Tresaguet, France's master road builder.

Born into a family of engineers, Tresaguet made his career in the Corps des Ponts et Chaussées, the national agency which carried out state-supported civil engineering projects. He served for a time as sub-inspector of roads in Paris, later rising to the post of chief engineer in Limoges. It was at this time that he developed his new road construction method, first used in a highway running from Paris through Toulouse to the Spanish border. In 1775 Tresaguet became inspector general of the Corps des Ponts et Chaussées, and his technique rapidly spread throughout the country.

French roads built before Tresaguet had several disadvantages: (1) Though solid, they were poorly drained, requiring considerable maintenance; (2) their camber (or rise from edge to center) was high, making them difficult for wheeled vehicles to negotiate; and (3) their great depth (generally 18 inches; 46 cm) made them costly in both materials and labor. Tresaguet's improved construction method (see below) produced roads which were much shallower (nine to ten inches; 23 to 25 cm) yet had better drainage and a lower camber. As a result, they were cheaper to build and maintain. Indeed, Tresaguet claimed that his roads, if properly built, should last 10 years with minimal maintenance. This was an important consideration for the state, since earlier roads had been built and repaired by the unpopular *corvée,* or forced labor draft. In 1776, one year after Tresaguet became inspector general of the Corps, the *corvée* was abolished.

By 1788, some 12,000 miles (19,300 km) of roads (over one-third of the national highway system) had been constructed according to Tresaguet's method. He further improved the system by organizing regular road patrols to locate problems before they became serious. Under Tresaguet and for many years after his death, the French road network was by far the best in Europe. His construction technique spread to other countries, influencing such important road builders as Britain's Thomas Telford [q.v.].

Tresaguet himself, however, suffered an undeserved fate. Dismissed from his post during the French Revolution, he died in poverty and obscurity.

Outstanding Engineering Achievement:

A Tresaguet road consisted of three layers: a base layer of long stones set vertically against the cambered foundation; an intermediate layer of smaller stones, hand-placed horizontally; and a top layer of small, hard stones compacted by rollers. Tresaguet set great importance on obtaining the hardest stone available for the top layer, even if this meant importing materials from outside the locality. Two features of Tresaguet's road design deserve special note: the vertical placement of the base stones (earlier roads had horizontally-placed base stones); and the cambered foundation running parallel to the road's surface (earlier roads had flat foundations). The vertical base stones and cambered foundation together permitted better drainage of the road. The cambered foundation also considerably reduced the road's depth, saving building materials and improving the transmission of shock from the surface to the foundation. All these factors made Tresaguet's roads much easier to build and maintain than earlier roads. Indeed, no great improvements in highway construction appeared in France until the advent of motor vehicles and hard surface roads in the twentieth century. ■

Further Reading:

Kranzberg and Pursell, *Technology in Western Civilization.*
Singer et al., *A History of Technology,* Vol. IV.

JAMES BRINDLEY
b. 1716, Derbyshire, England
d. Sept. 30, 1772, Turnhurst, England
British Civil Engineer

Life and Times:

Britain's transportation network suffered in the early eighteenth century from the political turmoil of the seventeenth. Without strong state support such as existed in France, building in England advanced slowly until the growing trade and manufacturing of the early industrial era

James Brindley, builder of canals essential to the development of England's industrial centers.

stimulated the opening up of England's interior areas. Along with a boom in road construction, canals began to appear on a large scale. Fortunately, the trades of the pre-industrial era had prepared a whole class of men for building the transportation arteries needed to sustain the Industrial Revolution. Almost invariably, the British engineer had some background as a millwright, charged with harnessing the power of wind and watermills. In this sense, James Brindley, England's first great canal-builder, was a representative figure.

Brindley was born into a poor farming family near Buxton. Fascinated with machinery since childhood, he apprenticed himself to a millwright at 17. Brindley proved a skilled and dedicated mechanic, and his services were soon in great demand in the Macclesfield area. At 26 he went into business for himself as a wheelwright. His first engineering opportunity came when the owner of a coal mine in Clifton sought his help in draining the mine of water. Harnessing the natural power of a nearby waterfall, Brindley built impressive mill machinery which hauled drainage buckets attached to a wheel. The success of this venture caught the attention of the Duke of Bridgewater, a wealthy and progressive property owner, who recruited him to help construct a canal between Worseley and Manchester in the heart of the burgeoning Midlands.

The Bridgewater Canal, as the project was called, was authorized by an Act of Parliament in 1759. Completed in 1762, it was soon extend-

ed to the Mersey River, connecting Manchester with Liverpool. Even before this undertaking was finished, Brindley was asked to plan a more ambitious one, the Grand Trunk Canal. Running 90 miles (145 km) south and east, it connected the Mersey with the Trent River and each with the Severn River, providing a direct inland link between the ports of Liverpool, Bristol and Hull. The Grand Trunk Canal was completed in 1777, shortly after Brindley's death. Its success stimulated the construction of several other canals, three of which had been designed by Brindley: the Coventry Canal, which connected the Grand Trunk with London, the Droitwich Canal and the Birmingham Canal. Brindley's advice was also important in the planning of other major canals, including the Leeds and Liverpool Canal, which connected Lancashire and Yorkshire.

Brindley's canals had an immediate impact on the cost of transporting goods in northwest England. The Bridgewater Canal gave Manchester a steady and cheap supply of coal for the first time in its history, cutting local coal prices in half. After the opening of the Grand Trunk Canal, the cost of transporting goods among the many towns along its route also fell drastically. The canal system made it easier for farmers to find new markets for their produce in the rapidly growing manufacturing towns. The canals even facilitated a redistribution of England's population by permitting workers and subsistence farmers to move from the wooded districts to the cities. For all these reasons, Brindley's canals played an important part in the development of the Manchester-Sheffield-Birmingham area, Britain's industrial heartland.

Outstanding Engineering Achievements:

From an engineering standpoint, Brindley's canals were remarkable mainly for their innovative use of aqueducts to reduce the number of locks, hitherto relied upon to bring ships from one altitude level to another. Although drainage conduits had been developed in France, Brindley's use of the aqueduct required construction techniques new to England. His first feat in this area was the Barton Aqueduct, which carried the Bridgewater Canal across the Mersey River. Known as Brindley's "castle in the air," it was 200 yards (180 meters) long and 12 yards (10.8 meters) wide, with an elevation of 39 feet (11.9 meters) to permit coal barges on the river to pass underneath. The aqueduct's center was bolstered by a bridge with three semicircular arches.

Barton Aqueduct that carried Brindley's Bridgewater Canal over the Mersey.

The Grand Trunk Canal was an even greater challenge to Brindley, for much of its course passed through very hilly terrain. From the Mersey River to its highest point at Harecastle, the canal rose 395 feet (120 m). The completed waterway, as planned by Brindley, had numerous aqueducts (one with 23 arches), 75 locks, 5 tunnels and over 100 bridges. ■

Further Reading:

Arthur Fleming, *A History of Engineering.* London, 1925.

R. Payne, *Canal Builders.* New York, 1959.

L. T. C. Rolt, *Navigable Waterways.* New York, 1964.

JOHN METCALF
b. 1717
d. 1818
British Civil Engineer

Life and Times:

By the sixteenth century, Great Britain's road system had reached a state of advanced deterioration. It was obsolete in almost every way; most of the roads had been built by farmers and forced laborers at a time when even the most elementary principles of civil engineering were unknown. During the eighteenth century, as demographic and economic growth placed increasing demands on all forms of transportation, England lagged far behind France in road construction. Parliamentary approval of road funds meant incessant bickering and compromise before any new project could be started. And, unlike the French, England had no national school for engineers, forcing British road-builders to learn by trial and error. Gradually, the various Turnpike Acts created the beginnings of a modern road network. Although many of the new highways were far from satisfactory, by the 1760s an increasing number of good roads and bridges had been built.

The first distinguished British road-maker was a blind man. John Metcalf, of Knaresborough, was stricken with smallpox and blind from the age of seven. To compensate for his handicap he sought by a strong effort of will to excel in outdoor sports and lead a daring, robust life. As a young man he traveled as a vagabond fiddler and volunteered as a musician with the forces sent to Scotland to quell the Rebellion of 1745. Following this, Metcalf worked as a trader between Aberdeen and Yorkshire and drove a carrier's wagon from Knaresborough to York, gaining first-hand knowledge of England's pressing need for better roads. In 1765, when Parliament authorized construction of a turnpike road from Harrogate to Boroughbridge, Metcalf embarked on a new career by contracting as engineer for some three miles of its proposed length.

Outstanding Engineering Achievements:

After successfully completing his first engineering assignment, Metcalf undertook a portion of the road being built between Harrogate and Knaresborough. While surveying the proposed route, he discerned an odd change in the ground's character. Excavations revealed the remains of an old Roman thoroughfare, which Metcalf used as a source of building materials for his new road.

While working on the same project, Metcalf devised a novel method of coping with a large bog which obstructed his path. Rather than building around the bog at considerable cost in time and money, Metcalf decided to build over it. He created the roadbed by having small bundles of heather laid across the bog in two layers, the bundles of the second layer at right angles to those of the first. These were covered by a layer of gravel, followed by two more layers of heather bundles and a final layer of gravel.

Road metals completed the surface. The result was a solid, well-compacted road that literally floated on the bog. This anticipated a method used by George Stephenson [q.v.] when he built a railway from Liverpool to Manchester across Chat Moss.

Metcalf went on to lay about 180 miles (290 km) of road in the counties of Lancashire, Yorkshire, Derbyshire, and Cheshire. He did not retire from civil engineering until he was 70, by which time the total value of his contracts amounted to some 65,000 pounds. He gave the remainder of his life over to writing his memoirs. ■

Further Reading:

Arthur Fleming, *A History of Engineering*. London, 1925.

Abraham Wolf, *A History of Science, Technology and Philosophy in the Seventeenth and Eighteenth Centuries*. London, 1950.

JOHN ROEBUCK
b. 1718, Sheffield, England
d. July 17, 1794, Borrowstounness, West Lothian, Scotland
British Chemical Engineer and Industrialist

Life and Times:

The heavy chemical industry in Britain arose largely from the production of sulfuric acid. Known to alchemists as oil of vitriol, the substance was used as a bleaching agent, in the extraction and cleaning of precious metals and in other types of metal-working. During the 1820s, with the advent of Nicholas Leblanc's [q.v.] process for synthesizing sodium carbonate, sulfuric acid also became important in the production of other chemicals. Fortunately, sulfuric acid could already be manufactured cheaply and in large quantities, due largely to the work of John Roebuck and his business partner, Samuel Garbett.

The son of a well-to-do cutlery manufacturer, Roebuck studied chemistry at the University of Edinburgh with the noted chemist Joseph Black, and in 1742 received his medical degree from the University of Leyden in Holland. Roebuck settled first in Birmingham, where he abandoned medicine to work as a consulting chemist in the jewelry trade. With Garbett he soon established a shop for refining precious metals, in this way becoming interested in the cheap production of sulfuric acid. In 1746 the two men set up a "vitriol manufactory" in Birmingham, and three years later a much larger plant at Prestonpans near Edinburgh.

Roebuck's operation completed a development begun some ten years earlier by Joshua Ward and John White, who first produced sulfuric acid on a factory scale. But Ward and White used glass equipment, essentially enlarged laboratory vessels with limited capacity. Roebuck overcame this problem by designing a retort lined with corrosion-resistant lead that was sturdier and handled larger quantities of acid than glass containers. The cost of Roebuck's product was 3.5 shillings a pound, down from 2.5 shillings an ounce earlier in the century.

Roebuck was also active in other branches of engineering, though more as an entrepreneur than as an innovator. In 1760 he joined with Garbett and William Cadell to establish the Carron iron works near Falkirk, Scotland. Modelled after Abraham Darby's [q.v.] Coalbrookdale iron works, the Carron works was the foundation of the Scottish iron industry and one of the first foundries to use John Smeaton's [q.v.] improved blowing cylinder in its blast furnaces. In 1768 Roebuck entered into a brief partnership with James Watt [q.v.], who had gone into debt while developing a separate condenser for his steam engine and needed financial help. In return for a two-thirds interest in Watt's patent, Roebuck assumed the inventor's debts and supported his work. But Roebuck himself went bankrupt before Watt completed his engine and was replaced in the partnership by Matthew Boulton.

Outstanding Engineering Achievement:

Roebuck treated his process for producing sulfuric acid as a strict trade secret, so that few of its details are known. It is likely that he obtained acid by burning sulfur and potassium nitrate, an old method first developed by Cornelius Drebbel [q.v.]. Roebuck's real accomplishment was the development of a lead chamber in which the combustion took place. Later retorts of similar design had a capacity of some 1,200 cubic feet (34 cubic meters). Sulfur and potassium nitrate were inserted on two trays and burned intermittently for six weeks before the resulting sulfuric acid was removed. ■

Further Reading:

Archibald and Nan Clow, *The Chemical Revolution*. London, 1952.

Henry Hamilton, *Economic History of Scotland in the Eighteenth Century*. Oxford, 1963.

F. S. Taylor, *A History of Industrial Chemistry*. London, 1957.

T. I. Williams, *The Chemical Industry*. London, 1953.

WILLIAM EDWARDS
b. 1719, Eglwysilan, Glamorganshire, Wales
d. 1789
British Bridge-builder

Life and Times:

One of the most remarkable bridge-building projects of the eighteenth century was undertaken by a Welsh farmer, William Edwards, who built the single-arch Pontypridd Bridge across the Taff River in Glamorganshire in 1756. As a child, Edwards had shown an aptitude for building walls, and by the age of 20 he was doing construction work in the port city of Cardiff. In 1746, when local businessmen in Pontypridd found their iron- and coalmining operations hindered by the frequent flooding and freezing of the Taff, Edwards volunteered to build a bridge for 500 pounds.

His first attempt, a three-arch structure for which he gave a seven-year guarantee, collapsed after two years when its heavy stone piers were knocked out by uprooted trees during a flood. Edwards replaced it with a single arch of 140 feet (43 meters); this too collapsed when floodwaters tore away the wooden centering that supported the arch while it was under construction. The third bridge gave way six weeks after completion, when the stone haunches that formed the base and sides of the arch sank during a storm and forced out the keystones. Recognizing that the haunches had been too heavy, Edwards incorporated into the haunches of his fourth bridge a set of cylindrical openings buttressed by masonry. This bridge was opened to traffic in 1755 and still stands, though the main road is now carried on a modern bridge alongside it.

Having made his reputation with the Pontypridd, which was considered one of the most picturesque bridges in the country, Edwards went on to build a number of other bridges in South Wales, employing a unique style of masonry derived from the stonework of the ruins of Caerphilly Castle. Edwards was also a farmer and a minister.

Edwards' bridge over the Taff at Pontyprydd, for 70 years the bridge with the longest single span.

Outstanding Engineering Achievements:

The fourth and successful version of Edwards's Pontypridd Bridge had a single arch of 140 feet (43 meters), with a radius of 175 feet (53 meters); it bore a carriageway 11 feet 7 inches (3.5 meters) wide. The stone arch-ring, its wedge-shaped joints held together by mortar made from a local hydraulic lime, was only 18 inches (46 cm) deep; together with the rubble fillings, roadway, and parapet walls, it measured no more than three feet six inches (1 meter) deep, nearly half again as slender as the contemporary French bridges of Jean Rodolphe Perronet [q.v.]. The haunches that support the arch on either side were made lighter and more stable by the inclusion of cylindrical tunnels which were buttressed into the spandrel-walls by rings of masonry. Although the arch and roadway are steep, the Pontypridd is regarded as one of the most beautiful bridges of its kind and has been designated a national monument. Its span was not exceeded until John Rennie [q.v.] and his sons built London Bridge in the early 1800s. ■

Further Reading:

Dictionary of National Biography, s.v. "Edwards."

Singer et al., *A History of Technology*, Vol. III.

ANDREW MEIKLE

b. 1719, Houston Mill (near Dunbar), Scotland
d. November 27, 1811, Houston Mill, Scotland
British Mechanical and Agricultural Engineer

Life and Times:

The eighteenth century brought great changes in British agriculture. Growth of the urban population made it profitable for farmers to expand their production, and the enclosure of common lands made it possible for them to introduce new tools and techniques. The times favored experimentation and the abandonment of age-old practices. One of the better-known agricultural innovators who flourished in these years was Andrew Meikle.

The son of a Scottish miller, Meikle inherited his father's mill and soon became interested in machinery that might improve its operation. This led him to experiment with improvements in the windmill, then one of the main power sources in the countryside. In 1750 he invented the so-called fantail, a device which automatically kept windmill sails facing at right angles to the wind. Meikle also sought to overcome the effects of sudden gusts of wind, which decreased the windmill's efficiency and often damaged the vanes. In 1772 he solved this problem with the "spring" sail, a device with shutters that opened automatically and "spilled" wind blowing above a certain velocity.

While still experimenting with the windmill, Meikle turned his attention to developing a

Andrew Meikle, inventor of the threshing machine with the design that became standard.

threshing machine that would speed one of the most arduous tasks of the harvest season. Attempts to mechanize the threshing process had begun in the previous century, and several devices were already available. Meikle, however, was the first to construct a machine using the "drum and concave" design (see below), which later became standard. He patented the machine in 1788 and one year later opened a threshing machine factory. Use of the device spread rapidly, and by the mid-nineteenth century improved versions of the threshing machine had largely displaced the hand flail on British farms.

Meikle's increasing age and other factors caused his business to decline to the point that in 1809 a subscription drive for his relief was organized, bringing in 1,500 pounds. Among the contributors was the famous civil engineer John Rennie [q.v.], who had worked as Meikle's apprentice from 1773 to 1775.

Outstanding Engineering Achievements:

Until Meikle's invention of the fantail, windmill sails were kept facing into the wind by turning them manually with a long "tail" pole attached to the rear of the vanes. The fantail was a small auxiliary windmill mounted at right angles to the main sail. The two were connected by a wooden worm and wheel, and a pinion and rack arrangement that produced a speed reduction of 3,000 to 1 and kept the mainsails perpendicular to the wind. The sails were generally made of louvered wooden slats instead of canvas because of wood's greater durability and resistance to stress.

Meikle's "spring" sail was divided into unequal sections. Each was pivoted and connected to a spring that released the section when a predetermined force acted upon it. The spring tension could be changed by adjusting the length of the rods that held them to the shutter.

Meikle's threshing machine consisted basically of a rotating wooden drum set within a concave surface. Grain was separated from chaff by the rubbing action of the two surfaces. The rapidly rotating drum blew most of the chaff away, while the grain dropped into a sieve-like trough which separated weed seeds and other small particles from the bulk of the grain. The machine could be powered by hand, water, horse or by steam engine. ▪

Further Reading:

John D. Bernal, *Science in History*. London, 1965.

Aubrey F. Burstall, *A History of Mechanical Engineering*. London, 1968.

Abraham Wolf, *A History of Science, Technology and Philosophy in the Eighteenth Century*. London, 1952.

JAMES HARGREAVES

b. 1720, near Blackburn, Lancashire, England
d. April 1778, Nottingham, England
British Mechanical Engineer,

Life and Times:

An imbalance between cotton weaving and spinning existed even before the invention of the flying shuttle in 1733. The work of five spinning wheels was required to supply one weaver's loom with sufficient yarn. As the export and domestic consumption of cotton expanded, increasing numbers of weavers entered the textile industry, creating a greater demand for yarn than spinners could supply. Widespread use of the flying shuttle in the 1750s aggravated an already critical problem. This situation created strong pressure for development of a spinning machine, first accomplished by James Hargreaves.

Hargreaves began his career as a Lancashire weaver. He introduced improvements in the hand-carding of cotton, and in the early 1760s his reputation as a skilled mechanic attracted the attention of Robert Peel, a cotton manufacturer. Like his competitors, Peel wanted badly to mechanize his spinning operation, and hired Hargreaves for this purpose. By about 1764 Hargreaves had developed the spinning jenny, though he did not patent the machine until 1770. The delay may have resulted from his desire for secrecy to guard against appropriation of his design by rival manufacturers, and also to prevent vandalism by spinners whose occupations were threatened by the device. But word of Hargreaves's invention spread when he sold several models to Lancashire businessmen, causing a group of spinners to destroy the machines. Peel quickly lost interest in mechanized spinning, and Hargreaves left Lancashire for Nottingham in 1768.

Nottingham was a center for the cotton trade in the Midlands. Here Hargreaves, in partnership with Thomas James, established a cotton mill equipped with his machines. But the venture was not the financial success he had hoped.

James Hargreaves, inventor of the spinning jenny, one of the first spinning machines.

Hargreaves faced strong competition from Richard Arkwright [q.v.], a rival cotton manufacturer who patented his own spinning machine, the water frame, three weeks before Hargreaves finally patented the jenny. The water frame was a superior machine in several respects, more fully automated and capable of operating a larger number of spindles. Arkwright's factory eventually employed three times the work force used by Hargreaves and James. The spinning jenny, moreover, was easily reproduced by entrepreneurs who refused to pay royalties to the inventor. Unable to collect license fees on his patent, Hargreaves offered a reward of ten guineas for information concerning illegal use of his machine. This effort failed, and he eventually sold rights to the jenny to a group of manufacturers for the lump sum of 4000 pounds. Later mechanics introduced significant improvements in the device, and Samuel Crompton [q.v.] incorporated certain features of it into his spinning mule.

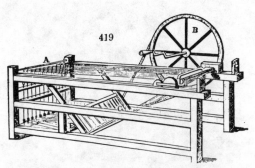

419

The spinning jenny of Hargreaves. Covvon rovings were placed at C; the operator spun the wheel, B, and pushed D forward and back; thread collected on spindles, A.

Outstanding Engineering Achievement:

Hargreaves's spinning jenny was modeled after the action of the human spinner using a one-thread spinning wheel. For the spinner's left hand, which drew out the thread as it was being spun, he substituted a drawbar consisting of two horizontal pieces of wood. The drawbar drew out the thread while it was being twisted by the machine's sixteen spindles. The spinner's right hand turned a wheel which revolved the spindles. Essentially, the yarn was spun by imparting a twist to the thread, which gave it durability, at the same time that the thread was being drawn out. On Hargreaves's jenny, the backward movement of the drawbar pulled out the threads and the revolution of the spindles affected the twist. The yarn was then wound on the spindles as the drawer returned to its original position.

Yarn produced by the jenny was fine and light, well suited for use in the weft of a loom. It was less suitable for the warp, which required a stronger yarn produced by the water frame and later by Crompton's mule. ∎

Further Reading:

C. Aspin and S. D. Chapman, *James Hargreaves and the Spinning Jenny*. New York, 1964.

David Landes, *The Unbound Prometheus*. Cambridge, 1965.

F. Nasmith, "Fathers of the Machine Cotton Industry," *Transactions of the Newcomen Society*. Vol. VI (1925–26).

Singer et al., *A History of Technology*. Vol. IV.

JOHN SMEATON
b. *June 8, 1724, Austhorpe, England*
d. *Oct. 28, 1792*
British Civil and Mechanical Engineer

Life and Times:

John Smeaton was one of the most versatile and prominent British engineers of the eighteenth century. So broad were his interests that it is impossible to describe him in terms of a single historical trend or line of development. He made important contributions to both mechanical and civil engineering, including power technology, marine construction and machine design. At a time when most British engineers were essentially craftsmen operating by trial and error, Smeaton insisted on the importance of theoretical considerations in assessing the efficiency of machines. He was known not only for his original inventions but also for his improvement of numerous existing devices. Indeed, it was said that Smeaton could not touch anything without improving it.

The son of an attorney, Smeaton was intended by his father for a legal career. The young man had ideas of his own, however, and apprenticed himself to a scientific instrument maker. In 1750 he opened his own instrument shop in London. His background and training were evident throughout his career in his desire to measure and improve the mechanical efficiency of any device that attracted his attention.

While still establishing himself in London Smeaton began to study water wheels, then the main source of energy for most British industries. He constructed a set of scale models which allowed him to measure and compare the power provided by various types of water wheels (see below). The result of these experiments was a set of rules for determining the efficiency of a given water wheel. Smeaton also turned his attention to the related subject of windmills, constructing another set of scale models to study the power output of different windmill sails. In 1759 he summarized his findings in both areas in two papers read before the Royal Society, entitled "Experimental Enquiry into the Natural Powers of Wind and Water to turn Mills." Smeaton remained interested in natural energy sources for the rest of his life, designing numerous water wheels for use in factories, foundries and pumping stations. In the view of modern engineering authorities, his improvements made water and wind power production as efficient as was possible at the time.

From natural forms of energy, Smeaton's at-

John Smeaton, a leading member of Britain's first professional society of engineers.

tention turned easily to the main artificial power source of his time, the steam engine. The then most commonly used steam engine, designed by Thomas Newcomen [q.v.], was a relatively inefficient device confined largely to pumping water from mines. In 1767 Smeaton built a Newcomen engine for supplying water to a London reservoir. Dissatisfied with its performance, he began to consider ways of manufacturing more precise and better functioning parts for the engine. In 1769 he designed a boring machine that produced a better engine cylinder. Using this and other improvements in workmanship, Smeaton constructed several Newcomen engines during the next six years that nearly doubled the efficiency of previous models. The Newcomen engine remained expensive to operate due to its high coal consumption. Yet, as in the case of water wheels, Smeaton's improvements brought the device to its peak performance, given the limitations of the design and existing machining methods. Further development of the steam engine had to await the revolutionary changes introduced by James Watt [q.v.].

Smeaton's extensive work in mechanical engineering did not prevent him from gaining even greater prominence as a civil engineer. In 1754 he took temporary leave from his London business, touring Holland to study canals and harbors. Two years later he was commissioned to rebuild the Eddystone Lighthouse off the southwest coast of England. Considering the fate of the island's two previous timber lighthouses—

one destroyed in a gale, the other by fire—Smeaton decided on a stone structure, tapering up from a broad base to ensure stability. Rough seas, however, prevented him from supplying the island with stone blocks large enough to withstand gale-force winds by sheer mass. Forced to use smaller blocks, Smeaton had the ingenious idea of borrowing a carpentry technique known as dovetailing (see below) to ensure firm adhesion. His search for a water-resistant lime to join the blocks (see below) also opened the way for the development of cement. Completed in 1759, the Eddystone Lighthouse withstood the worst Atlantic storms and became the most famous of Smeaton's creations. It remained at its original location until 1882, when erosion threatened to undermine its foundations. Too well-known to be destroyed, the tower was dismantled and reassembled on the mainland.

Smeaton remained active as a civil engineer in subsequent years, constructing several bridges and the Forth and Clyde Canal. In 1774 he was commissioned to build an artificial harbor at Ramsgate on the southeast coast after the failure of previous efforts. Smeaton succeeded in creating a safe and silt-free haven for ships, the first functioning artificial harbor (see below). He later constructed artificial harbors at Port Patrick and Eyemouth. This development in marine engineering was a great boon to British shipping, which suffered from coastal storms that frequently blocked access to natural ports.

The importance and diversity of Smeaton's work was widely recognized in his own time. As early as 1753 he was made a fellow of the Royal Society, which awarded him the Copley medal for his work on water wheels and windmills. Smeaton also contributed to the emergence and recognition of engineering as a separate profession in Britain. When a group of British civil engineers formed the Society of Engineers in 1771, he became one of its leading members. Though he never formally served as president of the group, its successor organization, the Society of Civil Engineers, honored him by calling itself "the Smeatonian." Smeaton's papers and engineering sketches were collected in three volumes by the Royal Society after his death; it also published a selection from them.

Outstanding Engineering Achievements:

At the time of Smeaton's researches on water and wind power, the most commonly used water wheel was the undershot type, turned by a stream of water flowing beneath it. Smeaton

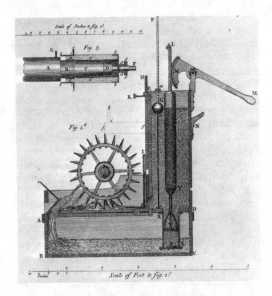
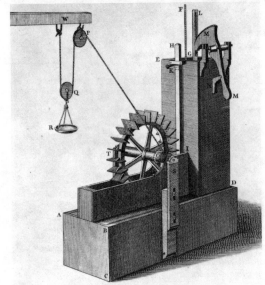

Smeaton's model for measuring the power of a waterwheel. Handle, M, operates a pump that maintains a standard head of water; weights loaded on pan, R, slow the wheel to a stop and show the force produced.

Artificial harbor built by Smeaton at Ramsgate on the east coast of Kent.

determined in his experiments that the undershot wheel operated at less than half the maximum efficiency of an overshot wheel, turned by water falling down across its top. Though opportunities to construct a water wheel beneath a fall were limited, Smeaton helped popularize a compromise type known as the breast wheel. Turned by water flowing down a grade, the breast wheel combined features of the undershot and overshot wheels and operated at an efficiency between the two. Many of the water wheels built

by Smeaton were breast wheels, ranging in diameter from 12 to 18 feet (3.5 to 5.5 meters) and in width from 2 to 7 feet (.6 to 2 m). He also introduced cast iron parts for both water wheels and windmills as a means of improving durability and efficiency.

In constructing the Eddystone Lighthouse, Smeaton had the stone blocks cut with flaring extensions (tenons) and indentations (mortises), which fit tightly together to form a joint. This was the carpentry technique known as dovetailing (see above). He also experimented with various types of lime for use in the mortar, discovering that limestone with a high clay content produced the most water-resistant substance. The dovetailed blocks, joined with strong hydraulic lime, formed in effect a solid stone ring at every level. Smeaton further increased the structure's solidity by having holes drilled in the top and bottom of each block and joining the stones of every level with strong wooden pegs. Finally, he had the foundations built into a rocky slope to prevent slippage. Although this technique had the desired effect, it made the lighthouse vulnerable to erosion (see above), ultimately forcing its removal.

The artificial harbor constructed by Smeaton at Ramsgate was formed by two piers extending 1,300 feet (395 meters) out into the sea, separated at their outer ends by 200 feet (60 meters).

Previous efforts to create a harbor at Ramsgate had failed due to the rapid accumulation of silt between the two piers. Smeaton solved this problem by constructing additional piers within the harbor to form an inner basin, which filled with water at high tide. When discharged through sluices at low tide, the rushing water scoured the main harbor, carrying the silt out to sea.

Of Smeaton's several bridges, the best known was the 900-foot (275 meters) span across the River Tay at Perth, supported on seven arches. Smeaton's main innovation in bridge construction was to introduce circular perforations into the arch cornerstones, or spandrels. This considerably reduced the weight of the arches and decreased stress on the piers, which could be made more slender than was previously possible. ■

Further Reading:

Arthur Fleming, *A History of Engineering.* London, 1925.

Singer et al., *A History of Technology,* Vol. IV.

NICOLAS JOSEPH CUGNOT
b. Sept. 25, 1725, Void, Meuse, France
d. Oct. 2, 1804, Paris, France
French Military and Mechanical Engineer

Life and Times:

While James Watt [q.v.] was developing his steam engine, the Frenchman Nicolas Joseph Cugnot was developing the world's first design for a self-propelled vehicle. In 1769, the year Watt obtained his first patent, Cugnot ran his first steam-powered truck. But whereas Watt's engine became the workhorse of the industrial revolution, Cugnot's invention was ignored and never advanced beyond the prototype stage. Credit for constructing the first fully operational steam carriage later went to Goldsworthy Gurney [q.v.].

Cugnot was a professional soldier from Lor-raine who served in the army of Maria Theresa, the Habsburg empress of Austria and Hungary, and then in the French army. While stationed in Belgium, Cugnot began experimenting with a steam-driven vehicle. In 1763 Cugnot, now an educational officer, arrived in Paris, where he continued work on his invention. Six years later the French Foreign Minister, the Duc de Choiseul, consulted the inspector-general of artillery, Gribeauval, about a steam wagon designed by a Swiss officer. Gribeauval had just become aware of Cugnot's work and found that the vehicles were similar. Choiseul chose to support Cugnot and provided him with government funds for building a full-size version of his working model.

Cugnot's first truck carried four passengers at a speed of about three miles an hour. Choiseul then ordered a second truck that would carry a load of four or five tons at a speed of 1,800 toises (2.2. mi or 3.5 km) per hour. The second truck, called the *fardier,* cost the government 20,000 livres, but by the time it was completed in 1771, Choiseul had fallen from power. The new ministry refused to provide wood for fuel or even the labor of two men for two days to test the vehicle. After 1789 the Revolutionary government also refused an appropriation for testing. In 1801, the steam truck was taken out of storage and placed in the museum of technology, the Conservatoire Nationale des Arts et Métiers, where it remains.

Cugnot wrote three military treatises. In 1779 he was awarded a pension of six hundred livres a year. The Revolution discontinued the pension, and Cugnot returned to Belgium, where he was supported by a woman. During the Consulate, Napoleon renewed the pension, this time for a thousand livres a year, which continued until Cugnot's death.

Outstanding Engineering Achievement:

The Cugnot steam wagon had three wheels, the single front wheel serving as the drive wheel. In the atmospheric steam engines of the day, cold water was injected into the steam-filled cylinder when the piston was at the top of its stroke. This produced a sudden condensation and vacuum, allowing atmospheric pressure to push the piston back to its starting point. Cugnot mounted two 13-inch (33 cm), 50-liter cylinders above the wheel, positioned so that the pistons descended as the cylinders filled with steam. The piston rods were connected to each other by a rocking beam, and the piston strokes were synchronized so that, as atmospheric pressure forced one piston up, high-pressure steam pushed the other down. The cold-water injection was thus dispensed with. A double ratchet and pawl system transferred the reciprocating motion to the axle, where it produced the rotary movement for turning the wheel. This was the first successful device for changing reciprocating to rotary motion. Moreover, it is the only high-

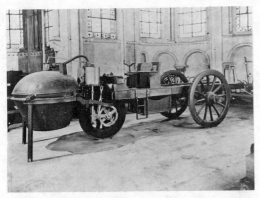

The Fardier *designed and built by Cugnot; the world's first steam-propelled vehicle.*

pressure steam engine known to have been built in the eighteenth century.

The *fardier,* which was almost as big as the tractor of a modern tractor-trailer, cannot have been very stable on any uneven surface. The twin cylinders were hung on the front wheel, which also carried the large copper boiler cantilevered out in front of it. All this weight had to be turned to steer the cart. In spite of its size, the boiler could produce only enough steam to last for fifteen minutes, and had no way to be refilled on the move. These were serious faults; denied money for improvements, Cugnot was unable to remedy them. ■

Further Reading:

Maurice Daumas, ed., *A History of Technology and Invention,* Vol. III. New York, 1979.

Kranzberg and Pursell, *Technology in Western Civilization.*

Shelby T. McCloy, *French Inventions of the Eighteenth Century.* Kentucky, 1952.

Ralph Stein, *The Great Inventions.* Chicago, 1976.

JOHN WILKINSON
b. 1728, Clifton, Cumberland, England
d. July 14, 1808, Bradley, Staffordshire, England
English Ironmaster and Inventor

Life and Times:

The commercial development of James Watt's [q.v.] atmospheric steam engine, patented in 1769, was delayed for nearly seven years by his inability to secure accurately bored cylinders. The creation of an effective vacuum in the engine depended on the fit of the piston within the cylinder; any gaps between them would permit the escape of steam. The boring mills of the time, however, could not offer workmanship of the quality required until John Wilkinson introduced his improvements in 1774.

Wilkinson's father was a manufacturer of box iron and utensils for the laundry trade. In the early 1740s, father and son set up a furnace and refinery near Lindale, where Wilkinson experimented with the use of peat fuel in iron smelting. He successfully used coke for that purpose at Bilston, Staffordshire, where he built the area's first blast furnace in 1748. By 1770 he was the owner or co-owner of several ironworks, producing grenades, shells, and cannon for the East India Company, the French government and other purchasers of ordnance. His weapons business expanded further with his invention in 1774 of a more accurate method of boring cannon.

Wilkinson first applied his new technique to the boring of steam-engine cylinders for the Boulton and Watt foundry in 1775, when he successfully cast and bored a cylinder of approximately 18 inches (49 cm) diameter. The following year, Matthew Boulton wrote: "Wilkinson hath bored us several cylinders almost without Error, that of 50 inches (127 cm) diameter for

John Wilkinson, the ironmaster whose technique for boring steam-engine cylinders helped make steam power a reality.

Bentley & Co. doth not err the thickness of an old shilling in no part. . . ." Wilkinson's method thus achieved a maximum error of only one in one thousand. Without this degree of accuracy, the Watt engine could not have achieved the efficiency of operation required for widespread commercial use. Wilkinson supplied several hundred cylinders for Boulton and Watt engines over the next two decades, until 1795, when the firm installed its own boring mill.

Wilkinson not only helped make steam power a reality, but was also among the first ironmasters to employ it in his own works. In 1776 he equipped his foundry at Willey, Shropshire, with a Boulton and Watt engine to work the blowing cylinders of the furnace—the first use of a steam engine for a purpose other than pumping water—and soon had four more engines installed in his foundries. His competitors had to follow his example or go out of business. By 1783 Wilkinson's Bradley ironworks employed a tilt hammer driven by a Boulton and Watt rotative engine, which he harnessed three years later to a rolling mill. He also installed the first large steam engine in France, used to operate pumps at the Paris waterworks.

Wilkinson led the British iron industry in other respects as well. He pioneered new uses for iron, building a 70-foot barge of bolted cast iron plates to transport his cannon on the Severn River. In 1779 he helped finance the world's first cast iron bridge, built by Abraham Darby III [q.v.] over the Severn at Coalbrookdale. Wilkinson's concern with the structural uses of iron became something of an obsession later in life; he is said to have built himself an iron coffin. He also joined with Darby in an early price-fixing agreement for iron products, the predecessor of a trade association of ironmasters in the developing Midlands industrial area. The group not only set prices but also sought to represent the industry's political interests with the British government.

Outstanding Engineering Achievement:

In the typical boring mill of Wilkinson's day, a water wheel rotated a shaft on which a cutting bit was fixed. Because it was supported only at the wheel end, the shaft tended to sag, and the bit was easily deflected by impurities in the cast iron of the cylinder.

Wilkinson solved this problem by passing the shaft completely through the hollow cylinder and supporting it in bearings at both ends. The cylinder itself was immobilized in a cradle.

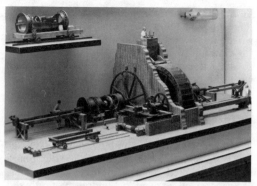

Model of Wilkinson's boring mill. Cutaways of the cylinder being worked are shown in place in the mill and on the shelf above; right, a smaller cylinder being worked.

Within the shaft was a non-rotating rod, joined to the bit through a longitudinal slot; a weighted lever, worked by a rack and pinion device, fed the bit forward on a steady course along this rod. Wilkinson's mill was equipped with three cutting heads, two for the initial boring and a third for finishing. ■

Further Reading:

Thomas S. Ashton, *Iron and Steel in the Industrial Revolution*. London, 1924.

Kranzberg and Pursell, *Technology in Western Civilization*, Vol. I.

LEWIS PAUL
fl. 1730
d. April 1759, Kensington, England
British Mechanical Engineer

Life and Times:

Before the changes in textile production in England that took the name Industrial Revolution, the making of cotton and woolen fabric was a cottage industry. In France and Italy, silk was produced in factories, but in England bundles of wool or cotton were assigned to workers to process at home. The washing and carding of the raw fiber, spinning it into thread, and weaving the thread into cloth were all manual operations. The chief limitation of this system was that five or six people were needed to spin the yarn that just one could weave. Mechanization of spinning would therefore considerably increase the output of finished textiles. This step was taken by

Lewis Paul, whose spinning machine was the forerunner of the water frame of Richard Arkwright [q.v.] and the spinning mule of Samuel Crompton [q.v.].

Paul's father was a French refugee who died when the boy was very young. Lewis was raised under the guardianship of the third earl of Shaftesbury and then his brother, Maurice Ashley Cooper. Lord Shaftesbury was a philosopher of considerable influence, so his ward had access to intellectual as well as noble society. Paul was known to Samuel Johnson, the famed dictionary maker, but died before Johnson's biographer, James Boswell, arrived in London. Not only did Paul enjoy the wit of Johnson's acquaintances, but he also persuaded them to invest in his projects. Even Dr. Johnson, acerbic critic though he was, helped Paul word the letters he sent to raise money for his inventions.

In 1728 Paul married the widow of a prominent lawyer. She died the following year, but this tragedy was partly mitigated by her legacy and by Paul's invention of a machine for pinking shrouds. The machine, which prevented the unravelling of cloth by cutting a scalloped edge, was successful and produced a good profit. This in turn led Paul to an association with John Wyatt in 1733.

Originally a ship's carpenter, Wyatt had developed an interest in machinery and invented a device for turning and boring metals. Unable to obtain financing for its manufacture, he sold the rights to Paul. Whether Wyatt or Paul invented the spinning machine is a matter of some conjecture; credit is usually given to both together or to Paul alone. Wyatt's descendants claimed that his role had been undervalued, but Wyatt's own writings indicate that Paul contributed essential ideas to the machine's development. It was Paul who received a patent in 1738 for applying rollers to the spinning of thread.

The partners opened their first spinning factory in 1740 in London, with others following in Birmingham, Northampton, and Leominster. But despite intense public interest and a promising beginning, the machines were not yet capable of doing a consistent job, and by 1748 all the factories had failed.

Undiscouraged, Paul continued to develop new textile machines. In 1748 he was awarded a patent on a machine for carding, the process that prepares a fiber for being spun. The principle of his machine was incorporated by Arkwright in the carder that he patented in 1775. When Arkwright sued several manufacturers for infringing on this and other patents, the hearings revealed that the carder owed too much to Paul

for Arkwright to be entitled to patent it. Ten months before his death, Paul patented another spinning machine, but this one was not produced. His personal papers, bought by a library after his death, were unfortunately destroyed in a fire.

Outstanding Engineering Achievements:

In hand carding, a wire-bristle brush is drawn over the fluffy mass of cleaned cotton until the individual fibers are all parallel. A rope of the fiber, or sliver, can then be taken off to be spun. The process is slow, and if not done properly the sliver will be uneven and prone to break during spinning. In Paul's carder, the cotton was drawn over a cylinder that was surfaced with the wire bristles. This is essentially the system still used.

Spinning is a process of pulling and twisting. In Paul and Wyatt's spinning machine, the slivers were drawn between a pair of rollers and then passed to a second pair of rollers revolving at a faster rate. This stretched the sliver, thinning it down to a string, called a roving. The roving could be similarly stretched and thinned into a yarn. Winding the yarn onto a spool added twist to it. But Paul never understood how important twist was in giving the sliver or roving its strength. In later, more successful machines, a twist was (and is) given to the sliver before stretching as well as after. Paul's machines broke the sliver far too often, especially when spinning the short-fibered American cotton. ■

Further Reading:

Maurice Daumas, ed., *A History of Technology and Invention,* Vol. III. New York, 1979.

Kranzberg and Pursell, *Technology in Western Civilization.*

Abraham Wolf, *A History of Science, Technology and Philosophy in the Eighteenth Century.* London, 1952.

JOSIAH WEDGWOOD
b. *July 12, 1730, Burslem, England*
d. *Jan. 3, 1795, Etruria (Hanley), England*
British Manufacturer and Chemist

Life and Times:

The impetus to Britain's early industrial development came mainly from the textile and metallurgical industries. A notable exception to

Josiah Wedgwood, pottery manufacturer, and pioneer of industrial efficiency and the use of the steam engine.

this rule was the pottery manufacturer Josiah Wedgwood, one of the first entrepreneurs to enforce a rigid work discipline in his factory. Wedgwood's researches into materials, his interest in chemistry, his business and factory organization and his promotion of improved transportation made him a leader of the Industrial Revolution.

The youngest son of a potter, Wedgwood went to work at his father's craft at age nine. Three years later he suffered a severe attack of small pox, which lingered for several years. (A quarter-century later, a persisting residual infection necessitated the amputation of his right leg. Wedgwood's recovery was painfully slow. Five years after his brother refused to accept him as a partner, Wedgwood teamed up with Thomas Whieldon of Fenton Low, a potter of some distinction and taste. Their five-year partnership was fruitful, producing notable imitations of tortoiseshell and agate ware, and a white stone ware.

In 1759 Wedgwood struck out on his own, purchasing the Ivy House works in Burslem. One of his most important products was a green glaze which became popular in a great variety of articles for home and foreign consumption. After moving to the nearby Bell

Works in 1762, Wedgwood created an inexpensive, sturdy, cream-colored earthenware—the "Queen's Ware"—the favorite of Queen Charlotte and Russian empress Catherine the Great.

Wedgwood's rapidly improving fortunes led him to collaborate with Thomas Bentley of Liverpool, a merchant with a considerable knowledge of classical and Renaissance art. Bentley ran the Wedgwood warehouse and showrooms in London. In 1769, the partners opened a large new factory near Hanley, named Etruria. Etruria soon produced two new brands of pottery which made Wedgwood famous. The first Etrurian ornamental ware was the "Black Basalt," a fine-grained, smooth black surface which closely resembled that of Greek and Etruscan vases. Several years later, after many experiments and refinements, Wedgwood's most outstanding invention, Jasper ware, appeared. Jasper ware, according to Wedgwood's *Catalogue* (1787), possessed a translucent quality which made it "peculiarly fit for cameos, portraits, and all subjects in bas-relief." Tremendously popular, it allowed Wedgwood to produce the famed Portland Vase, a design which Sir Joshua Reynolds, president of the Royal Academy, pronounced a most faithful imitation of the Roman original.

Outstanding Engineering Achievements:

Wedgwood built on technical advances in pottery-making introduced during the mid-eighteenth century, when Enoch Booth had first produced a liquid lead glaze and John Astbury had introduced flint and blue and white clays. Systematically experimenting with a wide variety of materials and techniques, Wedgwood helped make constant change and improvement an accepted part of his craft. The outstanding Jasper ware demonstrated his interest in chemistry and his precise use of pottery materials: its final composition was 59% calk (barium sulphate), 29% clay, 10% flint, and 2% witherite (barium carbonate).

Wedgwood's knowledge of chemistry led to his membership in the Lunar Society of Birmingham. His association with this scientific club enabled him to consult with the leading British chemists of the day. Wedgwood invented the pyrometer, a "thermometer for strong fire" as he described it, and supplied it to chemists Joseph Priestley and Antoine Lavoisier. Elected a Fellow of the Royal Society in 1783, he addressed it on several occasions, lecturing on such topics as the chemistry of clays. Although never really interested in scientific theory,

Wedgwood appreciated the practical connection between science and technology as a means of producing systematic advances in his craft.

In addition to his innovations in pottery-making, Wedgwood was a pioneering industrialist who helped make Staffordshire, the area where his factory was located, one of the largest centers of pottery manufacture in the world. In 1782 he became one of the first entrepreneurs in the area to introduce steam engines, which he used to power machines that ground and mixed pottery materials. Wedgwood was also a pioneer in promoting industrial efficiency through division of labor and strict work rules. By 1790 his factory employed 270 workers, all rigidly segregated by task. Wedgwood hoped in this way to end the drunkenness, sloppy workmanship and idleness which marked the habits of workers, at least in the eyes of that generation of English capitalists. As Wedgwood claimed, the punch clocks, the system of fines for breaches of work rules, the intense supervision—all of which he introduced at Etruria—"made machines of the men as cannot err." ■

Further Reading:

Dictionary of Scientific Biography, s.v. "Wedgwood."

R. E. Schofield, *Lunar Society of Birmingham*. London, 1963.

———, "Josiah Wedgwood and the Technology of Glass Manufacturing," *Tech. and Culture*, **3** (1962).

DAVID RITTENHOUSE
b. April 8, 1732, Paper Mill Run, Pennsylvania
d. June 26, 1796, Philadelphia, U.S.A.
American instrument-maker, horologist, and surveyor

Life and Times:

During the latter half of the eighteenth century, innovations in design by English engineers such as Jesse Ramsden [q.v.] markedly improved the precision of land-measuring and astronomical instruments. As a result, the art of surveying, for example, was transformed: chain surveying gave way to measuring land with more precise angle-measuring instruments. In North America,

David Rittenhouse, an engineer who incorporated many of the newer techniques into his own work, became the continent's leading designer of astronomical and surveying instruments in the late eighteenth century.

Rittenhouse was born in 1732 on the outskirts of Philadelphia, and grew up on a farm in Norriton, north of the city. Developing an early interest in clock-making, Rittenhouse established a workshop in Norriton, and from 1750 to the late 1760s, he built numerous weight-driven pendulum clocks, which had come into common use shortly before 1700. By the mid-1760s Rittenhouse had also begun to make astronomical instruments and to make observations with them. This drew him closer to the scientific community at the recently founded College of Philadelphia (now the University of Pennsylvania). On June 3, 1869, Venus was due to cross the face of the sun. Extensive preparations were made in Europe and America for observing this transit, since it could lead to a determination of the distance between the earth and the sun. Rittenhouse built a transit telescope for the event. The interest aroused by the transit led to the formation of the American Philosophical Society. Rittenhouse's activities gained him notice as a leading amateur scientist, and he later succeeded Benjamin Franklin as president of the society.

Rittenhouse constructed a variety of telescopes of various sizes and for astronomical and terrestrial purposes. He made orreries, geared to show the movement of the planets, clocks, astronomical clocks, and a variety of surveying instruments. These included a number of compasses with a subdivided, sliding scale. In Europe they were known as Vernier compasses; in the United States Rittenhouse's name was given to them. Rittenhouse himself used surveying instruments to settle disputes about the boundaries of Pennsylvania and neighboring colonies. After the American Revolution, he also explored the Western Reserve, the region due west of the Alleghenies.

The revolution in 1776 transformed Rittenhouse from a craftsman into a political figure. He helped write the Pennsylvania Constitution in 1776; then served as treasurer of Pennsylvania from 1777 to 1789. He designed telescopic sights for rifles and cannon. Finally, in 1792 he assumed the directorship of the U.S. Mint. With the aid of his long-time assistant, Henry Voigt, Rittenhouse designed the rolling and edging machinery required to mint coins. By then his health, never strong, began to decline markedly, and he died in 1796.

Outstanding Engineering Achievement:

Rittenhouse's accomplishments are noteworthy less for their innovative design than for their superior workmanship. He did, however, introduce the use of spider web for the cross hairs placed in the focus of telescopes; the thinness of the web allowed for greater precision in marking the path of celestial bodies.

The instrument built by Rittenhouse to observe Venus' transit followed the design of earlier European models. Made of brass, the telescope consisted of a tube 33½ inches (85 cm) long fixed perpendicular to a horizontal axis. This axis was placed across a brass stand, allowing the telescope to rotate up and down only. The American Philosophical Society has preserved the telescope; it may well be the oldest extant telescope in North America. Also preserved is the very accurate clock that Rittenhouse made for timing the transit. It is an 8-day clock with a mercury-compensated pendulum that beats exact seconds. ■

Further Reading:

Dictionary of Scientific Biography, s.v. "Rittenhouse."

Edward Ford, *David Rittenhouse: Astronomer-Patriot*. 1946.

Robert P. Multhauf, *A Catalogue of Instruments and Models in the Possession of the American Philosophical Society*. Philadelphia, 1961.

Howard C. Rice, Jr., *The Rittenhouse Orrery*. 1954.

EMILAND MARIE GAUTHEY
b. Dec. 3, 1732, Chalon-sur-Saône, France
d. July 14, 1806, Paris, France
French Civil Engineer

Life and Times:

French preeminence in European civil engineering, established under Louis XIV, continued through the eighteenth century. By this time the engineering skills and resources existed to carry out a number of projects conceived in earlier years. Among these was the ambitious Canal du Centre, or Charolais Canal, built by Emiland Marie Gauthey.

The son of a doctor, Gauthey was born in the province of Burgundy. His father sent him to be educated by his uncle, who taught mathematics at the school for royal pages at Versailles. When Gauthey's father died, the family was faced with financial problems. Fortunately, Gauthey was able to attend the Ecole des Ponts et Chaussées, France's national engineering school, by serving on its mathematics faculty. After completing two years of study and teaching, he returned to Burgundy and in 1758 became an assistant engineer for the provincial government.

The centrally located province contained navigable waters from four major river systems: the Rhône, the Loire, the Seine and the Rhine. Linking any two of them would considerably reduce transportation costs and contribute to the region's prosperity. As early as 1516, King Francis I had considered constructing a canal that would connect the Loire with the Saône, a tributary of the Rhône. The engineer Adam de Craponne [q.v.] surveyed the proposed route, but technical difficulties—chiefly the hilliness of the area—caused the project to be repeatedly postponed. It was Gauthey who revived the plan when he returned from a surveying expedition in 1767.

After 16 years, Gauthey was able to obtain official approval and financial backing for his proposal. Under his supervision, construction of the Canal du Centre began in 1783; work was completed in 1794. The canal was important in the early development of the mining and metallurgical area around Montceau-les-Mines. It also completed the first inland water route between the English Channel and the Mediterranean, by way of the Seine (connected to the Loire by the Briare Canal) and the Rhone River system.

Before taking responsibility for the Canal du Centre, Gauthey built numerous bridges and served as consulting engineer for other projects. In this role he became involved in the celebrated controversy over the reconstruction of the church of Ste. Geneviève in Paris (later the Panthéon Français) by his friend Jacques Soufflot [q.v.]. In his plan for the church's dome, Soufflot proposed a classical design that alarmed traditionalists with the thinness of the supporting columns. Called on for his opinion in 1770, Gauthey devised a machine to test the strength of the stone intended for the columns (see below); he found that Soufflot's design, though unconventional, was sound. This was the first time a testing device was used to help plan the construction of a building. When cracks later appeared in the dome and columns, Gauthey attributed them to faulty workmanship and proved his conclusion with further calculations.

The value of Gauthey's work was appreciated

in his lifetime. In 1782 he was made director general of canals in Burgundy; a promotion to inspector general and reassignment to Paris followed in 1791. Though he gained prominence in royal service, his career did not suffer under the Republic and the Napoleonic Empire. A medal was struck to mark the completion of the Canal du Centre, and Gauthey was later named to the Legion of Honor. He did not marry until his sixties and had no children; however, he trained several of his nephews as engineers. One of them, Louis Navier [q.v.], saw to the posthumous publication of Gauthey's important treatise on the construction of bridges and canals.

Outstanding Engineering Achievements:

The Canal du Centre, or Charolais Canal, was the largest engineering project of its day; its construction took 11 years. Some 70 miles long, the canal ran north-southeast across the Loire-Saône watershed, joining Chalon on the Saône to Digoin on the Loire. It rose 430 feet from Chalon with the aid of 50 locks and descended by 30 locks the 250 feet to Digoin. Gauthey also worked on other canals in Burgundy.

Of Gauthey's many bridges, the largest spanned the Saône and Doubs. One of these, at Lyon, was in wood. Following the lead of Jean Rodolphe Perronet [q.v.] and other French civil engineers, Gauthey streamlined the piers of his bridges to reduce their resistance to flowing water. Other structures that Gauthey designed included quays at Dijon, a chateau at Chagny, and a church at Givry. In his plans for the church Gauthey applied his ideas concerning the strength of stone and the weight of domes.

Like Charles-Augustin de Coulomb [q.v.], Gauthey was an important early figure in the study of statics, or the ability of structural materials to withstand stress. His interest in this field led him to construct the testing machine which figured so prominently in the controversy over the dome of St. Geneviève. Gauthey placed small stone cubes hewed to a standard size under a lever, near the fulcrum. He then placed progressively greater weights in a tray suspended from the far end of the lever, noting the effects of the pressure on the stone. A similar device was later officially adopted for tests by the Ecole des Ponts et Chaussées. ∎

Further Reading:

Aubrey F. Burstall, *A History of Mechanical Engineering*. London, 1968.

James Kip Finch, *Engineering and Western Civilization*. New York, 1951.

Emiland Gauthey, *Oeuvres de M. Gauthey*. Liège, 1843.

Kranzberg and Pursell, *Technology in Western Civilization*, Vol. I.

RICHARD ARKWRIGHT
b. Dec. 23, 1732, Preston, England
d. Aug. 3, 1792, Cromford, England
British Engineer and Industrialist

Life and Times:

The introduction of power machinery in the British textile industry gave rise to the rapid development of the factory system in the mid-eighteenth century. New spinning and carding machines made possible more efficient and centralized modes of production that liquidated once and for all the cottage industries of pre-industrial capitalism. The engineer most closely associated with these changes is Richard Arkwright. Although his reputation as an inventor

Richard Arkwright, developer of the "water frame" spinning machine, one of the industrialists who brought mechanization to the textile mill.

was tarnished by charges of unoriginality and patent infringement, he was an archetypal early industrialist, still given credit for bringing to textiles both the machines and organization of labor that brought about the Industrial Revolution. Arkwright was, in the bitter words of Thomas Carlyle, "this man [who] had to give England the power of cotton."

The son of a minor tradesman, Arkwright emerged from the mixed class of upwardly mobile artisans and small landholders that provided most of Britain's early industrialists. He began his career as a wigmaker before becoming interested in the textile trade, then in the early stages of mechanization. Arkwright first became involved in textiles as an inventor, developing improved versions of spinning and carding machines for the processing of cotton (see below). Rival entrepreneurs succeeded in nullifying his patents, however, on charges that all important elements of Arkwright's machines were borrowed from existing devices. The effect of this decision was to make automatic machinery generally available in the cotton industry, a powerful impetus to Britain's early industrial development.

Though disappointed as an inventor, Arkwright went on to prosper as an industrialist. By 1789 he owned eight textile mills, most of them in Derbyshire. After 1790 he converted most of his machinery, originally water-powered, to the use of James Watt's [q.v.] newly perfected steam engine. Always seeking to improve the efficiency of his operations, Arkwright was one of the first to introduce the rigid system of factory discipline that came to characterize the industrial workplace. The modern factory could not function, he reasoned, with the individualistic work habits of artisans accustomed to working at home with their own tools. Arkwright's labor standards aimed to make workers conform to the mechanized order of the new production process. What had once been skilled and creative labor now became machine-tending geared to the regular operation of the automaton. Knighted in 1786, Arkwright brought to the cotton industry a form of organization that during the next century spread throughout the British economy.

Outstanding Engineering Achievements:

Eighteenth century spinning machines were notable mainly for using rollers to treat the yarn, putting spindles on a movable carriage and enlarging considerably the number of spindles which could be used at once. Although Arkwright took a patent for his spinning machine in

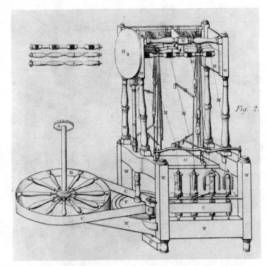

Drawing of Arkwright's spinning machine from the 1769 patent application. Each shaft, I, pulled on the thread, M, while a flyer, Q, twisted it onto a bobbin, P.

1770, it was not introduced in factory production for two more years. It was called the "water frame" because of the large, water-driven wheel which powered the device. Arkwright's spinning machine stood upright like a chair, with four pairs of rollers at the top and two pairs below which drew out strands of cotton (or "roving") to the required fineness. The roving was then pulled down to the flyer and bobbin, where it became yarn. The water frame produced much stronger cotton yarn than other spinning machines, allowing manufacturers to dispense with linen warp threads customarily used in the weaving process.

In 1775 Arkwright took out another patent, this time for a carding machine. Some types of carding machinery already existed, but Arkwright sought to improve them. Carding was necessary to prepare the roving for the spinning process. Arkwright's model used a cylinder equipped with card-teeth to secure the cotton, which was removed by a comb. This crank-and-comb method allowed the roving to pass beneath rollers and be deposited in continuous strips into a can. The cardings were then taken from the can and passed under the rollers to form thicker strands. The carding machine was as important as the spinning machine to the mechanization of the textile industry, efficiently performing an operation that was interminable when done by hand.

In 1785, after a long series of legal battles, Arkwright's spinning and carding machine patents were canceled on the grounds that they

Arkwright's spinning machine, known as the water frame since it was originally powered by water (later by steam).

were unoriginal and their language vague and unintelligible. Arkwright's opponents, manufacturers who desired free access to the machines, brought forth numerous witnesses to testify that Arkwright was not the inventor of the water frame. It was shown that he had borrowed extensively from the work of earlier inventors, including James Hargreaves [q.v.] (who had invented a spinning jenny some five years before introduction of the water frame) and John Wyatt and Lewis Paul [q.v.], who had collaborated as early as 1730 to develop a rudimentary spinning machine. Although Arkwright was able to make some claim for such innovations as the crank-and-comb mechanism on his carding machine, he failed to prove the originality of either the carding machine or water frame. ■

Further Reading:

John D. Bernal, *Science in History,* Vol. II. London, 1965.

Singer et al., *A History of Technology,* Vol. IV.

Kranzberg and Pursell, *Technology in Western Civilization.*

Abraham Wolf, *A History of Science, Technology and Philosophy in the Eighteenth Century.* London, 1952.

ROBERT MYLNE
b. 1734
d. 1811
British Civil Engineer

Life and Times:

The Scotsman Robert Mylne was the last noted British architect who was also an important engineer. Born into a distinguished line of masons to the Scottish crown, he qualified as a master mason in 1755 and began a four-year residence in Rome to further his education. He returned to England in time to present the winning design for the proposed Blackfriars Bridge in London. The new bridge, the third across the Thames, was a response to the city's rapid growth in the eighteenth century. After accepting Mylne's design, the city fathers charged him with completing the project. Begun in 1760, the bridge was opened to traffic nine years later. It was replaced in the mid-nineteenth century by a wrought iron structure.

Outstanding Engineering Achievement:

Among the innovative techniques Mylne used in building the Blackfriars Bridge was an improved method of centering arch stones. This involved constructing a wooden framework composed of multiple wedges in the shape of the arch. The voussoirs were lowered into place on top of the framework and tested for firmness. If any movement of masonry aroused suspicion of weakness, work could be halted without risk of

Robert Mylne, innovative bridge builder, canal engineer, and practicing architect.

Blackfriars Bridge under construction, showing Mylne's improved method of centering arch stones by means of a wood-frame arch.

In 1770 Mylne became engineer for the New River Company, reporting on canals, harbors and waterworks throughout England. After 1791 he spent his time designing country houses and was a founding member of Associated Architects in London. ∎

Further Reading:

Singer et al., *A History of Technology*, Vol. IV.

Kranzberg and Pursell, *Technology in Western Civilization*, Vol. I.

disaster. This was an advance over the prevailing practice of lowering arch stones permanently into place, with no precautionary drawing back.

Mylne also incorporated several French innovations into his design, including the elliptical arch and the use of caissons in constructing the piers. The elliptical arch, longer and more graceful than the semicircular arches of earlier bridges, was also far better suited to withstand the scouring action of flood waters. The Blackfriars Bridge had nine elliptical masonry arches, the largest of which spanned 100 feet (30 meters) in the center. Mylne was not the first British engineer to make use of caissons, large, watertight chests which facilitated underwater construction. But he did introduce the practice of emplacing the caissons, within which the bridge piers were constructed, on timber piles sunk into the riverbed. This technique retarded erosion and created a more stable bridge foundation.

To transmit the thrust of the bridge's nine arches, Mylne constructed a primitive but sound inverted arch in each pier. The junction between the main and inverted arches was a bit weak, but the structure was effective in distributing weight evenly from one span to the next.

In addition to the Blackfriars Bridge, Mylne designed the Jamaica Bridge in Glasgow and surveyed both St. Paul's Cathedral and Canterbury Cathedral. He also served as engineer for the Gloucester and Berkeley Canal, the ship canal between Berkeley Pill and Gloucester which permitted vessels to bypass treacherous parts of the Severn. Seventy feet (21 meters) wide and 18 feet (5.4 meters) deep, the canal improved access to the port of Gloucester so that, by the mid-nineteenth century, it had become a center of trade, bringing railways into the region.

JESSE RAMSDEN
b. Oct. 6, 1735, Salterhebble, Yorkshire, England
d. Nov. 5, 1800, Brighton, England
British Instrument Maker and Mechanical Engineer

Life and Times:

In the late eighteenth century, the demand for precision instruments grew as more sophisticated machines came into general use. Advances in metallurgy and manufacturing techniques enabled instrument makers to create more and more accurate measuring tools to satisfy the increasingly stringent requirements of navigators, scientists, geodesists, and makers of industrial machinery, all of whom required finely calibrated measuring rules and circles in their work. The prolific British engineer Jesse Ramsden, the most successful and famous instrument maker of his day, devised linear and circular dividing engines, theodolites (surveying instruments for measuring horizontal and vertical angles), and the first screw-cutting lathe for steel. His career exemplifies the changing character of the precision instrument maker from traditional handicraftsman to inventor of extremely accurate machinery for the production of interchangeable, standardized machine parts.

After several years as a clothworker's apprentice and clerk, the 23-year-old Ramsden apprenticed himself as an engraver to a mathematical instrument maker in London. He set up his own successful instrument-making and engraving shop in 1762. In the quest for more accurate measuring-rules and astronomical setting-quadrants and circles for his customers, Ramsden developed two dividing engines, devices which calibrated scales on other instruments, between

*Precision-instrument maker Jesse Ramsden invented
the first lathe for cutting steel screws.*

1766 and 1775. The later, more advanced engine, based on principles pioneered by the Duc de Chaulnes around 1765, was the first one suitable for industrial use. Ramsden found that the accuracy of dividing engines depends on the uniformity of the threads in their adjustment screws. In 1770 he invented the first screw-cutting lathes, which could cut threads of several pitches in hardened steel; until that time, all screws had been cut by hand, with variable results.

By 1790 Ramsden was employing over 60 craftsmen to produce measuring circles, sextants, balances, theodolites, and a variety of other instruments. A theodolite measuring over three feet (1 meter) in diameter was constructed for William Roy's geodetic survey of England and France in 1784. Ramsden's vertical circle, five feet (1.5 meters) in diameter, of the alt-azimuth mounting of the telescope at the new Palermo observatory was used by Giuseppe Piazzi to construct his star catalogue.

Ramsden was made a fellow of the Royal Society in 1786 and a member of the Imperial Academy of St. Petersburg in 1794. His instruments were famed for their fine workmanship and durability. During World War II, sea warfare created a sudden shortage of sextants in England. Since all instrument-making machinery was employed in more urgent tasks, one of Ramsden's old dividing engines was taken from a museum, equipped with a motor, and used to manufacture sextants.

Outstanding Engineering Achievements:

Ramsden invented or refined the designs of dozens of instruments and machine tools. His most important innovations were his screw-cutting lathes, the first of their kind, and his dividing engines for graduating circles and rules.

Before Ramsden, screw threads were cut laboriously by hand. In the design of his first screw-cutting lathe, the rod to be threaded was rotated by a crank. The same crank was linked by adjustable gears to a lead screw, parallel to the rod, which drove the tool holder and the diamond-tipped cutting tool forward. The number of teeth to be cut was regulated by changing the gearing ratio. Ramsden's second lathe was more complex and able to cut longer and more uniform screws. A crank rotated both the stock to be threaded and a large circular plate with a threaded edge with which the crank engaged at a tangent. As the threaded wheel was turned, it moved the cutting tool by means of a pulley.

Ramsden used these lathes to cut adjustment screws and threaded parts for his dividing engines. The dividing engine for calibrating circles for navigational and astronomical instruments incorporated a large, inscribed master wheel, turned in precise increments by a tangent screw, which also turned the circle to be marked at the

*Ramsden's dividing engine, the first machine for
calibrating accurate circular scales.*

Further Reading:

Dictionary of National Biography, s.v. "Ramsden."
Dictionary of Scientific Biography, s.v. "Ramsden."
Kranzberg and Pursell, *Technology in Western Civilization,* Vol. I.
Singer et al., *A History of Technology,* Vol. IV.

Geodetic theodolite built by Ramsden mounts a telescope between precisely calibrated horizontal and vertical scales.

same rate. The screw was advanced by a foot treadle. The divisions on the master wheel were read through a microscope with crosshairs; when the divisions and crosshairs were aligned, a mark was inscribed in the circle. This machine was accurate to less than three seconds of arc, or 1/432,000 of a circle. Ramsden's straight-line dividing engine used a rack-and-screw carriage that was also advanced by a foot treadle.

Ramsden excelled in the design of geodetic instruments. His theodolite for William Roy was the largest and most accurate yet built; it required three years to complete. It consisted of a horizontal, inscribed circle in a sturdy wooden framework with a centrally mounted sighting telescope. Azimuth angles between geographical points were measured with the horizontal circle and read with small microscopes mounted on the frame; an altitude scale on the telescope allowed measurement of vertical angles.

Ramsden's other designs included pyrometers, micrometers, dilatometers (devices for measuring the heat expansion of metals), sextants, telescope mountings, and precision balances. He also developed the first magnifying eyepiece with crosshairs. ■

JAMES WATT
b. Jan. 17, 1736, Greenock, Scotland
d. Aug. 19, 1819, Handsworth, England
British Inventor and Industrialist

Life and Times:

The work of James Watt forged an epoch. He lived to see the transition of England's economic base from the domestic or cottage industry to the factory system of modern industrial capitalism, a change that would have been unthinkable without his improvement of the Newcomen steam engine. Not content with the role of inventor, Watt was also an industrialist who supervised the manufacture and marketing of his engine. In this respect, he was a typical early capitalist—unconventional, innovative, self-educated and self-confident.

The young Watt, son of a merchant in Greenock, Scotland, seemed destined for an instrument-making career. He was a delicate child, however, whose predilection for tinkering with instruments was frustrated by an incomplete formal education that was continually interrupted by bouts of ill health. Still, he seemed a reflective youth and exhibited a genuine precocity in mathematics and the study of natural phenomena. (The popular story of Watt the youth staring enthralled at the spectacle of a steaming tea kettle is, however, almost surely apocryphal.) At eighteen he went to London to study mathematical instrument making. In 1765 he returned to Scotland to work as apprentice in a Glasgow instrument-making shop, but was turned down by the local guild that regulated entry into the trade. It is ironic that this craft guild, a remnant of the pre-industrial world, helped set in motion events that eventually consigned such organizations to oblivion.

From this educational hiatus, Watt was rescued by a faculty member of Glasgow University who had noticed his mechanical prowess. In

James Watt, developer, manufacturer, and distributor of the steam engine that mechanized British industry.

return for occasionally repairing university-owned equipment, he was given a room at the university and allowed to ply his trade. Watt concentrated on building scientific instruments, but supplemented his meager income by making pipe organs, guitars and fiddles. He soon found a partner, however, and went into business manufacturing nautical instruments.

Watt became interested at this time in the possibility of improving the Newcomen steam engine to broaden its usefulness. The idea was definitely "in the air." In 1759, Watt met a young scientist named John Robison who spoke enthusiastically of building a wheeled carriage propelled by steam. Watt became familiar with the operation of the steam engine four years later, when asked to repair one belonging to the university. After redesigning the machine, he secured the financial backing of Dr. Joseph Black, a famous chemist at the university, and John Roebuck, owner of an iron foundry. Working first in an unused pottery shed and later at Roebuck's country estate, he produced and patented the prototype of his invention in July 1769.

The first Watt steam engine did not function efficiently enough for industrial use. The technology available to Watt was simply inadequate

to produce parts of the size and precision demanded by his design. After several years of frustration (aggravated by Roebuck's bankruptcy), Watt was fortunate enough to meet the industrialist Matthew Boulton, owner of an ironworks in Birmingham. Boulton's factory was well ahead of the times in the skill of its workmen and the quality of its machines. In 1773 Watt and Boulton went into partnership, Boulton agreeing to manufacture steam engines at his factory in return for an interest in the patent.

The first engine built in Boulton's factory, completed in 1776, was used at an iron works in Broseley owned by another great engineer, John Wilkinson [q.v.]. Though a simplified and streamlined version of Watt's original design, the machine was still enormous for its time, with a piston and cylinder measuring 50 inches (127 cm) in diameter. It was nevertheless successful, using less than one half the fuel required by a Newcomen engine for the same amount of work. A second Watt engine was used to pump water from a Staffordshire coal mine, and orders soon began pouring in from other collieries.

By 1783 Watt perfected a method of converting the up-and-down motion of the working beam, suitable primarily for pumping, into rotary motion that could be used to operate other kinds of machines. This required the invention of several novel components such as a "double-acting" cylinder, the "parallel-motion" linkage, and sun-and-planet gearing (see below). Within a decade the Watt engine had begun to be adopted in the British cotton industry, then the main user of automatic machinery. This combination was a key factor in the Industrial Revolution. By freeing industry from its previous dependence on water power, the steam engine enabled manufacturers not only to build larger factories, but also to locate their works away from streams, near sources of labor and raw materials, which is to say in the growing cities of industrializing Britain.

Watt's engine not only contributed to but also borrowed from the new techniques of the machine era. In the absence of precision machinery such as lathes or boring tools, the accuracy of Boulton's mechanics was still an indispensable factor in the manufacture of the steam engine. To minimize the possibility of error, Watt and Boulton sought to restrict each workman to a particular task that could be performed time and again. Boulton's factory thus quickly came to depend on the division and rationalization of labor, a feature of industrialism that soon dominated the modern work place.

By the end of the century, Watt and Boulton

were both very wealthy men. At the expiration of his patent in 1800, Watt retired to lead a quiet life in the country. But he did not give up inventing. He worked on a machine for copying sculpture, and lived to see the steam engine applied to ships and railways.

Outstanding Engineering Achievement:

The Newcomen steam engine which Watt examined in Glasgow was inefficient. The entire cylinder had to be injected with cold water at the end of every stroke in order to condense the steam that filled it. This process wasted both steam and time, since the cylinder then had to be made hot enough for the next stroke. Watt's initial improvement consisted simply of creating a separate steam condenser outside the cylinder, allowing the cylinder to be maintained at a constant high temperature. Watt later created the so-called "double-acting" steam engine by designing a set of valves that introduced steam alternately on each side of the piston, exerting upward as well as downward force. He also discovered that the supply of steam could be cut off soon after the piston began its stroke, permitting the natural adiabatic expansion of the steam to drive the piston. This considerably reduced the engine's fuel consumption.

As in earlier steam engines, the motion of the piston was transmitted to the device being powered by means of a horizontal beam, one end of which was connected to the piston (hence the term "beam engine"). On the downstroke of the piston, the other end of the beam ascended, pulling a connecting rod which could be used either to operate a pump or turn a wheel. With the introduction of the "double-acting" engine, Watt had to connect the piston with the beam in a way that would transmit upward as well as downward force; the flexible chain which he had earlier used acted only on the downstroke. After some experimentation, he developed his famous "parallel motion" device, a set of three bars joined to the piston and beam in the form of a pantograph; this linkage ensured that the connecting rod would travel vertically.

Other improvements in Watt's steam engine included the centrifugal governor and the "indicator." The centrifugal, or fly-ball, governor was a set of spinning metal balls which acted as a restraint on the engine's speed. When an engine ran too fast, centrifugal force made the balls act as a brake on the throttle. The indicator was a device for determining simultaneously both the pressure in the cylinder and the volume of steam, thus giving a continual measure of the

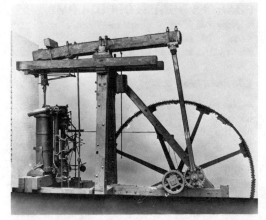

Watt's rotative beam engine of 1788; left, double-acting cylinder; left-rear, fly-ball governor; top left, parallel-motion linkage; bottom right, sun-and-planet gearing.

power output of the engine. This ingenious device facilitated both evolutionary improvement of the engine, and the convenient calculation of the royalties that customers owed the patent holders.

In addition to his work on the steam engine, Watt contributed significantly to the development of iron and steel manufacture. The larger steam engines created a need for greater forgings than could be made with hand-held hammers. Seeking to produce a heavier hammer-blow, Watt invented a powerful tilt hammer which was worked initially by a waterwheel and later by steam engine. He also patented an improved combustion furnace, invented a special ink for copying letters and originated the term horsepower. The watt, our primary unit of power, is named for him. He was named a fellow of the Royal Societies of both London and Edinburgh, was a corresponding member of the Institute of France and a foreign associate of the Academie des Sciences. ■

Further Reading:

D. S. L. Cardwell, *From Watt to Clausius*. Cornell, 1971.

H. W. Dickinson, *A Short History of the Steam Engine*. 1938.

Robinson and Musson, *James Watt and the Steam Revolution*. 1969.

Samuel Smiles, *Lives of the Engineers*. London, 1904.

Singer et al., *A History of Technology*, Vol. IV.

CHARLES AUGUSTIN COULOMB
b. June 14, 1736, Angoulême, France
d. Aug. 23, 1806, Paris, France
French Military and Civil Engineer and Physicist

Life and Times:

Nearly 50 years elapsed before the new physics of Isaac Newton [q.v.] and the new mathematics of Newton and Gottfried Wilhelm von Leibniz were together applied to engineering problems. Even then, the work of Daniel Bernoulli [q.v.] and Leonhard Euler [q.v.] was mainly theoretical. It took another generation before Charles Augustin Coulomb became the first to apply the methods of calculus to problems of engineering and electricity and to combine theory with experimentation. One of the great engineers of the eighteenth century, Coulomb is now regarded as the founder of structural analysis.

Coulomb graduated from the engineering school of the French Corps of Engineers in 1761, with the rank of first lieutenant. He was posted first to Brest, then to Martinique in 1764, back to France in 1774, and finally to Paris in 1781, retiring with the rank of lieutenant-colonel in 1791. He was engaged as a consultant in 1783 to inspect canal and harbor modifications in Brittany. When he produced a critical report, he was sent to jail for a week. This does not seem to have hurt his status, for the next year he was placed in charge of the water supply to all the royal buildings and to much of Paris. His last post, to which he was appointed in 1802, was that of supervisor of the establishment of France's secondary-school system.

Throughout his career, Coulomb combined his military work with basic engineering research. In Martinique, he supervised the construction of Fort Bourbon, which protected France's main naval base in the West Indies. He used this opportunity to study the strength of structural materials; his results were presented to the Academy of Sciences in Paris in 1773. Since Coulomb was not then a member of the Academy, this very important paper was published among the "works of outsiders." Written in a concise manner and using the latest, and therefore most difficult, calculus of variations, it was ignored for 40 years. When finally brought to light, it was found to lay the foundation of both structural analysis and soil mechanics.

While supervising hundreds of laborers at the fort, Coulomb also began a study of the efficiency and output of human work. Previous studies had considered only work done for a short time, ignoring the effect of fatigue. Coulomb returned to his investigations during the next 20 years, finally publishing his results in 1799. This significant contribution to ergonomics set a maximum of eight hours a day for productive work at heavy tasks and ten hours for light ones.

For its competition of 1777, the Academy called for essays on magnetism. Coulomb shared the first prize, his paper covering problems of the suspension of compass needles, particularly the torsion on a thread used to hang such needles. Two years later, while stationed in Rochefort, Coulomb conducted experiments on friction in the shipyards. The resulting paper on "The Theory of Simple Machines" won the first prize of 1781, and with it election to the Academy and permanent residence in Paris.

The Revolutionary authorities abolished the Academy of Sciences in 1793, but Coulomb was elected to the new Institut de France two years later, becoming its president in 1801. Work he published between 1785 and 1787 established Coulomb's law of electrostatic charge; it is appropriate that the unit of charge bears his name.

Outstanding Engineering Achievements:

The paper which Coulomb presented to the Academy of Sciences in 1773 was titled "Essay on the application of the rules of maxima and minima to several problems of statics relating to architecture." It contains the first explicit statement that the forces acting on a beam must be in equilibrium, and gave the laws that every engineering student now knows: the horizontal components (tensions and compressions) must be in balance; the vertical components must balance the load; and the sum of the moments of the internal forces must balance the moment of the load.

By testing to destruction, Coulomb determined the "cohesion," by which he meant both shearing and tensile strength, of materials such as timber, stone and brick. He also found their coefficients of friction. With these constants in his equations, he found the limiting conditions by what is now the familiar method of calculus. The problems that Coulomb treated included the pressure of earth on a masonry wall, the stresses and strains on pillars and beams, and the shape of vaults.

In preparing his 1777 paper on magnetism, Coulomb worked with the torsion balance that he invented. He suspended a rod by a thread connected to its midpoint, and showed that such a rod would settle in a particular direction because the thread would resist being twisted. He then proved that if the rod was subject to a turning force, the angle through which it rotated would be proportional to that force. This gave a method of measuring tiny forces such as the magnetic and electrostatic ones then available.

After fitting one end of the rod with a pith ball, Coulomb gave it a charge and brought a similarly charged ball close to the first. The repulsive force between them caused the rod to twist away, with an angle that could be measured. Bringing the second ball to different distances from the first demonstrated the fact that the force of repulsion is (like the force of gravity) inversely proportional to the square of the distance between the charged spheres.

Coulomb also showed that the attraction between spheres with unlike charges obeyed the inverse square law. Replacing the balls and rod with magnetized needles, he showed that the same law also holds for magnetism. His further observation that the force is directly proportional to the product of the charges resulted in the law that is known as Coulomb's law. ■

Henry Cort, inventor of the puddling-and-rolling process that produced great quantities of wrought iron at relatively low cost.

Further Reading:

Dictionary of Scientific Biography, s.v. "Coulomb."

C. Stewart Gillmor, *Coulomb and the Evolution of Physics and Engineering in Eighteenth Century France.* Princeton, N.J., 1971.

J.A. Ripley, Jr., *The Elements and Structure of the Physical Sciences.* New York, 1964.

J.P.M. Pannell. *Man the Builder.* New York, 1970.

Hans Straub, *A History of Civil Engineering.* London, 1952.

HENRY CORT
b. 1740
d. 1800
British Inventor

Life and Times:

In the course of the eighteenth century, Britain underwent a virtual revolution in iron production which vastly increased the metal's availability and reduced its cost. The first step in the process was the substitution of coke for charcoal in the smelting process by Abraham Darby I [q.v.]. Darby's innovation made possible the reduction of far greater quantities of iron ore and the use of plentiful coal instead of scarce wood as fuel. Cast iron made in a coke-fired furnace, however, absorbed impurities from the coal which could not be removed by the traditional refining process of beating the hot metal with hammers. As a result, coke-smelted iron could not be refined into wrought iron, a malleable form with superior resistance to stress. Some improvement in quality was achieved by remelting the iron over a reverberatory furnace, which kept the metal from direct contact with the fuel. But this extra step added to manufacturing costs, and still failed to produce iron of sufficient strength and ductility. Credit for removing this bottleneck in iron production goes to Henry Cort, inventor of the puddling-and-rolling process.

Owner of a forge and slitting-mill near Portsmouth, Cort did work for the British Admiralty. At that time the government imported large quantities of wrought iron from Sweden, and Cort began to seek some way of fostering domestic wrought iron production. Though encouraged by the industrialist Matthew Boulton and steam engine designer James Watt [q.v.], he went heavily into debt in the course of his experiments. Nevertheless, in 1784 Cort patented his innovative puddling furnace (see below). The new refining technique not only made possible the direct production of wrought iron in a coke-fueled furnace, but also proved much quicker than the traditional process of repeatedly heating and hammering the metal. As a result, wrought iron could be made in far greater quantities than before and at a correspondingly lower cost. The new supply situation encouraged manufacturers to make increased use of iron, substituting it for wood in machines, tools and buildings. Production of unrefined pig iron, a general indication of iron consumption, increased sharply in Britain during the later part of the eighteenth century, rising from 40,000 tons in 1780 to 400,000 tons in 1820. Cort's invention also definitively outmoded the traditional charcoal-fired smelting furnace, allowing the British iron industry to leave the country's shrinking woodlands and concentrate in the coal-producing Midlands.

As in the case of many inventors, Cort himself derived no material benefit from his invention. The debt which he had incurred developing the puddling furnace was so heavy that he was forced into bankruptcy and his patent rights were seized. Although his process was to make fortunes for nineteenth-century iron magnates, Cort was virtually penniless when he died.

Outstanding Engineering Achievement:

Cort's puddling process would have been impossible without the prior development of the coke-fired reverberatory furnace, capable of achieving higher temperatures and smelting

Section of Henry Cort's puddling furnace, in which iron was heated and stirred to separate out impurities.

greater quantities of iron ore than the earlier charcoal furnace. Puddling consisted of stirring the semi-molten cast iron with a long rod to separate out and partially burn off impurities. The result, when hammered into shape, was an iron bar or "bloom" with a coating of dross at or near the surface. The dross could then be removed by squeezing the bar between two rollers, a much faster method than the traditional hammering. Cort's complete process thus came to be called "puddling-and-rolling." The wrought iron which it produced was still inferior to charcoal-smelted iron, but so much cheaper that consumers readily overlooked the difference. ∎

Further Reading:

Maurice Daumas, ed., *Histoire Générale des Techniques,* Vol. III. Paris, 1968.

David Landes, *The Unbound Prometheus.* Cambridge, 1969.

Singer et al., *A History of Technology,* Vol. IV.

JOSEPH-MICHEL MONTGOLFIER
b. 1740
d. 1810

JACQUES-ETIENNE MONTGOLFIER
b. 1745
d. 1799

French Aeronautical Engineers

Life and Times:

The age-old dream of human flight began to attract serious scientific attention during the Renaissance. The protean Leonardo da Vinci [q.v.] conceived the idea of the parachute and designed several flying machines, including the helicopter. Francisco Lana-Terzi first proposed a lighter-than-air flying ship in 1670, and the Portuguese Jesuit Bartholomeu Lourenco de Gusmao demonstrated a model hot air balloon in 1709. The first manned flight, however, was the work of two French brothers, Joseph-Michel and Jacques-Etienne Montgolfier, who designed and built a passenger-carrying hot air balloon in 1783.

Owners of a paper manufacturing company near Lyons, the Montgolfier brothers turned to aeronautics from a general interest in science. Research on gases conducted by the chemists Joseph Priestley and Henry Cavendish focused

The Montgolfier brothers, Joseph-Michel and Jacques-Etienne, designed and made the balloon that was the vehicle in the world's first manned flight.

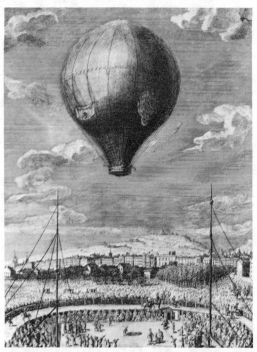

Record of the flight of the Montgolfier balloon, Lyon, January 29, 1784, carrying the elder Montgolfier, Pilâtre de Rozier, Prince Charles, and three counts.

attention on the composition of air, and the discovery of hydrogen in 1766 opened new possibilities for lighter-than-air flight. Hydrogen was difficult to manufacture, however, and the brothers turned instead to the hot air balloon. Evidently they knew nothing of Lourenco de Gusmao's demonstration; their early work duplicated his experiments with small model balloons. On June 5, 1783 they conducted their own first public demonstration with a much larger hot air balloon, 30 feet (9 meters) in diameter, which rose to 6,000 feet (1800 meters) and travelled half a mile (.8 km) in 10 minutes. The balloon came to earth in the farming village of Gonesse, whose frightened inhabitants, thinking it was a monstrous animal, attacked it with stones and pitchforks.

Though the demonstration flight was unmanned, it attracted the attention of the French Academy of Sciences, which invited the Montgolfier brothers to Paris for further work. On September 19 they sent up another balloon in the presence of the royal family, this one carrying several animals which returned to earth unharmed. The stage was set for manned flight.

Jean-Francois Pilâtre de Rozier, the court historian, volunteered to ride as passenger in a series of test ascents in a balloon tethered to earth. On November 21, Pilatre de Rozier and the Marquis d'Arlandes rose 3,000 feet (900 m) above Paris in the first human free flight, travelling 7½ miles (12 km) in 25 minutes. The trip created a sensation, and the Montgolfiers' balloon was soon imitated elsewhere. Pilatre de Rozier, however, had the misfortune of becoming the first air fatality, killed in an accident in 1785.

The first practical application of human flight was not long in coming: the transport of international air mail between Britain and France. Trips by hot air balloon, however, were strictly limited in altitude and distance. The future of ballooning lay with the hydrogen-filled balloon, developed by the French physicist Jacques-Alexandre-Cesar Charles only 10 days after the Montgolfiers' inauguration of human flight.

Outstanding Engineering Achievement:

The Montgolfiers' balloons rose due to the expansion of hot air, which becomes less dense and therefore lighter than the surrounding atmosphere. The brothers apparently did not understand this, believing that some gas released by fire lifted the balloon. For this reason they burned damp straw and other smoke-producing materials to fill their balloons with hot air. Initially, the fire was set on the launching platform beneath the balloon. For manned free flight, however, a brazier was suspended beneath the neck of the balloon and fed with burning fuel by passengers in the gondola. The balloon that carried Pilatre de Rozier and the Marquis d'Arlandes above Paris was nearly 50 feet (15 m) in diameter, with a capacity of 78,000 cubic feet (2210 cubic meters).

The Montgolfiers' scientific interests were not confined to aeronautics. Shortly before the end of the century Joseph-Michel invented the hydraulic ram, a non-mechanical pump that raised water by a combination of air inlets and valves. The device could handle only small amounts of water, but was easy to operate and did not require an engine. Introduced commercially in England, it was manufactured during the mid-nineteenth century. ■

Further Reading:

Feldmen and Ford, *Scientists and Inventors*. New York, 1979.

Kranzberg and Pursell, *Technology in Western Civilization*, Vol. I.

T. K. Derry and Trevor Williams, *A Short History of Technology*. New York, 1961.

Abraham Wolf, *A History of Science, Technology and Philosophy in the Sixteenth and Seventeenth Centuries*. London, 1950.

NICHOLAS LEBLANC
b. Dec. 6, 1742, Issondon, France
d. Jan. 16, 1806, Paris, France
French Industrial Chemist

Life and Times:

Industry in eighteenth century Europe suffered from an increasingly severe shortage of timber. Not only was wood the most common industrial fuel, but wood ash was the main source of alkali, which is necessary to the manufacture of glass, soap, bleaches and other common substances. From the early years of the century, scientists and manufacturers attempted to discover an economical process for synthesizing alkali, especially soda, from readily available materials. The first important success in this effort was the work of the French chemist and physician Nicholas Leblanc.

Leblanc began his career as an apothecary's apprentice, but took up the study of surgery and in 1780 became the surgeon of the future Duke of Orleans, Phillippe de Bourbon. Under the duke's sponsorship he seemed destined for great success. In 1775 the French Academy of Sciences had offered a prize of 2,400 livres for discovery of a practical means of synthesizing soda. In 1789 Leblanc developed his chemical process (see below). He patented the process in 1791 and one year later set up a factory for manufacturing soda. The prize was never awarded, however.

It was at this time that the French Revolution intervened. The Duke of Orleans was executed in 1793, Leblanc's patent was annulled and the factory he had built was confiscated and made public property. Only in 1801, was the factory returned to him. Leblanc meanwhile had become so destitute that he could not operate it; in 1806 he shot himself in the poorhouse of St.-Denis. Fifty years later his heirs received reparations from Napoleon III.

Despite the tragic end of its discoverer, the Leblanc process spread and ultimately brought revolutionary changes. It led to creation of the heavy chemical industry and the development of chemical engineering as a distinct profession. Leblanc's discovery also made possible for the first time the mass production of soap, with great effect on sanitary conditions in Europe. Introduced in Britain during the 1820s, the Leblanc process remained the principal means of soda manufacture for most of the nineteenth century, until development of a still more efficient method by Ernest Solvay in 1861. As late as 1885, half of the 800,000 tons of soda produced throughout the world was made by the Leblanc process.

Outstanding Engineering Achievement:

Leblanc produced soda by treating salt from seawater with sulfuric acid to form sodium sulfate. This was in turn mixed with chalk and charcoal and heated in a crucible. The resulting impure "black ash" was dissolved in water to recrystallize out the soda. Leblanc's process was neither fuel-efficient nor non-polluting. It was nevertheless far less expensive than previous methods of soda production. ■

Further Reading:

Archibald and Nan Clow, *The Chemical Revolution*. London, 1952.

Singer, et al., *A History of Technology*, Vol. IV.

T. J. Williams, *The Chemical Industry*. London, 1953.

IGNAZ VON BORN

b. Dec. 26, 1742, Karlsburg, Transylvania
d. Aug. 28, 1791, Vienna
Austro-Hungarian Metallurgist

Life and Times:

The use of mercury to extract gold and silver from their ores, known as the amalgamation process, was an old and well-established technique by the eighteenth century. Known by the Romans (Pliny had written of it in his *Natural History*) and widely employed by mining engineers working for the Spanish crown in Mexican and Andean mines during the sixteenth century, mercury amalgamation was less common in Europe, especially with the growing popularity of smelting, or "fusion," among European metallurgists. Smelting, however, consumed large quantities of wood, charcoal, and lead, and was thus quite costly. Metallurgists in areas where fuel and lead were scarce sought more efficient methods of recovering precious metals from their ores. In Hungary, where mercury was available and wood was becoming scarce, there was renewed interest in mercury amalgamation in the eighteenth century. A nobleman from Transylvania with a keen interest in mining, Ignaz von Born, developed a refined procedure for the amalgamation of gold and silver ores which he concluded was "at least as perfect as fusion and with less expence."

The son of a nobleman of German descent, Born attended a Jesuit school and was briefly a member of the Society of Jesus. He went on to Prague, where he studied law. Born's interest soon turned to natural history and mining, and by 1770 he had entered the department of mines and the mint at Prague. One of his first duties was to conduct a tour of Transylvanian and Hungarian mines owned by the Habsburg dynasty. While observing the use of fire to extract ore from a mine, Born entered a shaft too quickly, before the thick arsenic vapors had dissipated. Stricken by the fumes, he suffered periods of temporary incapacitation for the rest of his life.

Born's interests soon ranged far beyond mining. In 1775 he helped found an important Viennese literary society. During the ebullient years of Emperor Joseph II's reign, he belonged to a Masonic lodge. A staunch rationalist, Born adopted the widespread anticlericalism of the Enlightenment, publishing an acerbic satire on priests and the Jesuits in 1783.

Born's most important technical accomplishment was his discovery of an improved version of the amalgamation process for retrieving gold and silver from the rich Hungarian ore. After conducting years of private experiments at great expense, he tested his method at Schemnitz, Hungary before an audience of accomplished mineralogists. The observers were duly impressed, and in 1786, at the behest of the Emperor, Born published his treatise on amalgamation. Born's process consumed only one percent of the wood which smelting the same quantity of ore would have required. When the Hungarian mines adopted the process, Born was given a considerable portion of the savings by Joseph. After turning to paleontology for several years, he was stricken by spasms during the summer of 1791, and died soon afterward.

Outstanding Engineering Achievement:

Born's version of the amalgamation process utilized a great deal of salt and mercury but was fuel-efficient. The silver-bearing black copper ore was first crushed and mixed with salt. The ore was then calcined (roasted to eliminate the sulfur) in a special furnace. The calcined material was placed in large boilers, mixed with water and pulverized. Mercury was added to the resulting pulp, and the mixture was stirred for 14 to 18 hours. The silver, at times with small amounts of gold, coalesced with the mercury into an amalgam, which settled to the bottom of the containers. Finally, the mercury was separated from the amalgam by filtration, pressure, and heat, leaving the silver and gold behind.

The process was cheap for Hungarian metallurgy, and saved much fuel and lead. Only the exhaustion of the Hungarian mines in the early nineteenth century put an end to the production of silver and copper in eastern Europe. ∎

Further Reading:

Ignaz von Born, *New Processes of Amalgamation of Gold and Silver Ores*. London, 1791.

Chalmers, *Biographical Dictionary* (1812 edition).

DAVID BUSHNELL
b. 1742, Saybrook, Connecticut
d. 1824, Warrenton, Georgia
American Nautical Engineer

Life and Times:

The most ingenious mechanical device developed during the American Revolution was David Bushnell's one-man submarine, the *Turtle*. Although his vessel failed to cripple the Royal Navy, it was the first step toward realizing submarine navigation. A Yale student, Bushnell designed the *Turtle* in Westbrook, Conn. From its inception he envisioned the vessel as a potentially devastating new weapon in naval warfare. Bushnell's plan was to approach a ship stealthily under water and transfer a time bomb from the outside of the submarine to the ship's hull. After enough time had elapsed for the submarine to withdraw, the bomb would explode. The *Turtle*, however, failed to damage, much less sink, any British ships. On its first try, it did manage to get alongside the HMS *Eagle* but was unable to screw the bomb to its hull. Bushnell's subsequent trials were even less successful. The young engineer then abandoned his one-man submarine warfare to experiment with floating

mines in the Delaware and Hudson river. In 1783 he became commander of the West Point Corps of Engineers.

Outstanding Engineering Achievement:

Bushnell's submarine was made with oak planks, bound with iron and caulked and sealed with tar. Aptly named, the *Turtle* was higher than it was wide, giving it the appearance of two joined carapaces. On top it had a glassed-in conning tower and two ventilating tubes, the only parts to break the surface. It was submerged by allowing water into a tank at the bottom, which could be emptied by a foot pump. The submarine moved by means of a screw propeller turned by another foot pedal, and could be raised and lowered in the water by hand-operated cranks which turned other screw propellers. A compass and barometer to gauge depth were illuminated by phosphorus when the vessel was submerged. ∎

Further Reading:

Brooke Hindle, *The Pursuit of Science in Revolutionary America, 1735-1789*. Virginia, 1956.

Model of Bushnell's one-man submarine Turtle, *which was successful as a vessel but not as an engine of war.*

JOHN FITCH
b. Jan. 21, 1743, Windsor township, Connecticut
d. July 2, 1798, Bardstown, Kentucky
American Mechanical Engineer

Life and Times:

The application of steam power to transportation was suggested by Denis Papin [q.v.] as early as 1707. But the increased productive capacities of the Industrial Revolution and the improvement of the atmospheric steam engine by James Watt [q.v.] were necessary before steam transportation could become a reality, first on water and then on land.

In July 1783, the French aristocrat Claude de Jouffroy [q.v.] succeeded for the first time in moving a boat upstream by the power of steam. But subsequent innovations in steamship technology were achieved mainly in the United States. There, the existence of a vast Western interior devoid of roads spurred advances in water transportation. Furthermore, during the American War for Independence a number of

John Fitch, a better engineer than a businessman, built the first operative steamboat in America and ran the first regular steamboat service in the world.

entrepreneurs had developed mechanical skills as manufacturers of firearms and military equipment. Among them was John Fitch of Connecticut, who in 1786 demonstrated perhaps the first operative steamboat in America—his feat was almost simultaneous with a similar achievement by Virginian James Rumsey—and who established the first regular steamboat service in the world.

After working on his father's Connecticut farm, Fitch apprenticed himself to a clockmaker and learned the basics of brass working and founding. At 21 he established his own brass shop in East Windsor, Conn. During the American Revolution, he was in charge of a gun factory in Trenton, N.J. and later surveyed lands along the Ohio River. Captured by Indians, he was turned over to the British and held prisoner until near the end of the conflict.

After the war Fitch moved to Bucks County, Pa. There he saw a steam engine for the first time in 1785 and conceived the idea of building a steamboat. Most of his remaining 13 years were devoted to realizing that idea. His first working steamship, built in 1786, was powered by an engine with a horizontal 12-inch (30 cm) cylinder that moved six paddles on each side of the boat, an effort to convert the action of Indians paddling a canoe into mechanical terms. In July 1786, the vessel ran on the Delaware River at three miles per hour, too slow for practical purposes. Although Pennsylvania, New York, Delaware and Virginia gave him exclusive franchises in 1786-87, Fitch's efforts to obtain government subsidies were unsuccessful. But he persisted in his work with the help of private backers. Fitch replaced the horizontal cylinder with a vertical one and tried a new boiler for his second ship. He demonstrated it in August 1787 at Philadelphia before delegates to the Constitutional Convention. But this steamship, too, ran at only three miles (5 km) per hour.

Only after Fitch had reduced the size of the boiler and fully adopted the principles of James Watt's engine was he able to construct a practical vessel. In October 1788, his third steamship ran upstream on the Delaware River between Burlington, N.J. and Philadelphia, carrying 30 passengers and covering 20 miles (32 km) in three hours and ten minutes. During the summer of 1790, he used his fourth vessel to provide regular service between Philadelphia and Burlington. Although the steamship averaged over seven miles per hour, the stagecoach was faster. The operation, financially unsuccessful, was abandoned at summer's end. Had Fitch operated his steamship on the Hudson River, where the terrain was hilly, he might have established an advantage over land transportation. But he was not adept at recognizing such business considerations. Nor was he cost-conscious regarding construction and operating expenditures. As a result, his financial backers had abandoned him by the end of 1790.

In 1793 Fitch unsuccessfully sought financial aid in France. He returned to America the next year and settled in Boston. In 1796, after reputedly testing in New York a steamboat moved by a screw propeller, Fitch settled in Kentucky, where he died two years later. Although Robert Fulton [q.v.] is credited with inventing the steamboat in 1807, it is clear that he relied substantially on the earlier work done by Fitch.

Outstanding Engineering Achievement:

Fitch's third steamboat, tested in 1788, attained improved speed by use of a pipe boiler, a length of tube winding around inside a brick furnace. A model of compactness for its time, it enabled Fitch to eliminate 3 and one-half tons of brickwork.

Working on his fourth ship in 1789, Fitch replaced the 12-inch (30 cm) cylinder of his earlier ships with an 18-inch (46 cm) cylinder and placed his paddle system at the stern. But his real breakthrough came with his adoption of the small jet condenser that was part of James Watt's steam engine. Air was removed from the condenser by a pump, creating a vacuum that was filled by steam from the engine cylinder. The condenser was kept cool so that steam continued flowing into it until the cylinder was completely evacuated. The design was more effective than previous condensers used by Fitch; exhaust was more completely removed and a better vacuum was achieved within the cylinder, increasing the engine's efficiency. ■

Further Reading:

K. T. Rowland, *Steam at Sea: a History of Steam Navigation.* Newton Abbot, 1970.

EDMUND CARTWRIGHT

b. April 24, 1743, Marnham, Nottinghamshire, England
d. Oct. 30, 1823, Hastings, England
British Inventor

Life and Times:

Cartwright was a country minister by profession who dabbled in medicine, agriculture and inventing. Though educated at Oxford, he was typical of the mechanics who made the early British Industrial Revolution in that his engineering knowledge was largely self-taught. In 1784, he learned through a chance conversation that the widespread use of spinning machines developed by Richard Arkwright [q.v.] had begun to produce more cotton than could be turned into fabric by hand-loom weavers. Cartwright immediately realized that further mechanization of the textile industry might resolve this developing bottleneck. Though he had never seen a hand-loom in operation, he set out to reproduce mechanically the weaving process.

The machine that resulted from Cartwright's efforts was deficient in several crucial respects, and so the hand-loom continued to dominate the cotton industry until well after the conclusion of the Napoleonic Wars. By the time the power-loom came into general use, inaugurating a new phase of industrial capitalism, it reflected the work of other inventors, such as Richard Roberts [q.v.], as well as Cartwright. The latter

suffered a serious financial setback when he started a small factory at Doncaster equipped with his new weaving machine. A larger factory, established in 1791 at Manchester with 400 power-looms, was burned to the ground by weavers who objected to being rendered obsolete by mechanization.

Outstanding Engineering Achievement:

To reproduce the hand weaver's work, Cartwright's power-loom had to perform an intricate series of maneuvers: lift the warp, or lengthwise, threads for the shuttle; drive the shuttle, which placed the woof, or crosswise threads; batten the woof together; and, finally, wind the woven cloth. The machine also had to stop automatically in case of a broken thread, keep the cloth stretched appropriately and size the warp from time to time (an operation the hand weaver did almost without stopping). Cartwright's loom performed these functions, but operated eratically; the spring-propelled shuttle jerked and its motive force, provided by a single shaft, was too abrupt and harsh. In principle, Cartwright's design was sound; its problems can be attributed to the primitive engineering techniques which he had to work with.

Cartwright took a patent on the over-all machine in 1785. He worked continuously on its improvement, receiving patents for modifications in each of the three following years. He considered the power-loom in a state of marketable completion in 1787. Although his apparatus was a commercial failure, it demonstrated that weaving could be mechanized.

Cartwright also sought to develop a machine for combing wool, a process that separated long and short fibers preparatory to spinning. The device, completed in 1792, made use of a circular revolving comb which deposited the long fibers (or top) into a can. A smaller cylinder-comb teased out the short fibers (noils), which were then plucked off by hand. Cartwright was on the right track, but combing was even more difficult than weaving to mechanize satisfactorily, and the machine was not a commercial success. ■

Further Reading:

Singer et al., *A History of Technology.* Vol. IV.

Kranzberg and Pursell, *Technology in Western Civilization.* Vol. I. 1967

Abraham Wolf, *A History of Science, Technology and Philosophy in the Eighteenth Century.* London, 1952.

ALESSANDRO VOLTA
b. Feb. 18, 1745, Como, Italy
d. March 5, 1827, Como, Italy
Italian Physicist and Electrical Engineer

Life and Times:

Volta's electric battery was the first step toward developing the practical applications of electricity and putting its power in the hands of engineers. Invention of the battery was the result of a dispute between Volta and Luigi Galvani, a professor of anatomy at Bologna. Galvani discovered that an electric current caused the muscles of a frog's legs to contract, producing twitching. He attributed this, however, to "animal electricity," believing that animal tissue actually produced electric current. Volta discredited this notion by showing that the excitation was a chemical reaction resulting from the contact of two dissimilar metals that were moistened and touching at one end.

Volta's battery, developed in 1800, initiated what might be termed the second phase of electrical experimentation. The first period, one of general curiosity, began with Francis Hauksbee's [q.v.] static electricity machine and culminated in the Leyden jar, which aroused considerable public interest. The Voltaic continuous current pile, or electric battery, made it possible to sustain a continuous electric current in almost unlimited supply from a simple and accessible source.

The scientific value of the giant frictional electrostatic machines of the Hauksbee era was limited and their contribution to practical technology was nil, but the electric battery opened the door to new developments in research and technology. The simplicity of the wet battery greatly expanded experimentation with electrical power throughout Europe. Soon after Volta published his findings large electric batteries were constructed in a number of laboratories, which produced a steady series of new discoveries. Volta's work led to the study of the properties of electric current and eventually to the discoveries of Hans Christian Oersted [q.v.] and Georg Ohm. This was the beginning of the third phase in the study of electricity, which established the convertability of mechanical and electrical power and led to the development of the modern electrical industry.

Early electrical knowledge developed largely as a branch of pure science. It was thus natural for a physicist like Volta to become interested in the field. As a youth, Volta resisted his family's

Alessandro Volta, whose battery was the first to produce a steady flow large enough for serious experimentation in current electricity.

desire that he become an attorney to follow his intellectual interests. His earliest mentor was the Italian scientist Giovanni Beccaria, who studied the properties of atmospheric electricity. Under his influence, Volta began experimenting with devices to measure, store and transmit electricity. He soon demonstrated a talent for obtaining significant results from makeshift and economical instruments.

In 1774 Volta received an appointment as professor of physics at the Royal School in Como. Five years later he was named professor of natural philosophy at the University of Pavia. The debate with Galvani brought him wide recognition and many honors. In 1791 he was made a member of the Royal Society and three years later received its highest honor, the Copley Medal. During the French invasion of Italy, Volta pleaded successfully for academic freedom at the University of Pavia. Napoleon, who witnessed a demonstration of the electric battery, awarded Volta a pension and raised him to the rank of count. The unit of electromotive force or potential difference, the volt, is named for him.

Outstanding Engineering Achievements:

Volta first produced electric current with a pile or column of zinc and copper discs which was the basis of the wet battery. Each pair of discs was separated by a paper or cloth soaked in brine. Volta noticed that the current generated by the pairs of metal discs decreased as the wet paper dried. To remedy this he designed his wet battery, or "crown of cups." This consisted of a row of glass beakers partially filled with an electrolyte such as brine. To transmit current, Volta connected the row by inserting a plate of copper in one vessel and soldering it to a plate of zinc inserted in the next. This series of anywhere from thirty to sixty cups could be arranged in a straight line or a curve. The flow of current was demonstrated when an observer simultaneously touched the fluid in two cups, receiving a shock.

In addition to his work on the battery, Volta developed three devices that greatly advanced the quantitative study of electricity: the electrophorus, the condenser, and a modified version of the electrometer. These enabled scientists to detect and transmit small electrical charges and to standardize their experiments, permitting an objective comparison of their results.

Volta's electrophorus, capable of sustaining an electrical charge almost indefinitely, was perhaps the most interesting electrical invention since the Leyden jar. It consisted of a metal plate which held a cake, or bar, of non-conducting material; a wooden shield was enveloped in tin foil and attached to an insulated handle. The cake was charged by rubbing and the shield was grounded when brought into contact with the cake. The shield could then be detached to transfer its charge to a Leyden jar, which itself had been electrified by the shield. By substituting a thin layer of resin for the cake, Volta converted the electrophore into a condenser

which could detect minute degrees of electrification. The condenser was later used to determine that electricity is freed in the evaporation of water and the combustion of coals.

Volta's interest in meteorology and his support of Benjamin Franklin's [q.v.] concept of a single electrical fluid led him to improve the measuring capacities of the electrometer. This device used silver wires functioning as indicators to determine the amount of electricity in the atmosphere. After being grounded, it was raised into the air; the resulting spread of the wires indicated the strength of the atmospheric electrical charge. Volta's electrometer was a far more sensitive device. A glass vessel contained two straws suspended by a silver wire. The wire was charged by one of Volta's condensers, causing the wire to diverge. The divergence of the straws was proportional to the charge given to the electrometer.

While the method of exploding gases in a closed glass tube was originated by Joseph Priestley, the explosion of mixed gases owes to experiments conducted by Volta. Volta used a graduated glass vessel, called a eudiometer, in which he exploded a mixture of common air (oxygen) and "inflammable air" (hydrogen). The eudiometer was filled with water to which eight parts of oxygen and one part of hydrogen were subsequently admitted. The mixture was then exploded with a spark, causing the water to rise. Volta continued to spark the gases until the total volume diminished by one-eighth. He concluded that the maximum possible reduction in unit volume of common air was one-fifth. Volta's experiment led to one of the most important discoveries of the eighteenth century; sparking oxygen and hydrogen over mercury in a eudiometer, scientists were able to discover the composition of water. ■

Volta's "crown of cups," a series of wet cells in which the copper plate of one cup is connected to the zinc plate of the next; bottom center, the terminals.

Further Reading:

John D. Bernal, *Science in History*, Vol. II. London, 1965.

Dictionary of Scientific Biography, s.v. "Volta."

Robert Heilbron, *Electricity in the Seventeenth and Eighteenth Centuries*. Berkeley, 1979.

René Taton, *Science in the Nineteenth Century*. New York, 1965.

Abraham Wolf, *A History of Science, Technology and Philosophy in the Eighteenth Century*. London, 1952.

WILLIAM JESSOP
b. 1745
d. 1814
British Civil Engineer

Life and Times:

Jessop's father, an engineer, had met and become friends with the famous nautical engineer John Smeaton [q.v.] when they worked together on the Eddystone Lighthouse. After the senior Jessop died, Smeaton raised his son, William, and made him his pupil. William became an innovative builder who developed new techniques in the construction of ports, dams and railways.

The dock, a key feature of the modern industrial port, was little used until the last years of the eighteenth century. The dock allowed workmen to load and unload ships regardless of the tide; without it, vessels often settled at low tide on mudbanks. On an open riverside such as the Thames, freight ships were also vulnerable to theft by gangs of river bandits. The problem of systematic pilferage on the Thames became so acute that London commercial interests were finally roused to action. After the failure of a police brigade to halt the bandits, the West India Dock Company obtained a charter from Parliament in 1798 to build the first dock on the north side of the river. Jessop was appointed to supervise the project.

William Jessop, builder of the Thames River dock, the first self-contained loading and storage facility in England.

Outstanding Engineering Achievements:

Jessop is best known for his pioneering Thames River dock. Completed in 1805, it included quays, wet docks and large warehouses, all protected by a high wall and ditch. This was the first self-contained loading and storage facility in England, and proved an effective answer to the West India Company's security problem.

Jessop's work as a civil engineer directed his attention to dredging equipment, then in an early stage of mechanization. James Watt [q.v.] and Matthew Boulton had sought to construct a steam-powered dredger, but came up against the problem of how to avoid overstraining the engine when the scoop struck a large stone or other heavy object. Jessop suggested using an easily replaceable transmission belt that would break at a certain load, leaving the removal of heavy objects to workmen or a larger engine. This was the principle of a steam dredger which Jessop designed in 1805.

An engineer of great versatility, Jessop also contributed new ideas to railroad construction. When he served as engineering consultant to a railway being built in Leicestershire in 1785, wooden rails were still in use. Jessop suggested that the rails be cast with an iron flange in order to strengthen them. Though this proposal was initially rejected, it won through in time and became standard practice in British railroads.

Jessop served as consultant to Thomas Telford [q.v.] during construction of the Caledonian Canal in the early 1820s. This was a difficult project, involving eight bridges and numerous tunnels and culverts to accommodate the many streams that flowed beneath the canal. Though financially unsuccessful, the canal was nevertheless a notable engineering feat. ∎

Further Reading:

Arthur Fleming, *A History of Engineering*. London, 1925.

Singer et al, *A History of Technology*, Vol. IV.

JOSEPH BRAMAH
b. 1748, Stainborough, England
d. Dec. 9, 1814, London, England
British Mechanical Engineer

Life and Times:

In the late eighteenth and early nineteenth centuries, Britain led the world in the design and manufacture of precision machinery. Such instrument makers as Henry Maudslay [q.v.] established standards of exactness that made possible the mass production of interchangeable parts for many common devices. More than a few of these engineers, including Maudslay himself, received their training in the machine shop of Joseph Bramah, who was an inventor of note in his own right. Here took place some of the important initial steps in the development of the modern machine-tool industry.

Born in the English Midlands in 1748, Bramah grew up on a farm. An adolescent leg injury prevented him from doing farm work, and he eventually sought to become a carpenter and cabinet-maker. His new career led him to move south to London in 1770 and establish a woodworking shop there. As a carpenter Bramah had to install water-closets, which were quite common in the houses of the wealthy. In 1778, after tinkering with the design, Bramah devised an improved water-closet that quickly replaced the older model.

Bramah's invention was timely. The growing concentration of people in London had aggravated an already serious problem in waste disposal. As more water-closets came to be installed in homes, Bramah expanded his shop

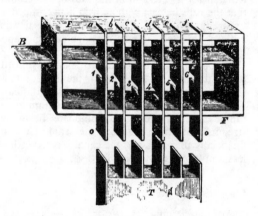

Bramah's lock, in which the slides a-g prevent the bolt from moving unless the notches 1-6 are all lined up; top, the key.

and began manufacturing the necessary parts. He then turned to a new field, lock design, and after much experimenting developed his famous patent lock. Patented in 1784 and again in 1798, the Bramah lock resisted all attempts to pick it for 67 years. A reward of 200 guineas which Bramah offered to anyone who could open the lock without its key went unclaimed until 1851, when an American locksmith named Alfred Hobbs succeeded after 51 hours of effort.

Development of the Bramah lock led its inventor into still another field of engineering. The lock's components required extraordinary craftsmanship to be reproduced. If the device was to turn a profit, accurate machine-tools were needed to mass-produce its parts. Bramah proceeded to develop these tools, aided by Maudslay, then 18, who became foreman of Bramah's shop in 1789.

Their collaboration proved very fruitful. With some direction from Bramah, Maudslay invented the slide-rest, a device for controlling the cutting tool of a lathe while objects were being shaped on it. Maudslay also made it possible for Bramah to build the first functional hydraulic press in 1795. Maudslay's self-sealing leather collar enabled the machine to remain watertight and continuously in motion, two requirements that had been hitherto unattainable in hydraulic press design. The press found many applications, including the baling of cotton and the forging of steel ingots.

At times contentious, Bramah chafed at the honors accorded to James Watt [q.v.], and in 1796 testified against him at a hearing on the validity of Watt's patent for the steam engine. The next year Bramah had a dispute with Maudslay over salary; as a result, Maudslay left Bramah's employ and founded his own workshop. But Bramah continued to invent machinery until his death; many of these devices are now curiosities, including a wood-planing machine, a device for stamping serial numbers on banknotes, and a pump for raising beer from kegs in the basements of pubs. All told, Bramah received 18 patents for his inventions.

Outstanding Engineering Achievements:

Although the first British water-closet dated from 1596, it long needed improvement. In 1775 an inventor named Alexander Cummings developed an improved model activated by a flush handle that simultaneously admitted water from a cistern and slid open an exit valve. Through this valve, the water and wastes emptied into a

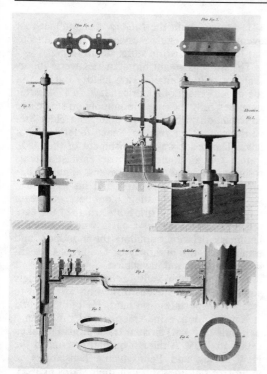

In the hydrostatic or hydraulic press of Bramah, force applied to pump handle, H, resulted in ram, E, being pushed with great pressure against plate, B.

waste pipe and thence into a sewer or cesspool. Unfortunately, the valve system did not always work properly. One of Bramah's improvements was the substitution of a hinged flap valve in place of the slide valve; the flap allowed the basin to empty quickly and sealed more tightly afterward. In 1782 Bramah further improved the design of the water-closet by introducing a trap with a water-seal to block out the noxious vapors from the cesspool.

Bramah's patent lock was an exceptionally well-made and sturdy tumbler lock, one containing movable parts (or tumblers) which permitted the device to be opened only when lifted from place by the proper key. The tumbler lock was widely known in ancient times; its invention in China was ascribed to the semi-legendary Kungshu P'an [q.v.]. But it had long fallen from use in Europe, where interest in it revived shortly before Bramah began his work. The effectiveness of the Bramah lock depended on the many possible combinations of positions in which the tumblers could be placed. A lock with five tumblers could be set to open in any one of 3,000 positions, while an eight-tumbler lock had over 1.9 million possible settings.

The overall design of the hydraulic press had

been established by Blaise Pascal [q.v.] in the 1640s: a slender force-pump, operated by a handle, was connected by a tube to a large cylinder within which a wide piston, known as the ram, was located. Water filled the spaces beneath the ram and the force-pump piston, as well as the intervening tube. Because the bottom surface of the ram was so much greater in area than the bottom surface of the pump piston, a small force applied to the latter created great pressure underneath the ram. Consequently the ram was driven upwards, and materials placed on the platform atop it were compacted against a sturdy retaining plate.

Previous hydraulic presses were inefficient. If the ram fit tightly against the enclosing cylinder, it would not drop down freely when the water pressure was reduced. If it fit loosely, water would squirt out and much of the force would be lost. Bramah and Maudslay surrounded the ram with a strip of inflatable leather. When pressure was applied, a flap on this collar was forced against the cylinder, ensuring that no water would escape. When the pressure was cut off the flap no longer pressed the cylinder tightly, and the ram's descent was easy. ∎

Further Reading:

Singer et al., *A History of Technology,* Vol IV.

Samuel Smiles, *Industrial Biography.* London, 1864.

JOHN STEVENS
b. 1749, New York, New York
d. March 6, 1838, Hoboken, New Jersey

ROBERT LIVINGSTON STEVENS
b. Oct. 18, 1787, Hoboken, New Jersey
d. April 20, 1856, Hoboken, New Jersey
American Engineers and Entrepreneurs

Life and Times:

The wealthy and influential Stevens family was responsible for many of the engineering advances in steam-powered transportation in nineteenth-century America. John Stevens was an early and impassioned advocate of steamship travel; he introduced several innovations in steamship design, including one of the first uses of a double screw propeller. Robert Stevens, working with his father and his brother Edwin, designed numerous steamships and ferryboats, created a distinctive American style of railroad track and coal-burning locomotive, and was ahead of his time in the development of armored warships.

The son of a shipowner and politician, John Stevens studied law at King's College (now Columbia University), but never practiced. Instead he joined the Revolutionary Army in 1776, served as treasurer of New Jersey, and, from 1782 to 1783, as Surveyor-General of eastern New Jersey with the rank of Colonel.

In 1787 Stevens saw John Fitch's [q.v.] steamboat as it traveled between Burlington and Trenton on the Delaware River. He immediately grasped the potential of steam-powered travel and decided to devote his wealth and energy to developing a steamship service for New York and New Jersey. Stevens patented a multitubular boiler in 1803 and used it the next year in his first steamboat, the *Little Juliana;* the ship was propelled by twin Archimedean screws similar in design to modern boat propellers. By 1808 Stevens and his sons had completed the *Phoenix,* a 100-foot (30 meters) passenger steamship. Robert Fulton's [q.v.] monopoly on steamship travel in New York State prevented the *Phoenix* from travelling the Hudson River, but John's son Robert piloted the craft to Philadelphia, the first time a steam-powered vessel was used at sea. In

John Stevens, an early advocate of steam travel, built the first steamship used at sea, the first steam ferry, and the first American steam locomotive.

1811 Stevens built the *Juliana,* a steamboat that eventually saw regular service on the Connecticut River as the world's first steam ferry.

The Stevens steamship activities were important not only in engineering history but also in the development of American law. In 1790, after unsuccessfully seeking a monopoly on steamship construction in New York State, the elder Stevens urged Congress to enact federal patent laws. The result was establishment of the U. S. Patent Office, some of whose earliest patents went to Stevens. The Stevens family later brought suit against Fulton and his associates, seeking to overturn their monopoly on steam navigation in New York State. In 1824 the case reached the Supreme Court, which issued a landmark decision annulling the monopoly and establishing the authority of Congress to regulate commerce and navigation.

As his steamship ventures became increasingly successful, John Stevens turned his attention to steam transportation on land. He built the first steam locomotive in America and ran it on a half-mile (0.8 km) circular track at his Hoboken estate in 1825. Although he had convinced the New Jersey and Pennsylvania legislatures to authorize rail lines through their states in 1823, the planned railroad did not open until 1834, four years before his death.

Robert Livingston Stevens, John's second son, carried on the family's work in steamship and locomotive design. In his late teens he began to assist his father in the design of steamboats, including the *Little Juliana,* which he operated during its trial runs on the Hudson. Robert incorporated a concave hull into the design of the *Phoenix,* giving it greater speed, and was manager of the Stevens Delaware River service, which, under his direction, became one leg of a transportation system that included steamships, railroads, and carriages linking New York and Philadelphia. In the course of his career Robert designed and built more than twenty steamships and conventional yachts, some of which were the fastest of his time.

In 1830 Robert became president and chief engineer of the Camden and Amboy Railroad and Transportation Company, the firm his father had begun organizing eight years before. On a trip to England to purchase the company's first locomotive, Robert designed the T-rail, the hook-headed railroad spike, and a rail joint, all of which became standard parts of American rail track. He also started the practice of laying track on wooden crossties rather than stone blocks, an improvement in cost and speed of construction. He invented the cowcatcher and the eight-wheel locomotive, and was the first to burn anthracite coal in a locomotive engine.

During the War of 1812, Stevens devised an explosive shell for naval cannon. Realizing the destructive potential of these shells on wooden vessels, he later petitioned the government for permission to construct an armor-plated steam warship, the first of its kind. Congress was slow to accept the idea, and construction was not approved until some thirty years later. Rapid advances in firepower forced Stevens constantly to upgrade his design, with the result that the ship was still unfinished at the time of his death.

Outstanding Engineering Achievements:

John Stevens' principal innovations in steamship design included the first American use of a screw propeller and the development of a marine multitubular boiler. His small steamboat *Little Juliana* successfully navigated the Hudson in 1804 at a speed of seven miles (11 km) per hour, propelled by twin screws with four adjustable blades rotating in opposite directions. They were connected by shafts and a gear system to a high-pressure steam engine mounted in the center of the boat. Stevens' inability to procure parts strong enough to withstand the stress of the high-pressure engine forced him to abandon the screw propeller in favor of paddlewheels, which could operate with low-pressure engines. His multitubular boiler, patented in 1803, was similar to that invented by Nathan Read [q.v.], with vertical copper tubes that circulated water around a brick-enclosed firebox.

Robert L. Stevens experimented extensively with the construction and design of steamship hulls and steam engines. To increase the rigidity of his hulls he installed an internal framework of iron and wooden braces, or "knees," and a "hog frame" of heavy timber. Stevens also designed a streamlined false bow that raised the speed of the Hudson River dayliner *New Philadelphia* to 14 miles (22.5 km) per hour. He improved the efficiency of his steam engines by reinforcing the multitubular boiler so that it could deliver steam to the cylinders at up to 50 pounds per square inch (345 kPa).

Another major improvement in marine and locomotive engines was the airtight fire-room or closed stokehold, developed by Robert and his brother Edwin. The device permitted wood or coal to be superheated by the introduction of pressurized air into the combustion chamber; the heart of the blast was further increased by venting exhaust with a fan. Fuel burned more cleanly and efficiently in this firebox, permitting the use of less fuel, a smaller boiler and a shorter smokestack.

Robert's efforts to produce a shot- and shell-proof steamship resulted in a vessel that resembled the Civil War-era *Monitor*. The ship incorporated twin screws and a cross-propeller near the stern so that the heavy ship could pivot quickly. It was scrapped after Robert's death in 1856. He also invented a cannon-fired bomb and an elongated percussion shell. ■

Further Reading:

Dictionary of American Biography, ss.vv. "John Stevens" and "Robert Livingston Stevens."

George Iles, *Leading American Inventors.* New York, 1912.

A. D. Turnbull, *John Stevens, an American Record.* London, 1928.

TIMOTHY PALMER
b. Aug. 22, 1751, Rowley, Massachusetts
d. Dec. 19, 1821, Newburyport, Massachusetts
American Civil Engineer

Life and Times:

The sixteenth century architect Andrea Palladio [q.v.] invented the properly-designed truss bridge. This was a purely theoretical exercise, for wooden bridges were no longer being built in Europe due to the scarcity of lumber. The Europeans who colonized America, however, found this commodity in abundance. A number of wooden bridges were built in the thirteen colonies during the seventeenth and eighteenth centuries. But Timothy Palmer, who has been called "the Nestor of American bridge builders," was the first to use the truss. His designs, arrived at intuitively, represented the first application of Palladio's principles.

Palmer was one of seven children, five of whom survived infancy. The family moved to Newburyport soon after Palmer's birth. Palmer marched with the Newburyport contingent to Concord on April 19, 1775. During the Revolutionary War he married a Newburyport woman, Anna Wyatt, who died in 1786. Although he remarried in 1794, Palmer had no children.

Palmer was active in civic affairs and in 1800 was chosen as surveyor of highways in Newburyport. But his bridge-building activities took him from the Kennebec River in Maine to the Potomac at Georgetown. Palmer apparently retired in 1815 and spent the remainder of his life in Newburyport.

Outstanding Engineering Achievements:

Palmer's first bridge, built in 1792, spanned the Merrimack river at Haverhill, Mass. It had two arched spans, one on each side of Deer Island. Long braces radiated from the abutments at each end of the span to points underneath the arch. The arch ribs themselves were stiffened by trusses, consisting of a single diagonal between adjacent posts. The arches were rounded to permit the passage of boats below; but a 30-foot (9 meters) drawbridge was soon installed in one span. Since the floor of the bridge rested directly on the arches, travelers had to negotiate a sharp climb followed by a steep descent as they crossed each arch. Nevertheless, the bridge achieved wide local popularity, perhaps because the merchants who underwrote it also established a tavern on the island.

As Palmer gained confidence, he designed longer bridges with flatter arches. His Piscataqua bridge had a span 244 feet long (74 meters). In 1796 Palmer bridged the Potomac at Georgetown, and in 1804 he received his most important commission: replacing the temporary Lancaster Turnpike bridge over the Schuylkill River in Philadelphia.

This "Permanent Bridge" had a center span 195 feet (59 meters) long and two 150-foot (45 meters) side spans. Palmer used no bracing in his design. The spans were continuous over the piers, which were made entirely of stone rather than the usual stone-filled wooden cribs. Especially notable was the western pier, which went down to bedrock more than 40 feet (12 meters) below the surface of the river. The Permanent Bridge lasted 50 years without major alteration and stood until 1875, when it was destroyed by fire.

Palmer was responsible for a number of technical innovations besides the truss. He designed his early bridges so that any timber could be removed for replacement without damaging the structure. He also may have originated the covered bridge: the one he built at Easton, Pa. over the Delaware was of this type and had a level floor. The Easton bridge remained standing for 90 years before being removed. ∎

Further Reading:

James Kip Finch, "A Hundred Years of

American Civil Engineering," *Transactions of the American Society of Civil Engineers,* Vol. CT (1953).

Robert Fletcher and J. P. Snow, "A History of the Development of Wooden Bridges," *Transactions of the American Society of Civil Engineers,* Vol. SCIX (1934).

Richard S. Kirby et al., *Engineering in History.* New York, 1956.

CLAUDE FRANÇOIS DOROTHEE, MARQUIS DE JOUFFROY D'ABBANS
b. ca. 1751, Beaune-les-Dames, France
d. 1832, Paris, France
French Mechanical Engineer

Life and Times:

Claude Jouffroy d'Abbans' development of the steamboat was premature on two counts. One was technological: James Watt [q.v.] had not yet invented the reciprocating steam engine, so Jouffroy had to work with the less efficient single-acting engine. The second was political: when the French Revolution broke out, Jouffroy and many other aristocrats went into exile. By the time the French monarchy was restored, Robert Fulton [q.v.] had achieved his commercial success in America, and technical progress had made d'Abbans' early work obsolete.

Jouffroy was born to a provincial family of the highest rank. His early aptitude for the applied sciences caused his family some distress; it seemed beneath their dignity. In 1772 Jouffroy joined the army. After a duel with his colonel, Jouffroy was banished to the south of France for two years. There he studied naval galleys and their maneuvers. Traveling to Paris in 1775, Jouffroy attached himself to a group investigating the application of steam power to navigation. Périer, a manufacturer of steam engines, used one to propel a boat down the Seine in that year, but the current proved too strong for the vessel to return upstream. Périer abandoned his efforts soon after this setback.

Jouffroy persevered. Returning to the province of his birth, he enlisted the help of a village coppersmith to construct the engine for his steamboat, the *Pyroscaphe.* Launched on the Doubs river in 1778, it was able to make some headway upstream. Ridiculed by his family and friends for his mechanical avocation, he soon moved his base of operations to Lyons. He commissioned two larger steam engines from a local foundry and installed them aboard a new

Pyroscaphe. Jouffroy tested it on the Saône River a number of times and finally conducted a public demonstration in 1783. After a successful half-hour voyage upstream, the *Pyroscaphe*'s boiler burst. Nevertheless, Jouffroy requested a patent and a thirty-year monopoly on steamboat travel from the French government. The matter was turned over to the Academy of Sciences, which asked him to conduct one more public demonstration on the Seine. This was an unexpected setback for Jouffroy, who had exhausted his funds, and he was unable to comply with the Academy's request.

With the outbreak of the French Revolution, Jouffroy emigrated and took up arms against the new regime. He returned to France in 1799 after ten years of exile. Financially ruined and closely watched by the police, he had to wait until 1816 for support from a friendly government. In that year he was allowed to set up a company to construct and operate riverboats, but soon faced competition from imports. It was not long before Jouffroy went bankrupt. He lived the rest of his life in obscurity and died at an old soldiers' home, the Invalides, in Paris.

Outstanding Engineering Achievement:

Jouffroy's first steamboat was 40 feet (12 meters) long and six feet (1.8 meters) wide. Toward the bow was a single-acting steam engine; the motion of its piston was communicated by a pulley and chains to two seven-foot (2.1 meters) rods. One of the rods was suspended on each side of the boat, parallel to its side and slightly above water level. At the forward end of each rod was a framework housing slats, which could open and close like those of a Venetian blind. The frameworks dipped into the water to a depth of eighteen inches. During the expansion stroke of the engine, the slats in the housing opened so as to minimize resistance to the water while the rods moved forward. When the condensation stroke began, the slats were shut and the rods moved quickly backward. This unusual mechanism provided the motive force for the boat.

In his second *Pyroscaphe* Jouffroy introduced several improvements. The disparity in power of the two strokes of the earlier engine had been a source of problems. Jouffroy solved this by installing two engines in a V shape, converging in a box with sliding valves. These directed the steam or cold water to each cylinder in turn; the alternation of strokes ensured a steadier source of power. More importantly, Jouffroy substituted paddle wheels for his previous arrange-

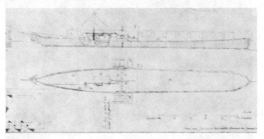

The Pyroscaphe, *Jouffroy's steamboat; an English drawing of a French print of the 1783 version.*

ment, which had proved difficult to operate in swiftly flowing water. The engines were connected with the wheel shaft by ratchets and pawls.

Jouffroy built this steamboat on a more ambitious scale, 140 feet long by 14 feet wide (43 meters long by 4.3 meters wide), with paddle wheels 14 feet (4.3 meters) in diameter. The boat drew three feet (1 meter) and displaced 182 tons including cargo. Its performance seems to have been satisfactory, poor workmanship being the cause of its misfortunes. Fulton, who spent a number of years in France and knew of Jouffroy's work, later designed his *Clermont* along much the same lines as the *Pyroscaphe.* ∎

Further Reading:

Biographie Universelle, s.v. "Jouffroy d'Abbans."

Maurice Daumas, *Histoire Générale des Techniques,* Vol. III. Paris, 1968.

René Théry, "Jouffroy d'Abbans et les Origines de la Navigation à Vapeur," *Techniques et Civilisations,* Vol. II (1952).

JOSEPH MARIE JACQUARD
b. July 7, 1752, Lyons, France
d. August 7, 1834, Ouillons, France
French Mechanical Engineer

Life and Times:

During the eighteenth century, France led Europe in the production of high-quality and skillfully designed fabrics. These textiles were woven on the draw loom, which placed each warp thread above or below the weft in a sequence that created the desired pattern of

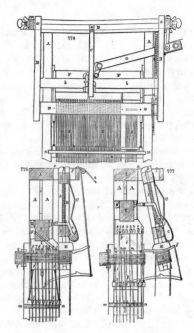

Joseph Marie Jacquard, inventor of an automatic system of weaving patterns through the use of punched cards.

Jacquard's pattern-weaving mechanism; the punched cards are connected in a strip or belt and fed over the perforated block, D.

different colored threads. In the course of the century French inventors gradually improved the silk draw loom. From 1725 to 1737 Basile Bouchon and a master silk weaver named Falcon developed a mechanism for automatically selecting the proper warp threads to be raised; the actual lifting of the warp, however, still had to be done by the weaver's assistant. In 1747 Jacques de Vaucanson [q.v.] designed a machine that eliminated the attendant, but the device was too unwieldy for practical use. It was finally Joseph Marie Jacquard who, by combining the ideas of these predecessors, invented the first workable, fully-automatic device for figure weaving in silk.

Jacquard, the son of a weaver, conceived his invention in 1790 while repairing Vaucanson's loom. But construction was delayed by the disruption resulting from the French Revolution. He finally demonstrated his machine at the Paris Exhibition of 1801 and introduced it in finished form in 1805. Silk weavers, afraid of losing work, destroyed many of the machines and assaulted Jacquard himself. But the advantages of the new device were obvious and attracted the attention of Napoleon I. Although the inventor did not have a patent, he received royalties and a government pension. In 1809 he was awarded the Cross of the Legion of Honor.

With Napoleon's encouragement, the Jacquard loom was soon widely used. By 1812 there were 11,000 in France, and during the 1820s their use spread to Britain. Though developed

for the silk industry, the Jacquard loom was later adapted for the weaving of other materials. As the machine that made automatic weaving practicable for the first time, it became the basis for all power looms used in modern textile manufacture.

Even more important, however, was the Jacquard loom's role in the development of modern computer programming. Its use of punch hole cards to raise the correct warp threads inspired the British mathematician Charles Babbage [q.v.] during the 1830s, when he developed a design for the first digital computer. Babbage envisaged the coding of mathematical instructions by means of punched cards. Although his machine was never completed, the American statistician Herman Hollerith used punched cards in 1886 to create a tabulating machine that manipulated mathematical sums represented by the holes in the cards.

Outstanding Engineering Achievement:

Jacquard's machine was actually a device attached to the top of the draw loom. A perforated block was covered by a card. On the card was a pattern of punched holes distributed so that some of the block's perforations were exposed and others were covered. The block was probed by a series of horizontal rods, each fitted with a spring at its other end. A rod encountering a hole in the card passed into the block. If the rod did not meet a hole, its spring was compressed. At a certain point along each horizontal rod was an eye through which passed a vertical wire. Each wire supported a warp thread attached to its bottom and had a hook at its top.

When a horizontal rod did not encounter a hole, it was pushed to the side by the card, moving the associated vertical wire's hook out of the perpendicular position. The wires linked to horizontal rods that did match with a hole remained in the vertical position. A rising bar, or griffe, lifted only the hooks attached to the latter wires and thus also lifted the warp threads attached to the bottom of those wires. The raised warp threads were then included in their appropriate place in the fabric's design.

. An endless belt of cards passed across the block's face. Each card represented the selection of rods required for a single shoot of the weft. Every time the flying shuttle made its traverse across the fabric carrying the weft, a new card appeared to raise the appropriate selection of warp threads for the shuttle's next throw. ∎

Further Reading:

D. S. L. Cardwell, *Turning Points in Western Technology*. New York, 1972.

Singer et al., *A History of Technology,* Vol. IV.

PIERRE ALEXANDRE LAURENT FORFAIT

b. 1752, Rouen, France
d. Nov. 8, 1807, Rouen, France
French Naval Engineer

Life and Times:

Pierre Forfait's career was moulded by the repeated naval conflicts between England and France in the latter part of the eighteenth century. Forfait served in European waters during the last phase of the American Revolution, which marked the high point of French naval success against its rival. England pulled ahead in the following years, and when hostilities resumed in 1793, the French were usually defeated on the high seas. To compensate for this weakness, France had a number of recourses: building more ships, fortifying ports, gathering intelligence and developing innovative weapons. Forfait had a hand in all these activities.

The son of a cloth merchant, Forfait studied with the Jesuits in his home town. The Rouen Academy awarded him prizes in mathematics and hydrography, and elected him to its ranks when he was 21 years old. As an engineering student he served at the port of Brest until 1782, winning admission to the Royal Marine Academy in 1781. Forfait left Brest to join the Franco-Spanish fleet off Cadiz, where he maintained and repaired ships.

With the end of the war in 1783, Forfait returned to Brest to conduct scientific investigations and construct ships. His last peacetime assignment was to England, where he studied naval developments in 1789. Later Forfait would inspect captured English ships to discover how the copper sheathing was fastened to the bottoms, a question of some importance.

Forfait was a member of the Legislative Assembly from 1791 to 1792; he also served as Napoleon's Minister of the Navy from 1799 to 1801. For most of the war years, however, Forfait directed the construction of ships and harborworks; he repulsed British attacks on Le Havre (1798) and Boulogne (1801). Forfait served on the commission that reviewed Robert Fulton's [q.v.] innovative naval weapons; although Fulton's floating batteries and torpedoes were tested and approved, the commission declined to fund construction of the *Nautilus*, a submarine. In 1798 Forfait was named president of a commission publicly charged with the task of preparing an invasion of Britain. In fact, this commission never met; it was intended to distract the English while secret plans were being made to invade Egypt.

Despite his numerous wartime services, Forfait was constantly embroiled in struggles with his colleagues in the Ministry of the Navy. Disgusted, he left government service in 1805 to spend time with his family, only to die two years later of an apoplectic fit.

Outstanding Engineering Achievements:

Forfait did notable work in ship construction. In 1787 the government decided to establish regular transatlantic navigational links with French colonies. The 800-ton packet boats Forfait designed and built for this service were much admired at the time. Although trim and swift, they had capacious stowage. The ships also incorporated a new capstan Forfait had developed. In 1796 Forfait was asked to solve the growing problem of shipping sufficient provisions up the Seine to Paris. He designed cargo boats of large capacity whose masts could be disassembled to go under bridges. A regular supply service was set up which covered the distance between Le Havre and Paris in the record time of six days. Forfait also designed and directed the construction of twelve divisions of gunboats for Channel defense, as well as five frigates or ships-of-the-line. His 1788 treatise on masts and sails became the standard work in its field.

Among Forfait's other accomplishments was the construction of harborworks at Le Havre, Boulogne and Antwerp. In less than three months he was able to deepen the Boulogne harbor by six feet (1.8 m) and erect fortifications that repulsed two attacks by British forces under Adm. Horatio Nelson. The military port he constructed at Antwerp was so formidable that the British demanded its destruction following Napoleon's defeat in 1814. ■

Further Reading:

Biographie Universelle, s.v. "Forfait."
Nouvelle Biographie Générale, s.v. "Forfait."
Maurice Daumas, ed., Histoire Générale des Techniques, Vol. III. Paris, 1968.

LAZARE-NICOLAS-MARGUERITE CARNOT
b. May 13, 1753, Nolay, Côte-d'Or, France
d. Aug. 2, 1823, Magdeburg, Germany
French Engineer and Military Strategist

Life and Times:

Lazare Carnot, a leading political and military figure of the French Revolution and the Napoleonic era, was also an engineer and mathematician and the earliest formulator of the principle of continuity in the transmission of power. Born to a middle class family in Burgundy, he joined the Royal Corps of Engineers as a young man and tried to win a name for himself by entering essay contests sponsored by learned societies. One such essay, on theoretical mechanics, won honorable mention from the Académie des Sciences of Paris in 1780; revised and published as Essai sur les machines en

général in 1783, and again revised as Principes fondamentaux de l'équilibre et du mouvement in 1803, the paper was the first theoretical analysis of engineering mechanics.

Carnot's study of fortifications and military strategy won a prize from the Académie de Dijon in 1784. The paper stood him in good stead eight years later, when, as a recently elected member of the Legislative Assembly, he was asked to reorganize the Army of the Rhine after the overthrow of the monarchy. His success in this task brought him to prominence and led to his appointment to the newly-formed Committee of Public Safety in August 1793. Responsible mainly for military affairs, Carnot was the only member of the 12-man Committee to remain in power after the arrest of Maximilien Robespierre the following year and the formation of the Directory in 1795. He was finally expelled from the government in 1797 by a leftist coup, which forced him to seek refuge in Germany and Switzerland.

Carnot spent most of the next ten years pursuing studies in mechanics, infinitesimal calculus, geometry and military fortifications. He returned to France in 1800 and served briefly as Minister of War under his former protégé, Napoleon. During Napoleon's retreat from Moscow in 1814 Carnot supervised the successful defense of Antwerp; later he served as Minister of the Interior in the final days of Napoleon's regime and headed the provisional government that followed it. Exiled by the restored monarchy, he settled in Prussia but left in France his son Sadi [q.v.], an engineer whose pioneering work on the thermal efficiency of steam engines helped establish the science of thermodynamics.

Outstanding Engineering Achievements:

Carnot was not an inventor but rather one of the first theoreticians of engineering mechanics. His most important work on this subject was the Essai sur les machines en général, in which he outlined a mathematical theory of power transmission in mechanical systems. He began with an abstract model of the machine as a motion-transmitting link between two otherwise unrelated bodies. Carnot went on to analyze the movement of energy from one part of the system to another; he found that power is transmitted most efficiently, and the largest amount of useful work done, when friction, turbulence, and other energy-wasting factors are kept to a minimum. This was an early and incomplete approach to the general law of the conservation of energy. Carnot theorized that all mechanical motions can be mathematically analyzed and expressed in terms of geometrical angles. Using this approach, coupled with his ideas on the conservation of mechanical energy, he derived the principle of conservation of momentum and torque. In the same work he argued persuasively against the persistent idea of perpetual motion.

Carnot's treatment of machines as systems was unusual for the time. Sadi Carnot was influenced by his father's work when he undertook his research into the thermal efficiency of the steam engine. Sadi's theoretical heat cycle, a system in which work is performed by the passage of heat through an ideal engine, incorporates his father's use of the concept of infinitesimal and reversible mechanical motions. ■

Further Reading:

Dictionary of Scientific Biography, s.v. "Carnot."

JONATHAN CARTER HORNBLOWER

b. July 5, 1753, Chacewater, Cornwall, England
d. March 1815, Penryn, Cornwall, England
British Mechanical Engineer

Life and Times:

James Watt's [q.v.] introduction of the separate condenser steam engine in 1776 encouraged other inventors to devise alternate designs that would improve the engine's efficiency and widen its applicability. There followed a series of legal battles in which Watt generally enforced his master patent on the steam engine. One engineer who tried to challenge Watt's early predominance was Jonathan Hornblower, inventor of the first single-acting, two-cylinder compound engine.

Hornblower came from a family of engineers. His grandfather had built one of the early Newcomen engines in 1725, and his father was one of the best-known engineers in Cornwall. As a young man Hornblower was employed with his father and three brothers by Boulton and Watt to build one of their engines. He was soon thoroughly familiar with Watt's single-cylinder engine and determined to improve on it. By 1781 he had obtained a patent for a single-acting engine with two cylinders that used steam expansively, hence much more efficiently. Though the first model seems not to have been a success, a subsequent version built in 1790 for a tin mine worked satisfactorily. But Watt immediately sued Hornblower for patent infringement because he had employed a separate condenser and air pump in his design. The case was finally decided against Hornblower in 1799, just one year before expiration of Watt's master patent.

Although Hornblower was prevented from undertaking further development of his engine, it showed how major improvements in efficiency and power would ultimately be achieved and so could not be ignored indefinitely. The multicylinder engine was revived and perfected by Arthur Woolf and others after 1804 and was later widely used in a variety of applications where fuel efficiency was important. Compound engines became increasingly popular during the course of the nineteenth century.

Outstanding Engineering Achievements:

Hornblower's single-acting compound steam engine of 1781 was composed of two cylinders, 19 and 24 inches (48 and 61 cm) in diameter, connected by piston rods to the same end of an overhead rocking beam. The bottom of the small cylinder was joined by a pipe to the top of the large cylinder. A separate condenser, boiler, and

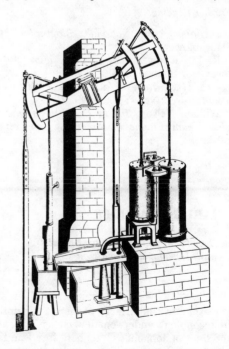

Hornblower's single-acting two-cylinder engine, the first compound steam engine and the first to use steam's expansive pressure.

air pump controlled the flow and temperature of steam. To start the cycle, steam was bled into the entire system; then a jet of cold water was shot into the condenser, creating a vacuum and drawing steam from the bottom of the large cylinder. As the large piston was pushed downward by steam initially at atmospheric pressure, taking the small piston with it, steam from the small cylinder was compressed and forced into the top of the large cylinder, where its expansion contributed to the force of the downstroke. This was the first use of expansive pressure in a steam engine, preceding Watt's application of the principle by one year. The discharged steam ran to the boiler through a pipe under the small cylinder, helping to keep it warm. Hornblower's design was more efficient than Watt's; because the steam was used twice before reheating, less fuel was needed. Also, each cylinder remained at a more constant temperature than in the Watt engine, so there was less energy lost in alternately heating and cooling the metal.

Hornblower wrote several treatises on the measurement of distances and forces, and obtained patents on rotary steam engines which were never built. He also invented the double beat valve. ■

Further Reading:

Dictionary of National Biography, s.v. "Hornblower."

R. L. Galloway, The Steam Engine and Its Inventors. London, 1881.

Ivor Hart, James Watt and the History of Steam Power. New York, 1949.

William Nelson, Josiah Hornblower and the First Steam Engine in America. New Jersey, 1883.

CHARLES STANHOPE
b. Aug. 3, 1753, London, England
d. Dec. 15, 1816, Chevening, England
English Inventor and Politician

Life and Times:

Despite the importance of the art of printing, its technology underwent few changes between the time of Johannes Gutenberg [q.v.] and the eighteenth century. The wooden hand-press, although improved by William Blaeu about 1620, required the strength of a ploughman to

The versatile Charles Stanhope invented the stereotype process which became an integral part of high-speed newspaper printing.

operate. Even Gutenberg's revolutionary technique of printing from movable type involved certain disadvantages. Once an edition of a book was printed, the pages were broken up and their type redistributed. If a second edition was desired, the entire work had to be reset. The storage of standing type in pages for a possible second edition represented a considerable capital investment. Moreover, individual letters could easily be jumbled or drop out when the set pages were moved. Charles Stanhope's solutions to these problems—the iron press and the technique of stereotyping—can be said to have introduced the modern era of printing.

Stanhope was the son of Philip, second Earl Stanhope, a distinguished mathematician and an ardent democrat. The young man early acquired his father's interests and, at the death of his older brother, became heir to the title as well. After a short time at Eton, Stanhope moved with his family to Geneva. There his tutor encouraged his interest in science; at 18, Stanhope wrote a book on engraving and a prize-winning essay (in French) on the pendulum.

Returning to England in 1774, Stanhope plunged into politics, supporting the second William Pitt's reformist measures. In 1780 Stanhope was elected to Parliament and began to agitate for electoral reform and against the

American war. A member of the House of Lords from 1786, Stanhope broke with Pitt over the French Revolution. Stanhope's enthusiastic support of the Revolution and his opposition to England's military intervention earned him the sobriquet "the minority of one." His proposals met with so little support that from 1795 to 1800 Stanhope boycotted the House of Lords.

Throughout his life Stanhope pursued a second career, that of inventor. His first inventions, two calculating machines, date from 1777. One performed addition and subtraction, the other, multiplication and division. Stanhope took out patents for steamships in 1790 and again in 1807. Several ships of his design seem to have been constructed. One, propelled by duck-foot oars, attained a maximum speed of only three miles (4.8 km) an hour. Few fields escaped his consuming curiosity: he investigated acoustics, electricity, tree surgery, canal and building construction, optics and printing.

Wishing to benefit mankind in general, Stanhope refused to take out patents for many of his inventions. He was less generous with the children of his marriages to Hester Pitt (1774) and Louisa Grenville (1781); he disinherited all six.

Outstanding Engineering Achievements:

The Stanhope press, still used in Europe for printing limited editions, was made entirely of iron except for a stout wooden base. In the centuries-old wooden press, a horizontal plate holding the page of type (the platen) was forced down onto the paper by the turning of a vertical screw. Attached to the screw was a bar, which the operator moved to tighten and loosen the screw. Stanhope's press featured a second vertical member, the arbor, on the side of the press nearest the operator. The bar was attached to the arbor, instead of to the centrally located screw, and thus was more convenient to operate. Power was transmitted from the arbor to an enlarged screw by an overhead system of levers and a coupling bar; the arrangement provided a much greater mechanical advantage than the old presses. The operator was further assisted by a counterweight, which helped raise the platen and return the bar to its original position after the page had been printed.

The Stanhope press was much more powerful than the old presses. With it, larger platens could be used to print larger pages, while firm, clear impressions could be made from the finest wood engravings. Printers who tried to install the Stanhope lever on their wooden presses soon found their presses broken to pieces. Nevertheless, the Stanhope was cumbersome and soon found competitors, notably George Clymer's [q.v.] improved Columbian press.

Stanhope was responsible for an even more important development, the adoption of the stereotype process by printers throughout the world. Stereotyping was a process for making facsimiles of pages composed of movable type. The facsimiles—solid plates of type metal cast in a mold—could easily be stored and transported, while the movable type from which they were cast could be redistributed and used again. Stanhope was not the first to attempt such a technique; two of his predecessors were Alexander Tilloch and Andrew Foulis of Glasgow. Stanhope paid them £800 to initiate him in their techniques, which he perfected and made practicable.

The stereotyping process began with a page of ordinary type, which was set and proofed for mistakes. After the type was rubbed with light oil, semi-liquid plaster of Paris was poured over it and worked in with a brush. Once it had hardened, the plaster mold was removed and baked dry. The mold was placed in a covered iron pan and lowered into a pot of molten type metal; holes at the corners of the pan allowed the metal to run in and form a thin plate reproducing the original page. Stereotyping was soon adopted by the leading university presses and steadily gained ground. Within a generation, improved stereotype processes dominated the fields of book and newspaper printing.

With David Hartley, Stanhope also devised a

The Stanhope printing press, made of iron, obtained firmer impressions on larger pages than the earlier wooden printing presses.

system for making fireproof houses. This involved embedding iron plates in the floors and ceilings of rooms, the surfaces of which were stuccoed. The method was expensive, although in one fire the contents of a room built in this manner were protected.

Stanhope further developed a cylindrical, biconvex lens with ends of unequal curvature. A microscope incorporating it, the Stanhoscope, was popular in nineteenth-century France. ■

Further Reading:

Dictionary of National Biography, s.v. "Stanhope."

George Kubler, *A Short History of Stereotyping.* Brooklyn, 1927.

Singer et al., *A History of Technology.* Vol. IV.

EDWARD TROUGHTON
b. Oct. 1753, Corney, Cumberland, England
d. June 12, 1835, London, England
English Instrument Maker

Life and Times:

An important step in the development of precise optical instrumentation was the invention of Jesse Ramsden's [q.v.] dividing engine. With this tool, circles could be graduated into degrees and subdivisions of a degree. Ramsden's theodolite of 1787 could be read with a vernier microscope down to five seconds of arc. Edward Troughton, Ramsden's younger contemporary, continued this quest for accuracy, exemplified in his famous statement: "The beauty of the instrument lies not in the flourishes of the engraver, chaser, and carver but in the uniformity of figure and just proportion alone."

The third son of a farmer, Troughton was prepared to follow his father's occupation when one of his brothers died. Edward replaced him as an apprentice to the eldest brother, John, who was a machinist in London. Two years later, the brothers became partners in a shop on Surrey Street in the Strand. Because both had inherited color-blindness they were unable to work in optics, where the central problem was the elimination of colored fringes in images. Instead, they restricted themselves to the design and manufacture of measuring instruments and mountings. In 1778 John built a copy of the

dividing engine that Ramsden had invented eight years before, and began making precisely graduated sextants and protractors.

As their business expanded, the brothers bought from Benjamin Cole the appropriately named "The Sign of the Orrery," an 80-year-old astronomical instrument shop. In 1826, after John's death, Edward entered into partnership with William Simms, who was the shop's chief instrument maker during the last year's of Edward's life.

The Troughtons produced a variety of navigational and astronomical instruments, from handheld quadrants to a wall-mounted measuring circle. They supplied the instruments for the 1815 American Coast Survey, and for the 1822 Irish and the 1829 Indian arc measurements. A transit circle made by Troughton, four feet (1.2 meters) in diameter, was used from 1806 to 1816 by the astronomer Stephen Groombridge in cataloging the position of 4,243 northern stars. Troughton also invented the dip-sector, used for determining how far the horizon is below the true horizontal, and the reflecting circle, a graduated circle with sighting scope that is kept horizontal and used for finding very accurate bearings.

Troughton was a founding member of the

Astronomical telescope by Troughton with an equatorial mounting in which one axis is pointed at the north celestial pole; when the telescope is rotated around that axis it follows the apparent path of the stars.

Royal Astronomical Society, and a Fellow of the Royal Society and the Royal Society of Edinburgh. A marble bust of him was placed at the Greenwich Observatory, and in 1830 he was awarded a gold medal by the king of Denmark.

Outstanding Engineering Achievements:

From the time of Ptolemy, measurement of the altitudes of stars in the observer's meridian (due north or due south of the observer) had been made with a wall-mounted quadrant. This gave the height of the star above the horizon (its altitude), or, by subtraction from 90 degrees, its distance from the zenith, the point overhead.

However, stars actually appear to rotate about the north celestial pole, near the Pole Star. Only for an observer at the earth's north pole is the celestial pole directly overhead. Elsewhere the pole is lower, according to the observer's latitude, so that the altitude of a star changes throughout the night and the year, and is different for different latitudes.

In 1806, at the request of future Astronomer Royal John Pond, Troughton constructed a mural instrument that was a full circle. With this, Pond could directly measure the angular distance of each star from the pole. Troughton then built a telescope mounting which, instead of turning vertically and horizontally, had one axis pointing at the celestial pole, and the other at right angles to it. The instrument could then be turned around the celestial equator; when focused on a star, movement around one axis would keep it trained on the star. (An equatorial mounting, as the device is called, can readily be power-driven and is now mandatory for all large instruments.) Troughton realized the value of the mounting but destroyed his first one, believing that it would make astronomy too easy to be appreciated. Fortunately, he reconsidered and built another.

The sextant, the most important tool in celestial navigation, was developed from the quadrant, a graduated greater circle, or more commonly, the octant, an eighth of a circle. In 1788 Troughton patented a type of brass sextant, a sixth of a circle. To overcome the softness of the metal, Troughton made all the parts of double strips of brass joined together with turned pillars. This double-frame design was used as late as 1830, when alloys were developed that could more readily take the strain of use.

Troughton's compensated mercurial pendulum kept the same rate of swing even when the temperature changed. The time of swing is

Troughton's altazimuth theodolite; tilting the telescope up or down sets the altitude; rotating it around sets the compass direction, or azimuth.

directly related to the length from the pendulum mounting to the center of gravity of the bob. As the temperature rises, the bob expands, its center of gravity drops, and its swing slows. Troughton solved this problem by fashioning a bob out of a container of mercury. As it expanded, the mercury rose in the container, keeping the center of gravity at the same level, and the swing at the same rate. ∎

Further Reading:

Henry King, *History of the Telescope*. London, 1955.

E. Wilford Taylor and J. Simms Wilson, *At the Sign of the Orrery; the origins of the firm of Cooke, Troughton and Simms*. England, 1950.

SAMUEL CROMPTON
b. *Dec. 3, 1753, Firwood, near Bolton, Lancashire, England*
d. *June 26, 1827, Bolton, Lancashire, England*
British Mechanical Engineer

Life and Times:

The mechanization of spinning—the process of drawing and twisting fibers to make yarn to be woven into fabric—began in mid-eighteenth century Britain. This development, in which Samuel

Samuel Cromptom combined features of the water frame and the spinning jenny in the highly versatile and successful spinning mule.

Crompton had a major part, helped make the British textile business the first in the world to use modern industrial methods of production. Advances in spinning technology were spurred in part by the increased demand for yarn created by John Kay's flying shuttle (1733). James Hargreaves' [q.v.] spinning jenny (c.1765) and Richard Arkwright's [q.v.] water frame (1769) both produced yarn in greater quantity and of superior quality than the traditional spinning wheel.

Crompton was responsible for the next important step in the progress of spinning. A farmer's son, as a youth he spun cotton at home on a jenny. Seeking to make a stronger and finer yarn, from 1774 to 1779 Crompton diligently worked to improve upon that machine, meanwhile earning money as a fiddler at the local Bolton theater. He devised a machine which, because it combined the best features of the jenny and the frame, aś a hybrid, became known as the spinning mule.

Either because its major features were borrowed from other inventions or because he lacked the money, Crompton did not take out a patent on the mule. Since he was able to produce large amounts of cotton yarn of extraordinarily fine quality, Crompton was beseiged at his home by people trying to discover the secret of the mule. Crompton decided to make his invention public in exchange for a legally nonbinding promise by various manufacturers to raise a subscription for him. The promise went largely unkept. Embittered, Crompton refused an offer from the first Sir Robert Peel to work in Peel's engineering shop and continued to work as a spinner. Later he failed as a bleacher and cotton manufacturer. He received a 5,000 pound grant

from the House of Commons but died a poor man.

Although Crompton personally saw little return from the mule, his device had great versatility and commercial success. It could make any grade of yarn, including the thin cotton yarn used in muslins and fine calicoes. The high-quality yarn previously used for these delicate fabrics had been a hand-spun variety imported from India at great expense. Now the material could be made by machine in Britain.

The mule soon began replacing its predecessors and, starting in 1790, was harnessed to the steam engine. In 1812 the number of spindles used on mules was 4,600,000 compared to 155,000 on jennies and 310,000 on water frames. Meanwhile, the great increases in production that it helped promote left weavers with more yarn than they could use. This situation stimulated Edmund Cartwright's [q.v.] invention of the power loom (c.1787). Soaring output of both yarn and fabric initiated a trend, particularly in and around Manchester, toward the replacement of local cottage industry by large factories employing wage labor during the last two decades of the eighteenth century. Attempts by spinners and weavers to destroy the new machines were in vain, and the application of steam power to spinning and weaving accelerated the growth of the factory system during the next several decades.

Outstanding Engineering Achievement:

On the mule, rovings—raw cotton made up into loose rolls—were wound around bars called creels. Each roving passed through two pairs of rollers, a principle borrowed from Arkwright's water frame. Then it went to a spindle mounted on a movable carriage, an arrangement taken in modified form from Hargreaves' spinning jenny. The first mule carried only about a dozen spindles, but later models held many times that number.

The second pair of rollers rotated faster than the first, so that the roving, stretched out in length and attenuated in width, was formed into a thread. While the rollers operated, the carriage moved away from them. Pulled at a faster speed than the delivery rate of the last pair of rollers, the thread was drawn out further. As the carriage moved, the spindles twisted the thread. Before the carriage reached the end of its travel, the rollers stopped rotating and clasped the thread. As the spindles continued to twist the thread, the carriage continued to move away from the rollers, although at a reduced rate. Thus, the thread was drawn out still more. Since

In Crompton's mule, the carriage, E, moves 5 feet forward and back; pulls on the rovings held at C; and twists the thread onto the spindles, D.

the twisting process was nearly complete at this point, the yarn was able to bear the additional tension. Consequently, the mule could produce particularly fine, thin thread. When the carriage stopped at the end of its run, the spindle was reversed for a few turns to disengage the yarn. Then a wire called the faller pushed down the thread so it could be wound onto the spindle.

The speeds of the rollers, carriage, and spindles could be adjusted independently. It was the great variety of possible relationships between these moving parts that enabled the mule to produce any type of yarn. ∎

Further Reading:

Hector C. Cameron, *Samuel Crompton*. London, 1951.

D.S.L. Cardwell, *Turning Points in Western Technology*. New York, 1972.

H. Catling, *The Spinning Mule*. Newton Abbott, 1970.

W. English, *The Textile Industry: An Account of the Early Inventions*. New York, 1969.

Samuel Lilley, *Men, Machines, and History*. London, 1965.

JEAN BAPTISTE MEUSNIER DE LA PLACE

b. June 19, 1754, Tours, France
d. June 17, 1793, Mainz, Germany
French Military Engineer

Life and Times:

Aerostation—the theory and practice of balloon flight—was largely developed, although soon abandoned, by the French. The names of some of the late eighteenth century pioneers in ballooning are still familiar, especially the Montgolfier brothers [q.v.]. Jean Baptiste Meusnier de La Place never ascended in a balloon; perhaps this accounts for his relative obscurity. Nevertheless, he did much to make balloon flight practicable. His premature death in battle deprived aerostation of one of its guiding spirits.

Although his family had been lawyers and administrators for generations, Meusnier decided to become an engineer. After being tutored in Paris, he passed the entrance examination for the military engineering school at Mézières. He graduated in 1775 as a second lieutenant in the Engineering Corps. While at Mézières he had studied mathematics with Gaspard Monge [q.v.] and done original work on the theory of surfaces. A paper he presented on this subject led to his admission at age 21 to the Academy of Sciences as a corresponding member.

In 1776 Meusnier compiled descriptions of machines presented to the Academy; the following year he continued his engineering education at Verdun. His first assignment, which would occupy much of the next ten years, was to the port of Cherbourg. There he worked on fortifications and a breakwater.

After the first balloon ascension in 1783, Meusnier took an active interest in the new field. His studies soon earned him a full membership in the Academy and yearly leaves from his duties at Cherbourg. Meusnier presented plans for the construction of balloons and worked with the chemist Antoine Lavoisier on methods of generating hydrogen to provide lift. His involvement in aerostation decreased after 1785, however, since official interest in balloons had waned.

Now that Meusnier was spending part of each year in Paris, promotions in the army began to come quickly. He was made a captain in 1787 and assigned to the general staff as a major in 1788. Meusnier participated in the Revolution, joined the Jacobins in 1790, and by 1792 had risen to major general. His first field command, with the armies of the Rhine, was brief and ill-starred. Captured by the Prussians early in 1793, he was soon exchanged and sent to defend Mainz. During a sortie he was struck in the leg by grape shot and died a few days later.

Outstanding Engineering Achievements:

Meusnier collaborated with Lavoisier in one of the most famous experiments of the eighteenth century. To confute Cavendish, who espoused the phlogiston theory, Lavoisier decomposed water into its components, carefully weighed them, and then reconstituted water, again weighing it. Meusnier helped Lavoisier design the apparatus for decomposing the water—a tube filled with red hot iron filings over which steam was passed. As the iron was oxidized, hydrogen gas was released. Meusnier further designed a gasometer, in which a bell for collecting the hydrogen gas was suspended from one arm of a balance beam, while a pan for weights hung from the other arm. The bell was immersed in water; to compensate for the upthrust of the water, Meusnier devised a means for varying the center of gravity of the system by turning a screw.

Quite aside from its experimental value, this procedure proved a practical means for generating hydrogen for balloons. The physicist Jacques-Alexandre Charles, who launched the first hydrogen balloon, needed weeks to obtain sufficient hydrogen by the action of sulfuric acid on zinc. In 1793, when the Revolutionary government became interested in the military value of ballooning, Lavoisier and Meusnier's technique was used. It produced enough hydrogen to fill a balloon in only fifteen hours.

Meusnier's visionary designs for dirigible balloons propelled by air screws were too expensive to implement. However, his successors benefited from the tests Meusnier conducted on various materials to be used in construction of gas bags.

Meusnier had a life-long interest in machines. During his years at Cherbourg he went into debt designing a still that desalinized sea water and an aerator that improved the taste of the distilled water. In Paris he worked with Lavoisier to reduce the amount of soot and increase the illumination produced by oil-burning lamps. For the revolutionary government he invented a machine for engraving bank notes too intricate in design to be counterfeited. ■

Further Reading:

Jean Darboux, "Notice Historique sur le Général Meusnier," *Eloges Académiques et Discours.*

Maurice Daumas, ed., *Histoire Générale des Techniques,* Vol. III. Paris, 1968.

Nouvelle Biographie Générale, s.v. "Meusnier."

WILLIAM MURDOCK
b. Aug. 21, 1754, Lugar, Scotland
d. Nov. 15, 1839, Handsworth, England
British Mechanical Engineer

Life and Times:

One of the many changes associated with the Industrial Revolution in Britain was the development of artificial lighting. Factory owners naturally wanted to maximize the use of their plant by running their machines continuously. But this meant night shifts and the necessity of providing bright and constant illumination for a large work area. Oil lamps and candles were expensive in Britain due to the American Revolution and the wars with France, and so hazardous that insurance companies had to set prohibitively high premiums for factories operating at night. During the early years of the nineteenth century, several inventors working independently developed gas lighting systems that provided for better light at less risk than before. Of these men, William Murdock was the first to see his method successfully marketed.

The son of a Scottish miller, Murdock trained as a mechanic and went to work in 1776 for the famous Boulton and Watt foundry. He soon gained a reputation as a skillful engineer, suggesting the sun-and-planet gear (see below) that

Boulton and Watt's chief engineer William Murdock introduced gas and lighting and invented the sun-and-planet gear in Watt's patent.

enabled James Watt [q.v.] to produce rotary motion with his steam engine. In 1784 Murdock anticipated Goldsworthy Gurney [q.v.] by constructing a three-wheeled, steam-powered model of a wagon that attained speeds of six to eight miles per hour. This aroused the hostility of Watt, however, who felt that he should control any practical application of his steam engine. Murdock chose to abandon the project and remained with Boulton and Watt, where he rose to the position of chief engineer and became known as one of the best mechanical engineers of his time.

Murdock's interest in gas lighting began when he was assigned by the firm to supervise the installation of steam engines in Cornish coal mines. He soon became aware of the possibility of decomposing coal and metal ores to obtain industrially useful substances. Among these was coal gas, which he used in 1792 to light a room of his house. After experimenting with different types of coal heated at various temperatures to produce the cleanest-burning gas, Murdock built equipment large enough to light the entire Boulton and Watt factory at Soho. The firm showed little interest in the invention, however, and work lapsed until 1801, when Philippe Lebon [q.v.] demonstrated the possibilities of gas lighting at the Hotel Seignelay in Paris. Now encouraged by Boulton and Watt, Murdock constructed two large gas flares which illuminated the front of the Soho plant to celebrate the peace of Amiens in 1802. The firm prepared to manufacture Murdock's apparatus, and in 1806 the Phillips and Lee cotton mill near Manchester, one of the largest in England, agreed to install gas lighting.

The decision considerably reduced the plant's lighting costs, and in subsequent years many other British factories and private homes followed suit. At first Boulton and Watt, backed by Murdock's reputation as the finest engineer in England, dominated the market. Yet within a decade, Murdock's equipment had been largely displaced by more efficient rival systems, including one developed by Samuel Clegg [q.v.] and Frederic Albert Winsor [q.v.]. Though quickly superseded, however, Murdock provided the first impetus for the establishment of the modern gas industry.

Outstanding Engineering Achievements:

Murdock produced coal gas by heating coal to decomposition in a retort. The escaping hot gases were led into a condenser, where tar was separated out by a jet of water. The remaining

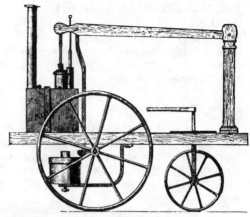

Murdock's experimental steam wagon achieved about 7 miles per hour on the floor of his house.

gas then moved into a holding tank, while the tar and water drained into a tar pit. From the holding tank, the gas was conducted into open-ended pipes, where it was ignited.

Murdock's system had two important flaws. Aside from the removal of tar, there was no provision for purification of the coal gas, so that the apparatus soon became encrusted with soot. The foul smell that resulted when the gas burned was called the "Soho stink." One of Clegg's innovations was to develop a water filter for the gas which eliminated this problem. Another drawback of Murdock's equipment was that it was designed to light only a single building. While this was practicable in the early years of gas lighting, it would have become prohibitively costly if applied on a mass scale. Winsor averted this problem with his idea of a gas company with central facilities that could provide gas to many customers.

The epicyclic or sun-and-planet gear conceived by Murdock was used by Watt to convert the vertical movement of the steam engine piston into rotary motion. The device consisted of a toothed wheel fixed at the end of a drive shaft and geared to another toothed wheel at the center of a larger wheel. The upper end of the drive shaft was fixed by a pin to the engine beam, so that it reproduced the vertical motion of the piston. Every piston stroke thus caused one revolution of the large wheel. ∎

Further Reading:

Archibald and Nan Clow, *The Chemical Revolution*. London, 1952.

Singer et al., *A History of Technology*, Vol. IV.

THOMAS-CHARLES-AUGUSTE DALLERY

b. Sept. 4, 1754, Amiens, France
d. June 1, 1835, Jouy-en-Josas, Seine-et-Oise, France
French Inventor

Life and Times:

The work of the unfortunate Thomas-Charles-Auguste Dallery, ignored in his own time and generally forgotten since, was instrumental in furthering the application of steam power to navigation. Later inventors perfected what he initiated.

Dallery, the son of a famous organmaker, showed rare mechanical ability as a child and by the age of 12 was building watches and clocks. He also constructed musical instruments, including an improved pipe organ and a clavichord organ; his device for adding semitones to the harp was patented by another harpmaker, and he derived no profit from it. A commission to build an organ for Amiens Cathedral, which carried a salary of 400,000 francs, was lost with the outbreak of the French Revolution, and Dallery thereafter made a poor living manufacturing miniature watches and gold jewelry.

Having witnessed an elementary steam carriage built by the Périer brothers in 1788, Dallery turned his mechanical skills to the development of steam power. A plan to build a steam-operated flour mill fell through when funds promised by the government did not materialize. His next project, the construction of a model steamboat to demonstrate the applicability of steam to the planned invasion of England, was entirely self-financed. The boat was launched at Bercy on the Seine in 1803, and incorporated four inventions—a twin screw propeller system, multitubular boiler, telescoping mast, and chimney fan—for which he received a patent in March of the same year. The refusal of the government to allocate funds for the development of the invention left the nearly bankrupt Dallery so desperate that he destroyed the boat and tore up the patent. Nine years after his death, the French Academy of Sciences, at the urging of Dallery's son-in-law, issued a report naming Dallery as the originator of the four inventions listed above; since then, however, Dallery has received virtually no recognition in accounts of the history of engineering, and his inventions have been credited to others.

Although the screw propeller was the subject of experiments by Daniel Bernoulli [q.v.] and John Fitch [q.v.] prior to 1803, Dallery was the first to apply this method of propulsion successfully to navigation; his patent preceded by two weeks the American patent awarded to John Stevens [q.v.] for a twin screw propeller system. His multitubular boiler closely resembled a 1793 invention by the American Nathan Read [q.v.].

Outstanding Engineering Achievements:

Dallery's propulsion system utilized two submerged archimedean screws driven by a two-cylinder steam engine. One propeller, with a mobile axis, was placed in the hull to act as a rudder; the other was set in the stern. Both were of two turns and, according to the patent, could be of variable lengths.

The other inventions covered by the 1803 patent included a boiler in which water was heated in vertical copper tubes feeding into an overhead reservoir, the greater surface area permitting faster and more efficient generation of steam; a collapsible mast of telescoping tubes, to permit the use of sails when necessary; and a screw propeller fan in the chimney of the boiler, to create a more powerful draft. The last-named innovation resulted in greater air circulation and a more powerful fire in the boiler, an idea later applied by George Stephenson [q.v.] to the steam locomotive. ∎

Further Reading:

Nouvelle Biographie Générale, s.v. "Dallery."

GEORGE E. CLYMER

b. 1754, Bucks County, Pennsylvania
d. Aug. 27, 1834, London, England
American Inventor and Engineer

Life and Times:

Charles Stanhope [q.v.], Earl of Stanhope, devised the first all-iron hand printing press in England. It was rather ponderous and tended to break down. The American George Clymer's improvement on it was practically the last word in the printing technology of the day before the development of the mechanical press.

Clymer (no relation to the George Clymer who signed the Declaration of Independence and the Constitution) developed a plow adapted to local soils at the age of 16. He continued as a carpenter, joiner and inventor in Bucks County

George E. Clymer improved on the iron printing press with one of the first major American contributions to printing.

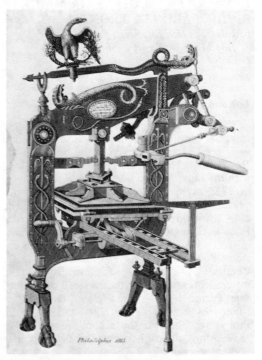

Clymer's press, the Columbian, one of the most widespread hand presses.

for 25 years. Around 1800 he moved to Philadelphia and developed a choke-resistant water pump used in construction of the first permanent bridge across the Schuylkill River.

About this time Clymer also became interested in improving the Stanhope press. After 16 years of effort, he developed the handsome and excellent "Columbian" hand press, one of the first real American inventions in printing. But the press cost $400 and sold poorly. The Ramage presses popular in the U.S. at the time cost only a third as much. In 1817 Clymer emigrated to England, where he mounted a sales campaign throughout Europe emphasizing the Columbian's excellence. After he presented the press as a gift to various European monarchs, he received valuable prizes from the King of the Netherlands and the Russian Czar. The campaign was successful, though the Columbian's American ornamentation and name inspired the development of the competing Albion press.

Outstanding Engineering Achievements:

The Columbian and Albion effectively displaced the Stanhope press. The Columbian had a longer stroke and was easier to use than the Albion, though it was slower than the Albion or even the Stanhope. The Stanhope is still used in Europe for printing limited editions, but the Columbian or Albion is used in England for such purposes.

The Columbian's mechanism used toggle joints to increase the efficiency of the elbowed pulling bar and diagonal connecting rod; these applied the pressure needed for a good impression on large sheets. The press could be used by a man of normal strength. A cast-iron counterweight, in the form of an American eagle, lifted the platen after the impression was made.

Clymer's water pump had a capacity of over 400 gallons (1,514 liters) per minute and could handle suspended matter. A single pump of this type was able to drain nearly half the area needed for construction of the piers of the Schuylkill River bridge. ■

Further Reading:

Edward C. Bigmore, *A Bibliography of Printing,* Vol. I. New York, 1945.

Dictionary of American Biography, s.v. "Clymer."

Sean Jennett, *Pioneers in Printing.* London, 1958.

Jacob Kainen, *George Clymer and the Columbian Press.* San Francisco, 1950.

Who Was Who in America: Historical Volume 1607-1896. New York, 1963.

GASPARD FRANÇOIS CLAIR MARIE RICHE, BARON DE PRONY

b. July 22, 1755, Chamelet, France
d. July 31, 1839, Paris, France
French Civil Engineer

Life and Times:

The career of Gaspard de Prony illustrates the essential continuity of the French scientific and engineering tradition, even at the height of the Revolution. The Academy of Sciences, along with the other royal academies, was swept away in 1793 as "parasitic," but reconstituted two years later as part of the Institute of France. The elite royal engineering school, the Ecole des Ponts et Chaussées, was viewed as a haven of the aristocracy and replaced with what became the Ecole Polytechnique; nevertheless, the Ponts et Chaussées soon re-emerged as a specialist school for graduates of the Polytechnique. The work of Jean Perronet [q.v.], who directed the Ponts et Chaussées from 1747 to 1794, and his pupil Prony, who headed the school from 1798 to 1839, forms a link between the old and new regimes in France.

Prony's family was of bourgeois stock; his father, a lawyer, had been elected to the provincial parliament at Dombes. After studying classics and mathematics at Dombes, Prony attended the Ecole des Ponts et Chaussées from 1776 to 1780. Perronet, who had been favorably impressed with Prony's work, called him to Paris in 1783 to act as his assistant. Prony soon became involved in a controversy over Perronet's bridge at Neuilly, whose innovative design offended traditionalists and evoked predictions of collapse. By analyzing the bridge in terms of Philippe de la Hire's [q.v.] formula for assessing the strength of arches, Prony established its soundness. In the following years Prony helped design the harbor works at Dunkirk and the Pont Louis XVI (later Pont de la Concorde) in Paris; he supervised the construction of both. He also taught at Ponts et Chaussées for several years.

After the Revolution broke out, the nature of Prony's work changed. In 1791 he was chosen to conduct a cadastral survey of the nation preliminary to reform of the tax system. The following year he was ordered to draw up new trigonometric tables required by the decimal division of the circle. In less than three years he supervised the production of 17 manuscript volumes of logarithms and trigonometric functions, calculated to 14, 19, or 25 decimal places. To assist him he had several hundred wig-powderers, thrown out of work by the change in fashions, who knew only addition and subtraction.

Despite these services to the Revolution, Prony came under suspicion in 1793; an anonymous warning, sent by Lazare Carnot [q.v.], saved him from possible imprisonment. Prony's fortunes soon improved, however. In 1794 he was appointed professor of mechanics and analysis at the Polytechnique, the following year named to the Academy of Sciences and in 1798 appointed director of the Ecole des Ponts et Chaussées. Napoleon respected Prony's professional ability and sent him to Italy on three occasions. There Prony studied river control, improved ports and drew up plans to drain the Pontine marshes. But these plans—as well as an 1827 proposal to control the Rhone River—were too costly to carry out.

Prony became inspector general of bridges and roads in 1805. He held this post for life and shaped the next 35 years of French civil engineering. Despite the continual changes of government in France, Prony never fell from favor; Charles X made him a baron in 1828, and Louis Philippe raised him to the peerage in 1835.

Between 1790 and 1815, when Prony retired from teaching, he published a number of textbooks on hydraulics, statics, analysis and mechanics. These tended to be practical and descriptive. His theoretical treatises on earth thrust and arches, like his textbooks, owed much to the work of his predecessors, especially Joseph Lagrange and Charles Augustin de Coulomb [q.v.]. However, his work on the flow of fluids had lasting impact. For example, Prony's *Nouvelle Architecture Hydraulique*, while updating the classic treatise of Bernard Forest de Belidor [q.v.], showed the use of descriptive geometry and Lagrangian analysis in solving engineering problems.

Outstanding Engineering Achievements:

Avoiding the theoretical controversies of the day concerning the behavior of fluids, Prony wrote several treatises on the flow of water for the use of field engineers. The formulas he developed involved four variables: the diameter of the conduit, the slope, the flow and the speed of the water. Given any two values, the remaining two could be calculated. Prony also set forth practical techniques for measuring the different values. When engineers installed water supply systems for the cities of France, they used Prony's equations at every level of the distribution network.

The Prony brake, which he developed in 1821 during tests of steam engines, is used even today. It is a dynamometric device which can be connected to the shaft of a motor running at any constant speed. Friction is applied to the turning shaft by means of brake shoes, and just enough weight is hung from the device to keep it from rotating with the shaft. The power of the motor can then be easily calculated. ∎

Further Reading:

Biographie Universelle, s.v. "Prony."

Maurice Daumas, ed., *Histoire Générale des Techniques,* Vol. III. Paris, 1968.

"Prony," Bulletin de la Société pour l'Encouragement de l'Industrie Nationale (March 1940).

OLIVER EVANS
b. Sept. 13, 1755, Newport, Delaware
d. April 15, 1819, New York, New York
American Inventor and Manufacturer

Life and Times:

One of the results of the American Revolution was to free the thirteen colonies from economic subjection to England. With Britain no longer able to restrict American manufacturing, native inventors quickly adapted and improved upon models of British machinery that were smuggled across the Atlantic. One of the most ingenious of these inventors was Oliver Evans, who did pioneer work in developing the high-pressure steam engine and introducing mass production techniques to the workplace. He has truly been called a symbol of American industrial independence.

Evans was the fifth of twelve children in a prosperous Delaware farm family that also engaged in milling. Apprenticed to a wheelwright in 1771, he invented his first machine, a device for cutting wire into short teeth, some seven years later. With one of his brothers he ran a small but successful general store in eastern Maryland until 1783. At this time Evans became conscious of improvements that could be made in the operation of grist mills, and from 1783 to 1785 he designed and built a semi-automated mill near Philadelphia.

In 1795 Evans published the first edition of *The Young Mill-Wright and Miller's Guide,* a manual which became a reference work throughout America and was frequently reprinted. Also in that year he became involved in the first of many patent infringement battles. However much trouble Evans had making money from his inventions, he was a capable businessman with a good sense for promotion. He was at this time building a dealership in millstones, bolting cloth and plaster of Paris. By 1802 he had enough money to undertake a great gamble, the manufacture of steam engines and other machinery. This business was a success and expanded to become the Mars Works in Philadelphia.

The most advanced steam engine in use when Evans began his venture was the low-pressure double-acting engine designed by James Watt [q.v.]. The Watt engine created motion by injecting steam at atmospheric pressure into a cylinder to move a piston. Along with the British engineer Richard Trevithick [q.v.], Evans realized that use of high pressure steam would create a more powerful and more efficient machine. Watt opposed such a step as dangerous; and indeed, the metal-working techniques of the time were so imprecise that any device operating under high pressure carried the risk of explosion. But Evans and Trevithick, working independently, each designed high-pressure steam engines and sought various applications for them. In Evans' case these included a steam-powered

The ingenious Oliver Evans, American pioneer of the high-pressure steam engine and of mass-production techniques.

crusher for pulverizing stone, an amphibious dredging machine and an iron-clad warship, the *Columbia*. Most of the steam engines made at the Mars Works were used in stationary tasks such as providing power in factories and water works.

The later years of Evans' life were filled with difficulties. Litigation over his patents, which required the services of up to 15 lawyers at a time, sometimes drove him to despair. Frustrated by endless legal battles, he even burned his papers in 1809. In 1817 the steamboat *Constitution*, formerly the *Oliver Evans,* suffered a loss-of-coolant accident that caused 11 deaths, and in 1818 a high-pressure boiler at Philadelphia's Fairmount water works exploded, killing three workmen. The Philadelphia Water Board did not consider Evans responsible for the explosion, but it was no help to his long campaign against Watt's strictures on allowable steam pressure.

Shortly before Evans' death of a lung infection, an explosion and fire destroyed the Mars Works. Many of his experimental projects, which included new methods of iron and steel production, were obliterated in the disaster. But Evans' influence on American industrial technology was still considerable. Largely as a result of his marketing skills, use of the high-pressure steam engine spread more rapidly in the U.S. than in Britain, and his enormously successful grist mills—George Washington was one of the first licensees—anticipated the technology of the production line.

Outstanding Engineering Achievements:

Much of our knowledge of what Evans actually contributed to steam engine technology was lost in his own despairing destruction of his papers in 1809, the Mars Works fire and the Patent Office fire of 1836. It seems, however,

that his line of high-pressure steam engines included various models. One whose description has survived dispensed with the rocking beam that transmitted the motion of the piston in most steam engines of the time. In this engine, a connecting rod ran directly from the piston rod to the hub of a flywheel, converting the piston's vertical motion to rotary motion. The flywheel in turn regulated stop-cocks which admitted high pressure steam into the double-acting cylinder. Other engines manufactured by Evans did have rocking beams, though these were modified in various ways to make them shorter and lighter.

The exact pressures which Evans achieved in his steam engines are uncertain, though in 1805 he proposed an engine operated at 120 pounds per square inch (830 kPa). In order to produce steam at such pressures he had to devote attention to boilers, modifying the box-like device used by Watt. Like Trevithick, Evans developed a cylindrical boiler with an internal fire-plate and flue. The boiler which exploded at the Fairmount water works was operating at a pressure of 220 pounds per square inch (1500 kPa).

Though Evans remains best known for his work on the steam engine, his semi-automated grist mill was equally innovative and important for his time. This design incorporated five labor-saving inventions. The first was a revolving rake, called a hopper-boy, which spread the grain over the upper floors of the mill for drying and guided it into the bolting hopper. This hopper led into the bolting chest or machine, apparently a sifter using the bolting cloth Evans also sold. The mill's other patented features were an elevator

The high-pressure engine of Evans, the first steam engine designed and built in the United States.

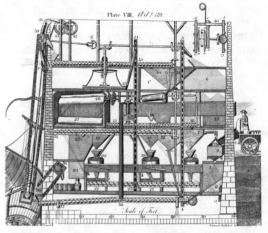

In Evans' semi-automatic grist mill of 1791, grain is moved by horizontal screw conveyors and vertical elevators, ground (25), sifted, and sorted.

consisting of an endless band or belt carrying small buckets; the conveyor and drill, two kinds of screw conveyor for transporting grain horizontally or up a slight incline; and the descender, a narrow conveyor belt which could be driven by the weight of the grain alone, though additional drive was preferred. Whereas previous mills required four men and one child to produce forty barrels of flour, with Evans' mill two workers were enough to produce the same amount. ■

Further Reading:

"An Eighteenth-Century Henry Ford," *The Mentor-World Traveller*. Vol. X (Feb. 1922).

Greville Bathe and Dorothy Bathe, "Oliver Evans: A Chronicle of Early American Engineering," *Pennsylvania Arts & Sciences*. Vol. I (Winter 1936).

Dictionary of American Biography, s.v. "Evans."

Encyclopedia of American Biography, s.v. "Evans."

Arlan K. Gilbert, "Oliver Evans' Memoir 'On the Origin of Steam Boats and Steam Waggons'," *Delaware History*. Vol. VII (Sept. 1956).

JOHN LOUDON McADAM
b. Sept. 21, 1756, Ayr, Scotland
d. Nov. 26, 1836, Moffat, Scotland
British Civil Engineer

Life and Times:

Despite the work of such accomplished road-builders as John Metcalf [q.v.], British roads still suffered from poor administration and chronic disrepair during the early years of the Industrial Revolution. The turnpike trusts, local associations responsible for maintaining much of the country's road network, were debt-ridden, corrupt and supervised by unpaid amateurs with little knowledge of engineering. Many roads were also poorly designed, with high, narrow surfaces that often buckled in cold weather. Much of the credit for improving Britain's road system, in both its administrative and structural aspects, must go to the Scottish surveyor John Loudon McAdam. Together with his countryman Thomas Telford [q.v.], McAdam played a major role in giving Britain a transportation system adequate to the needs of a growing industrial power.

Road builder John Loudon McAdam whose system was used in most industrial countries throughout the nineteenth century.

McAdam emigrated to New York at 14 to work for his uncle, who owned a prosperous mercantile business. Together they expanded the business and helped establish the New York Chamber of Commerce. McAdam's prospects in the New World became less favorable, however, when he supported the Crown during the American Revolution. Upon his uncle's death in 1779, his claim to the business was denied. Nevertheless, he had managed by then to accumulate a considerable fortune.

In 1783 McAdam returned to his native Ayrshire, where he received administrative appointments which gave him responsibility for upkeep of the area's roads. Disturbed by their poor condition, he began experiments in road construction which eventually led to the famous "macadamized" road surface (see below). By 1814 McAdam had inspected some 30,000 miles (48,000 km) of roads and spent £10,000 of his own money on road reconstruction. He continued his work on a larger scale after being named surveyor general of Bristol, a growing port city with badly over-used roads.

McAdam soon realized that his efforts to improve road construction would never be fully realized without a corresponding reform of road administration. His book *Remarks on the Present*

System of Road-Making, published in 1816, attacked "the alarmingly increasing debt and the loose state of the accounts" of the turnpike trusts. He later proposed centralizing authority over Britain's road network in a paid board of professional engineers. The protests of McAdam and his supporters moved Parliament in 1823 to convene an inquiry into road-making, which recommended the general adoption of McAdam's system. In 1827 he was named surveyor general of roads in Britain, a position which finally allowed him to put his ideas into practice on a national scale.

Offered knighthood for his achievements in road-building, McAdam declined due to age and infirmity. Upon his death he was succeeded as surveyor general of British roads by his son, James. McAdam's influence spread rapidly to the U.S. and to other countries of Europe, where 90% of all roads had been "macadamized" by the end of the century. The road surface designed by McAdam was used, with some modifications, in most industrial countries until the advent of rubber tires and automobiles in the twentieth century.

Outstanding Engineering Achievement:

McAdam departed from earlier road-building techniques in several ways, most notably in the structure of the foundation. Unlike Pierre Tresaguet [q.v.] and Thomas Telford [q.v.], who designed roads with a heavy foundation of large stone blocks, McAdam believed that the soil itself would serve as the best possible foundation if kept dry. All features of the macadam road had the all-important purpose of preserving the subsoil from dampness. To facilitate drainage, McAdam advocated raising the roadbed several inches above the surrounding ground and digging drainage ditches on both sides. He also sought to avoid sharp turns in the road and steep slopes, which tended to accumulate water. The earth foundation was covered with a relatively thin (10-inch; 125 cm) surface of dry, hard stone pieces, none more than six ounces (168 grams) in weight and two inches (5 cm) in diameter. McAdam had the stone laid in several layers, allowing each layer to be compacted by traffic. The resulting surface was highly resistant to water seepage. Unlike earlier road-builders, McAdam refused to use earth, chalk and other water-retentive substances as filler material in his roads.

The macadam road had several advantages over other designs. Above all, it used far less stone and thus was cheaper to build. Since the road was higher than the ground on either side, moreover, it did not depend primarily on its camber for drainage. McAdam could thus reduce the camber of his roads to a few inches, avoiding the steep grades which had overturned carriages on earlier roads.

Experience eventually showed that McAdam placed too much confidence in a foundation of dry earth. The yielding foundation of macadam roads proved unable to withstand the stress of heavy, sustained vehicular traffic. The "macadamized" surface of compacted stone pieces, however, was far more durable and cheaper than earlier designs. As a result, hybrid "Telford-McAdam" roads appeared frequently in nineteenth-century Britain, using Telford's stone foundation and McAdam's surface. The techniques developed by McAdam also proved suitable for repairing older roads with sound foundations. ∎

Further Reading:

Ray Devereux, *The Colossus of Roads.* New York, 1936.

Singer, et al., *A History of Technology.* Vol IV.

Abraham Wolf, *A History of Science, Technology and Philosophy in the Eighteenth Century.* London, 1952.

THOMAS TELFORD
b. Aug. 9, 1757, Westerkirk, Scotland
d. Sept. 2, 1834, London, England
British Civil Engineer

Life and Times:

Along with his Scottish contemporary John Loudon McAdam [q.v.], Thomas Telford was instrumental in creating the transportation network that served Britain during the Industrial Revolution. Roads, canals, harbors and bridges all fell within his purview. Though not a startling innovator, Telford was a virtuoso of large-scale projects; he took techniques developed by such pioneering civil engineers as James Brindley [q.v.], Abraham Darby III [q.v.] and William Jessop [q.v.] and brought them into widespread application. In 1820 Telford was elected first president of Britain's Institution of Civil Engineers. Also a noted architect, he became a Fellow of the Royal Society in 1827.

Thomas Telford, first president of Britain's Institution of Civil Engineers.

Telford was the son of a shepherd, and received scant formal education. He began his career as a stonemason, a trade that awakened his interest in architecture and technical drawing. At 23 he moved to Edinburgh and at 25 to London, where he found work in the architectural office of Sir William Chambers. His first civil engineering assignment came in 1787, when he was hired as surveyor for public works being built in Shropshire. This led to Telford's commission to build the Ellesmere Canal, a 103-mile (165 km) waterway in western England and Wales. Begun in 1793, the project was completed in 1805. This was the first of many canals built by Telford, including the Berkeley Canal (1813) and the Macclesfield, Birmingham and Liverpool Junction Canal (1825).

While the Ellesmere Canal was still under construction, Telford began a far more ambitious undertaking: the large-scale improvement and expansion of Scotland's transportation network. The region was already served by a system of military roads built by General George Wade following the rebellion of 1715. Telford added 1,000 miles (1,600 km) of new roads, reconstructed 28 miles of military roads and built numerous bridges. Improvement of harbor works at Aberdeen, Banff, Leith and other coastal towns was also part of the project. To accomplish these tasks, Telford had 32,000

Highlanders trained in construction techniques. Completed by 1820, the program contributed significantly to Scotland's economic development.

Among the important civil engineering developments of the late eighteenth century was the introduction of iron in construction, made possible by improvements in smelting and refining which brought down the cost of the metal. Though not the first to use iron as a structural material, Telford played an important role in popularizing it, especially among bridge builders. He built over 1,200 bridges during his career, many of them of iron. In 1798 he proposed replacing the London Bridge with a cast iron structure that would span the Thames with a single, 600-foot (180 meters) arch. His design required 6,500 tons of iron, far more than any existing bridge. Perhaps fortunately for Telford, the proposal was turned down by Parliament.

As the London Bridge plan indicates, many of Telford's projects were so ambitiously conceived that he had difficulty executing them with the resources available. One such white elephant was the Gotha Canal, commissioned by the Swedish government to connect the Baltic and North seas. Though only 120 miles (192 km) long, the waterway was far wider than existing British canals and required 58 locks to move boats across an altitude differential of 305 feet (93 meters). Begun in 1808, the canal took 22 years to complete and cost six times Telford's original estimate. The project's expense seriously drained the Swedish economy and, by some estimates, delayed the construction of railways in the country by 30 years. Nevertheless, Swedes were proud of the canal; King Gustav IV rewarded Telford with knighthood for his role in the project.

Outstanding Engineering Achievements:

Perhaps the most interesting of Telford's engineering works are his iron bridges, which became a common feature of the English countryside. Like other builders through the mid-nineteenth century, Telford used cast iron, a hard, brittle iron alloy with an admixture of carbon and silicon. He built his first iron bridge in 1795 at Buildwas in Shropshire; the 130-foot (40 meters) span weighed only 173 tons, considerably lighter for its size than earlier iron bridges. Telford also used cast iron in the construction of two large aqueducts which carried the Ellesmere Canal over rivers that flowed in its path.

The cast-iron suspension bridge built by Telford across the Menai Straits was used for 120 years and was then reconstructed.

Telford's largest bridge, built between 1820 and 1826, was a cast iron suspension bridge over the Menai Straits off the coast of northern Wales. The structure was part of an expensive road system that facilitated communication between central England and Ireland by connecting London with Holyhead on the island of Anglesey, an embarkation point for Ireland. Spanning 580 feet (177 m), the bridge hung from two stone towers, each 153 feet (46 m) high, on 16 wrought iron chains. The bridge's roadway, made of oak planking, was suspended 100 feet (30 meters) above the surface. The suspension chains, whose design Telford borrowed from Captain Samuel Brown, were capable of supporting weights of up to 24,640 pounds per square inch (170,000 kPa). The oak plank roadway was destroyed by a storm in 1839, and had to be replaced with a heavier timber deck. The entire bridge was reconstructed in 1940, leaving only the stone towers of the original still in use.

In road construction, Telford followed the three-layer stone design first developed by Pierre Tresaguet [q.v.] in late eighteenth century France. Telford's roads, composed of hand-laid stone pieces decreasing in size toward the top, had a smaller camber and better drainage than earlier British roads, facilitating the movement of fast coaches. Roads built by Telford were also relatively expensive due to their heavy foundations and thin top layer, which required frequent maintenance. ■

Further Reading:

W.H.G. Armytage, *A Social History of Engineering*. London, 1961.

James Kip Finch, *The Story of Engineering*. Garden City, New York, 1960.

Arthur Fleming, *A History of Engineering*. London, 1925.

Kranzberg and Pursell, *Technology in Western Civilization*, Vol. I.

Lionel T.C. Rolt, *Great Engineers*. London, 1962.

Singer et al., *A History of Technology*, Vol. IV.

NATHAN READ

b. *July 2, 1759, Warren, Massachusetts*
d. *Jan. 20, 1849, Belfast, Maine*
American Inventor

Life and Times:

One of the problems limiting the early improvement and application of the steam engine was the clumsy boiler used for generating steam. The boiler employed by James Watt [q.v.] was essentially a large vat lined with brick to provide insulation and protection against explosion. This model had several disadvantages: it was inefficient, consuming large amounts of fuel; it was heavy, limited mainly to stationary use; and it could not produce temperatures much above the boiling point of water. Notable improvement in all three respects came with the multitubular boiler, invented by Nathan Read of Salem, Massachusetts.

Read, who became a teacher and apothecary after graduating as valedictorian from Harvard University, first began experimenting with the application of steam power to marine and land transport in 1788. Realizing the difficulties posed

Nathan Read improved on the boiler of Watt's engine with a multitubular boiler that used less fuel and produced more steam.

by the standard brick boiler for mobile use of the steam engine, he designed a lightweight boiler built of copper or iron, which utilized a series of tubes to expose a greater surface area of water to the heat source. It was evidently more efficient than an earlier compact pipe boiler invented by James Rumsey, which circulated water through a length of coiled iron pipe but which was plagued by leaks and safety problems. Variations on Read's boiler were used by Robert Fulton [q.v.] in his steamboat *Clermont* and George Stephenson [q.v.] in his locomotive *The Rocket;* according to some writers, it was the progenitor of most later tubular boilers.

Read also designed a portable double-acting engine that operated on high-pressure steam, a chain-wheel method of boat propulsion, and a steam-operated land carriage. In 1791, following the establishment of the U.S. Patent Office, he successfully petitioned Congress for patents on all his inventions except the carriage, which he withdrew from consideration in response to ridicule from members of Congress.

Lack of funds hindered Read's attempts to develop a steamboat, and he returned to his home in Salem, where he helped to found the Salem Ironworks factory. In 1798 he patented and installed a machine for heading and cutting nails. After serving in Congress from 1800 to 1802, he was appointed a judge of the Court of Common Pleas for Essex County, Massachusetts, and later became chief justice of the court of Belfast County, Maine, where he had a farm. Satisfied with his legal career, he did not attempt to exploit the commercial possibilities of his inventions.

Outstanding Engineering Achievements:

Read's multitubular boiler, patented in 1791, consisted of a copper or iron cylinder in which were ranged concentric circles of interconnected tubes. (The size of the cylinder, and the number of tubes, varied according to the intended application. Seventy-eight tubes were used in the patent model.) Water flowing into these tubes from a reservoir atop the cylinder was surrounded by flames generated in a furnace underneath; the steam thus produced was channeled to the engine through a pipe. Both the pipe and the furnace funnel passed through the reservoir to preheat the water. This system, by allowing heat to reach a greater surface area of water, used less fuel than earlier boiler models and produced nearly twice the steam pressure; its light weight suited it for marine and locomotive use.

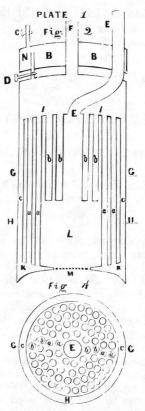

Vertical and horizontal cross-sections of Read's multitubular boiler.

Read's steam carriage utilized his multitubular boiler and two double-acting steam cylinders of his own invention, each of which turned one of the rear wheels by direct action of the piston rod. By using two atmospheres of steam in his cylinders rather than one, and venting the steam into the air, he was able to dispense with the condenser and reduce the weight of the engine.

In 1790 Read applied his multitubular boiler and double-acting cylinder to a paddleboat, but discontinued his experiments when he discovered that he was not the originator of the float paddlewheel, substituting in his patent petition a device that propelled boats by means of paddles attached to a revolving chain. ■

Further Reading:

Dictionary of American Biography, s.v. "Read."

David Read, *Nathan Read and the Steam Engine.* New York, 1870.

J. D. Storer, *A Simple History of the Steam Engine.* London, 1969.

WILLIAM COCKERILL SENIOR
b. 1759, Lancashire, England
d. 1832, near Aachen, Germany

JOHN COCKERILL
b. Apr. 30, 1790, Haslingden, Lancashire, England
d. June 19, 1840, Warsaw, Poland

CHARLES JAMES COCKERILL
b. 1789

WILLIAM COCKERILL JUNIOR
fl. 1830

British Industrialists and Mechanical Engineers

Life and Times:

William Cockerill Sr. and his sons John, Charles James, and William Jr. played a major part in bringing to the European Continent the new machinery and technical skills of early industrial England. They were particularly active in introducing spinning and weaving machinery and building engineering works in Belgium and other countries.

William Sr. began his career as a mechanic and carpenter, making textile machinery in Lancashire. Gifted with the ability to make models of almost any machine, he emigrated to Russia in 1794 after being recommended to Empress Catherine II as an artisan. But her successor, the capricious Czar Paul, sent him to prison for not finishing a machine on time. He escaped to Sweden and in 1799 went to Verviers, Belgium, where he established a factory for building textile machinery. In 1807, William Sr. began producing carding machines, spinning frames and looms for the woollen industry at Liège, thereby introducing machinery on the Continent which had previously been a monopoly of England.

Woollen clothing was much in demand for the armies of the Napoleonic era, and in 1810 William's eldest son, William Jr., began installing machinery for French woollen cloth manufacturers at Rheims and Sedan. His second son, Charles James, did the same in the French towns of Elbeuf, Louviers, Limoux, Chalabre, and Crest. Shortly after the Battle of Waterloo, the brothers William Jr., Charles James and John were invited by the Prussian government to extend their activities to Berlin, where they built a factory for manufacturing woollens by power-driven machinery and a large works that turned out steam-driven textile machinery.

As the demand for woollens declined following the end of the Napoleonic Wars, John and Charles James returned to Belgium to concentrate on building such machinery as steam engines, pumps and hydraulic presses. In 1816 they established an iron foundry and engineering works at Seraing, near Liège. Easily the most advanced ironworks on the Continent, the plant produced many types of light and heavy engineering products, including the latest inventions as they came out of England. By 1820, steamships were being constructed there.

In 1823, Charles James sold his share of the Seraing works and left for Aachen, Germany to build textile machinery. Left in charge of Seraing, John initiated a major expansion program with the aid of a loan from the Dutch government, which controlled Belgium at the time. The loan was used to erect a coke blast furnace, whose construction was supervised by the Scottish engineer David Mushet [q.v.], and rolling and slitting mills. The reorganization also involved the purchase of collieries to assure a supply of coal. The result was that Seraing became one of the largest enterprises on the Continent and an early example of vertical integration with pig iron and engineering products made under the same management. By 1830, the plant employed 2,500 workers.

John's efforts quickened the spread of British industrial technology. A condition of the Dutch loan to the Seraing works was that the latest inventions and engineering techniques be passed on to Belgian ironmasters. While skilled English workers were initially brought to Seraing, Belgian and other European workers were trained there and later used their knowledge in their own homelands. When the firm sold its products, a mechanic was sent with the purchase to instruct the customer on its operation and maintenance. Finally, during the 1820s and 1830s John dispersed industrial technology by establishing many new enterprises, including textile mills in Przelbudz, Poland, and Barcelona, Spain, and even a sugar refining plant in Surinam (Dutch Guiana). Ultimately, John created an empire—with Seraing at its center—of some 60 separate units that he owned or controlled.

When Belgium won its independence from Holland in 1830, the Seraing works suffered because of the new tariff barriers between the two countries. But by the mid-1830s John had reestablished his position as the leading Belgian ironmaster and became the Belgian government's major supplier of armaments, rails, rolling stock and locomotives. To meet the growing demand for railway equipment in Belgium and elsewhere, he again expanded Seraing. A second blast furnace, a copper smithy, and a hammering workship were built. He erected a new factory for building locomotive boilers at Sclessen between Liège and Seraing and a foundry at Tilleur. In 1839, the Seraing works were manufacturing one locomotive every ten days. It was largely due to John's efforts that Belgium became the most industrially advanced country on the European Continent, retaining this position through the mid-nineteenth century.

John's empire was shaken by the financial crisis of 1837. Unable to pay his creditors, he authorized his agents to sell gradually all of his assets except for the works at Seraing and Liège. Hoping to retrieve his position by selling railroad equipment to Russia, he went to St. Petersburg in 1840 to convince Czar Nicholas I to build an extensive railway network. His mission failed, and during his return trip John died of typhoid fever. His creditors continued to sell his assets, but the Seraing works, managed by a nephew, continued to thrive as a joint stock company. ∎

Further Reading:

W. O. Henderson, *Britain and Industrial Europe, 1750–1870.* 1965.

JACQUES VINCENT DE LACROIX DILLON

b. 1760, Capua, Italy
d. June 1807, Paris, France
Italian Civil Engineer

Life and Times:

Throughout the eighteenth century, France was the intellectual center of Europe. The French example penetrated to the most backward parts of the continent, and foreigners flocked to Paris to study the latest developments in their fields. The Revolution and the expansion of French power which followed at the end of the century only enhanced the country's attraction. If Robert Fulton [q.v.] is the most famous of the foreign engineers who worked in France at this time, Jacques Dillon left the best loved monument.

Dillon's ancestors had emigrated from Ireland to the Kingdom of the Two Sicilies. His father served the king as a brigadier general; Dillon accordingly entered military school at Naples and planned to pursue a career with the army.

When the corps of hydraulic engineers was formed, Dillon joined it and soon rose to the rank of captain. In 1795, the government decided to study the civil engineering techniques then in use in France. Dillon was chosen to lead a delegation of young officers and later that year took up residence in Paris.

The southern Italian delegation inspected the principal ports and canals of France. Dillon soon established close ties with leading scientists and engineers. Both sides benefited: Dillon instructed his hosts in Italian methods and caused the introduction of several Dutch machines, of which he had obtained models. His award-winning memoirs on various aspects of hydraulic construction were well received by the Academy of Sciences, which had them printed at public expense. Dillon was a candidate for admission to the Academy when Napoleon expressed interest in joining that body; not surprisingly, Napoleon prevailed.

After Dillon decided to settle permanently in France, he was charged with verifying the accuracy of the new decimal system of weights and measures and received an appointment as professor of arts and crafts at the Ecole Centrale at Paris. From 1798 his principal activity was the construction of bridges; in recognition of his accomplishments he was soon promoted to chief engineer. A sudden illness carried him off at the age of 47.

Outstanding Engineering Achievements:

Dillon was responsible for the construction of the Pont des Arts in Paris, the first iron bridge built in France and the first major bridge designed solely for pedestrians. The bridge was meant to beautify the capital, and Dillon's graceful and elegant design amply fulfilled this requirement. The bridge was lined with benches shaded by orange trees in tubs; glass roofing served to keep strollers dry when it rained. Although there was a toll of one *sou,* 60,000 Parisians paid to use the bridge on the opening day in 1798.

Dillon's other achievement was more practical. For five years he supervised the construction of drawbridges throughout France, a task cut short by his death. ∎

Further Reading:

Biographie Universelle, s.v. "Dillon."
Dictionnaire de Biographie Française, s.v. "Dillon."

JOSEPH EVE
b. May 24, 1760, Philadelphia, Pennsylvania
d. Nov. 14, 1835, Augusta, Georgia
American Inventor

Life and Times:

The cotton-cleaning engine, or cotton gin, was a simple device with enormous consequences. Large-scale cultivation of cotton began in the American South during the Revolution, when the tobacco trade with England was interrupted and English textiles could no longer be imported. As early as 1785 cotton became a regular export to England, where the mechanization of mills had sharply increased demand for that staple. Yet cotton could not be prepared for spinning until its seeds had been removed, and this was a laborious task when performed by hand: it took a person one day to pluck the seeds from a pound of cotton. The growth of cotton cultivation to its position of lopsided predominance in the Southern economy—and the consequent entrenchment of the plantation system and slavery—would thus have been impossible without an effective mechanical means of cleaning cotton.

The name most frequently associated with the cotton gin is Eli Whitney [q.v.], who in 1793 invented the model that eventually came into general use in the South. But popular legend ignores the fact that Whitney was not the first to develop and market a cotton gin. Gins of various designs had been used in the British colonies since the seventeenth century, and the new profitability of cotton during the Revolution aroused the interest of a half dozen inventors before Whitney. The most successful of these was Joseph Eve.

Eve was the son of a sea-captain turned merchant. The family left Philadelphia in the 1770s, possibly because of loyalist sympathies, and moved to the West Indies. Eve's first invention, his cotton gin, was in use there from 1787 onward. When Southern planters began to display interest, Eve applied for a U.S. patent.

In 1800 Eve moved to the vicinity of Charleston, South Carolina, married, and set up a factory. Ten years later he settled in Richmond County, Georgia, and in addition to gins began to produce gunpowder. He also experimented with steam power and writing poetry. Although his poetry was published in various Augusta newspapers, the steam engine he patented in 1818 apparently found no takers.

About 1824 Eve moved to Liverpool and in 1825 took out British patents on his steam engine and a boiler. The British Navy refused to adopt the engine. Goldsworthy Gurney [q.v.] considered using Eve's boiler for his steam wagon, but the project failed. In 1826 Eve returned to Augusta, where he spent the rest of his life.

Outstanding Engineering Achievements:

Eve's cotton gin was a form of the roller gin, a device known since ancient times. The principle is simple. Two cylinders lying close together are set revolving in opposite directions. When thinly spread cotton is fed into the rollers, the seeds will be expelled but the cotton will pass through. Colonial American gins ranged from hand-cranked models that could gin out five pounds of cotton a day to treadle gins capable of cleaning from 25 to 40 pounds (11 to 18 kg) a day. Eve's gin consisted of two pairs of rollers, placed obliquely one above another so that two persons could easily feed it with cotton. Since the gin could be worked by horses, oxen, or water power, it was capable of processing 35 pounds (16 kg) of cotton per hour. Although less sophisticated than Whitney's gin, Eve's sold for as much as $250.

Eve's less successful steam engine was an impulse turbine. Again the idea was not original, since many inventors before him—among them Giovanni Branca (1629) and James Watt [q.v.] (1769)—had tried to design such engines. Eve's consisted of a cylinder that could rotate within a casing. The cylinder had three projections, or vanes, that touched the walls of the casing. Steam was admitted through a valve in the casing into the space between the casing and the cylinder. It pressed against a vane and caused the cylinder to rotate; an exhaust valve removed the steam when the cylinder had made two-thirds of a revolution. The engine, which was woefully inefficient, also suffered from leakage and lacked adequate lubrication.

In contrast, Eve's water-tube boiler was well thought-out. It consisted of two large horizontal tubes linked by a number of small vertical pipes. These elements of the boiler were exposed to the fire. However, the upper and lower tubes were also joined by two "downcomers," vertical pipes encased in brickwork and thus shielded from the fire. The downcomers permitted water to flow down from the upper to the lower tube and prevent the burning out of the lower tube or the pipes. Eve was the first designer to realize the necessity of providing for circulation in water-tube boilers. Although the boiler had other ingenious features, it was apparently never built. ■

Further Reading:

John Leander Bishop, *A History of American Manufactures from 1608 to 1860.* Philadelphia, 1861.

John Bourne, *A Treatise on the Steam Engine.* London, 1852.

Dictionary of American Biography, s.v. "Eve."

Henry Powles, *Steam Boilers; Their History and Development.* London, 1905.

JOHN RENNIE

b. June 7, 1761, Phantassie, Scotland
d. Oct. 4, 1821, London, England
British Civil Engineer

Life and Times:

The son of a Scottish farmer, Rennie studied at Dunbar High School and the University of Edinburgh. He also trained as a millwright with Andrew Meikle [q.v.], known for his work on the threshing machine. In 1780 Rennie moved to London to begin his career as a civil engineer. A visit to James Watt [q.v.] led to a lifelong friendship as well as important contacts. Rennie's first major opportunity came when he was

One of Britain's greatest civil engineers, John Rennie was the first engineering contractor to take responsibility for all aspects of a project.

commissioned to design and construct a factory for the Albion Flour Mills at Blackfriars Bridge in London. Completed in 1784, the building was the first in Britain to be made entirely of cast iron, and established Rennie's reputation for skill, care and innovativeness.

Over the next 20 years Rennie rose to become, along with Thomas Telford [q.v.], the most prominent civil engineer in Britain. Perhaps best known as a bridge builder, he also constructed canals and docks, drained fens and designed harbors and coastal facilities. Beginning with his work on the Albion Mills factory, he helped popularize the use of cast iron as a structural material. He also originated the practice of giving a single contractor general responsibility for all aspects of an engineering project. In 1798 Rennie was elected to membership in the Royal Society. Two of his sons, John and George, became prominent civil engineers in their own right.

Outstanding Engineering Achievements:

Rennie's best known works are two masonry bridges in London: Waterloo Bridge, which stood from 1817 to 1939, and London Bridge, which was completed after his death in 1831. The Waterloo Bridge, the first in London made from granite blocks, was 1,080 feet (329 meters) long and 45 feet (13.5 meters) wide, with nine equal elliptical arches. The 690-foot (210 meters) long London Bridge has five semi-elliptical arches, with a central span of 150 feet (45 meters). This bridge was demolished in 1970, each stone being carefully marked and shipped to Arizona, where Rennie's London Bridge now stands. Rennie also built a number of cast iron bridges, the largest of which was the Southwark bridge in London. Completed in 1819, it was 660 feet (200 meters) long with three elliptical arches, the largest spanning 240 feet (73 meters); 3,620 tons of cast iron were used in the bridge's construction.

In constructing his masonry bridges, Rennie borrowed Robert Mylne's [q.v.] practice of building an inverted arch into each pier in order to transmit stress between arches. He also took over and improved Mylne's use of a framework composed of multiple wedges to guide the construction of every arch. Like Mylne, Rennie constructed his bridge foundations on piles; he preferred to carry out underwater work in semi-enclosed cofferdams rather than caissons, however, to keep the river bottom in view.

In 1805 Rennie completed work on the London Docks at Wapping, notable for their

Part of Rennie's nine-arch Waterloo Bridge, long regarded as, architecturally, London's finest bridge.

steam-operated cranes and warehouses with cast iron columns and roofs. He also designed the docks of the East India Company in London, as well as docks in Liverpool, Dublin and other cities.

Rennie's many canals included the 78-mile (125 km) long Lancaster Canal, from the coal district of Wigan connecting a lime-mining area near Lancaster to Liverpool; the Rochdale Canal, from Manchester to the Calder River; the Crinan Canal in Scotland; and the 57-mile (91 km) long Kennet and Avon Canal. Among Rennie's coastal works were the Bell Rock lighthouse, built with Robert Stephenson [q.v.] at the entrance to the Firth of Forth; and the first large breakwater on the English side of the Channel coast, built across Plymouth harbor.

Like John Smeaton [q.v.] before him, Rennie added to his engineering distinction by making significant improvements in the efficiency of the water wheel. He designed many large water wheels with iron axles that withstood greater stress than the wooden parts previously used. Rennie also developed a sliding sluice that regulated the amount of water flowing onto the wheel, permitting a steady rate of rotation. ■

Further Reading:

Arthur Fleming, *A History of Engineering*. London, 1925.

Richard Kirby and Philip Laurson, *Early Years of Modern Civil Engineering*. London, 1932.

John Pannell, *An Illustrated History of Civil Engineering*. London, 1964.

Singer et al., *A History of Technology*, Vol. IV.

Samuel Smiles, *Selections from Lives of the Engineers*. Cambridge, 1966.

Hans Straub, *A History of Civil Engineering*. London, 1952.

Neil Upton, *An Illustrated History of Civil Engineering*. London, 1975.

SAMUEL MOREY
b. Oct. 23, 1762, Hebron, Connecticut
d. April 17, 1843, Fairlee, Vermont
American Mechanical and Civil Engineer

Life and Times:

Although John Fitch [q.v.] built a steam-powered vessel as early as 1784, Samuel Morey was the first American to design, build, navigate and successfully demonstrate a paddlewheel steamboat. Others, better financed and perhaps more concerned with their own fortunes, took credit for the invention and commercialized it.

Born into a prominent New England family, Morey showed early mechanical aptitude as a local mechanic and repairman. He created a successful business in lumber and sawmills, at one point building an innovative system of chutes to bring timber down from a nearby mountain. Morey also served as local consulting engineer in the construction of locks for the Bellows Falls Canal.

Between 1790 to 1792, Morey and his older brother, Israel Jr., became interested in steam navigation and developed a paddlewheel steamboat. While waiting to see if the boat could survive the New England winter, Morey made a paddlewheel device to turn the spit in his fireplace, using steam from his wife's teakettle; he received the first of his many patents for this invention.

Morey's boat completed its test cruise successfully and attracted the attention of Chancellor Robert R. Livingston of New York. After inspecting the craft, Livingston encouraged Morey to continue his work on steam transportation with a substantial cash offer. Although Morey was not poor, developing the steamboat required the kind of support Livingston could give him. In 1797 Livingston, Robert Fulton [q.v.], John Stevens [q.v.] and others traveled in one of Morey's steamboats on Long Island Sound from New York to Greenwich, Connecticut. Unfortunately, Morey's financial arrangements for a steamship line subsequently collapsed and Livingston withdrew his support. The way was clear for Fulton's *Clermont,* which closely resembled one of Morey's boats, the *Lady Morey.*

Morey continued to run his profitable lumbering business. But the most he ever made from any of his inventions was $5,000. Even though one of his brothers was a successful judge, Morey never brought suit to win claim to his inventions.

Outstanding Engineering Achievements:

Morey's first steamboat was a dugout fitted with a paddlewheel in the prow and a series of steam engines which occupied most of the boat. The vessel eventually attained a speed of 4½ miles (7 km) per hour, enough to navigate the Connecticut River. After patenting a two-cylinder steam engine for steamboats in 1795, Morey continued to experiment. Following the suggestions of Benjamin Silliman of Yale University, Morey tried placing the paddlewheel in various locations; paddlewheels on the sides gave the best results. The *Lady Morey* was a sidewheeler, as was the still more powerful boat that Morey built in 1797 on the Delaware River at Bordentown, New Jersey. Morey's last steamboat, the *Aunt Sally,* measured 19 feet (5.7 meters). He lost interest in the *Aunt Sally* after 1830; vandals, or possibly Morey himself, sank it in Fairlee Lake, now Lake Morey.

Morey secured at least 20 patents from 1793 to 1833. In 1815 he patented a revolving steam engine and sold manufacturing rights to John L. Sullivan of Boston, who used the device to power cotton barge towboats in the South. Morey's American Water Burner, patented in 1817 and 1818, was ridiculed in its time but was a precursor of water gas. His 1818 patent for a Treble Pipe Steam Boiler also presaged later technology. Strikingly ahead of its time was a gasoline-powered internal combustion engine, which Morey patented in the U.S. in 1826 and throughout most of Europe. It included a carburetor, two cylinders, spark ignition, a designed combustion chamber and other modern features.

Though not the first to do so, Morey discovered the destructive distillation of wood to wood alcohol. He described the use of wood alcohol as a spirit lamp fuel and solvent in one of his many contributions to Silliman's *Journal of Science and Art.* ∎

Further Reading:

George Calvin Carter, *Samuel Morey: The Edison of His Day.* Concord, New Hampshire, 1945.

Dictionary of American Biography, s.v. "Morey."

Katherine R. Goodwin and Charles E. Duryea, *Captain Samuel Morey of Orford, N.H., and Fairlee, Vermont: The Edison of His Day.* Vermont, 1931.

Alice Doan Hodgson, *Samuel Morey: Inventor Extraordinary of Orford, New Hampshire.* Orford, New Hampshire, 1961.

JAMES FINLEY
b. 1762, Pennsylvania
d. 1828, Pennsylvania
American Civil Engineer

Life and Times:

New developments in bridge construction were especially important in the early United States, where many expanding towns had to be connected over yet unbridged rivers. Timber bridges, making use of the continent's most abundant resource, were first built in the U.S. The growing use of cast iron as a structural material opened further possibilities in bridge design, though the new country lacked the industrial facilities to produce the large castings needed for an all-iron bridge. One response to this situation was development of the suspension bridge by James Finley of Pennsylvania.

Finley was a judge of the Court of Common Pleas and justice of the peace in western Pennsylvania when he proposed building a bridge whose deck would be supported by iron chains suspended from the bridge's two towers. He finally persuaded authorities in Fayette and Westmoreland counties to support his project by giving the outrageous guarantee that the bridge, not including the roadway, would last fifty years. Completed in 1801, the bridge crossed Jacob's Creek on the road between Uniontown and Greensburgh. It was 70 feet (21 meters) long and 12½ feet (3.8 meters) wide, with a stiffened wooden deck.

Elevation drawing with details of Finley's chain suspension bridge over Jacob's Creek.

During the next eight years 40 bridges were built using Finley's design, although he did not receive a patent until 1808. The most famous of these was the Newburyport Bridge over one channel of the Merrimack River. Built in 1810 by John Templeman, its main span was 244 feet (74 meters) long and forty feet wide, supported by ten chains on each side. The suspension design was also adopted in Europe, most notably by Britain's Thomas Telford [q.v.].

The early suspension bridges were generally quite durable, partly because they dispensed with piers that could be undermined by floodwaters. Those that collapsed usually were overloaded or not faithfully built to Finley's designs. The Jacob's Creek bridge fell in 1825 under the weight of a six-horse team. The Newburyport bridge, however, did not have to be rebuilt until 1909.

Outstanding Engineering Achievement:

One advantage of Finley's bridges was that they had level, or only slightly arched, decks. The first bridge, over Jacob's Creek, had two towers at each end that reached a height of fourteen feet above the roadway. The two chains formed arches that touched the roadway at the halfway mark. To maintain the level roadway, iron pendants of different lengths were hung from the chain to each joist supporting the roadway. These pendants, or suspenders, then were clamped securely to the center of the joist and the center of the chain link.

Finley also realized that the angle of the chain going to the anchorage point gave the greatest strength if it was the same as the angle as it went to the bridge.

As a practical matter, he chose to make the length of the chain links the same as the distance between the floor beams, thus reducing the amount of smith work.

The roadway was rigid, with the load dis-tributed over several hangers which made the bridge resistant to deformation. Railings to protect the traffic were also rigid and contributed to the strength of the bridge. ∎

Further Reading:

Llewellyn Edwards, *A Record of History and Evolution of Early American Bridges*. Maine, 1959.

David Steinman and Sara Ruth Watson, *Bridges and Their Builders*. New York, 1941.

Charles Whitney, *Bridges, A Study in Their Art, Science and Evolution*. New York, 1929.

WILLIAM SYMINGTON
b. Oct. 1763 (or 1764), Leadhills, Lanarkshire, Scotland
d. March 22, 1831, London, England
British Mechanical Engineer

Life and Times:

Steam navigation underwent its earliest development in eighteenth-century America and Scotland, where the importance of water transport made it imperative to find sources of energy more reliable and effective than sail, human labor, or animal towing. Attempts to use modified Newcomen and Watt engines for this purpose were hindered by their weight, low power, and the instability of their vertical construction. The invention of the direct-acting horizontal steam engine by the Scottish engineer William Symington in 1801 overcame these difficulties and proved the feasibility of marine steam power.

Symington, the son of a miller, began to experiment with steam engines while assisting his brother in the construction and maintenance of Watt pumping engines in coal mines. In 1787 he patented a modified atmospheric engine that was used in mines, mills and distilleries. At the invitation of Patrick Miller, a banker and paddleboat enthusiast, Symington fitted a two-cylinder version of this engine to a small paddleboat; its trial on Dalswinton Loch in 1788 proved that a steam engine could operate safely on the water, although it had to be assisted by seamen working a windlass.

In 1801, Lord Dundas, a governor of the Forth and Clyde Canal Navigation Company, commissioned Symington to build a steam-powered

William Symington, who invented a horizontal steam engine specifically for use in a steamboat.

The Charlotte Dundas, *Symington's canal tugboat, was the first steamboat to prove itself capable of practical use.*

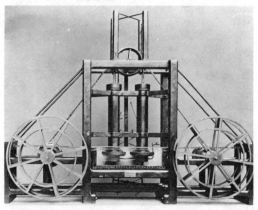

Symington's original two-cylinder steam engine for turning a boat's paddlewheels.

paddlewheel tugboat to replace the draft animals commonly used to tow boats through the waterway. This vessel, the first of two called *Charlotte Dundas,* was powered by a high-standing rotative beam engine. The Navigation Company cancelled funds for the boat's development after its first trials, claiming that wash from the paddlewheels could damage the banks of the canal.

The second *Charlotte Dundas* incorporated the direct-acting, reciprocating horizontal engine that Symington had perfected in 1802, following the expiration of Watt's patents. It successfully towed two sloops through the canal against a strong wind, but Lord Dundas and the Navigation Company were unimpressed and refused to pay the bills, and Symington lost most of his own money on the venture. The boat lay in the canal for five years and served for a time as a dredger before breaking up in a creek. Nevertheless, it has taken its place in naval history as the first steamboat fitted for practical use, and was a strong influence on other steamboat engineers, including Robert Fulton [q.v.].

Symington, reduced to poverty by a series of patent lawsuits, petitioned the government for an annuity, but was awarded nothing more than two small grants. During the last years of his life he designed a steam-operated diving bell, a breech-loading ship's gun, and a water-operated clock.

Outstanding Engineering Achievements:

Symington's low-pressure engine, patented in 1787, consisted of a combined working cylinder and condenser. A second, weight-operated piston, the "medium," forced out the condensed steam, eliminating the need for an air pump. A two-cylinder version of this engine, now in the Science Museum in London, drove the two paddlewheels of the wooden boat that was tested on Dalswinton Loch in 1788. The engine for the first *Charlotte Dundas* was an improvement on the Dalswinton model.

In 1801 Symington patented his most famous invention, the direct-acting engine, which he incorporated into the *Charlotte Dundas II.* It consisted of a double-acting steam engine, laid horizontally. The motion of the piston rod, which was guided in slides, was transmitted by a crosshead and crank mechanism directly to the axis of a wheel, producing rotative motion without the overhead beam of conventional steam engines. The arrangement provided the stability and regularity of movement necessary for a waterborne engine. The *Charlotte Dundas II,* designed by Symington to work as an integrated unit with the engine, was 56 feet (17 meters) long and eight feet (2.4 meters) deep, with an 18-foot (5.4 meters) beam. In 1803 it successfully towed two sloops, weighing 70 tons each, for a distance of 18.5 miles (30 km) in 9.5 hours on the Forth and Clyde Canal, against a wind that kept all other shipping at a standstill. ■

Further Reading:

Dictionary of National Biography, s.v. "Symington."

John W. Grant, *Watt and the Steam Age.* London, 1917.

W. S. Harvey and G. Downs-Rose, *William Symington: Inventor and Engine Builder.* London, 1980.

K. T. Rowland, *Steam at Sea: A History of Steam Navigation.* New York, 1970.

Claude Chappe, designer of a hand-operated semaphore system that relayed messages across France in minutes.

CLAUDE CHAPPE

b. Dec. 25, 1763, Brulon, Sarthe, France
d. Jan. 23, 1805, Paris, France
French Inventor

Life and Times:

Claude Chappe developed a semaphore telegraph which made possible, without electricity, the transmission of messages throughout France in minutes. Chappe's system, built in the revolutionary decade of the 1790s, was so efficient that it was still used in parts of France and England as late as the 1850s, when the electric telegraph was already well on its way to pre-eminence. Chappe in fact developed the semaphore system only after he failed in an earlier attempt to construct an electric telegraph. His was the last effort to satisfy the increasingly pressing need for rapid communication without the use of electricity.

Chappe was preparing for a career in the Catholic Church when his plans were interrupted by the French Revolution. The Revolution's campaign against the Church closed the College de la Joyeuse in Rouen, where Chappe was a student. But Chappe rallied to the newly-created Republic, and the scientific interests he had already developed in school were henceforth subsidized by the state. Chappe worked hard to develop a telegraph system using electricity, but abandoned the project in the summer of 1793 to begin work on a semaphore system. He built an initial apparatus, but a revolutionary crowd in Paris, acting on the false rumor that Chappe's device would be used by royalists to communicate with their foreign allies, destroyed Chappe's semaphore tower in August 1793. A second tower was built, and destroyed a second time for the same reason. Nevertheless, with government backing, Chappe had by October completed a system from Paris to Lille, building some fifteen relay stations in two months. The project was completed in time to transmit to Paris the news of the recapture of Le Quesnay from the monarchist forces of the Duke of Brunswick.

Chappe's success inaugurated a period of difficulties which plagued him for the rest of his life. Although he drew up ambitious plans for further extension of the system and began work several times, lack of funding frustrated him. Nevertheless, by 1799 the semaphore telegraph connected Paris with Strasbourg and Toulon at the eastern and southern ends of the country. But despite these limited successes, Chappe never regained the steady and adequate support he had known in the early phase of the Revolution. Financial difficulties drove him to suicide in 1805.

Model of one of Chappe's optical semaphore signaling towers, with the code that he devised.

Outstanding Engineering Achievement:

Before devising his semaphore network, Chappe built an electric telegraph capable of ringing a bell at a distance of 400 meters (1320 feet). Difficulties in insulating the conducting wire, however, prevented him from developing the instrument into a practical system. He then turned to the hand-operated semaphore, a wooden beam pivoted at the center and equipped with movable arms at both ends. Positioned at different angles, the semaphores stood for different letters, syllables and words. Chappe's most sophisticated device had 262 different combinations. Placed at stations six to eight miles (10 to 13 km) apart, the semaphores could be operated 24 hours a day by virtue of small lanterns placed at their tips for night use. The Paris-Lille system, for example, was able to transmit a message in two minutes. A message could reach Strasbourg in six minutes, and Toulon in 14. Chappe's system was adopted in England beginning in 1811 and, as in France, remained in use there into the 1850s. ∎

Further Reading:

Rollo Appleyard, *Pioneers of Electrical Communication*. New York, 1930.

Singer et al., *A History of Technology*, Vol. IV.

FREDERICK ALBERT WINSOR
b. 1763, Brunswick, England
d. May 11, 1830, Paris, France
British Entrepreneur

Life and Times:

The development of gas lighting in the early nineteenth century, spurred by the high cost of whale-oil and other fuels and by the high flammability of oil-lit textile mills, was initiated by the Frenchman Philippe Lebon [q.v.], who invented a "thermo-lamp" using charcoal gas in 1801. At the same time, two rival English engineers, William Murdock [q.v.] and Samuel Clegg [q.v.], both associated with the famous Boulton and Watt foundry, pioneered the production and purification of coal gas. The popularizing work of Frederick Albert Winsor, an eccentric entrepreneur, made gas a widely accepted fuel in London and resulted in the installation of the world's first centralized gas supply system.

Winsor, who grew up in Hamburg, Germany as Friedrich Albrecht Winzer, witnessed Lebon's demonstrations in Paris in 1802 and came away inspired by the thought of universal gas lighting. Lebon refused to sell him a "thermo-lamp" or to describe his production techniques, and Winsor had to reconstruct the model himself, despite his lack of technical training. Settling in London in 1803, he began to conduct experiments with coal-gas illumination in a vacant coach-building factory. He sought to bring his ambitious plans to the attention of the public through pamphlets, lectures (given by an interpreter), and exhibits at the Lyceum Theatre. His main task was to convince his audience that coal gas was safe, smokeless, more economical than candles or oil lamps, easily conveyed within pipes, and resistant to the elements; in the course of his demonstrations he installed gas lamps along a section of Pall Mall—the first street to be lit by gas—and in the garden and conservatory of the Prince of Wales.

Realizing that the Boulton and Watt plan of installing gas lighting on a house-by-house basis was impractical for large-scale use, Winsor conceived the idea of laying street mains, accessible to all customers and fed from a central generating plant. The proposal met with ridicule from most leading scientists, including William Wollaston, who commented, "They might as well try to light London with a slice of the moon." Nonetheless, in 1807 Winsor organized the New Patriotic and Imperial National Light and Heat Company, rashly advertising a return of £570 for every £5 invested. An application to Parliament for a charter granting exclusive gas-lighting rights in Britain and all its possessions was denied in 1803, thanks largely to opposition from Murdock, Boulton and Watt, and other rivals. The corporation was reconstituted as the London and Westminster Gas-Light and Coke Company, the first gas company in the world, and in 1812 was awarded supply rights to London, Westminster and Southwark.

The technical incompetence of Winsor and his associates, however, threatened to wreck the venture, which was saved only by the arrival of Samuel Clegg later in the year. By December 1813 gas lamps had been installed on Westminster Bridge; four months later the parish of St. Margaret's, Westminster, was entirely lighted by gas; and within the next two years, 26 miles (42 km) of gas mains had been laid under London's streets. The company's efforts were aided by the decision of insurance companies to lower their rates for gas-lit buildings.

Winsor took a leave of absence from the company in 1815 and settled in Paris, where he failed in an attempt to start another gas company. The officers of the Gas-Light and Coke Company rescued him from bankruptcy with an annuity of £200.

Outstanding Engineering Achievements:

Winsor was most important for his entrepreneurial role in conceiving and establishing the first central gas distribution system. Nevertheless, he also played a part in the early technical development of the field. In 1804 he patented an oven for producing coal gas. The gas was distilled in an iron retort and conveyed by a pipe to a beaker-shaped condensing vessel filled with water, where it passed through a series of perforated metal plates designed to thin the gas out and remove impurities. The method succeeded in removing ammonia, but had little effect on sulfurated hydrogen. Winsor also received patents in 1807 for a method of heating greenhouses with gas lamps and in 1809 for a method of using gas lamps in a semaphore telegraph system.

The pipes used by the Gas-Light and Coke Company to deliver gas from street mains to individual houses were originally made of musket barrels screwed muzzle to breech. Later versions used four-foot lengths of strip iron welded together. ■

Further Reading:

Samuel Clegg, Jr., *A Practical Treatise on the Manufacture and Distribution of Coal-Gas.* London, 1868.

J. D. Keating, *The Lambent Flame.* New South Wales, 1974.

William Matthew, *A Historical Sketch of Gaslighting.* London, 1832.

Singer et al., *A History of Technology,* Vol. IV.

JOHANN ALBERT EYTELWEIN
b. Dec. 31, 1764, Frankfurt am Main, Germany
d. Aug. 18, 1849, Berlin, Germany
German Mechanical and Hydraulic Engineer

Life and Times:

The Industrial Revolution produced an unprecedented demand for engineers and with it the new concept of formal engineering education. Mechanization also increased the need for better roads, for housing for a growing urban population, and all the other supporting civil engineering systems. In the same decade that the first Arkwright spinning mill began operation in Germany, Johann Albert Eytelwein established the first major German engineering school and the first German civil engineering journal.

The son of a poor tradesman, Eytelwein joined the Prussian artillery when he was 15, and studied engineering on his own. He passed the state examination in surveying, entered the Prussian civil service as a civil engineer in 1790, and was appointed to superintend the dikes near Berlin. Within three years he published his first textbook, a collection of applied mathematics problems, and in 1794 became director of the Board of Public Works in Berlin. Concerned mainly with rivers and harbors, Eytelwein's career continued to progress until 1816, when he became chief commissioner of hydraulic works in Prussia.

Meanwhile, Eytelwein played an important role in the development of engineering education in Germany. In 1797 he cofounded the *Journal für die Baukunst* (Journal of Architecture), followed by his engineering school (see below). Throughout his life, Eytelwein wrote a number of textbooks on mechanics, hydraulics, drafting and mathematics. In 1803 he was elected to membership in the Prussian Academy of Sciences.

Outstanding Engineering Achievement:

In 1799, five years after the founding of the Ecole Polytechnique in Paris, Eytelwein founded the Bauakademie in Berlin. The first German engineering school of university stature, it eventually merged with another school to become the Technische Hochschule Berlin, one of the world's leading institutes of technology. Eytelwein was the first director of the academy, holding that post for seven years, and taught courses in mechanics and machine design, hydraulics, hydrostatics and flood control. ■

Further Reading:

Dictionary of Scientific Biography, s.v. "Eytelwein."

Benjamin Henry Latrobe, the foremost civil engineer in America at the start of the nineteenth century.

BENJAMIN HENRY LATROBE
b. May 1, 1765, Fulneck, England
d. Sept. 3, 1820, New Orleans, Louisiana
Anglo-American Engineer and Architect

Life and Times:

In late-eighteenth-century Europe, engineering was rapidly acquiring professional status and a scientific and mathematical basis. The engineers of Britain and France, who led the world in the most important fields of technology, valued permanence and durability. The situation in North America was totally different. Bridges and buildings were designed by amateurs, and their plans were freely modified by the craftsmen carrying out the work. The American watchwords were expedience, rapidity and low cost. Transplanted to this alien soil, the British engineer Benjamin Henry Latrobe was able—though not without difficulty—to impose something of his European values and training. Latrobe's students, who included Frederick Graff [q.v.], William Strickland and Robert Mills, figured prominently among the first generation of American-born professional engineers and architects.

Latrobe was the son of a Moravian minister of French ancestry and an American-born mother. Educated in Moravian schools, first in England and then in Germany, he acquired a fine background in the humanities and sciences. About age 17 Latrobe showed an interest in his future vocation and was exposed to German engineering. After his return to England in 1783 he spent some time studying under the leading British engineer John Smeaton [q.v.]. For several years he specialized in canal work. About 1791, following architectural training with Samuel Pepys Cockerell, Latrobe established an independent practice in London. After his first wife's death and certain financial reverses, however, Latrobe suffered an emotional crisis. By 1796 he decided to seek a new life in the United States.

Latrobe spent two years in Virginia and then moved to Philadelphia to direct the construction of the Bank of Pennsylvania, a neo-classical structure without precedent in America. Soon he offered a design for a waterworks to the City of Philadelphia which was so impressive that he was employed to construct it. The completion of the bank and the waterworks in 1801 established Latrobe as the foremost engineer and architect in the U.S.

In 1803 Thomas Jefferson called Latrobe to Washington to take over the construction of the Capitol. Latrobe perceived flaws in the building, designed by the amateur architect William Thornton, and after heated controversy made major alterations in the plans. Work on the

Capitol continued until the outbreak of war in
1812. While in Washington, Latrobe also
worked on the White House, the Washington
navy yard, and the Washington Canal, as well as
on various out-of-town assignments—most notably the Baltimore Cathedral.

The next eight years were marked by disap-
pointment and tragedy. Latrobe moved to Pitts-
burgh in 1813, where he was associated with
Robert Fulton in a project to build steamboats.
The collapse of this scheme ruined Latrobe
financially and brought on another nervous
breakdown. In 1815 he returned to Washington
to repair the Capitol and White House, which
had been burned by the British, only to leave
government service in 1817. That year also saw
the death of his son Henry, on assignment in
New Orleans, and Latrobe's decision to declare
bankruptcy. After some time in Baltimore,
Latrobe moved to New Orleans in 1820 to
complete his son's project, the construction of a
waterworks; like his son, he died there of yellow
fever.

Outstanding Engineering Achievements:

Latrobe's Bank of Pennsylvania, with its 45-
foot (13.5 meters) brick dome, introduced the
large-scale vault to America. Latrobe later surpassed this achievement with his Baltimore Cathedral and daring Baltimore Exchange, whose
dome was 115 feet (35 meters) tall. Latrobe also
used masonry vaults to good effect in his work
on the Capitol; in 1808, however, the one in the
Supreme Court room collapsed because of faulty
design.

Other problems marred his additions to the
Capitol. Latrobe installed a hot-air system to
heat the first House of Representatives, but the
ducts were placed too high in the room to be
effective. Moreover, the acoustics of the room
proved faulty; to cut down the echoes, Latrobe
was forced to hang curtains between the columns. The acoustics of Latrobe's second House
chamber, dating from after the fire, were even
worse, for the spring of the vault began just at
the level of a man's head. Various solutions were
proposed to eliminate the rebounding echoes
until Robert Mills neatly solved the problem: he
raised the level of the floor four feet (1.2
meters).

Despite these flaws, most of Latrobe's work
on the Capitol was attractive and sound; visitors
are still charmed by the "corn-cob capitals" atop
the pillars of the east basement vestibule. The
White House also benefited from his talent, for
he designed its semicircular north and south

*The corn-cob capitals that Latrobe designed for the
pillars of the east basement vestibule of the Capitol in
Washington, D.C.*

porticoes, built colonnaded terraces that Jefferson had designed, and worked on the interior.

Latrobe's Philadelphia waterworks housed
two of the handful of steam engines then in use
in America; the boilers and flywheels had to be
made of wood, since there were no foundries to
cast metal parts. The engines pumped water
from the Schuylkill River below to an elevated
storage tank. The result was the first adequate
water supply system in an American city.
Latrobe's interest in steam engines was lifelong.
While in Washington he designed rudimentary
fire-tube and water-tube boilers. In 1810 he
installed a steam engine at the navy yard to
power a sawmill, forge, and blockmill. He was
also responsible for the erection of a steam-
powered woolen mill in Steubenville, Ohio
(1814-1815).

Latrobe served as a consultant on various
canal projects, most of which came to naught
through lack of funds. Nevertheless, in 1808 he
prepared a prescient report for Secretary of the
Interior Albert Gallatin on the communication
needs of the United States. In it he sketched out
a network of canal routes; in later years canals
were in fact built nearly everywhere Latrobe
suggested.

Other Achievements:

Latrobe's buildings determined the course of American architecture until mid-century. Besides introducing the neo-classical style, with its simple geometric shapes and Greek orders, he also built the first Gothic Revival house in the nation (1800). Among his numerous innovations in architecture were the use of scaled drawings, a practice hitherto unknown in America, and the provision of interior bathroom spaces in houses. ■

Further Reading:

Dictionary of American Biography, s.v. "Latrobe."

Talbot Hamlin, *Benjamin Henry Latrobe.* New York, 1955.

Carroll W. Pursell, Jr., *Early Stationary Steam Engines in America: A Study in the Migration of a Technology.* Washington, D.C., 1969.

ROBERT FULTON

b. Nov. 14, 1765, Little Britain, Pennsylvania
d. Feb. 24, 1815, New York, New York
American Nautical Engineer

Life and Times:

By the end of the eighteenth century, improvement of the steam engine by James Watt [q.v.] and others had made steam-powered water transport a viable proposition. Many inventors were working on the problem at the same time, and several could claim first achievements of some sort. The American John Fitch [q.v.] established the first regular steamboat service in the 1780s; the Scottish engineer William Symington [q.v.] built the first steam-powered tugboat in 1802; another Scot, Henry Bell [q.v.] launched the first British steam packet in 1812. It was in America, with its vast inland waterways, that river transport was more important and financially rewarding; and so it was appropriate that the world's first commercially successful steamship was the work of the American inventor Robert Fulton.

Like another famous American inventor, Samuel F. B. Morse [q.v.], Fulton began his career as an artist, studying for several years in London under the painter Benjamin West. Since public reaction to his work was lukewarm, however, he turned his attention to engineering.

Engineer and entrepreneur Robert Fulton, who designed the world's first commercially successful steamship.

Fulton first tried to design a canal system that used inclined planes instead of locks to lift boats onto different levels. After these plans proved impractical, he worked on improving the design of the submarine, first developed by David Bushnell [q.v.]. He hoped to arouse interest for the project in France, then at war with Britain; in 1797 he forwarded his plans to the French government and left for Paris. Three years later, with the encouragement of Napoleon, Fulton supervised the construction of the *Nautilus,* the first submarine to operate in European waters. He also developed a gunpowder charge that would explode underwater against enemy vessels. Though the French offered Fulton a reward for any British ships he could sink, the *Nautilus* proved too slow to overtake its intended victims. The problem of submarine propulsion, in fact, remained unresolved until the end of the nineteenth century. But the *Nautilus* gained an honored place in naval history, becoming the namesake of Jules Verne's fictional submarine and, through that, of the first nuclear submarine.

Meanwhile, Fulton had to look for some other way to make his fortune. He found it in 1802, when he met Robert Livingston, then U.S. ambassador to France. Himself an amateur engineer, Livingston was extremely interested in the commercial possibilities of steamboats; with considerable foresight, he had gained a 20-year monopoly on future steam navigation of New York State waters. He encouraged Fulton to design a steamboat for use on the Hudson River and furnished him with capital for research and development. Fulton, for his part, had closely followed the efforts of other inventors to construct a functioning steamboat. He realized that most earlier designs had failed because the power plant was too heavy and cumbersome, leaving no room for passengers or cargo. After some experimentation, he solved the problem in a small pilot boat which he launched on the Seine in 1803, reaching a speed of 4½ miles (7 km) per hour against the current. Fulton was so encouraged that he immediately ordered a larger engine from James Watt's Soho foundry for use in a boat to be built in New York.

Before fully committing himself to the steamboat project, however, Fulton made one more attempt to find support for his submarine. Turning this time to the British, he travelled to London in 1804. The Admiralty invited him to try to attack the French fleet at Boulogne, but the underwater explosive charges which he used proved defective. Left again without a sponsor, Fulton returned to the U.S. in 1806 after completion of the engine for his planned steamboat.

The *Clermont*, also known as "Fulton's Folly," was completed and fitted with its engine in mid-1807. On August 17, 1807, the boat began its memorable voyage from New York City up the Hudson to Albany. The 150-mile (240 km), 32-hour trip caught the public imagination, and the *Clermont* was soon running on a regular New York-Albany packet service. Livingston took on Fulton as a business partner; his monopoly on steam-powered river traffic in New York State made them both wealthy men.

Fulton supervised the construction of 17 steamboats and established and managed several packet lines. He also initiated numerous legal actions against what he charged were infringements of his steamboat patents.

The War of 1812 reawakened Fulton's interest in naval warfare. Hoping to protect New York harbor from invasion, he designed the first steam gunboat, the *Demologus*. The ship was completed in 1814, but the war ended before it saw action. Fulton also persuaded Congress to fund a study of a steam-driven submarine, his last effort to turn his earlier dream of undersea travel into a reality.

Outstanding Engineering Achievements:

The *Clermont* resembled the sleek sailing ships of its day; it was 133 feet (40 meters) long, 13 feet (4 meters) wide and seven feet (2 meters) deep, with a two-foot (0.6 meters) draught. Its Watt engine had a cylinder 24 inches (61 cm) in diameter with a four-foot (1.2 meters) stroke. The engine and boiler were located mid-ship and drove two side paddlewheels, which were 15 feet (4.5 meters) in diameter. An important feature of the ship was its use of the multitubular boiler developed by Nathan Read [q.v.], which was

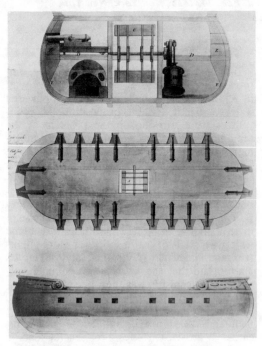

Fulton's steam packet boat the Clermont *on its regular run on the Hudson River between New York and Albany.*

The first steam gunboat, Fulton's Demologus; *top, midship section; middle, deck plan; bottom, broadside.*

much lighter and produced steam at higher pressure than the single tubular boiler used in earlier steamboats.

Fulton's submarine, the *Nautilus,* borrowed many features from its antecedent, David Bushnell's *Turtle.* Like the *Turtle,* the *Nautilus* was screw-propelled underwater and could be submerged by admitting the sea into ballast tanks. But Fulton's vessel had a number of original features. Its 21-foot (6.4 meters) hull, made of copper strips and an iron framework, was elongated like that of a normal boat. Indeed, the *Nautilus* was designed for use on the surface as well as underwater and was equipped with a sail for this purpose. When submerged, it was moved up and down by horizontal rudder. It used compressed air to support the four-man crew, and its hand-cranked propeller pushed rather than pulled the vessel through the water. The *Nautilus* was designed to remain submerged for three hours.

Fulton's steam warship, the *Demologus,* was enormous for its time, 156 feet (47 meters) long and 20 feet (6 meters) deep. Its steam engine cylinder was four feet in diameter, with a five-foot (1.5 meters) piston stroke. The ship's two rounded hulls held two paddlewheels between them, and were armed with thirty 32-pound (14 kg) cannon. ■

Further Reading:

Dictionary of American Biography, s.v. "Fulton."

William Barclay Parsons, *Robert Fulton and the Submarine.* New York, 1922.

ELI WHITNEY
b. Dec. 8, 1765, Westboro, Massachusetts
d. Jan. 8, 1825, New Haven, Connecticut
American Inventor, Engineer and Industrialist

Life and Times:

One of the key figures in American engineering and economic history, Eli Whitney was born into a Yankee farming family. His mechanical ingenuity was obvious even in his early years, when he built a small metalworking shop for making nails during the American Revolution. Hoping for a career in law, he entered Yale University and worked his way through college by constructing or repairing small mechanical

Eli Whitney, an inventor of the cotton gin, and a pioneer of mass production techniques.

devices. After graduating in 1792, he travelled south to Georgia to teach and prepare for the bar. There he met Phineas Miller, a fellow Yale graduate who managed the plantation of the late Revolutionary War general Nathaniel Greene. Greene's widow, Catherine, invited Whitney to live on the estate. It was here, in conversations with neighboring planters, that he learned of the region's economic problems and devised a mechanical solution to them.

The newly-mechanized British textile industry was demanding sharply increased quantities of cotton, staple crop of the South's plantation economy. The difficulty for Southern planters was that green-seed, short-staple cotton, which grew abundantly in the interior, could be cleaned of its seeds only with great time and effort by existing hand methods. In 1793 Whitney demonstrated a model of his cotton gin (short for "engine"), a mechanical device for cleaning and removing seeds from cotton. Financed by a $50,000 grant from the South Carolina government, he returned to New England to manufacture the gin.

Development of the cotton gin had enormous social and economic significance for the South. By making cotton cultivation vastly more profitable, it gave the plantation system—and the attendant "peculiar institution" of slavery—a new lease on life. It is ironic that this change, which increased regional conflict in the U.S. and finally contributed to the outbreak of the Civil War, was brought about by a "Yankee" invention. Whitney himself, however, reaped little reward for his effort. The basic elements of the gin were so simple and easily manufactured that he had great difficulty enforcing his patent. Whatever money he earned went into unsuccessful court battles, until the patent expired in 1807.

In 1798, when maritime disputes between France and the U.S. threatened to turn into war, Whitney obtained a government contract for manufacture of 10,000 muskets. By existing industrial methods, complex devices such as guns were made and assembled separately; replacement parts also had to be custom-made. Whitney apparently attempted to design machines that made exact replicas of each part of the gun—an early form of mass production that forecast the development of the assembly line and interchangeable parts. However, a variety of difficulties ranging from supply shortages to an epidemic prevented Whitney from fulfilling his government contract on time. But a fortunate marriage in 1817 finally brought him the financial gain he had sought in vain from the cotton gin.

Outstanding Engineering Achievements:

Whitney is undoubtedly best known for invention of a practical cotton gin, which consisted of

The original working model of Whitney's cotton gin. Cotton fed through a hopper onto the revolving cylinder was scoured by the bristles and emerged free of seeds.

four parts: a hopper that fed cotton into the gin; a revolving cylinder studded with wire hooks; a breastwork that strained out the seeds, leaving the cotton fiber on the hooks; and a second cylinder with bristles that cleaned the cotton from the hooks. The machine could be adapted to either horse- or steam power. Using the gin, a single operator could clean 50 pounds (23 kg) of cotton a day.

In terms of engineering achievement, Whitney's ideas on mass production of standard metal parts was certainly more significant than the cotton gin. Nevertheless, scholars have pointed out that Whitney's role in the development of these concepts has been overemphasized. The Swede Christopher Polhem [q.v.] manufactured interchangeable clock gears in the 1720s, while the Frenchman Honoré Blanc applied mass production techniques to the armaments industry. Nineteenth century American entrepreneurs, however, were the first successfully to manufacture interchangeable parts continuously and on a large scale, a strategy that became known as the American system. ■

Further Reading:

Edwin A. Battison, "Eli Whitney and the Milling Machine, *Smithsonian J. of History,* **1** (1966), 9–34.

David Landes, *The Unbound Prometheus.* Cambridge, 1965.

Singer et al., *A History of Technology,* Vol. IV.

R.S. Woodbury, "The Legend of Eli Whitney," *Tech. and Culture,* **1** (1960), 235–51.

MATTHEW MURRAY
b. 1765, Newcastle upon Tyne, England
d. Feb. 20, 1826, Leeds, England
English Inventor and Mechanical Engineer

Life and Times:

Matthew Murray was one of the most versatile mechanical engineers of the Industrial Revolution. The first inventor to improve the steam engine after the revolutionary changes introduced by James Watt [q.v.], he also developed new applications of steam power, new techniques of forging iron and new machines for the British textile industry. Murray has been called "the father of Leeds engineering," and his inventions helped put the Yorkshire city on the map as a manufacturing center. Although Murray's present reputation pales beside that of Watt, his engineering firm was for many years the only serious rival of Watt's great foundry and machine shop.

Born into a middle-class family, Murray received a fairly extensive education for his time, remaining in school until 14. He then became an apprentice in a blacksmith shop, where he had ample opportunity to become familiar with early steam engines designed by Thomas Newcomen [q.v.]. In 1788, after several years as a journeyman mechanic, Murray moved to Leeds, then just emerging as a center of the linen industry. He soon became chief engineer in the factory of John Marshall, a pioneering industrialist in the area of mechanical flax spinning. In 1790 Murray developed and patented a new machine for spinning flax yarn (see below), which Marshall promptly installed in his factory. Murray later introduced the so-called "wet spun" process, which produced a stronger and more silky yarn by wetting the flax during spinning.

Prompted by the industrial growth of Leeds, Murray left Marshall's firm in 1795 to establish his own general engineering and machine shop in the nearby town of Holbeck. Together with several partners he founded the firm of Fenton, Murray & Wood, serving in the new company as chief engineer and salesman. Murray's machine shop was among the first to rely entirely on steam power, and soon became one of the largest in England. The company manufactured not only the textile machinery that Murray had patented, but also steam engines which he designed.

It was after 1800, with the expiration of Watt's master patent on the separate steam condenser, that Murray began to introduce significant improvements in the steam engine (see below). Most of these were designed to make the basic Watt engine smaller, lighter, more efficient and easier to assemble; it thus became considerably cheaper to assemble and operate, spreading through British industry all the more rapidly. These developments and the rapid success of Murray's firm aroused the enmity of Boulton & Watt, the engineering company established by Watt and Matthew Boulton but operated at this time by the founders' sons. So strong was the competitiveness of the younger Watt and Boulton that they undertook one of the first known campaigns of industrial espionage to ferret out Murray's trade secrets. Though they succeeded in annulling one of Murray's patents in court, the incident did not slow the growth of

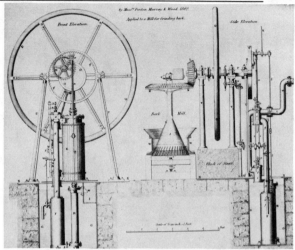

Murray's steam-powered mill for grinding bark with (left) the cycloidal straight-line-motion gearing.

his firm. But an intense rivalry between the two companies arose that lasted many years.

Undaunted, Murray went on to develop new uses of the steam engine. Among these was the first operating steam railroad, constructed in 1812 to haul coal from a mine at Middleton to Leeds. Four locomotives built in Murray's shop continued to run on the line until 1835. They proved too slow, however, for passenger service or general freight haulage. In this respect Murray stood midway between Richard Trevithick [q.v.], whose pioneering locomotive failed to run on tracks, and George Stephenson [q.v.], who developed the first rail system suitable for general use.

While still working on the locomotive, Murray became involved in the application of steam power to ships. In 1811 he joined with Trevithick to manufacture a high-pressure steam engine and boiler for *L'Actif,* a captured French privateer being outfitted as a packet boat. The engine was later used on another ship, the *Courier,* which made one of the first sea voyages by steam along the English coast. Murray also designed a much larger, two-cylinder engine which for many years was used in the U.S. as the standard power base of Mississippi paddle steamers. His achievements in this area, though not pioneering, certainly earned Murray an important place in the early history of steam navigation.

Murray's engineering influence continued even after his death. The factory which he founded became an important manufacturer of locomotives during the railroad boom of the mid-nineteenth century. A number of apprentices trained at Murray's machine shop went on

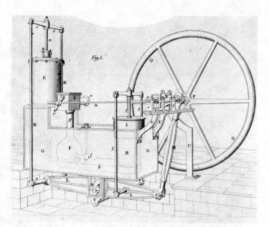

The 6 hp double-acting beam engine incorporating Murray's box or D-slide valve (center); 1806.

to become famous engineers in their own right; among them were Alfred Krupp, founder of the enormous machinery and armaments works in Essen.

Outstanding Engineering Achievements:

Murray's first important invention, the flax spinning machine, consisted basically of two rotating leather straps, pressed tightly together between two rollers; these drew out the flax and fed it into a second pair of rollers, from which yarn emerged. Murray originally powered the device with a Newcomen steam engine, switching after 1793 to a Watt rotative engine.

Of Murray's improvements on the steam engine, the most important was the so-called D slide valve or box valve. This was a single device which regulated both the entry of steam into the cylinder and its exit into the condenser. Use of the box valve meant that the steam inlet and outlet on the cylinder had to be much closer together than in the Watt engine; the latter used two separate valves for the process, a more cumbersome and less efficient arrangement. Murray also developed the "cycloidal straight line motion," an alternative to Watt's "sun and planet" gearing for converting the action of the piston into rotary motion. The advantage of Murray's method was that it required no beam or connecting rod to transmit the force of the piston to the flywheel. All this, as noted earlier, contributed to the development of lighter and more compact steam engines.

Murray also had to stress lightness in designing his steam locomotive; the relatively heavy locomotive constructed by Trevithick had fractured the brittle cast iron rails then in use. Murray achieved considerable economy in design by connecting his two-cylinder engine directly to the crankshafts which propelled the locomotive, dispensing with the heavy flywheel used by Trevithick. In order to give his locomotive sufficient traction to haul freight, Murray decided on use of a rack wheel, a large toothed wheel that engaged with corresponding teeth in one of the rails. The device worked, but severely limited the speed at which the locomotive could operate.

Of Murray's numerous other innovations, perhaps the most interesting is the first centrally heated building since the Romans. Murray incorporated the principle of central heating into a house next to his factory which he constructed for himself and his family. Heated by steam pipes, the structure was known locally as Steam Hall. ∎

Further Reading:

L.T.C. Rolt, *Great Engineers*. London, 1962.

JACOB PERKINS
b. July 9, 1766, Newburyport, Massachusetts
d. July 30, 1849, London, England
American Mechanical Engineer

Life and Times:

One of the first important American mechanical engineers, Jacob Perkins was active in several areas—printing and engraving, metallurgy and steam power. Born into a family that could trace its roots back to the early days of settlement in Massachusetts, he received little formal education. His mechanical ability was soon evident, however, and at 13 he was apprenticed to a goldsmith. In 1787 he worked briefly making dies for copper coins minted by the state of Massachusetts. This job ended when the states lost their authority to issue currency, and Perkins began his career as an inventor. Around 1790 he designed a machine that cut nails and shaped their heads in a single operation. Despite a lawsuit challenging his patent on the device, Perkins established a mill with several partners in Amesbury, Mass. The business failed, however, leaving him in financial difficulties.

Perkins spent the next two decades in Boston, New York and Philadelphia, where he applied his earlier experience with die-casting to the engraving of paper money. Europe and America were then flooded with a wide variety of bank notes; since all could easily be imitated, public confidence in currency was none too high. In 1805 Perkins invented a steel plate that could be used in the paper-engraving process. More durable than the copper plates used at the time, his steel plates could also be more elaborately engraved, and were thus harder to counterfeit. Perkins also invented an indenting cylinder for transferring engravings from one steel plate to another. By the 1820s many U.S. banks were using his plates to issue their notes.

In 1818 Perkins and his business partner, Gideon Fairman, moved to Britain with their equipment in the hope of being chosen to print notes for the Bank of England. Though they failed to obtain the contract, they remained in England and founded an engraving factory which in 1840 manufactured the first penny postage stamps.

Shortly after establishing himself in England, Perkins became interested in another field with which his name is now chiefly associated: the generation of high-pressure steam. Since the early years of the nineteenth century, Richard Trevithick [q.v.] and others had been working on the design of engines powered by high-pressure steam. Though such engines were smaller and more efficient than James Watt's [q.v.] atmospheric-pressure steam engine, most engineers still considered it dangerous to exceed twenty-five pounds per square inch (170 kPa). During the 1820s Perkins conducted pioneering experiments in the generation of high-pressure steam, attaining working pressures of 800–1,400 pounds per square inch (5500–9700 kPa).

Perkins' work led to his invention in 1831 of an early form of the water tube boiler. This boiler greatly improved upon earlier models by separating the upward flow of the hotter water near the furnace at the boiler's bottom from the downward flow of the colder water at its top. This separation inhibited the foaming up of useless "wet steam"—steam with water particles in suspension—that occurred when the upward currents interfered with the downward ones. Perkins' boiler also permitted a speeding up of fuel combustion, which made more efficient use of fuel but increased the "wet steam" problem in earlier boilers by intensifying the upward currents. Improved water circulation permitted quicker heating of the water and a more even temperature distribution within the boiler, which reduced stress and decreased the chances of explosion.

Though Perkins had gone a long way towards

Jacob Perkins, inventor of the bank note transferring machine.

removing the danger from high-pressure steam, he was unable to persuade other engineers to adopt his design. Discouraged, he gave up his experiments in 1834 and spent his later years in retirement.

Outstanding Engineering Achievements:

Perkins made steel plates for engraving bank notes with a new method of treating steel that allowed the plates to be impressed with an intricate design. He first softened the plates by subjecting them to intense heat for several hours in the presence of pure iron filings, which absorbed carbon from the steel. The plates were then slowly cooled, engraved with the desired pattern and re-carburized by being heated in the presence of finely-sifted carbon. Designs were engraved on the plates by means of steel indenting cylinders. A decarburized cylinder was rolled across an engraved plate until the pattern was impressed on it in relief. The cylinder was then hardened by carburization and rolled across the plate of soft steel, making a new engraving plate with the same design as the original.

In his experiments with high-pressure steam, Perkins used a copper boiler with a capacity of about 1 cubic foot (28l) and sides 3 inches (8 cm) thick. The water in this vessel was subjected to hydraulic pressure by means of a force pump, then super-heated by forced combustion. When the pump forced a small amount of water out through an escape valve, this water immediately flashed into high-pressure steam, which then moved through a pipe leading to the engine. One result of Perkins' work was to demonstrate that, contrary to accepted ideas, water could indeed be compressed.

Perkins' water tube boiler consisted of a U-shaped vessel with a second vessel, similarly shaped but smaller, fitted inside. The smaller vessel had a hole at the bottom. The water between the inner and outer vessels was nearer the furnace heat and therefore warmer than the water within the inner vessel. The warmer water rose between the two vessels, while the colder water descended down the inner vessel and through its hole to the area between the vessels. ■

Further Reading:

Robert H. Thurston, *A History of the Growth of the Steam-Engine.* New York, 1903.

Hugh P. and Margaret Vowles, *The Quest for Power.* London, 1931.

CHARLES MACINTOSH

b. Dec. 29, 1766, Glasgow, Scotland
d. July 25, 1843, Dunchatton, near Glasgow, Scotland
British Chemical Engineer

Life and Times:

A dyer's son, Macintosh became a counting house clerk, but his real interest was in chemistry. At 19 he left the counting house and became a manufacturer of sal ammoniac. His chemical experiments led to innovations in the production of dyes and other commercial products.

In 1823 Macintosh took out a patent for his most important achievement, the use of rubber as a coating for the waterproofing of garments. Within two years he had established Charles Macintosh and Company in Manchester to manufacture his rubber-treated fabric. The clothing made from his fabric by tailors became known as "mackintoshes" by an incorrect spelling of his name.

At first his raincoats sold well. But sales fell off for several reasons. Tailors, ignoring Macintosh's directions, punctured the rubber while making seams. This problem was eventually corrected by manufacturing the raincoats at Macintosh's factory. More seriously, the rubber stiffened and lost its elasticity in cold weather while becoming soft and sticky under heat and strong sunlight. In addition, sales decreased as railroads replaced open stage coaches and passengers were spared exposure to inclement weather. After Charles Goodyear invented the heat- and cold-resistant vulcanized rubber in 1839, sales of raincoats again climbed.

Outstanding Engineering Achievement:

Macintosh bought the by-products of the gas industry for use in dyes and pitch. One of the by-products of burning coal for gas was coal tar naphtha, which had no utility for him. Looking for a way to employ it, he found that naphtha was an excellent solvent for rubber, and decided to see if the resulting rubber solution could produce a waterproof fabric. With a brush he painted one surface each of two pieces of cloth, joined them together with the rubber-coated sides inward, and applied pressure, forming a double texture that avoided the problem of a sticky or brittle surface.

Macintosh also improved the quality of the dye known as Prussian blue. With Charles Tennant, he invented chloride of lime, or bleaching powder, during the 1790s. ■

Further Reading:

Meredith Hooper, *Everyday Inventions.* 1972.

Singer et al., *A History of Technology,* Vols. IV and V.

HENRY BELL

b. 1766 (or 1767), Torphichen Mills, Scotland
d. Nov. 14, 1830, Helensburgh, Scotland
British Inventor

Life and Times:

The Scottish engineer William Symington [q.v.] demonstrated in 1802 that a direct-acting steam engine could successfully drive a paddleboat without incurring an inordinate risk of instability or fire. Although his experiments were aimed at producing a tugboat that could replace draft animals on canal routes, his model ship did not generate enough towing power to make its development worthwhile in the view of prospective investors. Further progress in British steam navigation was delayed for another 10 years until the inventor Henry Bell realized that the steamboat, capable of operating on a schedule regardless of tide or wind, could profitably be put into service as a passenger carrier.

Bell was apprenticed as a millwright and formed his own building company in 1790. A man of little education but many ideas, he began experimenting with marine steam engines in 1800 and appealed to the Admiralty for permission to demonstrate the "practicability and great utility of applying steam to the propelling of vessels"; the Lords of the Admiralty, however, maintained their view that steam energy was of no value to warships. A second appeal three years later was also rebuffed, prompting a protest from Adm. Horatio Nelson in the House of Lords.

In 1807 Bell built a hotel in Helensburgh, a resort on the River Clyde opposite Greenock. To encourage visits from the wealthy residents of Glasgow, some 70 miles (112 km) away, he launched a manually-operated paddleboat service. In 1811 he arranged with a shipbuilding firm to construct a paddleboat, the *Comet*, to which he fitted a steam engine that had originally been built for stationary use.

For four years, beginning in 1812, the *Comet* steamed and sailed regularly between Greenock and Glasgow, reducing the length of passage from a day to a few hours. In 1819 it began serving a route from Glasgow to the Western Highlands, but was wrecked in a storm a little more than a year later. According to some accounts, Bell built a second *Comet* which served the Western Highlands route for another four years until it was sunk in a collision with a loss of 73 lives.

Bell, whose third appeal to the Admiralty in 1813 had met with as little success as his other attempts, later petitioned the government for acknowledgment of his work and was given an honorarium of £200; the Clyde Trustees provided an annuity. Although the *Comet* was apparently not a very profitable venture, it represented the first commercial use of a steamboat in Europe and led directly to the widespread application of steamboats on the Clyde River and other waterways.

The Comet, *designed by Bell, the first steamboat in regular use as a passenger carrier.*

Outstanding Engineering Achievements:

The *Comet* was built by John Wood of Port Glasgow with the following approximate dimensions: 43-foot (13 meters) keel, 10.5-foot (3.1 meters) beam, 5.5-foot (1.6 meters) draught, and with a carrying capacity of some 25 tons. The engine was a modified Watt model built for land rather than marine use by John Robinson of Glasgow; its overhead piston beam drove a six-foot (1.8 meters) flywheel which rotated four paddlewheels. The boiler was set in brickwork, and the long funnel doubled as a mast when necessary. Later the cylinder was replaced by a larger one, the hull was lengthened by some 20 feet (6 meters), and the pairs of radial paddles were replaced by a single paddle on each side, increasing the *Comet*'s speed to 6 or 7 knots (12 km/hr). After the wreck of the boat in 1820, the engine was retrieved and used to drive machinery in a Glasgow coachbuilding factory and later in a brewery; it is now in the Science Museum, London.

Bell's indebtedness to, and influence on, other steamship pioneers is a matter of controversy. He claimed to have given ideas and sketches to Robert Fulton [q.v.], but other writers have suggested that it was he who asked Fulton for advice. Some accounts indicate that Bell was present at the trial of Symington's *Charlotte Dundas II,* or at least studied its remains; Symington sued Bell in 1814 for infringement of patent, but withdrew his suit after Bell instituted a libel action. ■

Further Reading:

Dictionary of National Biography, s.v. "Bell".
John W. Grant, *Watt and the Steam Age.* London, 1917.
W.S. Harvey and G. Downs-Rose, *William*

Symington: Inventor and Engine Builder. London, 1980.

K.T. Rowland, *Steam at Sea: A History of Steam Navigation.* New York, 1970.

ARTHUR WOOLF

b. *1766, Camborne, England*
d. *Oct. 26, 1837, The Strand, Guernsey, England*
British Mechanical Engineer

Life and Times:

During the last quarter of the eighteenth century, the use of James Watt's [q.v.] steam engine spread in English mines and mills. But Watt's very success can be said to have retarded progress in steam engineering. His exclusive rights to the separate condenser helped him block rivals, among them Jonathan Hornblower, Jr. [q.v.], whose innovative compound engine was shown to infringe on Watt's patent. Watt was also reluctant to experiment with high steam pressure, which he considered unsafe, despite its potential for increased power and fuel efficiency. But after 1800, when Watt's patent expired, the separate condenser entered the public domain, and younger inventors with fresh ideas were free to incorporate it in their engine designs. One of the first to do so was Arthur Woolf.

Woolf, the son of a carpenter, was trained in his father's trade. After completing an apprenticeship in his native Cornwall and working in a mine, he moved to London and served as a millwright for Joseph Bramah [q.v.]. Woolf then became an engineer and in 1786 helped Jonathan Hornblower repair a compound engine he had installed at Meux's brewery. The assignment was doubly significant for Woolf. It introduced him to the idea of the compound engine and earned him an appointment as engineer to the brewery, a position he held for 10 years.

In 1803 Woolf patented a compound engine and a boiler. He convinced the brewery's owners to let him install his devices, a decision they would come to regret. Woolf was led astray for years by his erroneous beliefs on the relations between the volume and the pressure of steam. He persisted in making one of the cylinders too small, with the result that his engine failed to outperform the Watt models.

Leaving the brewery in disgust, Woolf entered into a partnership with Humphrey Edwards, a millwright. Together they established a steam engine factory at Lambeth, and finally arrived at a satisfactory design for a compound engine. But in 1811 Woolf broke with Edwards and moved back to Cornwall, where he provided steam engines to mines. After 1824 he stopped making compound engines and concentrated on perfecting the high-pressure Cornish engine devised by Richard Trevithick [q.v.]. Working until 1833 as superintendent of an engine factory at Hayle, Woolf earned a reputation as the best engine-maker in Cornwall and trained a generation of steam engineers. Woolf's foresight was in some sense vindicated at mid-century, when compound engines experienced a dramatic revival.

Outstanding Engineering Achievements:

Woolf's engine was designed to take advantage of the expansive power of steam, a principle discovered by Watt. Steam at a pressure of 40 p.s.i. (275 kPa) was admitted from the boiler to a small cylinder. When the piston stroke ended, the steam passed on to a second cylinder five to eight times larger than the first. There it expanded and acted on a second piston. At the same time, steam from the boiler reentered the first cylinder and pushed the piston back to its original position. A series of valves directing the steam alternately above and below each piston ensured that the two pistons always moved in the same direction at the same time, combining their power. Spent steam from the second cylinder was evacuated into the separate condenser.

To provide high-pressure steam safely, Woolf designed one of the first modern water-tube boilers. (An analogous device for warming liquids was found at Pompeii.) A number of cast-iron pipes about 10 inches (25.4 cm) in diameter, placed in tiers, ran the entire length of the fireplace. They sloped slightly upwards and opened into a large cylindrical water tank set in brick. The steam produced in the tubes by heating ran up the tubes and bubbled to the top of the water tank; from there it was admitted to the engine. Woolf's strongly built boilers never suffered an explosion; however, breakage of parts and leakage proved to be problems.

Hornblower's two-cylinder engine, from which Woolf drew his inspiration, had proved inefficient, overly complicated, and expensive to install and repair. With the use of high-pressure steam, Woolf was able to achieve fuel economies of 50 percent in comparison with Watt engines. Despite this advantage, compound engines remained somewhat more complicated and expensive to run than their single-cylinder competitors. Only in France, where fuel costs were quite high, did Woolf's invention find a ready market.

Under the supervision of Humphrey Edwards, the Chaillot engine works manufactured Woolf's engines and improved boilers in great numbers until 1870. ■

Further Reading:

Henry W. Dickinson, *A Short History of the Steam Engine*. London, 1963.
Dictionary of National Biography, s.v. "Woolf."
John Ross, *A Treatise on Navigation by Steam*. London, 1828.
Singer et al., *A History of Technology*. Vol. IV.

PHILIPPE LEBON
b. 1767, Brachay, France
d. 1804, Paris, France

Life and Times:

The increased use of coal to fuel and the Industrial Revolution led to the development of its by-products. One of them, coal-gas, became the subject of numerous experiments aimed at harnessing it for illuminating and heating rooms and buildings. Lebon was the first to demonstrate practically and in a commercially viable manner the vast possibilities of gas-lighting, although he did not use coal-gas. In 1801 he staged spectacular and widely publicized exhibitions at the Hotel Seignelay in Paris using gas derived from wood; his concept of gas-lighting was accepted and his method improved by distilling gas from coal, which was far more economical and fuel efficient.

Son of a charcoal-burner, Leban was trained at the famed national civil engineering school, the Ecole des Ponts et Chaussées. He began serious work on gas lighting as early as 1791, when he wrote that smoke contained a flammable gas. Gas had already been used to inflate balloons, but Lebon proposed employing it for the heating and lighting of buildings. In the scattered writings he left behind, he anticipated nearly all of its eventual applications. By 1797 he had constructed his first gas-making plant which distilled gas from wood, and he undertook a public campaign to persuade the French government to install gas lighting and heating systems in public buildings. In 1799 he obtained a patent on his technique.

In Lebon's 1801 exhibitions, what had previously been a laboratory experiment now

served to illuminate and heat a house and its garden. Two "thermolamps" devised by Lebon provided enough gas to warm and light the hotel's interior, illuminate its garden and shoot flames from one of its fountains. The display, performed regularly for several months, attracted popular attention but failed to win the support of French authorities. It did, however, stimulate the British engineering firm of Boulton and Watt to speed development of William Murdock's [q.v.] gas heating and lighting technique.

In 1804 Lebon was fatally attacked and robbed on a Paris street. His death stalled the progress of gas lighting on the Continent. Ultimately, the process developed by Samuel Clegg [q.v.] came into general use.

Outstanding Engineering Achievement:

Lebon's gas production and gas lighting devices are important not in themselves—they never saw commercial application—but for the widespread attention they attracted, which helped speed public acceptance of gas. His gas-making plant collected the flammable by-products of burning wood (oil and bitumen). Though no design of Lebon's "thermolamps" survives, his writings describe a glass globe within which gas could be burned. Gas and air were introduced into the globe by separate pipes and the products of combustion removed through a third pipe. The gas would pass from the vessel and rise into a varnished silk pipe. ■

Further Reading:

W.T. O'Dea, *Social History of Lighting*. 1958.
Singer et al., *A History of Technology*, Vol. IV.

BRYAN DONKIN
b. March 22, 1768, Sandree, Northumberland, England
d. Feb. 27, 1855, London, England
British Mechanical and Civil Engineer

Life and Times:

Originally an estate agent like his father, Donkin decided to develop his mechanical talents at the suggestion of noted engineer John Smeaton [q.v.]. He apprenticed himself to millwright John Hall in the 1790s, eventually became a business partner of Hall and went on to make important contributions to the processes of papermaking, printing, and food preservation.

Building on the ideas of Frenchman Nicholas Louis Robert, Donkin built the first practical automatic papermaking machine in 1804. Over many ensuing years, Donkin perfected the machine, and he ultimately produced almost 200 of them. The age-old hand process of papermaking could produce only small sheets of paper. Donkin's machines, capable of manufacturing continuous rolls of paper up to 40 feet (12 meters) long and over six feet (1.8 meters) wide, radically changed the papermaking industry.

Donkin and printer Richard Bacon patented a rotary printing machine in 1813 to replace the cumbersome flatbed press. Intended as a means of speeding the printing process, it proved inefficient. But the device employed inking rollers made from glue and treacle, and these composition rollers represented a significant advance in printing machinery because they did not harden on exposure to air or soften under the action of printing ink. Within a short time they were in general use.

In 1809 French chef Nicolas Appert developed a practical method of preserving food in glass jars. Within about four years Donkin had perfected Appert's methods and applied them to the preservation of food in air-tight tin cannisters, superior to glass because they could be completely sealed. Donkin's methods proved amazingly effective. A four-pound tin of roast veal produced by the firm of Donkin, Hall and Gamble was taken on an Arctic expedition in 1824. Never used, the tin remained sealed until 1938, when scientists finally opened it and found the veal still edible. Donkin, Hall and Gamble was selling canned meat and vegetables to the Royal Navy by the end of the Napoleonic Wars. With ships now able to carry indefinitely-preserved food, sailors could avoid scurvy by eating fresh fruit and vegetables as well as the traditional salt meat and hard biscuits.

Donkin won gold medals from the Society of Arts in 1810 and 1819 with two devices for measuring the velocity of the rotation of machinery. At the Great Exhibition of 1851, his papermaking machines won a gold medal. In 1818 Donkin helped establish the Institution of Civil Engineers. He was also an amateur astronomer and an ardent defender of phrenology.

Outstanding Engineering Achievements:

In the hand process of papermaking, a fine screen was dipped into a mixture of water and rag pulp. The water drained off, leaving a wet sheet of paper which was dried by pressing between layers of felt and by hot rolls. In Donkin's automatic process the water and pulp mixture was fed to a continuous moving roll of fine wire mesh. The thickness of the paper could be altered by changing either the speed of the roll or the rate of the feeding process. At the end of the wire mesh roll, the wet pulp was picked up by felt-covered rolls, which squeezed out the excess water. The pulp then fell onto a moving felt web which carried it through a second pair of rolls, further drying the paper. This method produced a continuous sheet of damp paper, which was wound on a drum and removed for drying on racks.

Donkin's method of food preservation entailed placing food in tin cannisters and heating them to sterilize the contents while air was driven off. The cannister was then sealed. Through extensive experimentation Donkin determined the temperatures and times needed to sterilize different types of food. To test the results, the cannisters were placed in chambers and kept at about 100° Fahrenheit (37.8° C) for a month.

To make inking or composition rollers, Donkin melted glue with treacle in a proportion of two parts treacle to one part glue by weight. The mixture was then heated and moulded into the desired shape.

Donkin invented the first steel pen in 1808. Two flat pieces of steel were placed at an obtuse angle to each other to form the ink duct. The two pieces were cut so as to form the pen point and were unjoined to about one-quarter inch from the point.

In 1810 Donkin designed a tachometer to measure the velocity of rotating machinery by counting revolutions. In this device he utilized the parabolic depression assumed by mercury when placed in a rotating cup. The cup was connected by a cone clutch to the equipment whose speed was to be measured. A tube calibrated on a scale of revolutions per minute was immersed in the mercury. Nine years later Donkin introduced a counter that would display the number of revolutions of a machine over a given time. Three dials were linked so that the "tens" dial moved the "hundreds" dial and the latter moved the "thousands" dial as the revolution rate increased. ■

Further Reading:

Meredith Hooper, *Everyday Inventions*. 1972.
Singer et al., *A History of Technology*, Vol. V.

SAMUEL SLATER
b. *June 9, 1768, Belper, Derbyshire, England*
d. *Apr. 21, 1835, Webster, Massachusetts*
Anglo-American Mechanical Engineer

Life and Times:

An English mechanic who introduced British cotton spinning machinery to America, Slater was a founder of the U.S. textile industry. he also initiated in America the manufacture and use of power-driven machinery and the adoption of the factory system of production.

The son of a prosperous farmer, Slater was apprenticed in 1783 to Jedediah Strutt, the business partner of inventor Richard Arkwright [q.v.] who employed the most advanced textile machinery in his cotton mills. Slater had opportunity to work in both the counting house and the mills, becoming familiar with the entire operation. By the end of his apprenticeship in 1789, he knew the details of Arkwright's water frame, Samuel Crompton's [q.v.] spinning mule and James Hargreave's [q.v.] spinning jenny, as well as carding machines and other devices.

Meanwhile, in the United States the surplus of imports over exports spurred societies for promoting manufacturers to offer bounties, premiums and prizes to skilled mechanics. Having

Samuel Slater, the mechanic who helped found the U.S. textile industry by bringing methods and machinery design from England.

seen such an offer in a Philadelphia newspaper, Slater decided to emigrate to America. At the time, however, Britain barred both the export of data on textile machinery and the emigration of textile workers. Fortunately for Slater, he had a photographic memory. Carrying the details of the new textile machinery in his head, he sailed from England in September 1789 in disguise and under an assumed name.

Slater disembarked in New York, where he worked for two months. He then met Moses Brown, a partner in the firm of Almy and Brown, which owned a struggling cotton mill in Pawtucket, R.I. On the basis of Slater's knowledge, he was hired to improve the spinning machinery at the mill. The machines at Pawtucket were woefully inadequate, as were those at other U.S. mills, and the yarn they produced could not compete with British imports. Slater had to begin construction from scratch. He made working drawings from memory and his mechanic executed them in wood and metal. In December 1790 Slater completed the machines. Soon they were harnessed to water power and later to steam. Almost immediately, the mill was producing prodigious quantities of cotton yarn competitive with the British product.

Slater became a partner in Almy and Brown, now Almy, Brown & Slater, and the firm built a new mill in Pawtucket in 1793. Soon the enterprise produced so much cotton yarn that its supply of raw material ran out, but this problem was remedied by Eli Whitney's [q.v.] invention of the cotton gin. In 1798 Slater and his in-laws formed a new partnership, known as Samuel Slater & Company, which erected a mill near Pawtucket. The firm also established cotton manufacturing plants at Smithfield (later Slatersville), R.I., in 1806 and Oxford (later Webster), Mass., in 1812. Other mills were opened in Jewett City, Conn., and Amoskeag, N.H. In 1814 Slater began manufacturing woolen cloth. Continuing as a textile manufacturer for 30 years, Slater died a wealthy man.

Outstanding Achievement:

The establishment of Slater's mills had great consequences for the development of industry in the U.S. Workmen came to his mills to learn the construction of his machines and then established their own enterprises. Soon knowledge of the textile technology he had brought from England became widespread, and mills were being built by competitors both within and outside of New England. In 1809 there were 62 spinning mills in the country with 31,000 spin-

The indenture papers by which Samuel Slater became an apprentice in the art of cotton spinning to mill-owner Jedediah Strutt.

dles, and 25 additional mills were being planned or built.

Slater's cotton mills also introduced the factory system to the U.S. As in English mills, the machines were driven by inanimate power and the manufacturing processes were divided into distinct steps, each involving simple tasks that could be performed by unskilled labor. ∎

Further Reading:

Roger Burlingame, *Machines that Built America.* New York, 1953.
Waldemar Kaempffert, ed., *A Popular History of American Invention,* Vol. II. New York, 1924.
G.S. White, *Memoir of Samuel Slater.* Philadelphia, 1836.

WILLIAM SMITH
b. March 23, 1769, Churchill, Oxfordshire, England
d. Aug. 28, 1839, Northampton, England
British Civil Engineer and Geologist

Life and Times:

The idea that fossils can be used to read the ages of rocks dates at least from Robert Hooke [q.v.] in the late seventeenth century. About a century later, the French naturalists Abbé Giraud-Soulavie and Georges Cuvier attempted to construct a geological history of the earth based on the fossil sequence found in layers of French limestone. But it was William Smith, an English civil engineer, who demonstrated conclusively that the succession of strata can often be identified from their fossil content, and who prepared the first colored maps showing England's underlying geological formations. Unlike the naturalists, Smith was not interested in constructing a theoretical chronology of the earth; his aim was to provide detailed stratigraphic information for the use of civil engineers and miners.

Smith, the son of a blacksmith, was educated at a village school and became assistant to a local surveyor. Between 1794 and 1799 he participated in the surveying, inspection, and construction of canals and mines in Somerset and as far north as Newcastle-upon-Tyne. His work allowed him to observe in detail the fossil aggregates visible in the cut rock. By 1799 he was able to dictate a complete description of the Somersetshire strata down the coal layer to two clergymen and fellow fossil collectors, Joseph Townsend and Benjamin Richardson.

Smith subsequently worked as a drainage, irrigation, and coal mining engineer, traveling from site to site and compiling extensive notes on each region's geological composition. His comprehensive map of the rock formations of England and Wales, begun in 1800, was printed in an edition of 400 in 1815. By 1824 he had published 24 geological maps and a number of treatises on fossils. Throughout this period, Smith found little support for his ideas from scientists and other engineers. In 1815, having lost his money in an investment in an unproductive stone quarry, he was forced to sell his huge collection of fossils and minerals to the British Museum.

Smith's contributions to geology finally achieved public recognition in 1831, when he became the first recipient of the Geological Society of London's Wollaston Award, given "for his having been the first, in this country, to discover and teach the identification of strata and to determine their succession by means of their embedded fossils." The careful accuracy and overwhelming detail of Smith's evidence had prevailed against professional skepticism, and the concept of stratigraphic succession was quickly adopted by the majority of geologists.

Outstanding Engineering Achievements:

Smith discovered that rock strata can be identified by their characteristic fossil content, and that these fossils always occur in the same stratigraphic sequence. Armed with this insight, geologists were later able to reconstruct the ages of rocks from the fossil record, and engineers gained the ability to locate ore and fossil fuels by searching for their associated rock formations. His major work, *Delineation of the Strata of England and Wales, with Part of Scotland* (1815), based almost entirely on his own observations and discoveries, was the first geological map on a large scale; it detailed approximately 65,000 square miles (168,000 square km), on a scale of five miles to the inch (3.2 km/cm), and showed 21 stratigraphic formations colored and shaded to indicate overlapping layers. The locations of tin, copper, lead, coal, salt, and alum works were represented by symbols. From 1816 to 1824 Smith also published a series of colored plates on the fossils of strata surrounding London, as well as geological maps of Kent, Sussex, Yorkshire and 18 other English counties.

Smith's first major work of civil engineering was the Somerset Coal Canal, which he helped design. After 1799 he was Britain's foremost drainage and irrigation engineer; he helped design sea defenses in South Wales and the east coast of England and repaired the failing water supply in the city of Bath. Shortly before his death he was engaged by the government to help select stone for the construction of the new Houses of Parliament. ◼

Further Reading:

William Berry, *The Growth of a Prehistoric Time Scale*. San Francisco, 1968.

Dictionary of National Biography, s.v. "Smith."

Dictionary of Scientific Biography, s.v. "Smith."

C. J. Schneer, ed., *Toward a History of Geology*. Cambridge, 1969.

Singer et al., *A History of Technology*. Vol. IV.

MARC ISAMBARD BRUNEL

b. *April 25, 1769, Hacqueville, Normandy, France*
d. *Dec. 12, 1849, London, England*
British Civil and Mechanical Engineer

Life and Times:

The father of the famous civil engineer Isambard Kingdom Brunel, Marc Isambard Brunel was important in his own right for developing new techniques of tunneling and mass produc-

Frenchman Marc Isambard Brunel, chief engineer of New York City, who supplied the Royal Navy with pulleys and tunneled under the Thames.

tion. Born near Rouen, he was sent to the seminary of St. Nicaise to begin a career in the church. But it soon became apparent that his talents and preference lay in construction, mechanics and navigation. At 17 he enlisted in the French Navy, serving for six years as an officer. Brunel had to flee France during the Revolution due to his royalist sympathies. He emigrated to the U.S. in 1793, beginning a career as a civil engineer and architect. After surveying a canal connecting Lake Champlain and the Hudson River at Albany, he served as architect and chief engineer for the city of New York.

In 1799 Brunel moved to England, where he did his most important work in civil and mechanical engineering. The British Admiralty was then seeking to reduce the cost of manufacturing pulley blocks for its ships, of which it needed some 100,000 every year. At the time, pulley blocks were made laboriously by hand. In 1801 Brunel proposed to Samuel Bentham, inspector general of Naval Works, a new system which would almost entirely mechanize the process. Bentham endorsed the proposal, and by 1808 a factory built to Brunel's specifications had been constructed at Portsmouth. The block-making machines, designed by Brunel and made by Henry Maudslay [q.v.], enabled 10 men to equal the output of 110 skilled manual workers. The new system was important as one of the first instances of mass production by machine tools. The Admiralty saved 17,000 pounds a year on an investment of 54,000 pounds, and rewarded Brunel with a royalty equal to one year of its savings.

In 1814 Brunel was elected to membership in the Royal Society. Although a prolific inventor, he could not manage his own financial affairs and in 1821 was imprisoned for debt. He was eventually bailed out of jail by a government grant of 5,000 pounds, and in 1825 began work with his son Isambard on the first tunnel under the Thames River. Richard Trevithick [q.v.] had failed in an earlier attempt to construct a Thames tunnel. The Brunels succeeded, but not without great difficulty. The excavation was flooded five times, and work was suspended for seven years in 1828. Finally completed in 1842, the tunnel was at first used by pedestrians, and ultimately incorporated into the London subway system. Brunel was knighted in 1841 for his role in the project.

Part of the cast-iron shield designed by Brunel to hold workers excavating his Thames tunnel and lining it with bricks.

Outstanding Engineering Achievements:

Brunel's pulley-making factory in Portsmouth contained 43 machines, driven by a single 30-horsepower steam engine. These included boring machines to drill holes, mortising machines to cut slits and scoring machines to shape grooves. Most of the machines worked on several blocks at a time, and all could be operated by unskilled workers. Only the final polishing and fitting of the pulley blocks remained to be done by hand.

Brunel's Thames River tunnel extended 12,000 feet (3600 meters) between Rotherhithe and Wapping, with a width of 37 feet (11 meters) and a height of 23 feet (7 meters). It was lined with brick and hydraulic mortar. To permit work on such a large face, Brunel designed a cast-iron shield with three levels that contained working space for 12 men. Large screw-jacks pressed the top and bottom of the shield against the sides of the tunnel and moved the structure forward when a section of the excavation was completed. Workers within the shield could both excavate the face and line the just-completed sides with bricks.

In addition to his main achievements, Brunel worked on a number of other inventions, including machines to bore cannon, knit stockings and mass-produce military boots. He also experimented with early methods of constructing a suspension bridge, work carried on by his son, Isambard. ▇

Further Reading:

James Kip Finch, *Engineering and Western Civilization*. New York, 1951.

Singer et al., *A History of Technology*. Vol. IV.

JOHANN GEORG REPSOLD
b. Sept. 19, 1770, Bremen, Germany
d. Jan. 14, 1830, Hamburg, Germany
German Instrument Maker

Life and Times:

Some noted engineers are innovators, creators of original designs. Others are improvers; not contributors of completely novel methods, but important because they make revolutionary designs practical. Johann Georg Repsold was an engineer of the second kind. A modifier of designs of Karl Friedrich Gauss [q.v.], he was instrument maker for the astronomers Heinrich Christian Schumacher and Friedrich Wilhelm Bessel.

Repsold was the son of a minister, intended by his father for a career in theology until the boy's interest in technology proved to be greater. In 1788 Johann went to Cuxhaven to study mathematics and technical drawing with Reinhard Woltmann, a pilot on the Elbe River. Seven years later Repsold replaced him. In 1799 Repsold married the daughter of a captain of the Hamburg fire department, an organization that he eventually headed.

In 1800 Repsold opened a machine shop in Hamburg. He also met the Swiss astronomer Johann Kaspar Horner, who was mapping the estuaries of the Weser, Elbe and Eider rivers. Their mutual interest in surveying and astronomical instruments led Repsold to construct a portable transit instrument which Horner used to make observations around the world. At this time Repsold also began an association with Heinrich Schumacher of the newly opened Hamburg Observatory.

When Gauss was appointed director of the Göttingen Observatory in 1807, he began a lengthy correspondence with Repsold. As a result, Repsold made a meridian circle which was installed at the observatory in 1818. The communications between Gauss the mathematician and Repsold the craftsman resulted in the development of a better quality of optical glass.

In 1821 Gauss invented the heliotrope, a reflecting device which provided surveyors with a bright point of light to sight on. Repsold built a heliotrope, with some improvements, for Heinrich Schumacher. The resulting measurements were so accurate that the astronomer Friedrich Wilhelm Bessel used them as a standard in calculating the earth's dimensions.

During the winter of January 1830, a fire broke out in a large building in Hamburg. Repsold, by now the chief of the fire department, was directing his men when a large beam fell and killed him. His work was continued by his son and grandson, who continued the family tradition into the twentieth century.

Outstanding Engineering Achievements:

Repsold specialized in making astronomical instruments, including transit circles and mountings for the large telescopes that were beginning to appear. Without sturdy and precise mountings such telescopes are virtually useless, since they cannot be pointed accurately or will not maintain their position. None of Repsold's instruments were strikingly different from those made in England and France at the time, though he did make improvements.

An example of Repsold's work is a telescope based on a design of the English optician John Dollond. Dollond had sought to increase the light entering the instrument while avoiding the faults that usually appeared in large lenses. His telescope had two object lenses that fed into the same eyepiece. The difficulty was that the two images did not focus exactly together, resulting in blurring. Repsold solved the problem by mounting each lens in its own small tube, which slid independently in the main tube. Each lens could be focused on its own by masking the other, and blurring was eliminated. This method is still used in adjusting the separate lenses of a pair of binoculars.

By making his instruments with extreme care and attention to detail and by effecting such design improvements, Repsold was able to build precise instruments at a time when astronomy was just beginning to need them. By constantly refining its precision techniques, the Repsold shop remained in the forefront of instrument making throughout the nineteenth century. ■

Further Reading:

Henry King, *History of the Telescope*. London, 1955.

R. J. Forbes and E. J. Dijksterhuis, *A History of Science and Technology*. Baltimore, 1963.

BENJAMIN WRIGHT
b. Oct. 10, 1770, Wethersfield, Connecticut
d. Aug. 24, 1842, New York City
American Civil Engineer

Life and Times:

Wright was the most important of the early American frontier engineers, helping to lay the foundation for settlement of upper New York State and other parts of the old Northwest. Trained as a lawyer and surveyor by his uncle, he moved from Connecticut to Fort Stanwix in the Mohawk Valley at the age of eighteen. He eventually settled there with his wife and their nine children, among them the future engineer Benjamin Hall Wright. A prominent surveyor,

Benjamin Wright, chief engineer of the Erie Canal and of the New York and Erie Railroad.

A lock gate on the Erie Canal.

judge and canal engineer, Wright became known as "Father of American Engineering" for his role in building the Erie Canal.

Outstanding Engineering Achievement:

Benjamin Wright was the chief engineer, along with the surveyor James Geddes, in the construction of the Erie Canal, the first major engineering project in America. Though not the first American canal, the Erie, connecting the Hudson River with Lake Erie, held the distinction of being the longest canal in the Western world, with a length of 363 miles (584 km). (Scholars are uncertain as to whether the Grand Canal of China, connecting Hangchow and Peking, exceeded the length of the Erie at that time.)

Wright divided construction of the Erie Canal into small geographical sections, employing workers indigenous to the areas through which it passed. Branching from the Hudson River near Albany, the canal extended northwest through upper New York State to join Lake Erie at Tonawanda Creek near Buffalo. Most of the land along this route was virgin forest. Eighty-three locks, most of them constructed between Schenectady and Utica, lifted boats across an altitude gap of 675 feet (205 meters). Begun on July 4, 1817, the canal was completed on November 4, 1825, the first reliable transport route linking the American interior with the Atlantic Ocean.

Wright also served as chief engineer for a number of other canals, including the St. Lawrence Ship Canal and the famous Chesapeake and Ohio Canal, constructed between 1825 and 1831. His expertise in overland construction also allowed him to become one of the country's first railroad engineers; after serving as chief engineer of the New York and Erie Railroad, he worked with his son Benjamin to plan the first Cuban railroad, linking Havana to the interior of the island.

As a surveyor, Wright plotted out 500,000 acres (20,000 hectares) in Oneida and Oswego counties, two million acres (800,000 hectares) in St. Lawrence County, and other parts of upper New York State. He also mapped part of the Mohawk River, beginning at Seneca Lake and moving southward to Rome. His work played a major role in opening the area to settlement. ∎

Further Reading:

American Society of Civil Engineers, *A Biographical Dictionary of American Civil Engineers.*

James Kip Finch, *Engineering and Western Civilization.* New York, 1951.

James Kip Finch, *The Story of Engineering.* Garden City, New York, 1960.

RICHARD TREVITHICK
b. April 13, 1771, Illogan, Cornwall, England
d. April 22, 1833, Dartford, Kent, England
British Mechanical Engineer

Life and Times:

Son of the manager of a Cornish mine, Trevithick came into contact with mining engineers as a boy and was himself an engineer in the mines by the 1790s. He modified the engines used there and invented a water-pressure engine at that time.

In 1800, when James Watt's [q.v.] inclusive steam-engine patent expired, Trevithick introduced a high-pressure steam engine as an alternative to Watt's low-pressure engine. Thomas Savery [q.v.] had conceived the idea of a high-pressure engine a century earlier, but construction of a practical model had to wait until advances in design permitted the building of lighter and sturdier boilers. Trevithick proceeded over the objections of Watt and others, who feared (with some justification, considering the metal-working techniques of the time) that the high-pressure engine would be extremely dangerous.

The new engine represented an enormous engineering advance. Watt's low-pressure engine was huge, stationary, and difficult and expensive

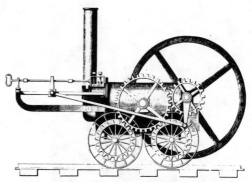

The first steam locomotive run on tracks, Trevithick's "tram-waggon" ran at Penny-Darran, South Wales.

to build. By designing a simpler, cheaper, lighter, more compact, and more efficient machine, Trevithick enormously expanded the potential application of the steam engine, which had previously been used mainly to pump water from mines. By 1804 he had built and sold more than 50 of his engines for use in factories, mines and food-processing plants. The high-pressure engine raised the possibility of steam-powered transportation.

Trevithick himself first attempted to use his engine in transportation. In 1801 he built a steam carriage, the first steam vehicle to carry passengers. Three years later he constructed the first steam locomotive used on a railway. Run at Pen-y-darran, the locomotive carried ten tons of iron, 70 men, and five wagons at almost five miles an hour for 9½ miles (15 km). Although the cast-iron rails used by Trevithick gave way under the heavy weight, the demonstration proved that the friction of smooth wheels on smooth metal could provide adequate traction. In 1808 he ran a locomotive, called *Catch-Me-Who-Can,* on an oval track in London and charged admission for rides. Although George Stephenson [q.v.] subsequently built the first practical steam-locomotive railroad system, Trevithick has a strong claim as the inventor of the modern railroad engine. He also adapted his new engine to create a number of other steam-powered devices, including a steam dredger and steam thresher.

Trevithick gained additional fame for the highly fuel-efficient stationary condensing steam engine that he introduced in 1812, which became known generically as the Cornish engine. Essentially a Watt-type engine with an improved boiler that could produce high-pressure steam, this type of engine was slowly improved during the nineteenth century and achieved a remarkable level of efficiency. In the fuel-poor non-

Richard Trevithick, pioneer of the high-pressure steam engine, built the first passenger-carrying steam vehicle and the first railway locomotive.

Trevithicks' high-pressure engine, with its cylindrical boiler and direct-acting connection between piston and wheel.

ferrous mines of Cornwall, such efficiency was crucial, and the Cornish engine continued to be used there until the middle of the twentieth century.

In 1816 Trevithick left England for Peru to work as a mining engineer, and returned penniless in 1827. He continued working on inventions during his last years but died destitute. For all his inventive genius, Trevithick's restless disposition drove him to new projects before he completed old ones.

Outstanding Engineering Achievements:

Watt's low-pressure steam engine, a massive structure containing cylinder, air pump and rocking beam, was driven by the force of expanding steam. Trevithick greatly multiplied this force by injecting steam into the cylinder at greater-than-atmospheric pressures, up to 145 pounds per square inch (1000 kPa). His engines could generate up to 100 hp (75 kw) (well above the average Watt engine), and were remarkable

at the time for their small size in relation to their power. They were also simpler than previous models. Though some of Trevithick's engines used the traditional rocking beam to transmit the motion of the piston, others were direct-acting, i.e. the piston rod was connected directly to a wheel to provide rotary motion. In addition, Trevithick dispensed with Watt's separate condenser and air pump by venting spent steam directly into the air. The loss in efficiency was more than compensated for by dramatic decreases in bulk and weight, and an increase in the power-to-size ratio.

Trevithick's engine would not have been possible without a more efficient boiler that could produce higher temperatures than previous models. Trevithick replaced Watt's huge, cube-like boiler with a cylindrical one. The boiler contained a cylindrical firebox with a return flue, so that the chimney and furnace door were on the same end of the boiler. The cylinder was built into the boiler so that it could be surrounded by steam and kept hot. The boiler for the Cornish engine was essentially a cylinder heated by a furnace tube within it. Heat was transferred to the water from the hot flue gases inside the tube, increasing the boiler's efficiency. ■

Further Reading:

Henry W. Dickinson and Arthur Titley, *Richard Trevithick, the Engineer and the Man.* Cambridge, 1934.

Robert James Forbes, *Man the Maker.* London, 1950.

Joachim G. Leithauser, *Inventors' Progress,* trans. by Michael Bullock. Cleveland, Ohio, 1959.

C. Matschoss, *Great Engineers.* London, 1939.

THEODORE BURR
b. Aug. 16, 1771, Torringford, Connecticut
d. 1822, Harrisburg, Pennsylvania
American Civil Engineer

Life and Times:

Although the truss was known in Europe from the sixteenth century, it was not used in European bridges until the advent of the iron bridge some 300 years later. In North America, on the other hand, the truss was in widespread use for the construction of wooden bridges from the end of the eighteenth century. The rediscovery and mastery of the truss is a tribute to the first generation of American bridge-builders. With little formal training, they had to use the materials at hand—the vast expanses of forest—and their intuitive engineering judgment. Theodore Burr, perhaps the chief of these early American bridge builders, developed the covered truss bridge in its classic form.

Burr is frequently called a native of Massachusetts, though in fact he was born in Connecticut. In 1789 he married a woman from Harrisburg, Pa., who is said to have been the daughter of the navigator Captain Cook. Although he lived much of his life in Pennsylvania, his bridge-building assignments often took him far afield.

In 1804, Burr received his first known commission, the construction of a bridge over the Hudson river between Waterford and Lansingburgh, N.Y. He was active for at least the next twelve years, building bridges over the Delaware, Mohawk and Susquehanna rivers. Burr patented his truss design in 1817 and may have retired from active work at that time.

Outstanding Engineering Achievement:

Burr's innovative bridge over the Hudson at Waterford represents his major contribution to the design of covered bridges. It consisted of four spans from 154 to 180 feet (46 to 54 meters) long. The arches sprang from the face of the abutment and rose almost to the roof of the bridge, for the body of the bridge lay between the arches instead of riding on top of them. The flat roof and floor were supported by vertical posts, which in turn were linked by diagonal braces. The posts, braces and floor were firmly connected to the segments of the arch that passed alongside, thus acting as stiffeners for the arches.

The whole design was a model of sturdiness, and the covering preserved its structure from the elements. The Burr arch truss, patented 13 years after the construction of this bridge, was adopted for use in hundreds of highway and railroad bridges. The Waterford bridge never required strengthening until its destruction by fire 105 years later.

Each of Burr's three other major bridges involved innovations, though these were not always successful. The Mohawk bridge at Schenectady, New York, was a wooden suspension bridge; it had to be supported by a trestle after 20 years. The bridge over the Delaware at

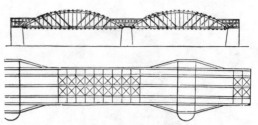

Two of the five arches of Burr's truss bridge over the Delaware at Trenton.

Trenton, N.J., supported by five arches, had two roadways and two sidewalks. Burr's most ambitious bridge spanned the main channel of the Susquehanna near Lancaster, Pa. The river was swift and 100 feet (30 meters) deep; each spring it was swept with ice floes. Burr and his construction crew built the bridge's single, 360-foot (110 meters) arch in sections, which they then stationed in the river on floats. When the river froze, they dragged the remaining sections over the ice and swung them into position. Work was completed in 1815. Only two years later the bridge was destroyed by ice during the spring thaw, never to be rebuilt. ■

Further Reading:

Herbert W. Congdon, *The Covered Bridge.* Brattleboro, Vermont, 1941.

James Kip Finch, "A Hundred Years of American Civil Engineering," *Transactions of the American Society of Civil Engineers.* Vol. CT (1953).

Robert Fletcher and J. P. Snow, "A History of the Development of Wooden Bridges," *Transactions of the American Society of Civil Engineers.* Vol. XCIX (1934).

Richard S. Kirby et al., *Engineering in History.* New York, 1956.

HENRY MAUDSLAY
b. Aug. 22, 1771, Woolwich, Kent, England
d. Feb. 14, 1831, London, England
British Instrument Maker and Engineer

Life and Times:

Henry Maudslay, the mechanical genius known as "the father of the machine-tool industry," was the son of a mechanic in the Royal Arsenal at Woolwich. He began working in the arsenal at the age of 12 as a powder-monkey,

The father of the machine-tool industry, Henry Maudslay, built one of the first totally mechanized factories.

later as a blacksmith. At 18 he was apprenticed to the tool- and lock-maker Joseph Bramah [q.v.], whose foreman he became and whom he assisted in the invention of the hydraulic press. In 1798 Maudslay left Bramah's shop after a dispute over wages and set up his own business; his first large order, from Marc Isambard Brunel [q.v.] and Samuel Bentham, was for the manufacture of 43 machines to make pulley blocks for the British Admiralty at the Royal Dockyards in Portsmouth. The machines, built over a period of 5½ years, constituted one of the first totally mechanized factories; they produced 130,000 blocks per year and did the work of 110 skilled laborers. Some of them were still in use at Portsmouth as late as the 1940s.

Maudslay, the maker of a vast number of machine tools, is best known for his screw-cutting bench lathe of 1799–1800. Screw-cutting lathes had been constructed earlier by Jesse Ramsden [q.v.], the French instrument maker Senot, and the American David Wilkinson; but Maudslay's improved version, incorporating a slide-rest, lead-screw, change-gears, and all-metal construction, was the first to achieve widespread industrial use. Maudslay also designed and built metal lathes, face lathes, marine steam engines, and stationary table engines, which dispensed with the conventional walking beam and were the first direct-acting steam

engines to be widely accepted. He held patents on a method of printing calico, on a differential motion for raising weights and turning lathes (with his friend Bryan Donkin [q.v.]), on air-purification of stored water (with Robert Dickinson), and on methods of desalinating and regulating the water supply of marine boilers (with Joshua Field [q.v.]).

Maudslay was a perfectionist who supplied the several hundred craftsmen in his Lambeth factory with standard plane surfaces against which to check their work. He also invented a bench micrometer accurate to 0.0001 inch (.0025 mm). His influence was felt well into the next generation of British engineers, of whom several—notably Richard Roberts [q.v.], Joseph Clement [q.v.], James Nasmyth, and Sir Joseph Whitworth—were his employees and students. Joshua Field, famous in his own right as a designer of marine steam engines, became a senior partner in Maudslay's firm, which was eventually known as Maudslay, Sons and Field.

Outstanding Engineering Achievements:

Maudslay's screw-cutting lathe consisted of a spindle, on which the work was mounted, connected by a series of gears to the lead screw, which propelled the sliding tool carriage. The earliest models required the operator to disassemble the lathe and remove the lead screw in order to change the pitch of the screw to be cut; later versions were designed to allow the pitch to be changed by a simple substitution of gears between spindle and lead screw. (This system had been devised by Jacques de Vaucanson [q.v.] 50 years earlier, but Maudslay evidently hit upon it independently.) His lathes were so accurate that he was able to cut a five-foot (1.5 m) brass screw, two inches (5 cm) in diameter,

Maudslay's original screw-cutting bench lathe, prototype of the first lathe to achieve widespread industrial use.

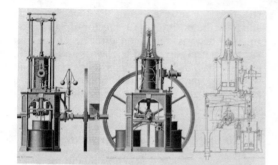

The table engine designed and built by Maudslay; a direct-acting steam engine seen here from the front (Figs. 1 and 2) and the side (Fig. 3).

with 50 threads per inch (20 per cm); the accompanying nut was a foot (0.3 meter) long. Maudslay's first lathe has been preserved in the Science Museum in London.

Another significant improvement which Maudslay brought to the lathe was the sliding tool rest, perfected in 1807 and used on his screw-cutting and other lathes. The tool rest, which held the cutting tool, slid along a bar parallel to the lathe bed or was attached to the lathe bed itself; it could be easily fixed and adjusted at any point by thumb screws. The tool rest made possible faster, more precise and more uniform operations on the lathe.

The Portsmouth block-making machinery that Maudslay built and helped design consisted of 43 wood-shaping tools organized into a mass production line. Blocks in three sizes were made by reciprocating and circular saws, boring machines, mortising machines, milling machines, and lathes, all powered by a 30-horsepower (2240-watt) steam engine.

Much of Maudslay's work was in steam engine construction and design, an area in which he cooperated closely with Field. Their principal innovation here was the table engine, a direct-acting engine in which two connecting rods fixed to either side of the vertical piston rod worked a crankshaft below the cylinder. The table engine's relative lightness and compactness made it especially suitable for use in machine shops and aboard ships.

One of Maudslay's lasting contributions to mechanical engineering was his approach to the art of toolmaking. An expert craftsman and toolhandler, he insisted on precision work and instituted the use of uniform taps, dies, and plane-testing surfaces throughout his shop. He was largely responsible for the switch from wooden to all-metal machine tools, with their superior stability and longevity. ■

Further Reading:

Maurice Daumas, *A History of Technology and Invention,* Vol. III. New York, 1969.

Dictionary of National Biography, s.v. "Maudslay."

Malcolm B. Gregory, *History and Development of Engineering.* London, 1971.

Singer et al., *A History of Technology,* Vol. IV.

GEORG FRIEDRICH VON REICHENBACH

b. Aug. 24, 1771 or 1772, Durlach, Germany (near Karlsruhe)
d. May 21, 1826, Munich, Germany
German Mechanical, Hydraulic, Military and Civil Engineer

Life and Times:

In the latter half of the eighteenth century, British engineers dominated the craft of instrument making. At the same time, innovations in the design of heavy machinery, including the steam engines of James Watt [q.v.], made possible the spread of mills and factories across the English countryside. But the nucleus of a precision instrument industry had taken shape in Germany by the early nineteenth century, and the technological mastery exercised by the English began to spread to engineers on the Continent. A central figure in this shift was Georg Friedrich von Reichenbach, whose inventions and career served as the catalyst for the development of precision engineering in Germany. A designer of measuring, surveying and astronomical devices, Reichenbach also founded two schools in which mechanical and optical engineers in Germany were trained.

Reichenbach spent his childhood in Mannheim. Because his father was a noted cannon borer who served the local ruler, the Elector Palatine, Georg had access to the most advanced training available locally in astronomy and instrument making. While attending the School of Army Engineers in Mannheim, Reichenbach came to the attention of the American-born scientist Benjamin Thompson, Count Rumford, then employed as a military engineer and administrator by the Elector.

With Rumford's help, Reichenbach was sent to England after graduation to study the most recent advances in engineering. There he was shown around Watt's plant. Bribing his way back later, he studied the steam engine, being careful to appear casual, and to ask no questions. He returned again many times over six weeks until he was able to complete a detailed drawing. He also met Jesse Ramsden [q.v.], whose instruments provided a precision never before attained.

Reichenbach returned to Germany after two years and settled in Bavaria, then ruled in personal union by the Elector Palatine. The state was then locked in a defensive struggle against the armies of Revolutionary France. Reichenbach joined the Bavarian army, for which he designed improved muskets and cannons. Among his inventions was a rifled cannon—one in which the inside of the barrel was spirally grooved in order to add spin, and therefore accuracy, to the motion of a shell.

While designing artillery, Reichenbach devised a way of improving the dividing engine that Ramsden had invented. This machine graduated scales with great accuracy and was the key to making precise measuring instruments. In 1804 Reichenbach established a firm in Munich for producing precision instruments. In collaboration with Johann Liebherr, another inventor, and Joseph von Utzschneider, a financier, he made a wide variety of surveying and astronomical instruments, including telescopes and theodolites. Some were made for leading astronomers, including Pierre Simon de Laplace, Friedrich Wilhelm Bessel, Friedrich Georg Wilhelm von Struve and Karl Friedrich Gauss [q.v.]. Though a private business, the firm was known as an institute and helped train the next generation of German instrument makers.

Besides the problem of precision, makers of optical instruments were concerned with improving the quality of glass and eliminating faults in lenses. In 1806 Reichenbach's company acquired a new junior partner, Joseph Fraunhofer, whose name has been given to the dark lines he discovered in the sun's spectrum. Fraunhofer's optical contributions later resulted in the manufacture of a telescope lens twelve inches in diameter, the largest then known. Reichenbach helped establish an optical institute along the lines of the existing mechanical institute, but severed his association with the partnership in 1814.

Between 1806 and 1817, Reichenbach supervised the construction of a pipeline to carry salt water from salt springs in the Alps near the Austro-German border to a plant located 67 miles to the northwest. During the line's construction, he resigned from the Bavarian army and took the position of Councillor of Saltworks. In 1820 he was appointed director of the Bavarian Central Bureau of Highways and Bridges, a post that included responsibility for urban water and gas supplies. His honors included a knighthood and election to the French Academy of Sciences.

Outstanding Engineering Achievements:

The pipeline that Reichenbach built took saltwater from Berchtesgaden to Rosenheim, rising at one point to an elevation of 1,200 feet (360 meters). To accomplish the pumping, Reichenbach used his version of the hydraulic ram invented in 1749 by Jozsef Karoly Hell. When located below a water supply such as a lake, the ram used the pressure of a large amount of water to pump a smaller amount to a higher level—a principle still employed in modern machines. Reichenbach built 11 of these water-pressure engines, of which the largest, pumping water across the line's highest point, was then considered the largest machine in the world. It was in use until 1958.

Reichenbach produced a number of large astronomical instruments for observatory use, including a meridian circle that carried a telescope of five-foot (1.5 meters) focal length. Others were small and portable. The terrestrial or azimuth circle was a surveying device in which a sighting telescope was mounted to swing up or down on supports that moved around a horizontal circle. The diameter of that circle was 16 inches (41 cm); it was precisely graduated and fitted with two verniers. The rotation up or down of the telescope could be read off a scale attached to its support, also supplied with two verniers. The instrument stood on three adjustable feet for perfect leveling.

Similarly accurate was the astronomical circle, in which the telescope was fixed to the diameter of a vertical circle. This 18 inch (46 cm) diameter circle could be rotated vertically, and it could be turned horizontally around a vertical shaft.

The universal instrument was a new type of measuring device that could be used for astronomical or surveying purposes. Reichenbach, who introduced it in 1812, regarded it as the result of all his former experience. Above the adjustable tripod of the instrument was a horizontal circle. Rotating around its circumference were a pair of vertical supports joined by an axle, fitted with two vertical setting circles. In the center of the axle, and perpendicular to it, was the telescope. A slight movement of the

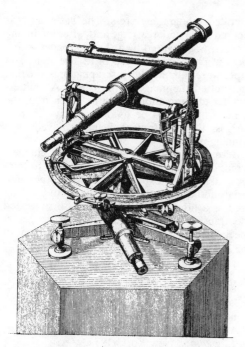

Reichenbach's terrestrial circle, equipped with a level at the top, adjustable feet, two verniers on each scale, to provide very accurate measurements.

telescope up or down was shown by the scales on the circumference of the vertical circles; movement of the telescope around the horizon was shown by the scale on the horizontal circle. A small angle of rotation of the telescope thus was multiplied into an easily read arc around a circle.

Further Reading:

Allgemeine Deutsche Biographie, s.v. "Von Reichenbach."

Maurice Daumas, *Les Instruments Sciéntifiques du 16ème Siècle.* Paris, 1953.

Dictionary of Scientific Biography, s.v. "Von Reichenbach."

Friedrich Klemm, *A History of Western Technology.* Cambridge, 1964.

ALOYS SENEFELDER
b. Nov. 6, 1771, Prague, Czechoslovakia
d. Feb. 26, 1834, Munich, Germany
German Chemical and Mechanical Engineer

Life and Times:

The son of an actor at the Theatre Royal in Munich, Senefelder began studying law at his father's insistence but subsequently became an actor himself and a playwright. Unable to get his plays published because of the expense, Senefelder tried to print them himself. This effort led to his discovery by 1798 of the basic principles of what was later called lithography, a planographic or flat-surface form of printing that involved impressing on paper designs drawn on a stone or metal plate. Senefelder developed the fundamentals of lithography so thoroughly that they have remained almost unchanged.

Senefelder secured a 15-year patent on his invention in Bavaria, where he resided. He went to England in 1800, secured a patent there the following year, and soon after obtained a patent in France. Senefelder then established printing houses and published sheet music. A book showing specimens of his process appeared in 1803. In 1818 he published *A Complete Course in Lithography* and later set up a lithographic workshop near Frankfurt-am-Main where craftsmen were trained in the lithographic method. He died a wealthy and respected man.

Remarkably sensitive in conveying detail, lithography was particularly well suited for the printing of maps, diagrams and pictures. At first the technique was used primarily for making reproductions by transferring already-produced designs to the stone or metal. But in the 1820s artists such as Delacroix, Géricault, and Goya began working directly on lithographic plates. The development around 1850 of color lithography and a mechanized lithographic press led to increased use of the process. From the time of the nineteenth century impressionists, lithography has been an important medium for original artistic work used by, among others, Degas, Manet, Toulouse-Lautrec, Whistler, and Picasso. Meanwhile, it also became an enormously successful and versatile commercial method of producing cheap prints.

Lithography spurred the early development of photography. Attempting to record the image formed by the lens inside the "camera obscura," or pinhole camera, Joseph-Nicéphore Niepce tried to fix the image on a lithographic stone by placing the latter at the lens' focus. He failed, but his attempts led to Louis Jacques Daguerre's

Aloys Senefelder, inventor of the lithographic process of printing.

invention in 1839 of the daguerreotype process of producing a silver image on a copper plate.

Outstanding Engineering Achievements:

After experimenting unsuccessfully with copper engraving, Senefelder accidentally took his first major step toward the invention of lithography in 1796. Having written a laundry list on limestone with a grease pencil, he tried to etch away the surrounding stone surface with nitric acid to leave the letters standing in relief like the type in printing. Attempting to improve the process over the next two years, Senefelder found that it was not necessary for the printing surface to be raised. By 1798 he had devised a practical form of lithography based on the mutual repulsion of grease and water.

Senefelder's process began with the polishing of a finely porous carboniferous limestone. Lettering or design was drawn upon it with a greasy pigment which was fixed into the pores of the stone by a slight acid bath. Then he applied a water solution which dampened the entire stone except for the greased portion, which repelled the water. Next, Senefelder used rollers to apply a greasy ink that adhered to the greased image but was rejected by the dampened portion of the stone. The ink, composed of wax, soap, and lampblack, was specially formulated by Senefelder so that it could be easily wiped off the stone's surface after having been absorbed by the image.

By 1798 Senefelder had designed a hand-operated lithographic press. The flat stone was secured to an undercarriage and, after the inking process, was covered by a sheet of paper with a sheet of pasteboard on top of it. The stone and paper were submitted to a scraping pressure that transmitted the image to the paper. A limitless number of impressions could be taken from the stone, which could be used for many different designs, the old drawing being removed by a grinding process.

Because the appropriate stone was cumbersome, limited in supply, and vulnerable to fracture, Senefelder experimented with other materials and demonstrated that zinc could also be used as a lithographic plate. He also suggested the transfer method of drawing an image on specially treated paper and then transferring it to the lithographic plate through pressure. ■

Further Reading:

Colin Clair, *A History of Printing in Britain.* London, 1965.

Anthony Feldman and Peter Ford, *Scientists and Inventors.* New York, 1979.

Michael Twyman, *Lithography (1800–1850).* New York, 1970.

WILLIAM CONGREVE
b. May 20, 1772, Woolwich, England
d. May 16, 1828, Toulouse, France
British Inventor

Life and Times:

The use of skyrockets as military weapons originated in China, where they were employed in the defense of the city of Kai-fung-fu against Mongol besiegers in 1232 A.D. Although introduced into Europe by the Arabs a few years later, rockets were not adopted on a large scale by European armies until the nineteenth century, when improvements by Sir William Congreve made them more portable and sometimes more effective than the artillery guns of the era.

Congreve joined the Royal Laboratory at Woolwich, of which his father was comptroller, as an artillery officer in 1791. His interest in rocketry was triggered by reports of the 1792 and 1799 battles of Seringapatam, in which the rockets corps of Hyder Ali, prince of the Indian state of Mysore, inflicted heavy casualties on British troops. After obtaining the support of military authorities, Congreve began experimenting with skyrockets and by 1805 had produced an explosive model for use by army troops, whom he trained himself. The rockets were responsible for the burning of Boulogne in 1806 and of Copenhagen in 1807; during the War of 1812 they enabled the British to open the road to Washington, D.C., and their impressive display at Fort McHenry inspired Francis Scott Key to write of "the rockets' red glare" in the poem which became the national anthem of the United States.

The following year, Congreve, by now a member of Parliament and a Fellow of the Royal Society, took one of his rocket companies to serve in the battle of Leipzig and in the siege of Boulogne, where they ignited food stores and forced the city's surrender. The absence of recoil in launching rockets made them ideal for firing from boats during naval attacks. But British soldiers, on more than one occasion, expressed horror at the devastation wrought by rockets on civilian populations.

Congreve, who succeeded his father as comptroller of the Royal Laboratory and second baronet of Walton in 1814, continued over the years to improve the range and payload capacity of his rockets. In 1826, in the aftermath of his involvement in a fraud scandal, he and his family moved to France, where he died a year later.

Congreve spoke of his rockets as "the soul of artillery without the body," and was convinced that the weapon would soon displace cannon. As a result of his work, rocket brigades were established by the armies of nearly all the European nations and by the United States. But Congreve had developed black-powder rockets virtually to their limit, and except for specialized applications in whale harpooning and lifeline throwing, the rocket eventually yielded to the development of lighter-weight, more accurate artillery pieces. Congreve-type rockets were last used by Russian forces in the Russo-Turkish war of 1881.

Outstanding Engineering Achievements:

The original model of the Congreve rocket consisted of a six-pound (2.7 kg) cylinder of heavy sheet iron, 40.5 inches (103 cm) long and 3.5 inches (8.9 cm) in diameter, to which a 16-foot-long (4.8 meters) guidestick was attached with copper and iron hoops. The incendiary payload, a mixture of saltpeter, sulfur, antimony sulfide, tallow, rosin and turpentine, was carried in a canvas container set into a conical cap. The charge, a mixture of saltpeter, sulfur and charcoal, was compressed into a slow-burning cake

William Congreve, British military engineer responsible for "the rockets' red glare" during the War of 1812.

dampened with alcohol. During the dangerous packing process, the cylinder was kept submerged in cold water as a safety precaution and was then dried for four months. When the fuse was lit, exhaust gases from the exploding charge propelled the rocket up a copper launching tube set at a 55-degree angle and through the air to a range of 2,000 yards (1800 meters).

In later years, Congreve replaced the cylinder with a conical container set back-to-back with the conical cap. These improved rockets ranged in size from 12 to 32 pounds (5.4 to 14.5 kg) and reached a maximum distance of 3,000 yards (2700 meters); besides explosives, they could carry other kinds of artillery ammunition, including spherical bombs, carbine balls and flares. In addition to being far more portable than artillery pieces of comparable range, they required fewer soldiers to move and operate them, cost less to manufacture and had the advantage of terrifying enemy troops and horses with their noise and smoke.

Apparently an inveterate tinkerer, Congreve improved or invented many devices in addition to the rocket. The *Dictionary of Scientific Biography* mentions 18 patents which he obtained during his career, including "new methods of mounting naval ordnance, gunpowder manufacture, printing unforgeable currency, gas lighting, 'hydropneumatic' canal locks, several kinds of clocks, a perpetual motion machine, a built-in sprinkler system, and a steam engine." He was the author of a number of treatises on technological subjects. ■

Further Reading:

Dictionary of Scientific Biography, s.v. "Congreve."
Dictionary of National Biography, s.v. "Congreve."
Willy Ley, *Rockets, Missiles, and Space Travel,* second rev. ed. New York, 1961.
William Reid, *Arms Through the Ages.* New York, 1976.
B.E. Epstein, *The Rocket Pioneers.* 1955.
Peter Young and J.P. Lanford, eds., *History of the British Army.* New York, 1970.

DAVID MUSHET
b. Oct. 2, 1772, Dalkeith, Edinburgh, Scotland
d. June 7, 1847, Monmouth, Wales
British Mechanical Engineer

Life and Times:

The application of the steam engine during the second half of the eighteenth century spurred a demand for iron in greater quantity and of higher quality than ever before. Ironmasters, lacking a scientific understanding of the process of converting ore to metal, continually experimented with new combinations of fuel, ore and additional substances to find ways of producing cheaper and better iron and steel.

One of the most diligent of these craftsmen was David Mushet, the son of a Scottish ironmaster. Working in Scottish foundries until 1805 and later in England, he was more systematic than most of his colleagues and, beginning in the 1790s, published many of his results in the *Philosophical Magazine.* His work contributed to the production of improved iron and cast steel. Through knowledge bequeathed to his son, Robert F. Mushet, he may also have contributed to the perfection of the Bessemer process of steel manufacture.

In 1801 Mushet discovered the Black Band Ironstone bed near Glasgow, so-called because of the black band of bitumen running through it. Most ironmasters regarded the ore as useless, and Mushet was widely ridiculed for asserting its fitness for smelting. But after James Beaumont

Neilson's [q.v.] invention of the hot blast in 1828, the Black Band ore was extensively used and became the underpinning of the Scottish iron industry.

Outstanding Engineering Achievements:

In 1800 Mushet patented a process for making cast steel by combining wrought iron with regulated amounts of charcoal in a crucible. This represented a step in the development of cheaper steel by starting with wrought iron instead of the uneven blister steel, which was convertible to a homogeneous product only through a time-consuming and fuel-costly process of melting and hammering. Mushet's discovery of the beneficial effects of manganese on iron and steel formed the basis of Josiah Heath's patent for making cast steel. By devising means for using oxides of iron—especially non-phosphorus, hematite ores—in the removal of chemical impurities from cast iron, Mushet also augmented the production and improved the quality of wrought iron.

Mushet's son Robert claimed that his father, by combining pulverized iron ore, oxide of manganese, and charcoal, was the first to make ferromanganese. It may have been the elder Mushet's work with ferromanganese that led Robert to mix it with molten pig iron in the refining process to prevent overoxidation of the metal. This step proved vital in the Bessemer steelmaking process. ■

Further Reading:

Fred M. Osborn, *The Story of the Mushets.* London, 1952.

GEORGE CAYLEY
b. Dec. 27, 1773, Scarborough, Yorkshire, England
d. Dec. 15, 1857, Brompton, Yorkshire, England
British Aeronautical Engineer

Life and Times:

The history of manned flight began in 1783 with the invention by the brothers Montgolfier [q.v.] of the hot-air balloon. The following years and decades saw an outburst of proposals for every conceivable kind of flying machine: airships (powered balloons), ornithopters (flap-

George Cayley, acknowledged as the father of modern aeronautics although, without a suitable engine, he could not put his ideas into practice.

ping-wing flying machines), and helicopters. But the enthusiasm of the designers could not make up for their ignorance of aerodynamic principles and the absence of an adequate source of power. George Cayley solved the first problem by single-handedly developing the science of aerodynamics; indeed, no further progress was made in this field until the twentieth century. Then, lacking a suitable means of propulsion, Cayley applied his theories to the construction of fixed-wing manned gliders. The airplane as we know it owes its existence to Cayley's achievements.

The family of Cayley's father, Thomas, was of ancient lineage. Raised largely by Isabella, his unconventional mother, Cayley early took to observing the work of village artisans as well as natural phenomena. He studied for several years under two Unitarian ministers, marrying the first one's unconventional daughter and adopting the second one's reformist political views. After a brief flirtation with republicanism and a trip to the continent, Cayley became more moderate and began to tend to his estate—his father had died in 1792.

Cayley fulfilled the obligations of a gentleman landholder by sponsoring an important drainage project, experimenting with land reform, and actively participating in Yorkshire politics; he was elected to Parliament in 1832. After leaving office in 1835, he founded a Polytechnic Institution in London and was an active philanthropist. Throughout his life, however, he pursued an interest in flight which dated from at least 1792.

In that year Cayley conducted his first aeronautical experiment, modifying a Chinese "flying top," or toy helicopter. In 1799 he began to set down his ideas concerning heavier-than-air flight. Realizing the inadequacy of the steam engine, he conceived a hot-air engine, similar to the Stirling engine of a few years later. He also entertained hopes concerning an internal combustion engine designed by William Chapman that used oil of tar as fuel. By 1804 he was using a whirling arm and a model glider to test his ideas on flight stability and aerodynamics. There followed observations of herons and experiments with kites and full-scale gliders. The result of this work was his classic two-part article in *Nicholson's Journal* (1809-10) on heavier-than-air flight.

Still lacking a suitable engine, Cayley abandoned the subject of heavier-than-air flight to turn to his many other technological and social interests, which included railroad safety, parliamentary reform, the design of airships, and a scheme for an artificial hand. Only when W.S. Henson published plans for an "aerial steam carriage" did Cayley again take up his pioneering work. Cayley eventually conducted two experiments with manned gliders, probably in 1849 and 1853. The pilots, a boy and a groom, both survived. He continued to experiment and tinker with his gliders until his death.

Outstanding Engineering Achievements:

Cayley early realized that the two functions of lift and thrust in flight could be separated. He thus originated the idea of the fixed-wing, independently powered airplane (1799) and was the first to construct a fixed-wing glider (1809). Cayley also observed that the outer edges of a bird's wing propel it, while the main portions provide lift.

His unprecedented practical experiments noted above led to a number of fundamental discoveries: that cambered (slightly arched) wings provide greater lift than flat ones; that a region of low pressure on the upper surface of a cambered airfoil contributes to the lift; that wings tilted upward at an angle impart lateral stability to an airplane; that a vertical tail surface gives directional stability; that rear rudder and elevator surfaces permit directional and longitudinal control; that streamlining reduces drag. Cayley introduced the cycle-type undercarriage

in his full-sized gliders and proposed that airplanes taxi to gain speed for take-off. He designed a biplane; the manned glider that flew
successfully was a triplane. It incorporated all
the features listed above, which are essential to
the modern airplane.

Cayley designed, but never built, various airships that were semi-rigid, streamlined, and
composed of separate gas cells. He also designed
helicopters and proposed the convertiplane—a
fixed-wing aircraft equipped with helicopter
blades. Cayley suggested that glider-like parachutes could be launched from balloons to fly
great distances. He realized that some form of
internal combustion engine was needed in order
to power aircraft.

It is perhaps reassuring that this genius had
certain blind spots. Several of his airship and
airplane designs called for propulsion by flap-
ping; Cayley was never an enthusiastic proponent of the airscrew. Not recognizing the
strength of trussed structures, he was hesitant to
build wide-span wings, preferring biplanes and
triplanes instead. Nevertheless, these failings
pale beside his achievements. He has rightly
been called the father of modern aeronautics
and, theoretically, the true inventor of the airplane. ■

Further Reading:

Gerard Fairlie and Elizabeth Cayley, *The Life
of a Genius.* London, 1965.

Charles Harvard Gibbs-Smith, *Sir George
Cayley's Aeronautics 1796-1855.* London, 1962.

J.E. Hodgson, "Sir George Cayley's Work in
Aeronautics," *Aviation and Aeronautical Engineering,* Vol. XV (Dec. 17, 1923).

John Laurence Pritchard, *Sir George Cayley,
The Inventor of the Aeroplane.* London, 1961.

FRIEDRICH KOENIG

b. April 17, 1774, Eisleben, Saxony
d. Jan. 17, 1833, Oberzell, Bavaria
German Mechanical Engineer

Life and Times:

At the start of the nineteenth century, the
hand-powered platen press employed in printing
produced 300 sheets per hour. By 1814 Friedrich
Koenig had increased the hourly rate to 1,100
sheets and enhanced the clarity of the print with

*Friedrich Koenig, inventor of the steam-powered press
that increased the speed of printing from 300 to 1100
sheets per hour.*

the most important typographic innovations
since those of Johannes Gutenberg [q.v.]. The
German-born Koenig, son of a peasant proprietor, served as apprentice to a compositor and
printer, and in 1803 established himself as a
printer and bookseller. He had ideas for building
an improved printing press, but failed to get
financial backing in Germany. Since England
had the most effective patent system in Europe,
Koenig moved to London in 1806.

Between 1810 and 1814, with financial backing
from the printer Thomas Bensley and in a
partnership with the engineer Andreas Bauer of
Stuttgart, Koenig radically altered the system of
printing. At first he applied steam power to the
cumbersome platen press, a significant but limited advance that increased the rate of impressions to 400 per hour. The following year,
Koenig introduced a machine of revised structure, the steam-powered single-cylinder flatbed
press, which printed 800 sheets per hour and was
used in printing books. In 1813, he patented a
double-cylinder machine suitable for newspaper
publication, printing 1,100 sheets per hour. *The
Times* of London began using this press in 1814
over the objections of its printers. In 1816,
Koenig completed a perfecting machine that
printed both sides of a sheet at the rate of 900 to
1,000 sheets per hour. *The Times* used this press
after other engineers had made modifications to
increase its speed.

Because of the many infringements of his
patents, Koenig realized little profit from his

inventions. He left for Bavaria in 1817 and with Bauer began manufacturing printing machines there. But publishers were intimidated by printers who resorted to violence to prevent the introduction of the new presses. Koenig's and Bauer's firm did not achieve significant success until after the former's death.

Introduction by *The Times* of Koenig's machines, which reduced costs by 25 percent, marked the beginning of the era of modern printing and cheap, mass-produced newspapers and books. The social ramifications were profound, for while the development of informed democracy was facilitated, so was the manipulation of public opinion.

Outstanding Engineering Achievement:

The hand press was laboriously operated by pressing the platen, a plate holding the paper, against a form that held the type and lay on a sliding flatbed. Ink was applied by hand with ink balls. Koenig's first steam-powered machine, patented in 1810, was a platen press. The only major change in design was the replacement of the ink balls with felt or leather-covered perforated brass inking cylinders. Fed from an ink box, they automatically spread ink over the type-form.

Koenig soon realized that the basic principle of the platen press—the pressing together of two flat surfaces—had to be changed if further progress was to be made in speeding up the printing process. In 1811 he introduced the single-cylinder flatbed press. The type again lay on a flatbed, but the platen was replaced by a horizontal cylinder whose circumference was divided into three printing surfaces, each bearing a sheet of paper. For each impression, the cylinder made one-third of a revolution, bringing to the top a printed sheet that was removed and replaced by hand. At the same time, the paper attached to the surface now at the bottom received an impression. With each partial revolution the type-form moved backwards and forwards. To utilize both directions of movement, Koenig introduced the double cylinder flatbed press. Each cylinder handled the impression in one direction of the bed. It was this machine, producing 1,100 impressions per hour, that was adopted by *The Times* in 1814.

The perfected machine consisted of two single-cylinder presses working in tandem. The sheet of paper was fed through both halves of the machine by a single endless web feeding apparatus and was turned by the use of an S-shaped course. ■

Double cylinder steam-powered flatbed press by Koenig that revolutionized the publishing industry.

Further Reading:

Warren Chappell, *A Short History of the Printed Word*. 1970.

Colin Clair, *A History of Printing in Britain*. London, 1965.

James Moran, *Printing Presses: History and Development From the Fifteenth Century to Modern Times*. Berkeley, California, 1973.

Singer et al., *A History of Technology*, Vol. IV.

FRANÇOIS EMMANUEL MOLARD
b. 1774, Cernoises, France
d. March 12, 1829, Paris, France
French Mechanical Engineer

Life and Times:

During the late eighteenth century, France lagged far behind England in the mechanization of industry. French industrialization did not really begin until the third decade of the nineteenth century, when the country had begun to recover from the constant warfare of the Revolutionary and Napoleonic periods. Despite the recent hostilities, the French acknowledged the achievements of the English. François Molard played an important part in bringing British technology to France by visiting England to study the industrial methods used there. In addition, Molard's own inventions contributed to the progress of French industry and commerce.

Molard was an adolescent at the start of the French Revolution. In 1793 he volunteered for the army, receiving the rank of lieutenant. He was withdrawn from active duty in 1795 to serve as commandant of the National Aerostatic School at Meudon. When the Revolutionary government abandoned its interest in the military application of ballooning, Molard attended the Ecole Polytechnique and served as an artillery officer until 1802.

By this time the Napoleonic government had begun to establish a system of technical and mechanical education, and Molard was enrolled in the effort. He served as director of technical schools at Compiègne and later Beaupréau, developing a curriculum and often teaching shop courses. He later returned to Paris to serve as adjunct director of the Conservatoire des Arts et Métiers and worked closely with the Ministry of Commerce on industrial matters.

In 1819 Molard visited England and observed industrial and agricultural techniques used in that country. His winning manner, expertise and willingness to share his own knowledge gained him admission to many factories. He published three books on the basis of his observations and supervised the construction of spinning and carding machines on the English model. Until his death ten years later Molard developed a great variety of inventions of his own.

Outstanding Engineering Achievements:

Molard developed a technique permitting sawmills to cut curved pieces, such as the felloes of wheels. The braking system he developed for wagon wheels, whereby a screw or lever controlled the brake shoes, was in use for decades. Molard experimented with new cables of superior strength for use in French mines, and developed geared cranes of the type long used in loading and unloading ships. Although mounted in one place, they could pivot 360 degrees.

Molard was much impressed by the agricultural implements used at the Coke farm in Holkham, England. Back in France Molard set up a shop that produced iron ploughs, threshers, winnowers, and machines for chopping up straw and roots to be used as animal feed. ■

Further Reading:

Marie Alphandéry, *Dictionnaire des inventeurs français*. Paris, 1962.

Biographie Universelle, s.v. "Molard."

ANDRE-MARIE AMPERE
b. Jan. 22, 1775, Lyons, France
d. June 10, 1836, Marseilles
French Physicist, Philosopher and Electrical Engineer

Life and Times:

If there has ever been a prepared mind waiting for a chance, it was that of Ampère in 1820 when Hans Christian Oersted [q.v.] discovered that an electric current generates a magnetic field. Since the previous century, it had been known that the contact of certain metals and acids could produce a flow in a wire of something that made frogs' legs jump, and that this flow could be used to decompose water into its constituent gases. But what it was that flowed was a mystery. Called galvanism, it was believed to have something to do with electricity, the crackling force produced by rubbing glass with silk.

But it was then that Oersted made his discovery, reported to the Academy of Sciences in Paris in September 1820, that a flow of galvanism deflected a compass needle. By the next week Ampère had confirmed and amplified the findings and presented his own paper to the Academy. He followed with two more papers within a month. The nature of current electricity was

André-Marie Ampère, the physicist who formulated the laws at the basis of the science of electrodynamics.

beginning to be understood, and the science of electrodynamics was born.

Ampère was born to a devout Catholic family at a time of social and intellectual ferment. His father was a rich merchant who had been elected to be a local justice of the peace. As such, he ordered the arrest of a political rebel, who was executed. In 1793, during the French Revolution's Reign of Terror, the elder Ampère was tried and guillotined. Young André-Marie was devastated. Although he had previously shown mathematical ability and had already studied theorems of Leonhard Euler [q.v.] and Jean Bernouilli (for which he taught himself Latin), he now withdrew into a deep depression, showing interest only in botany.

After a year, Ampère started to recover, helped by courtship and a happy marriage. He became a mathematics teacher and, in 1802, published his first paper, on probability theory. Then his wife died. In despair, Ampère moved with his infant son to Paris, where he obtained a teaching position at the École Polytechnique. A second marriage added a daughter to his household but ended in divorce.

Ampère's interests included not only the physical sciences but also biology and philosophy. He combined these in many years' work on the classification of the sciences and the philosophical basis of knowledge. In 1824, after teaching philosophy and astronomy at the University of Paris, he became professor of experimental physics at the Collège de France. These interests, and his religion, helped Ampère weather further personal disappointments: his daughter's husband was a violent drunkard, and Ampère's son wasted his life in the entourage of one of the town's beauties.

In 1808 Ampère had been appointed Inspector-General of the Institut Impérial. While on an inspection tour he contracted pneumonia and died. Forty-five years later the International Congress of Electricians named the practical unit of electric current after him; the ampere, or amp, continues to be used in the modern system.

Outstanding Engineering Achievement:

Oersted had noted that the magnetic effect caused by an electric current appeared to circle the current-carrying wire. Ampère gave a rule for the direction of this effect. He imagined a man in the wire, swimming headfirst with the current; if he faced a magnetic needle, its north pole would be deflected towards his left.

To formulate this rule, Ampère had to decide in which direction current flowed. Franklin had arbitrarily assigned the terms "plus" and "minus" to the two types of charges; the charge on a glass rod rubbed with silk was called "plus." Ampère followed Franklin in assuming that the flow was from plus to minus. (We now know that electrons flow from the negative terminal and we must distinguish between the positive-to-negative current flow of Ampère's rule and the actual negative-to-positive electron flow.)

Ampère demonstrated that two parallel conductors attract each other if the direction of current flow is the same in both, and repel if the directions are opposite. Also, if one of the wires is suspended so that it can rotate, Ampère showed that it does so about the common perpendicular, settling when the wires are parallel with the current flowing in the same direction.

Further magnet-like properties were revealed when Ampère discovered that a current flowing in a circular wire attracts another as if they are flat disc magnets with poles on their faces (now called magnetic shells). Putting a number of these magnetic shells together is comparable to coiling a wire into a helix. Ampère showed both mathematically and by experiment that such a solenoid, as he termed it, produced a magnetic field strong enough to magnetize steel needles.

Mathematically Ampère proved that the magnetic force produced at a point by a small element of current is inversely proportional to the square of the distance between the wire and the point. Current electricity was thus seen to obey an inverse square law comparable to those of gravity, magnetism, and electrostatics. Ampère also suggested that the mutual actions between magnetized bodies were caused by tiny electric currents flowing around minute particles. This idea could be neither confirmed nor denied at that time, but it is related to the modern concept of molecular dipoles. ■

Further Reading:

Rollo Appleyard, *Pioneers of Electrical Communications.* New York, 1968.

Dictionary of Scientific Biography, s.v. "Ampère."

William Magie, *A Source Book in Physics.* New York, 1935.

René Taton, ed., *Science in the Nineteenth Century.* New York, 1959.

Lloyd W. Taylor, *Physics: The Pioneer Science.* New York, 1959.

Clarence Tuska, *Inventors and Inventions.* New York, 1957.

PHILIPPE HENRI DE GIRARD

b. Feb. 1, 1775, Lourmarin, France
d. Aug. 26, 1845, Paris, France
French Mechanical Engineer

Life and Times:

In 1806 Napoleon prohibited the subjugated nations of Europe from importing English goods. This Continental System proved ineffective as a means of economic warfare. Moreover, it brought into sharp relief the inadequacies of French industries, now cut off from the world's leading source of technological innovations. Napoleon's subsequent efforts to encourage native talent should have brought the ingenious Philippe de Girard success and wealth. Instead, the result was the ruin of his family's fortune and a 28-year exile in Eastern Europe.

De Girard's father, the head of a wealthy provincial family, was an amateur botanist. The son showed an early aptitude for mechanics, constructing small water wheels by the brook that ran through the gardens of the de Girard estate. He also studied botany, painting and sculpture and composed poetry until the family's comfortable way of life was interrupted by the French Revolution.

De Girard's eldest brother, a member of the king's bodyguard, was wounded during the attack on the Tuilleries, and the family was compelled to leave France for Italy. For a time de Girard supported the family by painting portraits, but he soon undertook the first of his industrial ventures, a soap factory in Livorno. In 1794 the family felt it safe to return to France. De Girard set up a factory for chemical products in Marseilles and taught chemistry at the Marseilles Academy.

De Girard soon moved to Paris, where he displayed a number of mechanical devices at an exposition in 1806. When in 1810 Napoleon offered a prize of one million francs for invention of an improved method for spinning flax, de Girard soon patented his solution to this problem. But despite the economic value of de Girard's process, the government seems to have repented of its offer; it published stricter specifications and postponed awarding the prize until Napoleon fell from power. Although de Girard had gone deeply into debt while he strove to win the prize, Louis XVIII did not feel bound by his predecessor's promises. With the family yarn factory on the brink of bankruptcy, de Girard accepted an offer from the Austrian government and in 1816 had half his machinery shipped to

Vienna. The remaining machines and the family's estate were eventually seized by creditors.

Some years later de Girard, at the urging of the Russian government, moved to Warsaw to supervise a mechanized spinning factory. He continued to invent useful machines and processes until his long-delayed return to France in 1844. De Girard repeatedly tried to exact some sort of payment from the French government, but it took no action until 1853, when his heirs were awarded a pension of 6,000 francs a year.

Outstanding Engineering Achievements:

Flax, the raw material of linen, is more difficult than cotton to draw and spin mechanically because the filaments composing it are held together by a gummy substance. Attempts to mechanize these operations dated back to 1787 in England; heavy weights were hung from the flax to draw it out, and the thread was moistened to soften the gum before spinning. But heckling—the process of disentangling and aligning the filaments in the thread—still had to be done by hand if fine yarn was to be spun. De Girard's innovation was to successfully mechanize the heckling process and to improve the drawing and spining operations.

De Girard first passed the flax through a hot alkaline solution to separate the filaments. After drying, it was drawn through a machine equipped with combs for heckling. The strick of flax hung down between two vertical plaques lined with combs; mounted on cranks, the plaques repeatedly brushed the opposite sides of the strick, removing the tangles and lengthening it. The resulting thread was once more plunged into an alkaline solution before being twisted into yarn. Within a few years, de Girard's heckling process was in general use throughout Europe.

Another of de Girard's inventions was a desk lamp that maintained a constant level of oil at the base of the wick. The principle involved had been used long before by Heron [q.v.]. As the wick burned, the oil level fell until a partial vacuum was created; oil then was drawn through a tube from a reservoir to reestablish the original level. The lamps, bearing frosted glass globes and engravings designed by the young Dominique Ingres, were a great success.

While still in France, de Girard invented an achromatic lens using a liquid instead of the usual flint-glass and designed a steam-operated machine gun (never manufactured). In Eastern Europe he designed machines for extracting and evaporating beet juice and for manufacturing rifle stocks. He also improved the process of smelting zinc, designed and built 100-horsepower rotary-motion steam engines, and helped establish steamboat lines on the Danube. ■

Further Reading:

Maurice Daumas, ed., *Histoire Générale des Techniques,* Vol. III. Paris, 1968.
Nouvelle Biographie Générale, s.v. "Girard."
Singer et al., *A History of Technology,* Vol. III.

HENRY ECKFORD
b. March 12, 1775, Kilwinning (near Irvine), Scotland
d. Nov. 12, 1832, Constantinople, Ottoman Empire
American Shipbuilder

Life and Times:

The opening years of the nineteenth century were prosperous ones for the American shipbuilding industry. Seemingly limitless supplies of timber were readily available, permitting ships to be built for $35 a ton. In depleted and war-torn Europe, the equivalent cost was considerably higher—$50 in England and $60 in France. Despite President Jefferson's trade embargo, dozens of new shipyards sprang up along New York City's East River. That of Henry Eckford soon became noted for the quality of its ships.

Eckford left his native Scotland at age 16 to work in the Quebec shipyard of his uncle, John Black. After five years' study of ship design, Eckford moved to New York and found employment. He married in 1799 and in the following year began his own yard, where he mostly did repair work. During this time Eckford carried out his first important commissions in partnership with others: the *Beaver,* a 427-ton trading vessel for John Jacob Astor, and several gunboats for the U.S. navy.

With the opening of the War of 1812 Eckford moved to Sackett's Harbor on Lake Ontario, where he built war vessels. He worked quickly and well. It took him only 40 days to build the 24-gun sloop *Madison,* a shallow-draft ship capable of carrying a 600-man landing force. Back in New York, Eckford served from 1817 to 1820 as naval constructor for the Brooklyn Navy Yard.

Dissatisfied with government service, Eckford

Marine engineer Henry Eckford, builder of fast sailing ships, warships, and a three-master with a steam paddlewheel.

devoted himself after the war to his lucrative private work and became active in New York politics. But the financial troubles of 1825 caused the collapse of an insurance company in which Eckford had invested a half-million dollars. Personal tragedy followed in 1828, when three of his children died. In 1831 Eckford built his last ship, the war corvette *United States,* and took it to Europe to exhibit and sell. He found a willing buyer in the Sultan of the Ottoman Empire, who even placed Eckford in charge of the imperial naval yard. A year later, Eckford was struck down by a mysterious illness; his body was returned from Constantinople to the United States preserved in a barrel of spirits.

Outstanding Engineering Achievements:

Eckford was a pragmatic builder. He routinely interviewed the masters of the ships he had built each time they returned to port. He thus obtained an accurate analysis of the properties of his ships in all kinds of weather, which he used to revise his designs.

From these reports and his Great Lake experience in the War of 1812 Eckford developed a characteristic style of ship that foreshadowed the "clipper" class. His corvettes were built with an extreme deadrise, their sides rising sharply from the keel, and with little bilge, or curve at the bottom of the hull. Stern frames were reduced in size and extraneous details were eliminated. As a result, his ships were fast and stable. His

United States easily outdistanced the U.S.S. *Constellation* across the Atlantic.

Eckford's frigates were less severe than these smaller ships. Typical were the 64-gun, 2,000-ton ships that he built for four South American countries in the early 1820s. Eckford displayed his usual efficiency in their construction. Though framed with live oak, a wood quite difficult to work, all four frigates were completed within 18 months.

Eckford built even larger warships as well. His design for the *Ohio,* a 74-gun ship-of-the-line completed in 1820, was subsequently used in the construction of five sister ships. It was in connection with the *Ohio* that Eckford introduced the use of half-models, an idea suggested by his apprentice Isaac Webb.

Eckford designed only one steamship, the 100-ton *Robert Fulton.* Built in 1819, this square-rigged, three-masted vessel had an engine and paddlewheel mounted amidships. In 1822 it made the first successful steam voyage from New York to New Orleans and Havana. ■

Further Reading:

H.I. Chapelle, *The History of American Sailing Ships.* New York, 1935.

Cooper, *History of the U.S. Navy.*

Dictionary of American Biography, s.v. "Eckford."

Wheelock, "Henry Eckford (1775-1832), an American Shipbuilder," *The American Neptune.* (July, 1947).

NATHAN S. ROBERTS
b. July 28, 1776, Piles Grove, New Jersey
d. Nov. 24, 1852, Lenox, New York
American Civil Engineer

Life and Times:

Descended from early Puritan settlers of New England, Roberts worked as a farmer and teacher in Vermont, New York and New Jersey until 1816. In that year he was chosen by Benjamin Wright [q.v.] to plan and construct the western portion of the Erie Canal from Rome, N.Y., to its terminus at Lake Erie. Performing this work from 1816 to 1825, he completed one of the most difficult stretches of a waterway that proved vital in developing both economic and political links between the agricultural West and the commercial Northeast. Roberts later worked on many other engineering projects, including the Chesapeake and Ohio Canal and the Pennsylvania Canal.

Outstanding Engineering Achievement:

In 1816 and 1817 Roberts worked under Wright as a surveyor and assistant engineer on the section of the Erie Canal around Rome, and in 1818 he was made resident engineer in charge of the work between Rome and Syracuse. From 1819 to 1822 he planned the canal route from the Seneca River through the Cayuga marshes and designed the locks between Clyde and Syracuse. In 1822 he took charge of the locks to be built at Lockport and supervised construction of the remainder of the canal to its western terminus. Of all his Erie Canal work, the locks were Roberts' greatest challenge, for at Lockport the canal had to be built through a 60-foot (18m) rise followed by a cut 30 feet (9 m) deep and over seven miles (11 km) long. His successful plan was an unprecedented system of five double locks, each with a 12-foot (3.7 m) lift. The locks were combined into a continuous staircase, each lock feeding into the succeeding one.

Roberts completed the canal to its westernmost point in 1825. In 1835 he and two other engineers devised a plan to enlarge the canal to accommodate growing traffic. From 1839 to 1841 he supervised the enlargement of the canal from Rochester to Buffalo as chief engineer of its western division. He rebuilt one tier of the combined locks at Lockport and enlarged portions of the canal to cope with the increased traffic of packet boats traveling between the Great Lakes and the port of New York.

After completing the Erie Canal, Roberts

Combinations of five double locks on the Erie Canal at Lockport, engineered by Nathan Roberts.

became chief engineer of the Pennsylvania Canal. In 1828 he joined the board of engineers of the Chesapeake and Ohio Canal Company, planning and supervising work on large portions of the canal. For two years in the early 1830s, he worked for the federal government as chief engineer in a study of the Muscle Shoals in Alabama's Tennessee River, conducted with a view to opening a ship canal around the shoals. ■

Further Reading:

Charles B. Stuart, *Lives and Works of Civil and Military Engineers in America.* New York, 1871.

PETER BARLOW
b. Oct. 13, 1776, Norwich, England
d. March 1, 1862
British Mathematician, Physicist and Optician

Life and Times:

While working in a mercantile establishment, Barlow devoted himself to the study of mathematics and in 1801 obtained a post as a teacher of mathematics at the Royal Military Academy at Woolwich. For the next 15 years he gave his primary attention to pure mathematics and wrote several mathematical works.

Barlow then began experiments on the strength of wood, iron, and other materials. The tests formed the basis of his *On the Strength of Materials,* published in 1817. He later served as an adviser to civil engineers and architects. Turning to the subject of magnetism, he published an *Essay on Magnetic Attractions* (1820) and sought to use his discoveries to enhance the accuracy of the compass and for other practical purposes.

During the 1820s Barlow became interested in yet another field, optics. He first applied himself to improving achromatic objectives or lenses capable of refracting white light without breaking it into its constituent colors. This work led him to design telescope lenses with enhanced power of magnification. A modified form of this lens, known as the Barlow lens, is still used.

During the 1830s and 1840s, Barlow sat on railroad commissions, conducting experiments to determine the best shape for rails and to test the effects of gradients and curves.

Pater Barlow, inventor of the lens that is added to a telescope's optics to double or triple the magnification.

Outstanding Engineering Achievement:

Barlow's telescope lens was of concavo-convex shape. Finding it difficult to obtain large pieces of good flint glass, he sought a liquid substitute. He chose carbon disulfide, a colorless, transparent liquid with roughly the same refractive power as flint glass and twice as much dispersive power. The lens consisted of the transparent fluid enclosed in a glass capsule of appropriate curvature. It improved upon previous lenses by increasing the effective focal length of the telescope, i.e., the distance between the point at which light entered the telescope and the point at which it focused. This in turn increased the telescope's magnification.

Because of Barlow's knowledge of the strengths of materials, Thomas Telford consulted with him on the design of the Menai Straits suspension bridge in Wales. In 1820 Barlow proposed a simple way of correcting ships' compasses by the use of a small iron plate. He also made a primitive electric motor consisting of a star-shaped wheel, periodically dipped in mercury, suspended over a magnet.

Other Achievements:

Barlow's *New Mathematical Tables* (1814) gave the factors, squares, cubes, square roots, cube roots, and reciprocals of all numbers up to 10,000. So accurate were these tables that they have been reprinted many times since, even as recently as 1947. ■

Further Reading:

Dictionary of National Biography, s.v. "Barlow."

Dictionary of Scientific Biography, s.v. "Barlow."

Henry C. King, *The History of the Telescope.* London, 1955.

KARL FRIEDRICH GAUSS

b. April 30, 1777, Brunswick, Germany
d. February 23, 1855, Göttingen, Germany
German Electrical Engineer, Mathematician, Physicist and Astronomer

Life and Times:

One of the main industrial achievements of the nineteenth century was the efficient transmission of energy to machines via electricity. The application of electricity as a source of power proceeded through a series of small inventions, culminating in Michael Faraday's [q.v.] discovery of electromagnetic induction and invention of the dynamo. Karl Friedrich Gauss, a contemporary of Faraday, is known mainly for his sophisticated theoretical work in mathematics. But he also contributed to the practical development of electricity by devising one of the first electric telegraphs (an antecedent to which had been invented by Sir Francis Ronalds [q.v.] in 1816). Gauss furthermore advanced understanding of electromagnetic induction through his mathematical treatment of the flow of electrical currents and their magnetic fields through conductors. The stature of Gauss' work was displayed when his name was given to the unit of magnetic flux.

Gauss' contributions to science encompassed many disciplines. Although born into a poor and uneducated family, Gauss' mathematical precocity gained him entrance to the University of Göttingen under the patronage of the Duke of Brunswick. In 1799 he elaborated the first unassailable proof for the basic theorem of algebra (see below) and, two years later, published his *Inquiries into Arithmetic,* a pioneer work for both algebra and number theory. In 1804 he was named a Fellow of the Royal Society of London. Also in the nineteenth century, Gauss helped develop theoretical astronomy. From very few observations, he was able to calculate the orbits of the newly discovered asteroids Ceres and Pallas and correctly predict their returns. He also published an influential work on celestial mechanics, *Theory of the Motion of Celestial Bodies* (1809). In 1807 he was appointed director of the new observatory at Göttingen, a post he held until his death in 1855. From this position Gauss turned to the study of geodesy, the mathematical determination of points of location taking into account the size and shape of the earth's surface. He concluded the triangulation of Hannover for the government in 1847, advancing survey techniques and the mathematics of curved surfaces. He also invented a heliotrope, which permitted highly accurate angle measurements by reflecting sunlight to a distant observer.

The decade of the 1820s produced a sound theoretical understanding of electromagnetism which resolved years of speculation on the affinity between electricity and magnetism. When Hans Christian Oersted [q.v.] found in 1820 that an electric current induced through a wire coil would deflect a magnetic needle, the sciences of electricity and magnetism were linked. Gauss' work in geodesy had deepened his interest in terrestrial magnetism, and Oersted's discovery provided him an experimental basis for its study. In 1831 Gauss began a collaboration with the physicist Wilhelm Weber, a colleague at the University of Göttingen, and their use of the deflection of a magnetic needle led to the invention of an electric telegraph. German industrialists, however, believed that commercial development of the telegraph would be too expensive. As a result, the device was neglected and exer-

Karl Friedrich Gauss, one of the greatest of all mathematicians, and physicist Wilhelm Eduard Weber, whose collaboration led to the invention of an electric telegraph.

cised no appreciable influence on the later course of telegraphy, based on Samuel F.B. Morse's [q.v.] telegraph.

Outstanding Engineering Achievement:

Gauss' telegraph produced its signal by the motion of a large wire coil over a magnet. The generated electric current was sent through long wires to another coil, where it caused deflections in a magnetic needle. The telegraph was rudimentary but successful, allowing the Observatory to communicate with the Physics Laboratory across Göttingen.

Gauss' heliotrope served as a useful instrument for map-makers and surveyors until the twentieth century, when it was superseded by aerial cartography. It consisted of a small mirror fixed to a wooden stand so that it could be revolved. It reflected sunlight to an observer stationed farther away, allowing the direction and distance between the two points to be determined. This was accomplished by mathematically coordinating the angle between the reflecting mirror, a stationary observer and the position of the sun. Gauss helped make geodesy a science by providing a mathematical understanding of curved surfaces.

Other Achievements:

In mathematics Gauss demanded absolute logical strictness in all proofs. While still in high school, he had been dissatisfied with Newton's proof of the binomial theorem, and had replaced Newton's proof with a more rigorous one. He formulated the first detailed proof of the fundamental theorem of algebra that every algebraic equation has at least one real root, with the corollary that every equation of nth degree has n roots; and the fundamental theorem of arithmetic that every natural number can be factored into a product of primes in only one way. He also provided the first cogent proof of the law of quadratic reciprocity. Gauss formulated the properties of the bell-shaped Normal, or Gaussian, curve and further helped the beginnings of statistics by developing the method of least squares. He discovered Cauchy's theorem before Cauchy, non-Euclidean geometry before Bolyai, and left a notebook which showed that he had discovered, but not published, many of the mathematical developments of the nineteenth century. ∎

Further Reading:

Dictionary of Scientific Biography, s.v. "Gauss."

Tord Hall, *Carl Friedrich Gauss, A Biography*. Cambridge, 1970.

William L. Schaaf, *Carl Friedrich Gauss, Prince of Mathematics*. New York, 1964.

WILLIAM BRUNTON
b. May 26, 1777, Dalkeith, Scotland
d. Oct. 5, 1851, Camborne, Cornwall, England
British Mechanical and Civil Engineer

Life and Times:

The grandson of a colliery viewer and son of a watch and clockmaker, Brunton worked at Richard Arkwright's [q.v.] New Lanark cotton mills from 1790 to 1796 before gaining employment in the Soho works of Matthew Boulton and James Watt [q.v.] in Birmingham. He remained with Watt and Boulton until 1818, becoming superintendent of the engine manufactory. After further work as a mechanical and civil engineer, Brunton became in 1835 a partner in the Cwm Avon Tin Works, where he supervised the erection of copper smelting furnaces and copper rolling mills.

Brunton's most widely adopted invention was the calciner, a special furnace for extracting arsenic and sulphur compounds from tinstone, or tin oxide. Replacing the reverberatory furnace, by the mid-nineteenth century it was used in virtually all of Cornwall's tin mines and in Mexico's silver mines as well.

Outstanding Engineering Achievement:

In Brunton's calciner the bed was a revolving cast iron table. A hopper was placed in the arch above the bed. During the smelting process sulphur oxides exited from the furnace through a wide flue. The arsenic collected in several chambers, while the tin oxide fell from the table into a compartment below.

One of the pioneers of steam transport, Brunton designed some of the first engines used on ships sailing the Humber, Trent and Mersey rivers. Believing that locomotive engines would not grip railroad tracks except on level ground, Brunton built a "steam horse" in 1813 for a colliery. This was a locomotive fitted with human-like legs, including knee joints, that

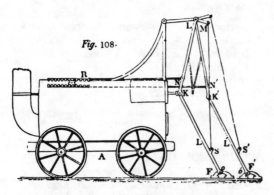

Fig. 108·

Brunton's "steam horse" in which the piston of a horizontally mounted engine is attached to the knee-joint, K, of a leg, L, alternately pressing on and raising the foot, F.

took six-foot-long steps. The locomotive operated through 1814 but exploded the following year. ∎

Further Reading:

Singer et al., *A History of Technology*, Vol. IV.

HANS CHRISTIAN OERSTED
b. Aug. 14, 1777, Rudkoebing, Langeland Island, Denmark
d. March 9, 1851, Copenhagen, Denmark
Danish Physicist

Life and Times:

In the first decades of the nineteenth century, the relationship between electricity and magnetism was not understood, although similarities between the phenomena were recognized. Both were known to have two types of poles, called positive and negative for electricity, and north and south for magnetism. Like poles repelled and unlike poles attracted. The force of this attraction was known to obey an inverse square law, comparable with that of gravity.

In 1751, Benjamin Franklin [q.v.] had shown that the discharge of a Leyden jar could magnetize iron needles, but 20 years later Charles Augustin de Coulomb [q.v.] found that a charged condenser had no effect on a compass needle. It was not realized at the time that it is the flow of electricity that is important. In fact, "electricity" then meant electrostatics, and "gal-

vanism" was the term for current electricity. It was Hans Christian Oersted who made the key observation that the flow of electricity causes a deflection in a magnetized needle.

Oersted reported his findings in July 1820. Astonished physicists in Europe and America verified them, and by the end of the year the mathematical laws governing the magnetic field of an electric current had been formulated, particularly by André-Marie Ampère [q.v.]. Research in electromagnetism led to the discovery that electricity is produced when a conductor moves in a magnetic field. This is the principle of the generator, which made possible the development of electricity as a major form of energy.

The son of an apothecary, Oersted showed an early interest in physics and chemistry, but since these subjects were not offered at the University of Copenhagen, he took a degree in pharmaceutical science and a doctorate in philosophy. After a year managing a pharmacy, he won a travel scholarship, which he spent visiting universities in Germany and France. In 1806 Oersted was appointed the University of Copenhagen's first lecturer in physics. He progressed to professor and eventually became Rector. In 1829 he initiated the founding of Copenhagen's Polytechnic Institute.

Oersted was widely respected, receiving honorary degrees from the universities of Erlangen and Prague, and he was also happily married and well liked. He encouraged Hans Christian Andersen, who, Oersted foretold, would be as famous for his stories as Oersted then was for his physics. The unit of magnetic field strength in the centimeter-gram-second electromagnetic system was named the oersted. It was in regular use for many years until the modern International System substituted others.

Outstanding Engineering Achievement:

As early as 1807 Oersted had stated his belief that both galvanism and magnetism were aspects of one force, but he found the connection only in the spring of 1820. At the end of a demonstration lecture, he placed a length of wire connected to his battery over a compass needle, and observed that the needle moved. He reversed the current, and the needle turned in the opposite direction. After further experimentation he also found that when he placed the wire at right angles to the needle, the needle did not move. All previously known forces—gravity, static electricity, magnetism—had influenced bodies directly towards or away from each other; here was one in which one body settled at right

Hans Christian Oersted holding a current-carrying wire over a magnetized needle and observing the deflections caused by the wire's magnetic field.

angles to the other. Oersted saw this as indicating that "the electric conflict . . . acts in a vortical or whorling movement" outside the conducting wire. This characterization was correct, as Ampère very soon demonstrated.

Oersted also did important early work in measuring the compressibility of liquids. The instrument which he developed for this task, the piezometer, consisted of a strong glass cylinder filled with water. Inside it was a glass bulb ending in a capillary tube that was dipped into mercury. The liquid under examination was placed in the bulb, the volume of which was known. When pressure was applied to the surface of the water, the compression of the liquid in the bulb caused more mercury to be drawn into the tube. Oersted included manometers to measure the pressure on the water and on the liquid; his results were so accurate that his value for the compressibility of water, .000047 of its volume for each increase of one atmosphere in pressure, is still the accepted value.

Although aluminum is the third most common element on earth, it occurs naturally only in compounds, and before Oersted's time had never been isolated. In 1825 Oersted mixed aluminum chloride with potassium dissolved in mercury. The more active potassium displaced the aluminum from the chloride. When the resulting aluminum amalgam was heated in a vacuum, the mercury evaporated, leaving a material that resembled tin. Two years later, the metal was identified as a new element. ∎

Further Reading:

H. Fyrth and M. Goldsmith, *Science History and Technology*. London, 1969.

B. Dibner, *Oersted and the Discovery of Electromagnetism*. New York, 1962.

Dictionary of Scientific Biography, s.v. "Oersted."

R. Stauffer, "Speculation and Experiment in the Background of Oersted's Discovery of Electromagnetism," *Isis*, **44** (1953), 33–50.

HUMPHRY DAVY
b. December 17, 1778, Penzance, England
d. May 29, 1829, Geneva, Switzerland
English chemist and inventor

In the second half of the eighteenth century, the English mining industry shifted the locus of its primary activity from the seabeds of the Severn and Tyne rivers to deeper, subterranean seams. While these new shafts increased both the supply and available reserves of British coal, they posed serious safety hazards for the men who worked the mines. Among the problems confronting the miners, explosions caused by the ignition of a mixture of coal-dust and air became increasingly common. By the early nineteenth century, attempts were made to combat the dangers of firedamp, as the mixture was called. One signal attempt was undertaken by an English chemist, Sir Humphry Davy, who developed a safety-lamp that bears his name. The Davy safety-lamp was intended to reduce the likelihood of firedamp explosions, and was regarded as a significant development in the history of the coal-mining industry. Its effect upon the safety of miners, however, was decidedly mixed.

Apprenticed to an apothecary, Davy developed an abiding interest in chemistry. At age twenty he wrote an essay on the nature of heat and light, in which he asserted that heat was the result of motion, rather than a substance, and thus rejected Lavoisier's theory of caloric. Shortly afterward, he was installed as a lecturer at the newly-formed Royal Institution, becoming a professor of chemistry within a year. One of his early chemical discoveries was of nitrous oxide, first used as an intoxicant, laughing gas, later as an anesthetic. Allessandro Volta's [q.v.] invention of the pile, or battery, enabled chemists to examine the effect of electrical charges upon the composition of elementary and compound substances. Through electrolysis Davy isolated the elements sodium, potassium, calcium, magnesium, barium, boron, and strontium. He was knighted in 1812.

In 1815 Davy was asked to investigate fire-damp explosions in coal mines. Within three months, he discovered that the primary component of firedamp was methane, which had been heated to a certain temperature and ignited, possibly by a spark from a miner's lamp. Davy then turned to ways of preventing the lamp flame from heating up the methane. He found that metal provided better insulation than glass, and on this basis he designed a safety-lamp. A similar lamp was designed by George Stephenson [q.v.] at the same time, but Davy was awarded priority.

The introduction of the Davy safety-lamp into coal mines did not, however, reduce the number of mine explosions. The safety-lamp afforded mine owners the opportunity of digging deeper and more extensive shafts. Thus the safety feature of the lamp was offset by the heightened risk of opening many new seams; moreover, air turbulence proved to be a source of ignition not accounted for by Davy's lamp.

Davy became President of the Royal Society in 1821; but in 1826 he suffered a stroke, and died in 1829.

Humphry Davy, discoverer of several chemical elements and inventor of a miner's safety lamp.

Outstanding Engineering Achievement:

Davy modified the design of the standard oil lamp, in which oil held in the base was burnt with an intense flame at the lamp's center. To disperse the heat, Davy surrounded the flame with a cylinder made from iron wire of about $\frac{1}{50}$ inch (0.5 mm) diameter, having 28 strands of wire per inch (11 per cm). Shortly after the lamp appeared, a second layer of gauze was added around the cylinder. To prevent this from weakening the light too much, part of the second layer was replaced with a glass tube. In the presence of methane the flame burns with a blue light. Because of this warning signal the lamp is still in use as a back-up to modern electronic systems. ∎

Further Reading:

Dictionary of Scientific Biography, s.v. "Davy."

The Collected Works of Sir Humphry Davy. 1839–40.

PAUL MOODY

b. May 21, 1779, Newbury, Massachusetts
d. July 8, 1831, Lowell, Massachusetts
American Mechanical Engineer, Inventor

Life and Times:

The Industrial Revolution took form in eighteenth century England with the invention of highly productive textile machinery and the introduction of the factory system. Hoping to keep the new industrial processes secret, the British government passed laws in 1774 and 1781 to prevent the export of machinery and the emigration of skilled workmen. England's monopoly was nonetheless broken in the 1790s, when Samuel Slater [q.v.], using his knowledge of modern textile machinery, established the factory system in the United States. America was to forge ahead of the mother country only 20 years later, when the first fully integrated, water-powered factory began converting raw cotton to finished cloth under a single roof. Although the concept was Francis Cabot Lowell's, the mechanical skill that made his idea a reality was Paul Moody's.

Moody displayed an early interest in mechanics and at 12 years of age became a weaver. Moving from one factory to another, he learned all he could about various types of mill machinery and was soon a master mechanic.

In 1800 Moody married and entered into a 14-year career as manager of a cotton mill in Amesbury, Massachusetts. Towards the end of this period he was approached by Francis Cabot Lowell, a wealthy entrepreneur who had just returned from a two-year stay in Britain. Posing as a merchant, Lowell had been able to observe the latest British textile machinery, including the recently invented power loom. Lowell now wished to build a mill on the British model at Waltham, where a 10-foot waterfall would provide power. But his mechanical ability was not great, and he enlisted Moody to help him reconstruct the loom. Moody succeeded and was placed in charge of the mill's engineering department.

In that capacity Moody equipped the Waltham mill with 1,700 spindles; several years later a larger factory with 3,600 spindles was built alongside. Once the Waltham complex was a thriving concern, its proprietors bought land in East Chelmsford—which they renamed Lowell—and prepared to build the prototypical New England mill town. Starting in 1823, Moody oversaw the installation of equipment and in 1825 took charge of the newly-built Lowell Machine Works. There, until his death six years later, he supervised a force of several hundred skilled mechanics who produced every type of machinery needed in cotton mills. The Lowell works' reputation as the best establishment of its kind in the nation was in no small part a legacy of Moody's.

Outstanding Engineering Achievements:

The wooden loom which Moody and Lowell built differed enough from its British inspiration, the power loom patented by William Horrocks of Stockport, to be virtually a separate invention. Though soon superseded, it was probably the first effective power loom used in America. The difficulty with power looms was that they subjected the warp threads to great stress, causing breakage. This problem could be solved if the warp was "dressed" with a coating, for instance starch, to strengthen it. Lowell was able to obtain a drawing of Horrocks' patent dressing machine, which Moody soon improved. He replaced the wooden rollers with soapstone ones which were unaffected by the moist warp threads, and devised a warper for putting the yarn on the beams of the loom. Moody's dresser, more than twice as efficient as Horrocks', remained in general use in the U.S. until mid-century.

Moody also improved the means by which the weft threads, or "filling," were conveyed to the loom's shuttle quills, which performed the actual weaving. Previously the threads had gone from a bobbin to a winder, which twisted them, and thence to the shuttle. Moody's filling-frame or filling-throstle allowed the threads to be spun directly on the bobbin, thus eliminating the expense and complication of separate winding.

In 1819 Moody and Lowell collaborated in improving the fly frame for roving cotton, the step preparatory to spinning. The English fly frame took no account of the changes in movement required as the receiving spool was filled. Lowell spent a week in mathematical calculations to determine how the roving could be fed smoothly onto the spool. Moody then built his "double speeder" to Lowell's specifications. This highly sophisticated device may have been Moody's greatest achievement.

Moody was also responsible for powering the machinery, both at Waltham and at Lowell. The Lowell falls were 30 feet (9 meters) high; there Moody oversaw construction of two waterwheels 30 feet (9 meters) in diameter and 12 feet (3.6 meters) long. He then regulated the flow of water onto the wheels by the use of the centrifugal governor, a device which Lowell had seen used in mills in England but could only vaguely describe. (James Watt [q.v.] had used this same sort of governor to regulate his steam engines.) An increased flow of water caused the governor to spin faster. The "fly-balls"—heavy metal balls suspended from the device's vertical axis—would then fly outwards, reducing the water flow. This was accomplished through a series of wires and levers joining the balls to a valve or watergate in the dam above the waterwheel. The result of this feedback system was a smooth, steady rotation of the wheel. Moody also eliminated the clumsy English gear drive system, substituting leather belts to transmit power from the wheel to countershafts and thence to the machines on each floor of the factory. ■

Further Reading:

Nathan Appleton, *Introduction of the Power Loom and Origin of Lowell.* Massachusetts, 1858.

Dictionary of American Biography, s.v. "Moody."

Steve Dunwell, *Run of the Mill.* Boston, 1978.

Waldemar Kaempffert, *A Popular History of American Invention,* Vol. II. New York, 1924.

WILLIAM HEDLEY

b. July 13, 1779, Newburn, England
d. Jan. 9, 1843, Burnhopeside Hall, England
British Mechanical Engineer

Life and Times:

The application of steam locomotives to railed wagon ways was first attempted by Richard Trevithick [q.v.] in 1804. This experiment attracted the interest of a number of inventive coal engineers, whose work over the next 30 years paved the way for George Stephenson [q.v.] and the *Rocket.* Locomotive designs of the era included an engine propelled by a chain pump and another propelled by mechanical legs.

The main problem in locomotive development—more a perceived problem than a real one—was the attainment of sufficient traction between wheels and rails to prevent slipping. Trevithick's experiments with smooth wheels had been conducted on cast-iron angle plates with standing flanges. A locomotive built by Matthew Murray [q.v.] in 1812 was dragged by a gear along a toothed rackrail laid between the two outer rails. The following year, however, William Hedley demonstrated that smooth wheels and rails could produce ample friction.

Hedley, born near Newcastle, had studied and worked in coal mines since his youth and by the early 1800s was a viewer (inspector) at the Wylam Colliery in Northumberland. At the request of his employer, Christopher Blackett, who was interested in steam transport but disliked Murray's locomotive, Hedley conducted traction tests. He concluded that no teeth were needed on either wheels or rails, and in 1813 built a smooth-wheeled locomotive. Its engine proved inadequate, and a second locomotive, called the *Wylam Dilly,* was built by Hedley and Timothy Hackworth [q.v.], the foreman of the Wylam blacksmith shop, later that year. For many years afterward it hauled eight loaded coal wagons at a speed of 4–5 miles (6.4–8 km) per hour on the Wylam plateway. Hedley's 1814 locomotive, *Puffing Billy,* which also ran in the colliery for many years, was equipped with the first grasshopper-beam engine.

Among Hedley's innovations was the "steam blast," in which exhaust steam was emptied into the chimney of the boiler, creating a greater draft and a hotter fire. However, because the blast produced a high-pitched screech that frightened the colliery horses, he chose instead to vent the steam quietly into the atmosphere through a reservoir. George Stephenson, who had no such

Puffing Billy, *Hedley's locomotive; on each side of the boiler is a cylinder with its piston attached directly to a grasshopper beam.*

inhibitions, used the steam blast and got the credit for its invention. Stephenson is said to have seen the *Puffing Billy* in action in 1814, when he was a mine foreman at a nearby colliery, and to have modeled one of his first locomotives after it.

Outstanding Engineering Achievements:

Hedley took out a patent in 1813 for a variety of methods of increasing engine traction, including the attachment of flanges or teeth to both sides of the wheel. Neither of his locomotives were equipped with them, however. His first successful engine, the *Wylam Dilly,* built in 1813 for the colliery plateway, had four smooth wheels, a wrought-iron boiler utilizing a return flue invented by Trevithick, and a silencer for the venting of steam.

The *Puffing Billy,* built in 1813 or 1814, was the first locomotive to employ grasshopper beams, which transmitted motion vertically from the engine's two cylinders to spur wheels and thence to the track wheels, 39 inches (99 cm) in diameter. The boiler, which was partially heated by an extension of the furnace and had a return flue, was lagged with wood. The engine is now in the Science Museum in Kensington, London.

Some writers credit Hedley with being the first to demonstrate the economic advantage of steam railway transport over horses; others give the credit to Matthew Murray. Hedley is also credited with being the first to put smooth-wheeled locomotives in regular operation in collieries. They were not thought to be safe except on dead levels, however, and stationary steam engines were used to haul them up even gentle inclines until 1836, when the American William Norris proved smooth-wheeled traction adequate for steep grades. ■

Further Reading:

R. L. Galloway, *A History of Coal Mining in Great Britain*. London, 1882.

———, *The Steam Engine and Its Inventors*. London, 1881.

Angus Sinclair, *Development of the Locomotive Engine*. Cambridge, Massachusetts, 1970.

J.N. Westwood, *Locomotive Designers in the Age of Steam*. Rutherford, New Jersey, 1978.

JOHN STRINGFELLOW
b. Dec. 6, 1779, Attercliffe, England
d. Dec. 13, 1883, Chard, England
British Aeronautical Engineer

Life and Times:

The hundred years preceding the success of the Wright brothers saw important developments that prepared the way for the first manned, powered, heavier-than-air flight. At the beginning of this period George Cayley [q.v.] clearly stated the principles of aerodynamics, an accomplishment equalled only by Leonardo da Vinci's [q.v.] writings on the same

John Stringfellow, designer of a steam-powered model airplane which proved that a self-propelled aircraft was a possibility.

subject. Midway through the century heavier-than-air flight became a reality with the launching of Cayley's manned glider and John Stringfellow's steam-powered model airplane. Fifty years of experimenting and technical advances would elapse before the crowning achievement at Kitty Hawk.

Stringfellow's experiments might seem of minor importance today, when model airplanes are largely flown by children. Nor, in truth, did they impress Stringfellow's contemporaries. Yet he deserved the wide recognition given by the ancient Greeks to Archytas [q.v.], who was credited with the invention of a mechanical dove. For until Stringfellow flew his model there was no proof that an aircraft could be sustained and propelled by its own power.

Stringfellow's father was a skilled mechanic. His son, who inherited this talent, was apprenticed to a lacemaker in Nottingham and became known as a maker of bobbins. Stringfellow moved in 1820 to Chard in Somerset, a center for lace manufacture, and within a few years he set up a machine shop to serve the lace industry. Some time before 1842 he met the engineer William Henson, a fellow townsman who was eager to design and build a steam-powered flying machine. Stringfellow probably assisted Henson with the design of the airplane's steam engine; he then joined Henson and others in an attempt to form an Aerial Transit Company.

The public greeted this project with amused disbelief. Since no funds could be raised for the construction of a full-sized airplane, in 1843 Stringfellow and Henson agreed to work on a model, which they hoped would prove the practicability of powered flight. The two tested their model on a hill near Chard during the summer of 1847, but it failed to fly. Discouraged, Henson left for America. The determined Stringfellow built a smaller model, tested it indoors in an unused lace factory, and in 1848 succeeded in making it fly.

After repeating this exploit in London later that year, Stringfellow seems to have abandoned model-making for two decades. His interest revived with the foundation of the Aeronautical Society of Great Britain. At the society's 1868 exhibition Stringfellow displayed a model triplane and won a prize of 100 pounds for constructing a light but powerful engine. Stringfellow remained an avid experimenter until shortly before his death.

Outstanding Engineering Achievements:

Stringfellow and Henson's model plane, with

its 20-foot (six-meter) wing span, was too large and too unstable to fly in the open air. The 1848 model embodied several changes, chiefly in the wings. These were 10 feet (three meters) from tip to tip, and instead of being completely rigid had trailing edges of silk unsupported by a spar. Da Vinci had proposed this general mode of wing construction, based on the bird's wing, and nineteenth century theoreticians advocated it as well. The rigid front section was supposed to impart strength, while the flexible rear edge permitted the wings to adapt to local air disturbances. A few later airplane builders would follow Stringfellow's lead, though how valuable this feature really was may be questioned.

Stringfellow also devised an ingenious launching method. A carriage holding the airplane was suspended from a wire. When the engine's steam pressure had built up, the carriage and the airplane traveled to the end of the wire; there the carriage automatically released the airplane, which continued its trajectory in the air without support. Thus launched, the model flew 40 feet (12 meters), climbing at a rate of one in seven, before striking a large canvas that had been set up to stop it. When the experiment was repeated at Cremorne Gardens in London, Stringfellow's airplane flew 120 feet (37 meters).

The wings and tail had a total surface of 18 square feet (1.6 sq. meters). Even so, the model weighed under nine pounds (four kg), including engine, water, and fuel. The cylinder was three-quarters of an inch (19 mm) in diameter, with a piston stroke of two inches (50 mm). Power was communicated to two pusher propellers 16 inches (41 cm) in diameter; these were the first airscrews used to propel a heavier-than-air craft. A spirit lamp provided heat for the boiler.

Little can be said of Stringfellow's 1868 triplane, which was never flown. His prize-winning engine, however, was remarkable. The two-inch (50 mm) cylinder contained a piston with a three-inch (75 mm) stroke. It was estimated to generate more than one horsepower, although engine and boiler together weighed only 13 pounds (six kg). By comparison, the three-horsepower engine that Henri Giffard used in 1852 to propel his navigable balloon weighed 350 pounds (160 kg), and it was considered a model of lightness. ∎

Further Reading:

Richard Bishop, *From Kite to Kitty Hawk.* 1958.

M. J. B. Davy, *Henson and Stringfellow: Their Work in Aeronautics.* London, 1931.

JOSEPH ASPDIN
b. 1779, Leeds, England
d. 1855
British Inventor

Life and Times:

By the late eighteenth century, the growing shortage of timber in Britain had put a serious squeeze on the building trades at a time when the country's industrialization demanded more canals, tunnels, docks and other structures. Some builders sought to reduce their use of wood by developing an effective hydraulic mortar or cement, i.e., one that could be used in water. Though some succeeded, the materials they used—including marble and tertiary limestone—were themselves scarce. John Aspdin overcame this problem by producing a hydraulic cement of consistent quality from readily available substances.

A stone mason and bricklayer turned builder, Aspdin discovered that clay heated together with common chalk or limestone formed a dull gray concrete. He patented the product in 1824, calling it Portland cement after the whitish limestone popular in Britain as a building material. Aspdin's son William took over large-scale production of Portland cement, establishing a works on the Thames in 1843 and another at Gateshead in 1851.

Civil engineers soon learned the value of Portland cement in heavy-duty construction work. Marc Isambard Brunel [q.v.] used it to fill holes in his Thames River tunnel, which opened in 1843. Aspdin's concrete was also used to rebuild the foundations of the Westminster, Blackfriars and Waterloo bridges in London, undermined by tidal waters. Sir Joseph Bazalgette chose Portland cement as the main structural material in the reconstruction of the London sewage system; 70,000 tons of the substance were used in the project, which began in 1858 and lasted for 17 years.

Outstanding Engineering Achievement:

Aspdin's process called for grinding chalk or limestone into a powder, mixing it with clay, then mixing this combination with water. The mixture was allowed to dry, either in the sun or by being heated in pans. The lumps of clay-limestone were then heated in a kiln until they formed a glassy sinter. This clinker-like material was ground into a powder.

Aspdin's 1824 patent indicated that the clay-limestone mixture was to be heated in a kiln at low temperature. The material eventually marketed as Portland cement, however, was produced at much higher temperatures. Aspdin evidently discovered after taking out his patent that more intense heat produced superior results, and secretly incorporated the change into his process.

The cement works operated by William & Aspdin made use of large, conical kilns with truncated tops. One surviving example is 36 feet (11 meters) high and 17 feet (5.2 meters) in diameter at the base, tapering to 2 feet 9 inches (83 cm) in diameter at the top. Its capacity is some 32,000 pounds (14,500 kg) of cement. ■

Further Reading:

Norman Davey, *A History of Building Materials.* London, 1961.

Kranzberg and Pursell, *Technology in Western Civilization.* New York, 1967.

Abraham Wolf, *A History of Science, Technology and Philosophy in the Eighteenth Century.* London, 1952.

JOSEPH CLEMENT
b. *1779, Great Ashby, Westmoreland, England*
d. *1844, Newington Butts, London, England*
British Mechanical Engineer

Life and Times:

The development of increasingly complex machinery during the Industrial Revolution made the standardization and interchangeability of machine parts a matter of critical importance. In the early nineteenth century, when Joseph Clement served as chief draftsman for Britain's leading engineering firm, Maudslay, Sons, and Field, standards of accuracy in the toolmaker's shop were still lax. Clement and Henry Maudslay [q.v.] sought to improve this situation by insisting on the production of true plane surfaces for machine parts. Clement helped make this possible by developing the first reliable planing machine.

Joseph Clement's earliest professional ambition was to be a mechanic. But as the son of a hand-loom weaver, he had no childhood opportunity to learn the technical skills such as drafting which were required of mechanical engineers. In 1802 Clement moved to Kirby Stephen, where he worked in the construction and repair of power looms and began to teach himself the craft of mechanical drafting. In 1813 he went to

London, finding employment in the tool shop of the noted inventor Joseph Bramah [q.v.]. His reputation as a first-rate "tool improver" attracted the attention of Maudslay, who made Clement his chief draftsman in 1814. Three years later, Clement established a small workshop of his own in Newington Butts.

Clement's planing machine, built in 1825, was the best early model. Other planing machines had been constructed by Matthew Murray [q.v.], an important steam-engine manufacturer, and Richard Roberts [q.v.], inventor of the self-acting spinning mule. Clement's planer, however, was for more than a decade the only machine capable of surfacing large pieces of cast iron. The device could take work up to six feet (1.8 meters) square and was in sufficient demand to become Clement's principal source of income. Charging eighteen shillings per square foot, Clement could earn 20 pounds per day. In 1842 Joseph Whitworth significantly improved the planing machine by making it self-acting.

Outstanding Engineering Achievement:

Clement's planing machine was equipped with two stationary cutting tools. The work was held on a table moved back and forth by hand on rollers, passing beneath the cutting tools in both directions. ■

Further Reading:

Singer et al., *A History of Technology.* Vol. IV.

Samuel Smiles, *Lives of the Engineers.* London, 1904.

ROBERT HARE
b. *Jan. 17, 1781, Philadelphia, Pennsylvania*
d. *May 15, 1858, Philadelphia, Pennsylvania*
American Chemist and Inventor

Life and Times:

Until 1815 Hare managed a family brewery, but he had an abiding interest in chemistry. He learned the subject by studying on his own and attending lectures at the University of Pennsylvania. Hare's obvious ability earned him a post as professor of natural philosophy at the Medical School of the University of Pennsylvania in 1810. He remained at the university, except for a six-year interval ending in 1818, until 1847. He became recognized as an outstanding teacher who excelled in illustrating his lectures by performing experiments with apparatus of his own invention. Hare's major achievement, however, came in 1801, long before his academic career began, with his invention of the oxyhydrogen blowtorch.

Capable of producing far higher temperatures than had ever been achieved, Hare's blowtorch could melt large quantities of substances previously regarded as infusible. These included platinum (melting point: 1,769°C), a metal valued for its resistance to corrosion. Though not immediately put to commercial use, the oxyhydrogen blowtorch made possible the founding of the platinum industry in the mid-nineteenth century. All modern methods of cutting and welding metals are based on improvements on Hare's blowtorch. In addition, Thomas Drummond [q.v.] found in the 1820s that by playing the blowtorch on a block of calcium oxide (lime), a brilliant light could be created. This device became known as the Drummond light or limelight.

Because Hare was an American, he was not in the mainstream of scientific activity during the early nineteenth century. If he had lived in Europe, his blowtorch and many other inventions might have earned him considerably more attention than he received.

Outstanding Engineering Achievement:

Seeking to produce higher temperatures than ever achieved, Hare decided to create a flame by the combustion of hydrogen and oxygen. He obtained these gases by the electrolysis of water. Using a keg from his father's brewery, Hare constructed a device with two compartments to hold both gases. Oxygen and hydrogen could be forced from the gas holder by pumping in water. From sheet tin, he rolled two long, thin, and somewhat flexible tubes. Hare attached one end of each tube to the gas holder and the other end to a device built from two blowpipes, in which the gases were mixed and ignited.

During his academic career, Hare invented or improved a number of electrical devices. These included the calorimotor (1819), a powerful galvanic battery that served as a model for Gaston Planté in his construction of the secondary battery. His deflagrator (1821), a device in which any series of cells could be activated or rendered passive at will, generated high electric current. In 1829, Hare invented the first electric furnace ever used. With it he converted charcoal into graphite, produced calcium carbide and purified phosphorus and calcium. Ten years

later, Hare discovered the utility of the mercury cathode in the electrolysis of aqueous solutions of metallic salts.

Hare also invented several eudiometers for gas analysis; synthesized ammonia by aiming a jet of a gaseous mixture of two parts nitric oxide to five parts hydrogen at a heated platinum sponge; devised new methods for isolating a number of elements, including boron and silicon; and developed a chemical process for denarcotizing the opiate laudanum. ■

Further Reading:

Edgar F. Smith, *Life of Robert Hare, An American Chemist (1781–1858)*. Philadelphia, 1917.

SAMUEL CLEGG
b. March 2, 1781, Manchester, England
d. Jan. 8, 1861, Haverstock Hill, Middlesex, England
British Mechanical Engineer

Life and Times:

Eighteenth-century efforts to make good coke from coal demonstrated that heated coal gives off an inflammable gas. In the 1790s Englishman William Murdock [q.v.] and Frenchman Philippe Lebon [q.v.] began experiments with gas that led to its first commercial use in illuminating buildings at the start of the nineteenth century. Meanwhile Napoleon's blockade, by creating a shortage of whale oil and tallow in England, spurred new advances in gas illumination there from 1800 to 1815. Much of this progress was the work of Samuel Clegg, who was uniquely qualified in the field of gas illumination because of his background in both chemistry and engineering.

After receiving a scientific education from the famous chemist John Dalton, Clegg became an apprentice at the Boulton and Watt engineering works where he witnessed Murdock's early experiments with gas. He left the firm in 1805 and shortly after installed gas lighting at a cotton mill near Halifax, introducing an improved method of purifying gas with lime.

Clegg's success in lighting a London establishment by gas led to his appointment in 1813 as chief engineer of the Chartered Gas Company, and in 1814 he completed a gasworks that illuminated an entire district of London. The first central gasworks for lighting an entire area, including streets, it represented the beginning of gas illumination on a large scale.

Gas lighting was safer than candles or oil lamps, and therefore reduced fire-insurance premiums. It also produced better light, allowing factories to remain open at night. As a result, Clegg's success in constructing a practical central gas-lighting system spurred the rapid spread of gas illumination to Baltimore, Paris, Boston, New York and Hanover by 1825.

Between 1815 and 1817, when he left the Chartered Gas Company, Clegg patented important innovations in gas engineering. He devised an improved method of gas purification by lime, a gas meter that became the model for all later devices measuring gas consumption, and a self-acting governor to maintain a constant gas pressure. His coal-efficient rotating retort for producing gas was ahead of its time but very costly to build and did not come into general use until later.

Outstanding Engineering Achievements:

Clegg first used lime to purify gas around 1805. He simply added lime to the water through which the gas was transmitted for cooling. Ten years later he patented a semi-fluid lime machine containing cream of lime. Through the machine passed a shaft to which paddles were attached so that the mixture could be constantly agitated while the gas went through it. This ensured that all of the mixture was used in removing malodorous substances and impurities.

The self-acting governor invented by Clegg consisted of a hollow upright cylinder closed at top and bottom, inside of which a small conical gasometer floated in water. Gas entered the gasometer by a pipe ascending perpendicularly through the center of the cylinder's bottom. A conical valve at the bottom of the gasometer was constructed so that the orifice by which the gas entered was contracted or enlarged by the rising or falling of the gasometer in the water as the pressure increased or decreased.

Clegg's rotating retort, in which coal was heated to produce gas, was built in light of the experimentally discovered fact that gas was manufactured most efficiently when the coal was burned quickly in thin layers. His retort consisted of a tray divided into fifteen sections by the spokes of a horizontal wheel that could be rotated manually. A thin layer of coal was placed in each section. The wheel was rotated every two hours so that at any time five sections were over the red heat, five were waiting to be placed over the heat, and five, having been processed, were ready to be emptied and refilled. ■

Further Reading:

W. T. O'Dea, *Social History of Lighting*, 1958.

Singer et al., *A History of Technology,* Vol. IV.

GEORGE STEPHENSON
b. July 9, 1781, Wylam, Northumberland, England
d. Aug. 12, 1848, nr. Chesterfield, Derbyshire, England
British Mechanical Engineer

Life and Times:

The introduction of steam-powered machinery and the emergence of the factory system in eighteenth-century Britain greatly increased the burden upon the nation's transportation system. Canal transport, impeded by ice for part of the year and too slow besides, could not cope with the ever-growing amounts of raw materials and finished goods flowing in and out of Britain's manufacturing centers. The transportation revolution that met the expanding requirements of commerce was led by George Stephenson. For although he invented neither the high-speed engine, the steam locomotive that employed it, nor the railway, Stephenson brought them together to create the first economically practical modern railroad.

The son of a poor colliery engineman, Stephenson followed in his father's footsteps. Though he received no formal schooling, Stephenson learned how to read at age 19 so that he could find out more about the steam engines and other mechanical devices that fascinated him. In 1814 he built a steam locomotive for the railway at the Killingworth Colliery. Hardly an improvement over the first steam railway locomotive, built by Richard Trevithick [q.v.] in 1804, Stephenson's machine ran at only four miles per hour and consumed large quantities of coal. It proved less efficient than the horse-drawn carts normally used on colliery railways. But in succeeding years he made improvements in both the locomotive and tracks that he built for other collieries.

Stephenson won an opportunity to apply his talents to public transport in 1822, when he became the engineer in charge of building a railway line between Stockton and Darlington along the river Tees. It was originally intended to be a horse railroad, but he convinced its directors to permit him to build a locomotive for

George Stephenson (standing left) and his son Robert Stephenson (seated). Robert is holding the miner's safety lamp that his father invented, while George is pointing to the Rocket, *the locomotive on which father and son collaborated.*

the line. In 1823 he established an engine works at Newcastle, named Robert Stephenson and Co. after his son, to construct the locomotive. Tested in 1825, the "Locomotion" hauled 90 tons over a nine-mile level stretch of the railroad at an unheard-of maximum speed of 12 miles (19 km) per hour. The Stockton and Darlington Railway, the first general freight-and-passenger locomotive railroad in the world, became a great financial success.

But it was Stephenson's work on the Liverpool and Manchester Railway that unquestionably established the modern railroad's reputation. The line's promoters, seeking a means to handle the huge output of Manchester's cotton mills, planned to employ stationary engines and haulage cables. Stephenson, appointed chief engineer to survey the 30-mile (48 km) railway in 1824, again convinced his superiors to employ the locomotive. He laid out the line in the face of great public resistance, for literature sponsored by canal interests had convinced many people that the steam locomotive would poison the air, terrify livestock, ruin arable land, and otherwise wreak havoc on the countryside. Then, in 1829, his locomotive, the *Rocket*, built with the help of his son Robert, bested its competitors in the famous Rainhill Locomotive Trials. Carrying thirty passengers, the locomotive reached a maximum speed of 30 miles (48 km) per hour, and its passengers, contrary to some predictions, did not go insane. Without trailers, the *Rocket* reached 35 miles (56 km) per hour.

The amazing success of the Liverpool and Manchester line spurred a railroad-building fever in Europe and the United States. Recognized as the world's foremost railroad expert,

Stephenson was consulted by engineers from many countries, and his engine works was called upon to supply an ever-increasing number of locomotives. In 1847 he became the first president of the Institution of Mechanical Engineers.

The railroad systems that Stephenson pioneered accelerated industrial growth by enlarging markets, reducing the price of raw materials, and increasing the mobility of the labor force.

Outstanding Engineering Achievements:

Stephenson's success was not founded primarily upon startling innovations. Rather, it rested largely upon his ability to conceive of the steam locomotive railroad as a comprehensive system within which locomotives and rail lines had to be upgraded in mutually-supporting tandem.

Soon after testing his first locomotive in 1814, Stephenson began making improvements. He replaced the locomotive's cast iron wheels with less brittle wrought iron ones and initiated the use of wrought iron rails. He also substituted "edge rails" for the popular "tram-plate rails" to increase lateral strength through increased depth. To increase the engine's power, Stephenson borrowed the device, first used by Richard Trevithick [q.v.], of ejecting steam through a pipe in the boiler chimney after the steam had performed its work in the engine cylinder. The chimney blast caused a suction draft through the furnace and stimulated combustion.

Seeking to cope with the problem of friction, Stephenson created a device to measure the drag of the train against the pull of the engine. He discovered that friction was constant at all speeds but that a gradient of only 1% more than tripled resistance. He concluded that inclined planes should be avoided if at all possible.

Stephenson applied this lesson to the construction of the Liverpool and Manchester line, performing remarkable engineering feats in doing so. A two-mile (3.2 km) long cut was hewn out of solid rock at Olive Mount near Liverpool. About 48,000 cubic yards (36,700 cubic meters) of stone were removed, and at some points the track ran eighty feet below the surface. Over Chat Moss, a swamp extending four miles along the line, he laid a floating platform made of loose turf and heather covered with gravel. Stephenson also built sixty-three bridges and two tunnels to keep the track level.

In constructing his locomotive, the "Rocket," for the L & M Railway, Stephenson and his son Robert built a multitubular boiler to increase the thermal efficiency of the engine. Twenty-five

The Stephensons' locomotive the Rocket, *the first engine of the first commercially successful railway line.*

three-inch (7.6 cm) copper tubes conveyed hot furnace gases from the rear of the boiler to the chimney. The water in the boiler thus came into contact with more heat than before, and a greater amount of steam was generated. Whether the Stephensons invented this arrangement independently or borrowed it from the French engineer Marc Seguin [q.v.] is not clear. In addition, the firebox at the back of the boiler was surrounded by water compartments to conserve heat.

Stephenson did not restrict his attention entirely to the steam locomotive. In 1815, spurred by a serious mine explosion, he invented the miner's safety lamp, which enabled colliers to work safely in gas-filled areas. In the oil lamp previously used, air reached the flame through a wide funnel which the gas could also enter, resulting in explosions. But the safety lamp, constructed on the premise that the gas could not penetrate small apertures, brought air to the flame through a narrow tube and surrounded the flame with a perforated metal plate. Sir Humphrey Davy [q.v.], an eminent London scientist, invented an almost identical lamp at virtually the same time. ∎

Further Reading:

James Kip Finch, *The Story of Engineering.* Garden City, New York, 1960.

Robert S. Kirby, et al., *Engineering in History.* New York, 1956.

Joachim C. Leithaüser, *Inventors' Progress,* trans. by Michael Bullock. Cleveland, Ohio, 1959.

Lionel T.C. Rolt, *The Railway Revolution: George and Robert Stephenson.* New York, 1962.

WILLIAM STURGEON
b. May 22, 1783, Whittington, Lancashire, England
d. Dec. 4, 1850, Prestwich, Lancashire, England
British Electrical Engineer

Life and Times:

William Sturgeon, inventor of the first electromagnet capable of holding its own weight, was a former cobbler's apprentice who taught himself basic mathematics, science, Greek, and Latin while serving in the Royal Artillery. He continued to conduct electrical experiments after leaving the army in 1820, at the age of 37, and became a lecturer and contributor to scientific journals while supporting himself as a bootmaker.

Sturgeon was acquainted with the recent discovery by Hans Christian Oersted [q.v.] that an electrified wire generates a circular magnetic field, and with the subsequent realization by André-Marie Ampère [q.v.] that an electrified wire coil, or solenoid, will act as a magnet. In 1823 he created the first actual electromagnet, for which he won the 1825 silver medal of the Society of Arts, by winding a solenoid around a

Sturgeon's electromagnetic motor; the switching on and off of four vertical electromagnets caused two horizontal magnets to spin.

bar of soft iron, producing a magnet able to lift twenty times its own weight. A year later he was appointed lecturer in science and philosophy at the East India Company's Royal Military College in Addiscombe.

During the next 16 years, Sturgeon engaged in numerous researches into electricity and electromagnetism, including the electrical ignition of gunpowder, the amalgamation of zinc with mercury for use in voltaic batteries, and the large-scale production of inexpensive batteries. In the course of 500 kite experiments he established the positive charge of the atmosphere in calm weather. His inventions included the commutator, a device for giving a single direction to opposing currents; an electromagnetic rotary engine; the first suspended coil galvanometer for measuring current; a device for preventing the breaking of Leyden jars during experiments involving electrical explosions; and an electromagnetic machine for producing shocks, later widely used as an alleged cure for assorted medical problems.

In 1836 Sturgeon founded the *Annals of Electricity,* a monthly periodical that continued publication until 1843, at which time he tried unsuccessfully to start the *Annals of Philosophical Discovery and Monthly Reporter of the Progress of Practical Science.* He encountered financial difficulties the following year with the failure of the Royal Victoria Gallery of Practical Science in Manchester, a technical school which he had superintended for four years. During the last years of his life Sturgeon supported his family through occasional lecturing and with a small grant and annuity provided by Lord John Russell. A volume of his collected scientific papers was published in Manchester in 1850.

Outstanding Engineering Achievements:

Sturgeon's electromagnet of 1823 consisted of a copper wire wrapped 18 times around a horseshoe-shaped bar of soft iron, one-half inch (13 mm) thick and insulated with varnish. Ampère had already determined that a coil of wire will become magnetized when it serves as a conductor of electric current; Sturgeon's addition of the iron core greatly increased the level of magnetization and enabled the seven-ounce (196 grams) device to support a weight of nine pounds (4 kg). Joseph Henry [q.v.] later increased the holding ability of the electromagnet to 3,600 lbs (1630 kg) by insulating the closely-packed wire coil with silk. The electromagnet was essential to the development of the telegraph, telephone and the electric motor. ∎

Further Reading:

Dictionary of National Biography, s.v. "Sturgeon."
Dictionary of Scientific Biography, s.v. "Sturgeon."

RICHARD JOHN GRIFFITH
b. Sept. 20, 1784, Dublin, Ireland
d. Sept. 22, 1878, Dublin, Ireland
Irish Civil Engineer and Geologist

Life and Times:

The 1801 Act of Union politically linked wretched and turbulent Ireland to Great Britain. That Act did nothing to solve Ireland's grievous social conditions—absentee landlords, rack rents, and overpopulation. Its passage did, however, lead Richard Griffith to take up a new career, that of civil engineer. During the ensuing half century Griffith's work speeded the modernization of his country's agriculture, transportation, and mining, and earned him the title of "father of Irish geology."

Griffith's father was a merchant and member of the Irish House of Commons. Griffith himself at first embarked on a military career, joining the Royal Irish Artillery as a lieutenant in 1799. After the Union, his regiment was consolidated with a British unit. His patriotic feelings offended, Griffith left the service and turned instead to civil engineering.

Griffith went to London for two years to study chemistry and geology with William Nicholson, editor of the *Journal of Natural Philosophy.* During the following five years he acquired practical experience, working in the mines of Cornwall and touring all the other mining districts in Great Britain. Griffith's abilities were impressive; at 23 he was elected a fellow of the Royal Society of Edinburgh. Refusing offers of employment, he returned to his native land and in 1809 was appointed engineer to a commission on waste lands.

In 1812 Griffith became inspector general of Irish mines and was appointed mining engineer to the Royal Dublin Society. When famine struck in 1822, he was assigned to conduct relief work and to build roads in the undeveloped southwest. He subsequently supervised the surveying of territorial boundaries and the valuation of properties throughout Ireland. Aside from their public value, these assignments helped him to prepare a superb geological map of Ireland, a project on which he worked intermittently from 1812 until 1855. His official responsibilities meanwhile continued to grow. He was involved in practically every public works project in Ireland from 1830 until 1864, and his influence continued even after he retired.

Outstanding Engineering Achievement:

Griffith conducted important road building activities in the rugged southwestern counties of Cork, Kerry, and Limerick. Work began in 1822 and was completed by 1830. The 250 miles (400 km) of coach road he built, presumably using the advanced techniques recently developed in England, were some of the finest in Ireland. Griffith's careful location work opened up a lawless and poverty-stricken area to trade and encouraged the growth of towns and the spread of agriculture. Had the government followed his equally well-thought-out recommendations for the siting of railroads, many detours would subsequently have been avoided.

Griffith's survey of the waste lands of Ireland, carried out between 1809 and 1812, was considered authoritative a generation later. Reports based on his work estimated that some 2.8 million acres (1.13 million hectares) of bog could and should be reclaimed, either for farmland or for pasture. The government was slow to act, although at intervals between 1834 and 1851 it permitted Griffith to experiment with land reclamation in Cork. Griffith's work was not, however, followed up with large-scale projects.

Dublin was the scene of an important urban renewal project carried out by Griffith. To rid the area near the Royal Barracks of a pestilential slum, Griffith diverted the flow of the river Liffey and literally washed the district away. In its stead he laid out healthful ornamental grounds. Griffith proved to be a practical architect as well, gracing the capital with its National Gallery and Museum of Natural History.

Other Achievements:

Griffith's geological map of Ireland, drawn on a scale of four miles to the inch, contained forty different stratigraphic horizons. The map won praise as "one of the most remarkable productions . . . ever effected by a single geologist." In the course of his years of field work, Griffith amassed a collection of carboniferous fossils that included 450 previously unknown species. ∎

Further Reading:

Dictionary of National Biography, s.v. "Griffith."

Dictionary of Scientific Biography, s.v. "Griffith."

George O'Brien, *The Economic History of Ireland in the Eighteenth Century.* Dublin, 1918.

"Sir Richard Griffith," *Dublin University Magazine.* Vol. LXXXIII (April 1874).

ITHIEL TOWN
b. Oct. 3, 1784, Thompson, Connecticut
d. June 13, 1844, New Haven, Connecticut
American Architect and Civil Engineer

Life and Times:

Early American bridge builders faced problems different from those of their European counterparts. Capital and labor for engineering projects were scarce. Bridges often had to be constructed quickly, with readily available materials, to meet the needs of growing communities. For these reasons American engineers pioneered in the construction of large wooden bridges, which were relatively easy to assemble and made use of the continent's most abundant resource. These bridges were first designed with wooden arches, reinforced by only a few diagonal struts. But it was later discovered that a bridge consisting of a horizontal wooden framework, or truss, would bear at least as much weight as an arched wooden bridge. One of the early popularizers of this design was Ithiel Town, inventor of "Town's patent lattice bridge."

Descended from early settlers of Massachusetts, Town worked as a carpenter and teacher before moving to Boston to study architecture at a school run by Asher Benjamin. By the time he turned his attention to bridges he was a prominent architect, known for buildings in New Haven, Hartford, New York and other cities. His work showed a classical taste and innovation in engineering and design.

Town patented his design for a wooden truss bridge in early 1820. His income from this source soon exceeded his earnings as an architect, and he improved on his own patent with another granted in 1835. Success brought him the acquaintance of such contemporaries as Eli Whitney [q.v.] and allowed him to assemble one of the finest early American collections of books on architecture and the fine arts. In 1829–30 Town toured Europe in the company of Samuel F.B. Morse [q.v.]; afterwards he became an active promoter of transatlantic passenger steamship service.

Outstanding Engineering Achievements:

Town's wooden truss bridges rested on masonry piers spaced as much as 200 feet (60 meters) apart—he spoke of going to 300 feet (90 meters)—to prevent ice and debris from collecting between the spans and to allow the dead weight of the truss to stabilize the supports. In his improved design of 1835, the rigidity of the truss was secured by a double series of lattice braces along the sides of the bridge, each series resembling a trellis but made of strong lumber rather than laths. The double series was reinforced by a continuous series of horizontal string pieces nailed between the two sets of diagonals at the first complete diamonds near the top and bottom of the structure. Most of Town's bridges were covered to preserve the wooden truss.

Town's design had several advantages over others. The truss structure gave only vertical thrust on the masonry supports, so that even if part of a span were destroyed, the bridge would not collapse completely. Also, it was easy to construct drawbridges in which a span pivoted on a support. Different principles were later required for really long spans, but many wooden truss bridges were quite large, able to support twin railroad tracks. The longest bridge built according to Town's design crossed the James River at Richmond, Va. with 18 spans measuring 130 to 150 feet (40 to 45 meters); it was completed in 1838.

Other Achievements:

Town was an important architect of churches and public buildings, including the Center Church in New Haven, circa 1812; Trinity Church in New Haven, 1814; Christ Church in Hartford; state capitol buildings in Connecticut, Indiana and North Carolina; the customs house on Wall Street; and the asylum building on the grounds of the Cathedral of St. John the Divine in New York. In constructing Center Church Town took the unusual step of assembling the spire inside the church and raising it to position by a windlass and tackle of his own devising. ∎

Further Reading:

Dictionary of American Biography, s.v. "Town."

Who Was Who in America, Historical Volume 1607–1896. New York, 1963.

Ithiel Town, *A Description of Ithiel Town's Improvement in the Principle, Construction and Practical Execution of Bridges for Roads, Railroads, etc.* New York, 1839.

PIERRE CHARLES FRANÇOIS DUPIN
b. Oct. 6, 1784, Varzy, France
d. Jan. 18, 1873, Paris, France
French Naval Engineer and Mathematician

Life and Times:

Known mainly as a pioneer in popular technical education, Charles Dupin also did important work in differential geometry with applications to optics and to nautical and civil engineering. Dupin's father was a lawyer and provincial legislator. At 17, Dupin entered France's new scientific and technical institute, the Ecole Polytechnique; under the tutelage of the school's first director, Gaspard Monge [q.v.] he quickly developed his interest in geometry, discovering the surface known to this day as the cycloid of Dupin. He graduated in 1803 and went on to the school of naval engineering. Over the next seven years Dupin was assigned to Antwerp, Genoa, Toulon, and Corfu. While restoring the arsenal at Corfu, he found time to do research and give public courses at the Ionian Academy; this was Dupin's first attempt to popularize mechanics and physics.

Dupin remained a naval engineer until 1816, serving at Toulon and Dunkirk. But the defeat of Napoleon in 1815 and the subsequent occupation of France led him to pursue new interests. In 1816 Dupin obtained permission to visit England and survey its military installations and industries. More visits followed; in 1820 he published the first of numerous statistical analyses of the British and French economies, works which achieved great popularity on both sides of the Channel.

Dupin admired British institutions. His glowing report concerning the school of applied science in Glasgow led to the inception of public lectures at the Conservatoire des Arts et Métiers in Paris. From 1819 until 1854, Dupin taught courses on the industrial applications of chemistry, mechanics, and physics. Aimed at the poorly educated, his courses were greeted with enthusiasm. Similar efforts were soon begun in the provinces and abroad, and the textbooks based on his lectures were translated into eight languages.

Dupin developed a great popular following; during the political crisis of 1830, he was able to convince unemployed Paris workers not to smash printing presses and other machines. Beginning in 1828, Dupin was repeatedly elected to the Chamber of Deputies by large majorities. During his long political career he worked to strengthen the navy, promote the use of steamships and encourage the construction of roads, railroads and bridges. In recognition of his accomplishments, Dupin was elected to the Academy of Sciences in 1818 and to the Academy of Intellectual and Political Sciences in 1832. Made a baron in 1824, Dupin was raised to the peerage in 1838 and appointed to the Senate in 1852.

Outstanding Engineering Achievements:

While stationed on Corfu, Dupin conducted experiments on the flexibility, strength, and elasticity of wood. These tests were of practical rather than mathematical value. In later years he continued to work on the resistance of materials to deflection, correcting hypotheses of Galileo [q.v.] and Edme Mariotte.

A more important contribution to shipbuilding resulted from Dupin's interest in differential geometry. Having created the theory of curvature of surfaces, Dupin determined what curvature would assure the maximum stability of a ship. His previous work testing materials contributed to the practical value of his suggestions. ■

Further Reading:

Nouvelle Biographie Générale, s.v. "Dupin."

CLAUDE LOUIS MARIE NAVIER
b. Feb. 15, 1785, Dijon, France
d. Aug. 21, 1836, Paris, France
French Civil Engineer

Life and Times:

The ancients discovered the arch, in various forms, but did not develop the girder. Even in the sixteenth century, engineers puzzled over why a system would work for a small model but fail when the full-size mechanism was constructed. It was Galileo [q.v.] who first pointed out that, since a beam's own weight increases with its volume, then multiplying each length by 10 would increase its weight 1,000-fold. The simple linear proportionality used in scaling-up did not take this into account. Galileo considered a beam which had one end embedded in a wall; at the other end was the load that the beam was to support. In such a position it was obvious that the beam was a lever in which the resistance force in the wall balanced the weight of the beam and the weight of the load. But, in 1638, when Galileo published propositions on the behavior

and strength of beams, he had no conception of elasticity or the importance of elastic deformation. Other investigators, including Robert Hooke [q.v.], the Bernoullis and Charles Augustin de Coulomb [q.v.], continued to study the problem of stress in beams and columns. The solution, the flexure formula that is still used, was first stated by Claude Louis Marie Navier nearly two centuries after Galileo.

The son of a lawyer who died when the boy was 14, Navier grew up with his mother's uncle, the eminent engineer Emiland-Marie Gauthey [q.v.]. Gauthey educated his ward as an engineer, and when Navier graduated from the Ecole des Ponts et Chaussées in 1806 he was first in his class. The following year Gauthey died, leaving the unfinished manuscript of a treatise on bridges and channels. Navier completed this work, added editorial notes, and published it in three volumes between 1809 and 1816. During the same period, Navier also revised Belidor's *Science des Ingénieurs* and *Architectural hydraulique.*

In 1819 Thomas Telford [q.v.] began the construction of his greatest bridge, the Menai Suspension Bridge between Wales and Anglesey. The French government twice sent Navier to observe it, and in 1823 he wrote his *Report and Memoir on Suspension Bridges,* which became the standard work on the subject for the next 50 years.

Navier's major work of construction was to have been a suspension bridge over the Seine in Paris. The Municipal Council opposed the bridge, however, and when the breaking of a sewer damaged the incomplete project the government was persuaded to abandon it. Nevertheless, Navier was well-respected. He taught at the Ecole des Ponts et Chaussées until 1830 and then, until his death, at the Ecole Polytechnique. He was elected to the French Academy of Sciences in 1824 and awarded the Legion of Honor in 1831.

Outstanding Engineering Achievement:

Navier's work in structural analysis and the strength of materials laid down the theory used afterwards in much of civil engineering. Collected in his 1826 book *Leçons sur l'Application de la Méchanique,* his contributions cover the maximum load that a particular beam can sustain; the deflection curves of beams; statically indeterminate problems, such as that of built-in beams; eccentric loading; and work on thin shells, the two-hinged arch, flat plates, girders and trusses.

Particularly well known is Navier's flexure, or bending-stress, formula, $s = Mc/I$, which relates the maximum stress, s, on a beam to the moment, M, of the bending forces, the distance, c, from the neutral axis, and the moment of inertia, I.

Navier also formulated three partial differential equations that describe the conservation of momentum for the motion of a viscous, incompressible fluid. Although his theories of heat and molecular forces are unacceptable today, the equations are still valid. Discovered independently, and later, by the British mathematician, George G. Stokes, they are known as the Navier-Stokes equations. The work of Navier was also important in the evolution of the concept of mechanical work. ■

Further Reading:

Dictionary of Scientific Biography, s.v. "Navier."

H. F. Moore, "The History of the Flexure Formula," *J. Engineering Education*. Vol. XXI (Oct. 1930).

J.P.M. Pannell, *The Illustrated History of Civil Engineering*. London, 1964.

PIERRE LOUIS FREDERIC SAUVAGE

b. Sept. 19, 1785, Boulogne, France
d. Jan. 17, 1857, Paris, France
French Mechanical and Naval Engineer

Life and Times:

Although the second and third decades of the nineteenth century saw a rapid increase in the commercial use of steamships, their mode of propulsion had important drawbacks from the military point of view. Paddlewheels were vulnerable to enemy fire, and their presence reduced the number of cannons that a ship could carry. The use of an underwater screw for propulsion, an idea suggested as early as 1729, would solve these problems. Beginning with David Bushnell [q.v.] in 1776, many inventors in Europe and America designed and tested screw-driven ships. Few of them, however, endured as many hardships as Frédéric Sauvage.

Sauvage was born in the port city of Boulogne, where his first job was that of naval engineer. In 1811 he became a shipbuilder; ten years later he began a stone-cutting business at a marble quarry near Boulogne. Sauvage's innovative spirit led him to investigate the navigational

Pierre Louis Frederic Sauvage, whose design for a screw propeller was rejected.

use of the screw. For ten years he tried to interest the Academy of Sciences, the government and the public in the propeller he had developed and installed aboard a small boat. The consensus was that a screw might well propel Sauvage's boat, but surely not a large ship. Some months after patenting his screw in 1832, Sauvage found himself in debtors' prison, bankrupted by his long and fruitless publicity campaign.

Sauvage got a second chance when Augustin Normand, a shipbuilder, received a commission to construct the *Napoleon* (later renamed the *Corse)*. Wishing to investigate the benefits of the propeller, Normand arranged to test Sauvage's design, as well as several others. In 1843 Sauvage's screw was tested and found wanting in comparison to other designs, despite Sauvage's furious protests. A beaten man, Sauvage was awarded a small pension by the government in 1846. In 1854 he went insane and spent his remaining three years in a rest home.

Outstanding Engineering Achievements:

After testing various designs for a propeller, Sauvage had correctly determined that a screw with several turnings (for instance, an Archimedes screw) was less efficient than a screw with just one turning. The propeller Sauvage patented in 1832 was a single helicoid blade with one turning. But Normand discarded this design in favor of a propeller with several blades.

Sauvage invented other devices, although only

one was a commercial success. This was a horizontal mill that he used in his marble-cutting and polishing business. In 1836 he adapted the pantograph to the reproduction of sculpture in the round and tried to market small-scale copies of masterpieces. Sauvage's *physionomètre* was a system for taking casts of objects and using these casts as molds for full-scale reproduction. He also developed a hydraulic bellows but failed to market it as a replacement for the pump in fire-fighting equipment. ■

Further Reading:

Biographie Universelle, s.v. "Sauvage."
Maurice Daumas, ed., *Histoire Générale des Techniques,* Vol. III. Paris, 1968.

LOUIS JOSEPH VICAT
b. March 31, 1786, Nevers, France
d. April 10, 1861, Grenoble, France
French Civil Engineer

Life and Times:

The eighteenth century saw the rebirth of underwater concrete construction, a technique known to the Romans and forgotten by their successors. The Romans had used naturally occurring cement for their concrete, especially the pozzuolana, or volcanic ash, that abounds in the vicinity of Naples. Unlike most natural cements, pozzuolana does not require the presence of air to harden, and mortar made from it resists the ravages of fresh or salt water. But eighteenth century builders could find few deposits of naturally-occurring hydraulic, or water-resistant, cements. What was needed was an artificial hydraulic cement that could be manufactured in large quantities. Along with Joseph Aspdin [q.v.] in England, Louis Joseph Vicat played a major role in fulfilling this need.

In 1804 Vicat entered the Ecole Polytechnique, going on to study civil engineering at the Ecole des Ponts et Chaussées. He worked on various road and canal projects until 1812, when he was given the assignment that would make him famous. In that year Vicat was sent to build a bridge at Souillac on the Dordogne river. The task was considered virtually impossible, since the spring floods were strong enough to scour the river bottom down to the rock. Moreover, funds were scarce because of Napoleon's war effort. Vicat set about sampling various local rocks to

see if any might serve as a substitute for pozzuolana, but soon decided he would have to manufacture his own. His work was entirely empirical, since the chemical reactions governing the hardening of concrete were unknown. He found, as John Smeaton [q.v.] had before him, that when lime is mixed with a small proportion of clay and then heated, the resulting product will harden even if immersed in water. This substance he christened "hydraulic lime."

Vicat published the results of these researches in 1818 and finally completed the Souillac bridge in 1824. Over the next four years he worked on a number of projects, notably the bridge over the Dordogne at Argentat. But that bridge, completed in 1828, was his last construction job. For the next 20 years he criss-crossed France looking for deposits of limestone and clay suitable for the manufacture of hydraulic lime; during that time he identified more than 900 quarries.

A steady stream of publications marked his continued investigations of mortar, hydraulic lime and concrete. By 1828 he had realized the important role that silica, and to a lesser degree alumina, played in the hardening process. With the continued progress of chemistry he was able to identify the chemical reactions that caused the hydraulic lime to set. But much of his work continued to be empirical, dealing with the proper temperature and duration of heating, the means of extinguishing the fire, the action of seawater on hydraulic lime, the speed of setting and the use of clinker.

By 1830 the use of concrete was common in bridge foundations and harbor works, and 1832 saw the construction of an all-concrete house in Marsac, France. But the imprint of Vicat's work on the French construction industry was long-lasting as well as swift. Until 1925 France continued to produce more hydraulic lime than artificial cement, the material generally used in Britain and the U.S.

Outstanding Engineering Achievements:

The bridge at Souillac represented the first use of artificial concrete on the European continent. Mixed at the construction site, it was poured into large molds to form the foundation for the stone piers. Vicat's bridge at Argentat was a further step in concrete construction: here the piers themselves were made of concrete blocks, and no quarry stone was used at all.

The Argentat bridge was the second suspension bridge constructed in France. Vicat introduced a technique for spinning the bridge's iron cables on site. He used traveling sheaves hung from temporary cables that had been strung above the towers of the bridge. This technique was independently developed by John Augustus Roebling. ∎

Further Reading:

Biographie Universelle, s.v. "Vicat."
"Centenaire de Louis Vicat," *Annales des Ponts et Chaussées,* Vol. II (1962).
Kranzberg and Pursell, *Technology in Western Civilization,* Vol. I. New York, 1967.

MARC SEGUIN

b. April 20, 1786, Annonay, Ardèche, France
d. Feb. 24, 1875, Annonay, Ardèche, France
French Mechanical and Civil Engineer, Physicist

Life and Times:

Seguin became a successful, pioneering engineer with no formal education beyond boarding school. He learned science informally from his famous granduncle, Joseph-Michel Montgolfier [q.v.], who made the first balloon ascent in 1783. Although not an integral member of the scientific community, Seguin also did theoretical work in the 1820s and 1830s on the conversion of heat into mechanical work.

After establishing a reputation for innovative bridge-building, Seguin won a concession in 1826 to build the first steam-locomotive railway in

Marc Seguin patented the multitubular boiler that was an important improvement in locomotive engines.

France. Running between St. Étienne and Lyons, it was completed in 1832. The locomotive introduced by George Stephenson [q.v.] in 1825 on the British Stockton and Darlington Railway travelled at a speed of 12 miles (19 km) per hour, too slow for Seguin. Seeking to improve the thermal efficiency of the engine, Seguin built a multitubular boiler that circulated water through several chambers. Stephenson was the first to use such a boiler, employing it on the Liverpool and Manchester Railway in 1829 and attaining speeds up to 35 miles (56 km) per hour. Whether he copied Seguin's design or conceived of it independently is not known. In any event, Seguin became the first to receive a patent for the device, which he later utilized on his own railway. For his accomplishments in engineering, Seguin was elected a corresponding member of the Académie des Sciences in 1845.

Outstanding Engineering Achievements:

Seguin faced two major problems in constructing the multitubular boiler. First, in order to produce additional steam, he had to find a way to transmit heat more readily to the water in the boiler. He achieved this by increasing the heating surfaces in contact with the water. Hot furnace gases were passed through tubes immersed in the water rather than through the boiler chimney. Second, Seguin had to create a draught in the furnace great enough to force the gases through the narrow tubes. This he accomplished by placing centrifugal fans in the furnace.

In addition to his work on the steam boiler, Seguin is known for his accomplishments in civil engineering. In 1825 he built across the Rhône, between Taine and Tournon, the first suspension bridge that used iron-wire cables instead of iron chains. Recommended by its cheapness, simplicity, and elegance, this form gradually replaced its predecessor.

Other Achievements:

In his theoretical writings, Seguin related heat to molecular velocity. When molecules transmit their momentum to external objects, he contended, heat is converted to mechanical work. However, it was Joule and Mayer who, in the 1840s, first stated the principle of the conservation of energy. ∎

Further Reading:

John D. Bernal, *Science and Industry in the Nineteenth Century.* London, 1965.
Dictionary of Scientific Biography, s.v. "Seguin."

P. E. Marchal and L. Seguin, *Marc Seguin (1786–1875): La Naissance du Premier Chemin de Fer Français*. Lyons, 1957.

JOHANN GEORG BODMER
b. Dec. 6, 1786, Zürich, Switzerland
d. May 28, 1864, Zürich, Switzerland
Swiss Mechanical Engineer

Life and Times:

Of the many inventors whose efforts contributed to the Industrial Revolution, few were as prolific and wide-ranging as the Swiss engineer Johann Georg Bodmer. His numerous patents (18 in Britain alone) include improvements to textile machinery (cleaning, carding, drawing, roving and spinning); improvements to metalworking machinery (cutting, planing, turning, drilling, rolling and screwing); armaments (cannon, bayonets, rifles, percussion shells, and gun and mortar carriages); steam engines for stationary, marine, and locomotive use, along with grates, furnaces, and boilers; screw propellers; locomotives; and machinery for treating rubber. He was among the first to adopt the metric system and helped pioneer the manufacture of interchangeable parts.

Born in Zurich of German and Huguenot descent, Bodmer was a child prodigy with unusual mechanical genius. After serving an apprenticeship to a millwright, he built a workshop at Kussnacht, where in 1805 he developed a 12-pound (5.4 kg) percussion shell for use in a breech-loading rifled cannon of his own invention. The following year he designed and built the waterwheels and spinning machinery for a cotton mill which he operated in partnership with Baron d'Eichthal at St. Blaise, Baden, meantime working on the use of machine-made parts in small-arms manufacture and the development of detachable bayonets for breech-loading rifles.

While serving as Director General of the Government Iron Works in Baden, Bodmer tried, without success, to sell his percussion shell to Napoleon, the British government, and Tsar Alexander of Russia. In 1824 he settled in Lancashire, England, where he established a factory to produce his revolutionary carding-spinning machine, a device that was not accepted in England but was later widely adopted in continental Europe and the United States. After a period in Switzerland devoted to flour mills, rolling mills, bridges and blast furnaces, he returned to England for further work on textile machines and on specialized machine tools. In 1834 he took out patents on a mechanical stoker for steam boilers and a double-piston steam engine. Later inventions in the area of locomotive apparatus included a rolling mill for steel tires, rocking furnace grates, variable speed gears, corrugated fireboxes, expansion valves, and a railway coach with a center corridor. He built two locomotives himself for a British railway company in the 1840s.

Bodmer lived in Austria and Alsace from 1848 to 1860, working on safety valves, feed-water meters, and other improvements on steam boilers.

Outstanding Engineering Achievements:

From the time of his involvement in the St. Blaise firearms factory, Bodmer was active in designing machines for the manufacture of standardized, interchangeable parts, although the idea was not widely applied for many years. Over the course of his career he designed improved planes, lathes, cranes and other tools to promote greater accuracy and uniformity of workmanship, including a metal blank for cutting precise gear teeth. He was also the first to use the pantograph as a tool for cutting and shaping metal wheels.

The most noteworthy of Bodmer's numerous textile inventions was an 1824 machine that made the carding and spinning of cotton a one-step process. A traveling belt caught the slivers of carded cotton as they were pushed through rollers on the carding engines and delivered them to a lap-machine, where they were wound on a wooden roller with a smaller risk of stretching than in the conventional manual method.

The percussion shell that Bodmer developed in 1805 for use in a rifled breech-loading cannon replaced the usual fuse with an explosive capsule set above the charge and covered with a cap. The impact of the shell against the target ignited the compound and set off the charge.

Bodmer's double-piston (compensating) steam engine, patented in 1834, was equipped with two balanced pistons of equal mass connected by a double crank. The pistons were pushed in opposite directions by a jet of steam admitted through a tube joining the two cylinders; a second jet at the end of each cylinder provided the power for the return stroke. This arrangement achieved a reduction of stress in the foundation, frame and bearings of the engine, enabling it to work at a speed twice that of the single-piston engine. The two locomotives which

Bodmer built for the South-East Railway Company in 1845 were equipped with compensating engines.

Many of Bodmer's most ingenious inventions met with resistance from those unwilling to accept too rapid change. Bodmer's commercial enterprises regularly failed, and he is rarely mentioned in reference works that give ample space to engineers of lesser accomplishments. Some inventions credited to others, including certain kinds of expansion valves and mechanical stokers, have been attributed by later writers to Bodmer. ■

Further Reading:

J. G. Bodmer, "Memoirs," *Proceedings of the Institution of Civil Engineering.* Appendix to Vol. XXVIII (1869).
Brockhaus Enzyklopädie, s.v. "Bodmer."
David Brownlie, "John George Bodmer, His Life and Work," *Transactions of the Newcomen Society.* Vol. VI (1925/26).

JOSHUA FIELD
b. c. 1787, England
d. Aug. 11, 1863, Surrey, England
British Inventor and Mechanical Engineer

Life and Times:

The development of steam navigation in the first decade of the nineteenth century opened a new area of activity for engine makers. The firm of Maudslay and Field—later Maudslay, Sons and Field—soon became a leader in the field, manufacturing marine engines that served as a standard for other manufacturers for a generation. Much credit is due to Joshua Field, long the firm's senior partner, whose vision and inventiveness helped bring about transatlantic steam navigation.

Details of Field's early life are curiously lacking. As an adolescent he worked as a draftsman at the Portsmouth dockyard; he may have had some training as a civil engineer. In 1804 Field joined Henry Maudslay's [q.v.] firm, famous for the production of precision instruments and machines. He soon specialized in the design and manufacture of steam engines. The firm began fitting ships with engines in 1816, when it provided a pair of 14-horsepower (10.4 kilowatt) engines for the coastal paddlewheeler *Regent.* Maudslay and Field was soon providing engines

for ocean-going ships as well; in 1821 two auxiliary 35-horsepower (26 kilowatt) engines were installed on the privateer *Rising Star,* bound for Chile. Demand for the company's products was international, for in 1822 Field testified before Parliament that engines had been sent to Germany, Canada, and China.

Field was a prominent spokesman for his profession as well as for his company. In 1817 he helped found the Institution of Civil Engineers (a term which then applied to all engineers engaged in non-military work) and served as one of its earliest vice presidents. He was elected a fellow of the Royal Society in 1836. During the 1830s Field took an active part in the public debate over the feasibility of transatlantic steamship navigation. His opponents claimed that a steamship could not possibly carry enough coal for the voyage. They were refuted in 1838, when the *Great Western,* with engines built by Maudslay and Field, steamed from Bristol to New York in 13 days.

Together with the junior partners in the firm, Field continued to take out patents on various kinds of engines until 1845. In 1848 he was elected to a two-year term as president of the Institution of Civil Engineers, the crowning honor of his career.

Outstanding Engineering Achievements:

The engine used in most transatlantic paddle steamers, the side-lever engine, was given its standard form by Maudslay and Field. The beam engine typically used on land was unsuitable for ocean-going ships: it was too top-heavy, and the overhead beam which transmitted the motion of the pistons would hardly fit in the hold. The side-lever engine was an adaptation of this engine. The cylinder remained vertical, though it was made shorter and wider. The piston rod terminated in a T, the arms of which extended beyond the cylinder on either side. From the end of each arm a connecting rod descended to a beam below. As in a beam engine, the motion of the connecting rod at one end caused the beam to rock about a center; its motion was communicated via a connecting rod at the other end to a crank, which turned the shaft of the paddlewheel.

Side-lever engines were typically installed in pairs, one per paddlewheel. Those on the *Great Western* had cylinders 73½ inches (187 cm) in diameter, with a piston stroke of seven feet (2.1 meters). They worked up to 450 horsepower (336 kilowatts), turning paddlewheels 28 feet (8.5 meters) in diameter whose paddles were 10 feet (3 meters) long. The engines took up 45 percent of the ship's hull space, and 660 tons of coal filled most of the rest.

Clearly, some form of direct-acting engine—one without intervening beams—would be less bulky. In 1839 Field and Joseph Maudslay patented two such designs, but neither proved entirely satisfactory. The last of the Cunard paddle steamers, the *Scotia* (1861), still had side-lever engines.

A technical problem of a different sort arose with the introduction of the screw for propulsion. Whereas paddles functioned well at 15 revolutions per minute, screws needed to be turned at 100 or more revolutions per minute. Maudslay and Field's solution was displayed in the engine they installed in the *Rattler* (1845). It turned a shaft carrying a huge gear wheel. This meshed with a smaller gear wheel carried on the propeller shaft. Since the gear wheels were in the ratio of four to one, the engine acting at 27 revolutions per minute could turn the screw at the required 108 rpm. After the *Rattler* won several tug-of-war contests with paddlewheel steamers, the British Navy began converting to screws. The design of the ship's engine, however, was soon superseded. ∎

Further Reading:

Maurice Daumas, ed., *Histoire Générale des Techniques,* Vol. III. Paris, 1968.

Dictionary of National Biography, s.v. "Field."

John Ross, *A Treatise on Navigation by Steam.* London, 1828.

Singer et al., *A History of Technology,* Vol. V.

David Tyler, *Steam Conquers the Atlantic.* New York, 1939.

JONATHAN KNIGHT

b. Nov. 22, 1787, Bucks County, Pennsylvania
d. Nov. 22, 1858, East Bethlehem, Pennsylvania
American Civil Engineer

Life and Times:

With the opening of the Erie Canal in 1825, New York City became the principal port for trade with the American interior. Threatened with economic decline, the citizens of Baltimore reacted quickly. In 1827 a railroad company was chartered to link the port on Chesapeake Bay with Wheeling, on the Ohio River. This vision-

Jonathan Knight who surveyed the route for the Baltimore and Ohio Railroad.

ary project, completed 26 years later, was begun in complete ignorance of the art of building railroads. Pushing its way westward, the Baltimore and Ohio Railroad served as an experimental laboratory for the rest of the nation. The person who first grappled with the problems of location, of curves and grading, and of track and wheel design was Jonathan Knight. The results of his theoretical and practical work, which were subjected to intense scrutiny, provided a sound basis for the subsequent boom in railway building.

Knight's father worked variously as a weaver, surveyor, and teacher. Though he received little beyond a primary education, the young man showed a natural aptitude for mathematics, a subject he pursued largely on his own. At 21 he began a career as a surveyor. After mapping Washington County for the state of Pennsylvania, Knight participated in the first surveys for the Chesapeake and Ohio Canal and for the portion of the National Road between Cumberland and Wheeling. In 1825 he was appointed by the federal government to extend that road from Wheeling as far west as Illinois. During this time Knight also served for six years as a member of the Pennsylvania legislature.

In 1827 the board of directors of the newly formed Baltimore and Ohio chose Knight and Col. Stephen H. Long to survey a route for the railroad. Their report was accepted the following year. Construction soon began on the first stretch of line, from Baltimore to Ellicott's Mills, 14 miles (22.5 km) away. Knight, however, went

The 80-foot span of the Carrollton Viaduct carried the Baltimore and Ohio railroad over Gwynn's Falls, near Baltimore.

to England to study civil engineering and railroading, returning in 1830 to an appointment as chief engineer of the company.

From Ellicott's Mills, Knight directed construction of two lines, one west to Point of Rocks on the Potomac River and one south to Washington, D.C. Once the Potomac was reached Knight was forced to conduct a dispute over right of way with the Chesapeake and Ohio Canal Company. However, by 1834 the main branch had reached Harper's Ferry, 82 miles (131 km) from Baltimore, and by 1836 both lines were in operation. From 1839 until 1842 the main branch was extended from Harper's Ferry to Cumberland, 98 miles (157 km) upstream. Knight's general duties for the company left him little time to inspect the work. He stepped down as chief engineer in 1842, though continuing until 1850 to serve as a consulting engineer. His retirement was interrupted by one term as a United States Congressman.

Outstanding Engineering Achievements:

Knight carried out a series of careful experiments in order to determine the safety of curves and the best shapes for wheels and rails. At the time it was generally supposed that locomotives would fly off the track on curves with a radius of less than 1,000 feet (300 meters). Vertical flanges on the wheels provided a margin of safety at the cost of considerable friction. The wheel Knight designed had a tread with a cone-shaped edge, permitting an almost imperceptible accommodation to curves. Peter Cooper's [q.v.] engine *Tom Thumb* was equipped with these wheels. The safety of high-speed locomotive transport was demonstrated in 1830 when that engine negotiated curves of 400-foot (120 meters) radius at 15 miles (24 km) per hour. Knight's design was later modified, since it was found that this wheel wore the inner edges of the rails very rapidly.

As work progressed on the Baltimore and Ohio, Knight continued his experiments. It was on a spur off the main track that he first

introduced several important innovations. He had longitudinal beams, or stringers, placed below as well as above the crossties; on the upper stringers were laid the first T rails used in the United States.

Knight's concern about the sharpness of curves was well founded. He wished to avoid the expense of driving tunnels through ridges and building embankments across valleys; the result was a sometimes circuitous route. Even so, the granite district of Maryland, which began some eight miles (12.8 km) out of Baltimore, proved troublesome. On the Washington branch line Knight was able to limit gradients to 20 feet per mile (4 meters per km), or four-tenths of one percent, despite the accidented terrain. Slightly steeper grades occasionally proved necessary on the main branch until the Potomac River valley was reached. Nevertheless, Knight had done his location work well. The stretch of track over the Alleghenies, from Cumberland to Wheeling, generally followed the route Knight had surveyed, and even it had grades no steeper than four percent. ■

Further Reading:

Harold L. Dorwart, "Biographical Notes on Jonathan Knight (1787–1858)," *The Pennsylvania Magazine of History and Biography,* Vol. LXXV (Jan. 1951).

National Cyclopaedia of American Biography, s.v. "Knight."

Charles Beebe Stuart, *Lives and Works of Civil and Military Engineers of America.* New York, 1871.

FRANCIS RONALDS
b. Feb. 21, 1788, London, England
d. Aug. 8, 1873, Battle, Sussex, England
British Electrical Engineer

Life and Times:

As knowledge of electricity gradually increased during the eighteenth century, it became apparent that electrical transmissions could be used as a means of communication. Improvements in the frictional machine invented by Otto von Guericke [q.v.] gave serious experimenters a reliable generator of static electricity. When Stephen Gray discovered in 1729 that electricity could be transmitted over a distance through a conductor such as metallic wire and that insulation could be provided by common substances such as rubber, the groundwork was laid for the invention of the electric telegraph. The first—and last—practicable telegraph using static electricity was invented by Francis Ronalds in 1816.

The son of a prosperous London merchant, Francis Ronalds elected to follow a career in physics rather than enter the family business. Influenced by the French meteorologist Jean André de Luc, whom he met in 1814, Ronalds devoted himself to electrical experimentation. Between 1814 and 1815, he published several papers on the practical uses of electricity. An experiment conducted in 1816 to determine the speed of electrical impulses led Ronalds to the invention of an electric telegraph; he transmitted static electricity through eight miles of wire that was charged by a frictional machine. Ronalds abandoned electrical experimentation when efforts to have the telegraph commercially developed failed. In 1843, Ronalds was appointed honorary director and superintendent of the Meteorological Observatory at Kew, near London, and was named a Fellow of the Royal Society one year later. While working at Kew, Ronalds devised a system for continuously recording data registered by meteorological instruments by means of photography. Ronalds retired in 1852 and was knighted for his years of public service and contributions to science in 1871.

Ronalds' lack of success with his electric telegraph owed to the unreadiness of British industry and government for such a device and the development of electromagnetic transmission. Ronalds had offered to demonstrate his telegraph for the British Admiralty, but traditionalists were disinclined to replace the relay semaphore, a visual system of communication which had been effectively used in the French wars. Moreover, Hans Christian Oersted's [q.v.] discovery of electromagnetism in 1820 and Michael Faraday's [q.v.] discovery of electromagnetism induction in 1831 turned experimentation away from static electricity. Electrical engineers found that electromagnetic transmission was more efficient and more reliable than static electricity. The large-scale development of electromagnetic telegraphy in Britain was accomplished by Sir Charles Wheatstone in 1837. Years later, however, Wheatstone acknowledged that his interest in electric telegraphy had been stimulated by Ronalds' antecedent work.

Outstanding Engineering Achievement:

Ronalds suspended some eight miles (13 km) of copper wire between a pair of large wooden

The wooden frames of Ronalds' experimental electric telegraph which enabled the sending and receiving stations (foreground) to be separated by eight miles of wire.

frames; the line was charged by a frictional machine. The sending station was provided with a dial inscribed with numbers and the letters of the alphabet; the dial was enclosed behind a plate with an opening which disclosed each symbol. The receiving station had a similar dial, and the two revolved synchronously by means of clockwork. The sending discontinued the charge generated by the frictional machine when the appropriate letter appeared, causing an identical symbol to be exposed at the receiving station. ∎

Further Reading:

Dictionary of National Biography, s.v. "Ronalds."

Singer et al., *A History of Technology,* Vol. IV.

AUGUSTIN JEAN FRESNEL
b. May 10, 1788, Broglie, Normandy, France
d. July 14, 1827, Ville-d'Avray, near Paris, France
French Physicist and Engineer

Life and Times:

An architect's son, Fresnel entered the École Polytechnique in Paris and subsequently was trained as an engineer at the École des Ponts et Chaussées. He became a government civil engineer but temporarily lost his post for opposing the return of Napoleon in 1815. During his period of enforced leisure, he began an experimental and mathematical study of optics. His

Augustin Jean Fresnel, inventor of the lens which concentrates light by a series of refracting prisms.

work provided the decisive evidence in support of Huygens' wave theory of light, for which he was admitted to the French Academy of Sciences in 1823.

Appointed to the lighthouse commission of the Department of Public Works in 1819, Fresnel employed his knowledge of optics to improve substantially upon existing beacons, which were based on inefficient metal reflectors.

Outstanding Engineering Achievement:

Fresnel created the first lighthouse apparatus employing the refractive properties of glass in place of metal reflectors. Glass lenses had been tried before; but because an ellipsoidal shape was required, no one had been able to make a lens thin enough to offer the necessary refractive properties while providing the proper curvature. Fresnel was able to reduce the thickness of the glass because, rather than employing a single lens, he surrounded the light source with a series of refracting prisms. With this technique, he obtained the necessary curvature by stepping back the surface of the glass in zones. In addition, Fresnel was able to produce several revolving beams of light by using rotating lens panels.

Fresnel's refracting system offered a more intense, brighter concentration of rays than the reflecting method. By the mid-nineteenth century, it had been adopted at almost 300 locations in Europe and was gradually replacing the old method of illumination.

In 1811 Fresnel developed a new method of producing sodium carbonate, which is an alkali used in the manufacture of soap, glass and other substances. Fresnel's method relied on the chemical reaction of salt, ammonia and carbon dioxide; unlike the prevailing process developed by Nicholas Leblanc [q.v.], this procedure was fuel efficient and permitted the recycling of byproducts. Practical difficulties, however, prevented industrial use of Fresnel's proposal until the 1860s when Belgian chemist Ernest Solvay commercialized the process.

Other Achievements:

Fresnel's reputation is founded more on his theoretical work in the field of optics than on his engineering work. Isaac Newton's [q.v.] corpuscular theory of light, prevalent throughout the eighteenth century, was challenged in 1800 by Thomas Young's wave theory. But Young was unable to explain the polarization of light. In a distinguished series of papers published from 1815 to 1821, Fresnel independently created a sophisticated mathematical wave theory of light that could explain polarization, diffraction, interference, refraction, and other optical phenomena. ■

Further Reading:

Dictionary of Scientific Bigoraphy, s.v. "Fresnel."

Eduard Farber, ed., *Great Chemists*. New York, 1961.

AUGUSTUS APPLEGATH
b. June 17, 1788, London, England
d. Feb. 9, 1871, Dartford, England
British Printer and Inventor

Life and Times:

As newspapers increased in size and circulation during the nineteenth century, their publishers searched constantly for improvements in printing technology. The steam-powered press invented by Friedrich Koenig [q.v.] in 1813 was the first major advance over the traditional, hand-operated platen press. Koenig's device greatly increased the speed and reduced the cost of printing. But, like the platen press, it relied on a flat surface to hold type and make impressions on paper. Even before Koenig, some inventors realized that type mounted on a rotating cylinder would print more rapidly. As early as 1790, William Nicholson patented a design for a rotary press in which both the type and the impression surfaces were cylindrical. But technical difficulties in the manufacture of the cylinders prevented the press's construction. The first workable rotary press was built by Augustus Applegath in 1848.

Applegath, a London printer, first experimented with rotary presses in 1816, when he assisted his brother-in-law, the mechanic Edward Cowper, in the construction of a machine with curved papier-mâché stereotype plates for the printing of unforgeable currency. Two years later Cowper patented an ink-distributing table for use in flat-bed presses. The device used a composition roller of melted glue and treacle that Applegath had made in imitation of pattern-stampers used in potteries. Applegath's own patents included a system for moving ink-rollers diagonally across the forme, or printing frame (1823), a rocking cylinder that allowed a single forme to give the impression alternately to two sheets of paper (1824), and a machine for casting type.

In 1827 Applegath was asked by the management of *The Times* of London to build a better version of the Koenig flat-bed press it had been using since 1814. Applegath's improved model, which incorporated his rocking cylinder, remained in service at *The Times* for the next 20 years. But the jarring back-and-forth movement of the flat type bed was a constant problem, and in 1846 Applegath undertook to design and construct a rotary press with a vertical type cylinder. His machine began printing *The Times* in October 1848. Yet despite subsequent improvements, it was soon made obsolete by a rotary press built by the American Richard Hoe, which had a more efficient horizontal drum and required fewer attendants. Both presses used columns of printer's type locked up in forms and secured to the cylinder; these were superseded in 1860 when engineers of *The Times* perfected a method of casting type in curved columns. A few years later they added a mechanical reel for feeding paper into the press in continuous webs, making the press very nearly automatic.

Applegath spent the remainder of his career as a printer of books and textiles.

Outstanding Engineering Achievements:

Applegath's improved version of Koenig's press was a steam-driven machine about 13 feet (3.9 meters) high and 14 feet (4.2 meters) long, with four impression cylinders which were fed sheets of paper by hand from four boards. The cylinders were on rockers, with alternating pairs receiving the imprint during the forward and backward movements of the type bed; the bed gave 40 to 45 strokes per minute and was linked by composition rollers. This machine used fewer moving parts than did Koenig's and produced between 4,000 and 5,000 impressions per hour.

The 1848 rotary press made by Applegath for *The Times* used a central drum, 200 inches (5 meters) in circumference, mounted vertically. Locked-up columns of printer's type were fixed to the drum, which was a polygon rather than a true cylinder. Eight impression cylinders, each about 13 inches (33 cm) in diameter, were grouped in a circle around the drum. Attendants fed sheets of paper into the machine from horizontal boards; the sheets were carried to and from the cylinders by tapes and were removed by other attendants. Vertical composition rollers inked the central type drum. Irregularities caused by the polygonal shape of the drum were compensated for by strips of paper pasted under the blankets of the impression cylinders; a later model of the press, which had two drums of 70-inch (1.8 meters) circumference, used tapered type to achieve a smoother, less angular surface. By then, however, Applegath's machine had been eclipsed by Hoe's.

The original rate of production of the press was 8,000 impressions per hour, which was raised by subsequent improvements to 10,000. Thomas Middleton, the engineer who built Applegath's presses, claimed that an eight-feeder model built for *The Standard* averaged 12,000 impressions per hour and a nine-feeder for *The*

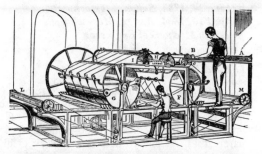

In Applegath's steam-driven perfecting press, belted rollers feed the paper to the cylinder, F, and G, to be printed first on one side, then on the other, with perfect coincidence of pages.

Printing the Times of London in 1848 by feeding vertical sheets to Applegath's rotary drum press.

Times 16,000; a ten-feeder made for *The Morning Herald* was alleged to have achieved a rate of 20,000 per hour with the use of stereotype plates.

Other printing devices patented by Applegath included machines for printing colored maps, wall charts and fabrics. ■

Further Reading:

Robert A. Hoe, *A Short History of the Printing Press*. New York, 1902.

James Moran, *Printing Presses*. Berkeley, California, 1973.

THOMAS BLANCHARD
b. *June 24, 1788, Sutton, Massachusetts*
d. *April 16, 1864, Boston, Massachusetts*
American Mechanical Engineer

Life and Times:

A farmer's son, Blanchard displayed remarkable mechanical aptitude at an early age despite lack of encouragement from his father. He invented a highly efficient hand-cranked apple parer at 13. At age 18 he went to work in his brother's shop, where tacks were made by hand. Over the next six years Blanchard developed an automatic tack-making machine until it was capable of producing 200 tacks per minute. He sold

the patent for five thousand dollars, far less than its worth. But the machine earned him a substantial reputation throughout New England, and Blanchard was hired by a private armory to devise a lathe for automatically turning the irregularly-shaped gun butt. He built a lathe capable of turning both the flats and the ovals of the butts.

Around 1818, Blanchard produced his most important invention, a lathe that automatically made the still more irregularly-shaped gunstock by copying a precut pattern. The fast-working, precision machine was soon used to produce duplicates of many articles, including shoe lasts, tool handles, tackle blocks, wheel spokes and, after some refinements, even marble busts.

By manufacturing identical copies of irregular forms in large quantities, Blanchard played a great role in implementing Eli Whitney's concept of mass-produced interchangeable parts. The United States Armory at Springfield, Mass. began employing the invention in 1819, and hired Blanchard to supervise its operation. The British government later purchased copying lathes, which created a sensation at the Exposition Universelle at Paris in 1857.

Because other entrepreneurs infringed on his patent, Blanchard received little compensation for his greatest achievement. He earned large sums, however, from a significant though less important invention completed in 1851. This was a machine that could bend timber without reducing its strength. The device was used in shipbuilding and in making handles for plows and other farm tools. Blanchard also invented a steam wagon, steamboats that could run against strong currents and in shallow waters, and machines for cutting and folding envelopes.

Outstanding Engineering Achievement:

Blanchard's copying lathe contained a revolving axle which held the model to be copied and the block from which the copy was to be made. Parallel to the axle was a rectangular carriage, carrying a friction wheel and a cutting wheel, that moved gradually from one end of the lathe to the other. The friction wheel followed the contour of the model and pushed the cutting wheel in a duplicate pattern of movement against and away from the block, so that an identical copy of the model stock was created. Once the lathe was started, the entire process worked automatically.

With modifications, Blanchard increased the versatility of the lathe. By revolving the model and the block in opposite directions, for example, he could make a left-foot last from a right-foot last. He could also make copies larger or smaller than the original by using copying wheels of different size from the friction wheel and by making the lengths of their paths proportionately different.

In designing his automatic tack-making machine, Blanchard replicated the necessary movements of the human hand. A thin steel strip, equal in width to the tack's length, was fed into the machine. The right amount of steel for a blank was cut by the contact of two upper knives with a lower bed knife below. Then the left-hand knife stopped operating, and a steel finger appended to the right-hand knife pushed the blank into gripping dies, which closed around it. A tool then struck the dies to form a head on the blank. The dies opened, and the finished tack was driven down into a pan by a knock-out attachment.

Blanchard also created a machine for bending timbers without fracturing or weakening the wood. Unlike earlier processes, his did not stretch the wood's fibers. Employing only compression, it did little or no damage to the timber. ■

Further Reading:

George Iles, *Leading American Inventors.* 1912.

Merritt Roe Smith, *Harper's Ferry Armory and the New Technology*. Ithaca, 1977.

Holland Thompson, *The Age of Invention.* 1921.

Thomas Tredgold, author of widely read and influential books on engineering, particularly on the steam engine.

stitution, Thomas Tredgold, was known for writings that helped define both civil and mechanical engineering as emerging fields.

A cabinet maker's apprentice in Durham from 1802 to 1808, Tredgold studied mathematics and architecture in his spare time. After working as a journeyman carpenter in Scotland, he came to London in 1813 and for 10 years served an an architect in the office of William Atkinson while reading widely in many areas of science. He then established his own architectural firm.

During the 1820s Tredgold became known for his pioneering efforts to establish through experimentation scientific principles applicable to machinery and construction work. His textbooks, which incorporated his own results and introduced engineering theory developed in eighteenth-century France, became standard reading for British engineers at a time when the rapid introduction of new structural materials and the development of new uses for the steam engine increased the need for systematic knowledge. Most of Tredgold's writings were published by John Weale, a businessman who helped establish technical publishing in Britain.

In 1827 the Institution of Civil Engineers turned to Tredgold for a definition of engineering to incorporate into its application for a royal

THOMAS TREDGOLD
b. Aug. 22, 1788, Brandon (near Durham), England
d. Jan. 28, 1829, London, England
British Civil and Mechanical Engineer

Life and Times:

In early nineteenth-century Britain, the newly-established engineering profession had yet to become divided into specialties. The term "civil engineer" encompassed most types of nonmilitary engineering, and the Institution of Civil Engineers, established in 1818, included many members who would later be recognized as mechanical engineers. One member of the In-charter. His response described the field as "the art of directing the great sources of power in nature for the use and convenience of man" and as the "practical application of the most important principles of natural philosophy." He viewed the major goal of engineering as the promotion of economic growth.

Although Tredgold's books were widely read by the engineers of his time, they contained many errors. In particular, they were marred by his inadequate knowledge of mathematics and his unfamiliarity with the theory of elasticity. Considering Tredgold's laboriously acquired education, these shortcomings are understandable. Perhaps more remarkable was his failure to foresee impending developments in machine technology. He viewed steam navigation, for instance, as limited to short voyages due to the weight of fuel which had to be carried on board. Tredgold joined James Watt [q.v.] in opposing the use of the more powerful and efficient high-pressure steam engines, which he viewed as dangerous. Indeed, Tredgold believed that the steam engine of his day had reached the limit of its power, and could be improved only by new manufacturing techniques which would reduce energy lost in performance.

Outstanding Engineering Achievements:

In his testing of materials and structural forms, Tredgold devoted particular attention to determining the strength of timber and cast iron. His first work, *Elementary Principles of Carpentry* (1820), examined problems relating to the resistance of timber in the erection of buildings, bridges and other structures. This was the first important effort by an English engineer to acquire data on resistance. In 1822 Tredgold published *A Practical Essay on the Strength of Cast Iron and Other Metals*, which incorporated Thomas Young's theoretical work on the principles of construction. In later works, including *A Practical Treatise on Railroads and Carriages* (1825), *Remarks on Steam Navigation* (1825) and *The Steam Engine* (1827), he used his knowledge of construction materials to suggest improvements in recent engineering innovations.

Tredgold's *Steam Engine*, republished in two volumes in 1838, was particularly influential in the growing field of machinery design and construction. The work traced the history of the steam engine, discussed its applications and presented the structure and proportions of various engine parts. Two chapters were devoted to discussion of boilers, a subject often ignored in writings on the steam engine. Tredgold also

originated two units of measurement which later became standard in describing the performance of engines and boilers: the unit of heat generation, later known as the British Thermal Unit (the amount of heat needed to raise one pound of water one degree Fahrenheit); and the measure of efficiency for a pumping engine (foot pounds delivered by a bushel of coal). Especially noteworthy were Tredgold's designs for cast iron steam engines, a great improvement over Watt's engines, made mostly of wood. ■

Further Reading:

James Kip Finch, "Tredgold: the Steam Engine," in Neal FitzSimons, ed., *Engineering Classics of James Kip Finch*. Kensington, Maryland, 1978.

Charles M. Norrie, *Bridging the Years: A Short History of British Civil Engineering*. London, 1956.

Singer et al., *A History of Technology*, Vol. IV.

DANIEL DOD
b. Sept. 28, 1788, Virginia
d. May 9, 1823, New York, New York
American Inventor and Mechanical Engineer

Life and Times:

After Robert Fulton [q.v.] demonstrated that steamship service was commercially viable, steam navigation quickly became established on America's inland waterways. The development of oceangoing steamers (as distinct from coastal packets) was slower, since their equipment had to withstand the rigors of an Atlantic crossing. In fact, early transatlantic steamers were essentially sailing ships with auxiliary steam engines used mainly in calm weather. The first of these hybrid ships was the U.S.S. *Savannah*, whose machinery was designed by Daniel Dod.

The son of a clock and instrument maker, Dod was trained in his father's trade and studied at Queen's College (now Rutgers) in New Brunswick. With his two older brothers he established a factory for the production of textile equipment, but this failed in the depression that followed the War of 1812. About this time Dod became interested in steam power, taking out U.S. patents on the manufacture of steam engines based on James Watt's [q.v.] design. He soon went into business with former New Jersey Governor Aaron Ogden manufacturing engines and other equipment for use on steamboats. The partners also intended to establish a steam ferry service but were prevented from doing this by Fulton's monopoly on the operation of steamboats in New York waters.

Dod and Ogden dissolved their partnership in 1818, shortly after manufacturing the *Savannah's* steam engine and equipment. The ship made its maiden voyage from New York to Liverpool—the first transatlantic steamboat crossing—in May-June 1819. At about this time Ogden defaulted on loans which Dod had underwritten, putting the latter in financial difficulties. Losses from the *Savannah's* voyage worsened Dod's predicament, and he was soon forced to declare bankruptcy. He managed to recover his equipment, however, and reestablished his business in 1820. Three years later Dod was killed in a boiler explosion while inspecting a steamboat in New York.

Outstanding Engineering Achievement:

The *Savannah* was a small boat, 98½ feet (30 meters) long with a weight of 170 tons. It was equipped with a low-pressure, 10-horsepower steam engine capable of attaining a maximum speed of four knots. The ship's collapsible paddle wheels, 15 feet (4.5 meters) in diameter, could be detached from their shafts when not in use and folded up for storage. The journey from New York to Liverpool, made partly under sail, took 31 days. After the *Savannah* returned to the U.S. its engine was removed, and the vessel was never again used as a steamship. ∎

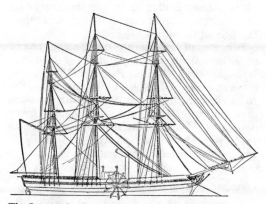

The *Savannah of the Seas equipped by Dod with an auxiliary engine, was the first ship with steam power to cross the Atlantic.*

Further Reading:

Maurice Daumas, *A History of Technology and Invention.* New York, 1964.
Dictionary of American Biography, s.v. "Dod."
Singer et al., *A History of Technology.* Vol. V.

SETH BOYDEN

b. Nov. 17, 1788, Foxborough, Massachusetts
d. March 31, 1870, Hilton, New Jersey
American Inventor and Mechanical Engineer

Life and Times:

Called by Thomas Edison "one of America's greatest inventors," Seth Boyden introduced important improvements in a wide variety of areas, including iron smelting, leather-working and steam engine technology. Boyden came from a family of considerable engineering distinction: his grandfather reportedly cast the first American-made cannon, his father invented a leather-splitting machine and his younger brother Uriah became a noted hydraulic engineer. Despite lack of formal education, Seth quickly developed his mechanical talents, designing file- and nail-cutting machinery as a teenager. After improving his father's leather-splitting machine, he moved to Newark in 1813 to manufacture materials for bookbinding. The variety of trades in Newark stimulated his inventive capacity and guided it in many directions. He spent the rest of his life developing new processes or devices and turning them into successful businesses, which he eventually abandoned to move on to new interests.

In 1819, after examining a piece of European ornamental leather, Boyden developed a lacquer that would not leave leather too stiff for practical use and established the first factory for varnished or "patent" leather. Six years later he developed a process for converting cast iron into a malleable form, until then a European trade secret. In 1831 he sold his successful patent leather factory after establishing a foundry to manufacture malleable cast iron. Boyden sold this enterprise as well in 1837, turning first to locomotive construction and then to the manufacture of stationary steam engines. He also invented a furnace grate bar in 1847, which he used to devise an improved process for smelting zinc ore.

In the midst of all this activity, Boyden left for

California to join the gold rush. He returned in 1850, no richer than before, but quickly re-established himself by developing an inexpensive process for manufacturing "Russia" sheet iron. He finally slaked his thirst for gold by developing the ornamental alloy "oroide," or "near gold," in 1868. Boyden is also credited with making the first daguerreotype in the U.S., and apparently gave some assistance to the inventor Samuel F.B. Morse [q.v.]. He spent his last years breeding hybrid strawberries at his home in Hilton, N.J. He developed a number of new strains, gaining considerable repute in an area where strawberries were an important cash crop.

Outstanding Engineering Achievements:

Although Boyden's improved leather-splitting machine was still in use as late as 1925, his most important work involved the stationary steam engine. He improved the engine's cast iron frame or bed, substituted the straight axle for the crank axle to transmit motion and developed a cut-off valve controlled by a governor to replace the throttle that regulated the engine's speed. Boyden failed to patent these improvements, however, and derived little financial benefit from them. ■

Further Reading:

Dictionary of American Biography, s.v. "Boyden."

Seth Boyden, Newark's Foremost Mechanic and Inventor. Newark, New Jersey, n.d.

Who Was Who in America, Historical Volume 1607–1896. New York, 1963.

WILLIAM FAIRBAIRN
b. *Feb. 19, 1789, Kelso, Roxburghshire, England*
d. *Aug. 18, 1874, Moor Park, Surrey, England*
British Civil and Mechanical Engineer

Life and Times:

An expert in the use of iron as a building material and one of the most highly regarded engineers of his era, Fairbairn opened a machinery works with John Lillie in Manchester in 1817 after serving as a millwright's apprentice and journeyman millwright. He manufactured improved cotton-mill machinery and waterwheels in the 1820s. At that time he became one of the

first engineers to experiment systematically with the properties of iron beams. Encouraged by canal operators, who faced stiff competition from railroads, Fairbairn conducted experiments in the construction of iron steamships in the 1830s and pioneered their early use. In 1835 he opened a new engineering works in London to handle orders for the boats.

When his workers went on strike in 1837, Fairbairn invented a steam-powered riveting machine that operated twelve times faster than hand riveting. Around 1840 he began erecting some of the first iron buildings in England, and in 1844 he patented the double-flue Lancashire boiler. Safer and more effective in producing steam than Richard Trevithick's [q.v.] single-flue Cornish boiler, it was used well into the twentieth century.

In 1845 Fairbairn extended his experimentation with iron when he began designing the Britannia Bridge. The structure was to span the Menai Straits in northern Wales as part of Robert Stephenson's railroad from Chester, England to Holyhead, Wales. By systematically testing stresses and materials, Fairbairn introduced scientific bridgebuilding and laid the groundwork for modern structural engineering theory. He used wrought iron to make the Britannia the first tubular suspension bridge with a rectangular cross section. Completed in 1850, its two hollow tubes (or girders) extended side by side for over 1,500 feet (450 meters) across four spans. This was an amazing advance in engineering practice, since until then the longest wrought-iron girder span was only 31½ feet (9.6 m). The structure was so strong that suspending chains were not needed, and remained in service without alteration and with virtually no repairs until badly damaged by fire in 1970. The Britannia Bridge design was the forerunner of many thousands of plate or box girder bridges throughout the world.

Because of Fairbairn's outstanding record of achievement, his *Application of Cast and Wrought Iron to Building Purposes* (1854) quickly became established as the standard text in the British construction industry. Fairbairn served as president of the Institution of Mechanical Engineers in 1854 and of the British Association in 1861, won the Royal Society's gold medal in 1860, and was created baronet in 1869.

Outstanding Engineering Achievements:

Because of the great width and depth of the Menai Straits, Robert Stephenson faced considerable difficulties in designing the Britannia

Floating the second tube of the Britannia Bridge that Fairbairn designed to carry the railroad over the Menai Straits.

Bridge. To allow passage of large ships through the Straits, the Admiralty rejected his proposed series of arches, which might interfere with navigation. Stephenson next turned to the idea of a bridge suspended from two circular or elliptical wrought-iron tubes. He called upon Fairbairn to test variously shaped tubes and determine the best design for the beams.

By applying concentrated loads at mid-span, Fairbairn tested 33 tubes of cylindrical, elliptical, and rectangular cross section and of various proportions. He determined that rectangular tubes were best and conducted final tests on a model rectangular tube of one-sixth the dimensions of the actual bridge. Discovering that the scale model could support up to 86 tons, he persuaded Stephenson that suspending chains were not necessary.

The bridge's two tubes ran continuously for 1,511 feet (461 meters). Its two central spans were each 459 feet (140 meters) long, and the two end spans 230 feet (70 meters) long. Both tubes were 30 feet (9 meters) high at the center and 14 feet 9 inches (4.5 meters) wide. For added strength, Fairbairn built rectangular hollow cells into the top and bottom of the tubes. The immense beams were supported on the abutments at either end and on three towers. Fixed bearings were installed on the central tower. To allow for expansion and contraction resulting from temperature changes, the tubes were fixed to expansion bearings at the other two towers and the abutments.

In addition to his work as a civil engineer, Fairbairn made important contributions to mechanical engineering. Among these was the cylindrical Lancashire boiler, similar to the Cornish boiler except that it substituted two small parallel flues immersed in water for one immersed large flue. This alteration gave Fairbairn's model several advantages. The additional heating surface provided by the two flues, or tubular furnaces, enabled it to generate more team than the Cornish boiler. Because the Lancashire flues were smaller, the depth of the water above them was greater than in the Cornish boiler. This reduced the possibility of explosion by an inadvertent lowering of the water level to the point where the top of the flues, exposed to the most intense action of the fire, would become overheated. The water level could also be lowered to create more room for steam between the surface of the water and the top of the boiler.

During his early years as a manufacturer, Fairbairn enhanced the quality of cotton-mill machinery by substituting lighter but stronger gearing equipment through the use of wrought iron instead of timber and cast iron and through improved workmanship. With more efficient bearings, couplings, frames, wheels, and pulleys, the operating speed of cotton-mill equipment increased greatly.

Fairbairn also improved the waterwheel, particularly with a new form of bucket introduced in 1828. It was ventilated to facilitate the escape of air as water entered from above and its readmission as the water emptied itself out below. This enabled the water to act with maximum impact upon the wheel.

In 1830 Fairbairn began conducting tests for the Forth & Clyde Canal Company on the resistance of water to various vessels at different velocities. He found that when vessels exceeded eight miles per hour, they rose and skimmed the water, thereby reducing resistance. To achieve such a speed he urged the introduction of strong but light ships powered by steam. Since a light wooden vessel would not be strong enough to carry a steam engine powerful enough to propel boats at the necessary speed, Fairbairn advocated the use of iron. During the next few years he built many iron vessels employing a new principle of construction, with angle-iron ribs and wrought-iron sheathing plates. ∎

Further Reading:

William Pole, *The Life of Sir William Fairbairn*. Baltimore, 1877.

Nathan Rosenberg and W. G. Vincenti, *The Britannia Bridge*. Cambridge, Mass., 1978.

Singer et al., *A History of Technology*, Vol. V.

EATON HODGKINSON

b. Feb. 26, 1789, Anderton, Cheshire, England
d. June 18, 1861, Higher Broughton, Salford,
England
British Materials Engineering Scientist

Life and Times:

Eaton Hodgkinson was a leading theorist, experimenter and writer on the strength of mechanical members used in fixed and moving structures. The son of a farmer, he was originally intended for a clerical career, but he had no talent for languages. His school discipline was so severe that it left him with halting speech and trembling hands for the rest of his life. He did much better when allowed to study mathematics at a private school, and worked diligently on the farm following his father's death. In 1811 he persuaded his mother to open a pawnbroking business in Salford, Manchester, where he made the acquaintance of the chemist John Dalton and other members of the local scientific community.

Hodgkinson read his first paper, "On the Transverse Strain and Strength of Materials," in 1822. The work corrected the prevalent belief that the "neutral line" in a beam under bending stress should be located where the moment of forces across the member is zero; Hodgkinson pointed out that the simple sum had to be zero. After studying the stress on suspension bridge members, he joined with the metallurgist William Fairbairn [q.v.] to determine the most stress-resistant shape for an iron beam. A series of tests in Fairbairn's foundry enabled him to develop a formula which resulted in the famous Hodgkinson's beam, a design described in the 1830 paper "Theoretical and Practical Researches to Ascertain the Strength and Best Forms of Iron Beams." Hodgkinson then turned his attention to stress on metal columns, publishing his results in the 1840 paper "On the Strength of Pillars of Cast Iron and Other Materials." In all, he prepared 19 scientific and technical papers. Much of his research was summarized in his book *Experimental Researches on the Strength and Other Properties of Cast Iron*, published in 1846.

Hodgkinson was elected to the Royal Society in 1840 and in 1847 was named professor of the mechanical principles of engineering at University College, London. Despite his serious speech impediment, his lectures were in great demand. From 1847 to 1849 he also served on a board of royal commissioners studying the application of iron to railroad structures. He was a member of numerous societies, including the Manchester Literary and Philosophical Society, before which he read many of his papers.

Outstanding Engineering Achievements:

Before his association with Hodgkinson, Fairbairn had experimented with iron beams in the shape of an inverted T. But Hodgkinson determined that the ideal beam was shaped in cross-section like an I, with the bottom flange larger than the top to equalize tension. This became known as the Hodgkinson's beam, described as "the pole star for engineers and builders." Manufacturers, however, found that the bottom flange was so much larger than the other parts of the beam that it cooled more slowly after casting, resulting in internal strains. Hodgkinson's ideal beam design thus had to be modified in practice.

Hodgkinson's work on the strength of beams and columns was important in the construction of the first wrought iron bridges during the mid-nineteenth century. Hodgkinson assisted Robert Stephenson, designer of the Britannia and Conway tubular railroad bridges, by determining the size of the girders to be used in the upper and lower sections of the two structures. ∎

Further Reading:

Maurice Daumas, *A History of Technology and Invention*. New York, 1964.

Dictionary of National Biography, s.v. "Hodgkinson."

Robert Rawson, "Memoir of Eaton Hodgkinson," *Smithsonian Institution Annual Report*. (1968).

Singer et al., *A History of Technology*, Vol. IV.

LOUIS JACQUES MANDE DAGUERRE

b. Nov. 18, 1789, Cormeilles, France
d. July 10, 1851, Paris, France
French Inventor

Life and Times:

Inventor of the first practical photographic process, Daguerre was the son of a magistrate's court crier. Apprenticed to the chief designer at the Paris opera in 1804, he launched a career as a painter of backdrops for the stage. From 1807 to 1816, Daguerre was assistant to panorama painter Pierre Provost.

Daguerre became an independent stage de-

Louis Jacques Mande Daguerre photographed by his own process, the daguerreotype.

signer in 1816 and with Charles-Marie Bouton invented the Diorama six years later. The Diorama consisted of real objects plus huge scenic backdrops painted on semi-transparent canvas. By changing the lighting behind and in front of the canvas, the illusion of change—as from season-to-season or day to night—could be created. Audiences in Paris were greatly impressed, and Daguerre became famous.

Daguerre's interest in the photographic process grew from his work on the Diorama. He obtained preliminary sketches for his backdrops by etching over the images of actual outdoor scenes as they appeared in a *camera obscura.* That 16th century device was a dark box having a hole fitted with a lens. It projected an inverted image of a lighted scene outside the box onto the interior surface opposite the hole. Daguerre wanted in some way to fix that image.

The early nineteenth century was an auspicious time for the development of photography, because the light sensitivity of silver salts had just been discovered. This was a crucial precondition to the development of photography.

In the early 1820s Daguerre began inserting plates coated with silver chloride or silver nitrate into the camera to obtain a permanent reproduction but achieved only a fleeting, darkening image. Then he learned about the work of Joseph Nicéphore Niepce. Using a different chemical process from Daguerre, Niepce had produced the first fixed photographic image in 1826 or 1827. But his method was impractical, since it required a seven to eight hour exposure.

In 1829 the ambitious Daguerre convinced Niepce to form a partnership with him. They worked jointly until Niepce's death in 1833. Continuing the effort, Daguerre by 1837 had created a practical photographic process that required an exposure of 20 to 30 minutes.

At first Daguerre could not arouse interest in the process, but by 1839 he had stirred the enthusiasm of influential French astronomer François Arago. Arago worked out an arrangement whereby the French government obtained the rights to the daguerreotype process, as its inventor called it, in exchange for a life pension for Daguerre and Niepce's son.

The secrets of the daguerreotype were revealed by Arago at a public meeting in Paris on Aug. 19, 1839. No invention before or since created such a public sensation. Within an hour after Arago's talk, opticians' and chemists' shops were crowded with people seeking the necessary paraphernalia to duplicate the process. People from all walks of life became amateur daguerreotypists. Subjects gladly sat still in the sun for half-an-hour to have their images recorded. Within months the process was being used in the United States, where by 1850 there were some 10,000 daguerreotypists. By the end of 1839, publishers were sending photographers around the world to take images of the Egyptian pyramids, the antiquities of Greece, and Niagara Falls. In the 1840s the process was used to record heavenly objects.

So sweepingly popular was the daguerreotype that some painters feared their craft would become obsolete. In fact, photography, with its realistic, objectively accurate images and its technical procedures, was more suited than the art of painting to the positivist, scientific, and matter-of-fact outlook of the 19th century. And it was highly appealing to the new middle class, which could participate in the invention both as photographer and subject.

Daguerre profited handsomely from his invention. Besides his lifetime pension, he received income from teaching the process through lectures and from his instruction manual, published in 32 editions in 1839–40.

Although the daguerreotype was faithful in detail and clarity and reduced exposure time to not more than 30 minutes, it had many disadvantages. Perhaps the most important problem was that, since the daguerreotype was a positive, no copies could be made. Exposure time was still too long for convenient portraiture; sitters had to rest their heads in a special clamp. And without adequate artificial lighting, portrait studios could operate only on sunny days. Large windows and glass roofs were required, making the studios hot and uncomfortable. The images came out in reverse as in a mirror image, and they lacked natural color. Mercury, which was used to fix the image, came off the plate easily, and the plate therefore had to be covered with glass. The daguerreotypists' equipment, including camera, a box for metal plates and containers for chemicals, weighed over 100 pounds (45 kg).

But Daguerre retired comfortably in 1840, leaving it to others to improve the photographic process. Soon his method was being challenged by the calotype system of William Henry Fox Talbot and the collodion photographic process of Frederick Scott Archer, both of which obtained positive prints from negative images. By the end of the U.S. Civil War, the daguerreotype had been superseded both in Europe and America.

Outstanding Engineering Achievement:

The daguerreotype process began with a lightly silver-coated copper plate. When this plate was exposed to iodine vapor, its surface became covered with a thin layer of light-sensitive silver iodide, which Daguerre and Niepce found in 1831 to be superior to the silver salts they had used previously. The plate was then placed in the *camera obscura* and exposed to light for 20 to 30 minutes. There was no apparent change in the plate at the end of the exposure period, but a latent image had been formed that needed to be developed.

To develop the image, Daguerre used mercury vapor. The inventor discovered its utility in 1835 when, according to one account, he placed an apparently spoiled plate into a chemical cupboard and found a perfect picture on it the next day. By a process of elimination, he discovered that the responsible agent was some drops of mercury that had spilled in the cabinet.

From then on, Daguerre developed his plates by putting them in a developing box and exposing them to the fumes of a cup of heated mercury for about 20 minutes. The mercury vapor condensed on those portions of the silver iodide which had been affected by the light. The greater the intensity of the light, the greater the condensation and the lighter the color.

To fix the image, Daguerre in 1837 began using a solution of common salt, altered in 1839 to a solution of sodium thiosulfate at the suggestion of astronomer Sir John Hershel. The solution washed away the unchanged iodide, leaving the bare silver of the original plate to form the shades of the picture. ■

Further Reading:

Helmut and Alison Gernsheim, *L.J.M. Daguerre: The History of the Diorama and the Daguerreotype*. London, 1956.

Reese Jenkins, *Image and Enterprise*. Baltimore, 1975.

Ralph Stein, *The Great Inventions*. Chicago, 1976.

RICHARD ROBERTS
b. 1789, Carreghofa, Wales
d. 1864, Manchester, England
British Mechanical Engineer

Life and Times:

During the early decades of the nineteenth century, there was a burst of technological innovation in the British textile industry which produced major advances in automation. An important figure in this process was Richard Roberts, who invented the self-acting spinning mule in 1825 and designed an improved version of the power loom.

Trained in Henry Maudslay's [q.v.] machine-tool building shop, Roberts made important contributions to the craft of precision mechanics as well as to the textile industry. In 1817 he designed and built one of the earliest metal-planing machines and the same year improved the lathe by equipping it with a back-geared headstock. His tool business, established in an up-to-date shop with the best lathes and screw-cutting machines, made dependable screws and

The daguerreotype is shown outdrawing all other spectacles of the day in this 1840 cartoon "Daguerreotypomania."

Richard Roberts, machine-tool craftsman who invented the fully automatic spinning mule.

gearing machinery. In 1847 he designed a punching machine for making rivet-holes in railway bridges. Roberts' background and career made him the pattern of the British engineer of the Industrial Revolution in all respects but one—his business failed and he died in poverty.

The son of a Welsh shoemaker, Roberts labored in a quarry until he was twenty, when he went to work for John Wilkinson [q.v.], inventor of the boring bar, at his Bradley ironworks. After working two years as a turner and fitter for Maudslay, Roberts left in 1816 to set up his own machine-tool business in Manchester. While Roberts' improvements in machine-tools were useful, the self-acting mule was certainly his greatest achievement. For years attempts had been made to automate spinning. By 1800 the mule invented by Samuel Crompton [q.v.] was steam-powered and a true factory machine, but it still required skilled operators who commanded high wages. It could stretch and twist the cotton fibers simultaneously, but the carriage came to a halt while the spindles continued to twist. Here the operative manually took over the winding-on, just as with the hand mule. Motivated by a spinners' strike which broke out in 1824, Roberts sought to eliminate this manual step. His machine of 1825 was not entirely successful, but by 1830 he had brought the self-acting mule to a nearly perfect state. Nevertheless, the machine did not take hold industrially

for some years, and Roberts and his partners in the firm of Sharp Brothers sustained heavy financial losses. From 1830 to 1839, their return on an investment of 12,000 pounds amounted to only about 7,000 pounds.

Roberts' power loom, based on an earlier model designed by William Horrocks, was a more immediate success. First demonstrated in 1822, it soon proved the most practical and popular machine of its kind, especially for weaving intricately designed fabrics. Using it, a factory operative could produce seven and one half times as much cloth as a hand loom weaver. Roberts set up a company to manufacture his loom, which was introduced in France in 1826. Beginning in the 1830s, however, it was gradually displaced in most branches of the textile industry by Joseph-Marie Jacquard's [q.v.] power loom, a more sophisticated machine adapted from silk manufacture.

Outstanding Engineering Achievements:

To make the spinning mule fully automatic, Roberts had to apply power to the carriage and to the turning or twisting motion of the spindles, both operating at varying speeds, and to the movement which reversed the spindles off the yarn. He introduced three driving pulleys and two driving belts to the machine. The belts interacted with the pulleys to effect the backing-off motion (which preceded the twisting by the spindles); the moving-in of the carriage was accomplished by means of a scroll (or spiral) pulley. Roberts' machine also ensured the tension of the yarn when the backing-off process occurred. The entire mechanism was powered by a drive shaft that moved through quarter-turns, engaging in succession the parts involved in each phase of the spinning process.

In 1830 Roberts solved the problem of how to vary the speed of the spindles in harmony with the movement of the carriage. He did this with a quadrant—part of a toothed wheel with a grooved arm which affected the movement of the spindles in accordance with that of the carriage. With this refinement, the self-acting mule was fully realized.

Roberts' power loom was operated by two shafts. One operated heddles that raised the warp, or lengthwise, threads, the other, pickers that threw the shuttle, which placed the woof, or crosswise threads. Both of these operations had to be carefully coordinated. The second shaft drove the batten, which pushed the thrown woof threads together. Roberts' loom was capable of weaving both plain and fancy fabrics.

Roberts' metal-planing machine. The work (here a short I-bar) is clamped on the table that slides along tracks below the blade.

Roberts also developed a planing machine, the earliest still existing model, which held the work on a table that moved back and forth beneath a traversing tool. The blade shaved the work on each motion, producing a plane surface. The table was moved by chains wound on a drum which was rotated manually, and the tool was raised and lowered by means of a screw. The tool clamp was spring-loaded and hinged so that the cutting instrument was held firmly during its performance. The later planing machines of Joseph Clement [q.v.] and Joseph Whitworth, however, could handle much larger work. ∎

Further Reading:

David Landes, *The Unbound Prometheus.* Cambridge, 1965.

Singer et al., *A History of Technology.* Vols. IV. and V.

Kranzberg and Pursell, *Technology in Western Civilization*, Vol. IV.

GEORGE EVEREST
b. July 4, 1790, Gwernvale, Brecknockshire, England
d. Dec. 1, 1866, London, England
British Surveyor and Geodesist

Life and Times:

The history of geodesy—the science of determining the size and shape of the earth—dates from the time of Erastosthenes (276–194 B.C.), who made the first reasonably accurate estimate of the earth's circumference using a geometrical formula. In the sixteenth century the Dutch astronomer Tycho Brahe originated the idea of geodetic triangulation, a method of surveying extensive distances over uneven terrain by taking successive measurements at the vertices of a triangular network plotted over the face of the earth. Two hundred years later, Sir George Everest applied this technique to his survey of the Indian subcontinent, during which he computed the longest arc of meridian, or segment of a polar great circle, yet measured.

Everest, a graduate of the Royal Military Academy at Woolwich, was a cadet with the East India Company and an officer with the Bengal artillery when he first went to India in 1806. In 1817, having participated in surveying expeditions in Java and in engineering projects in India, he was appointed chief assistant to Sir William Lambton, supervisor of the Great Trigonometrical Survey of India, which the British government had initiated fifteen years earlier. Everest spent three years conducting the geodetic survey of the swampland and jungle of central India and became superintendent after Lambton's death in 1823.

Everest returned to India as Surveyor-General in 1830 after a five-year recuperative stay in England, during which he studied recent developments in geodetic science. He reorganized

George Everest, who used the method of triangulation to survey the entire subcontinent of India.

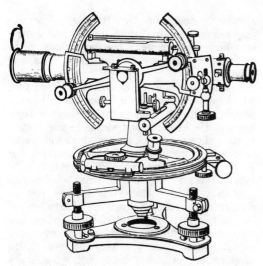

The theodolite designed by Everest and used during the survey in which he discovered the world's highest mountain.

the Survey and undertook the remaining measurements and calculations needed to establish the Grand Meridional Arc of India (see below). He retired in 1843 and was knighted in 1861. The highest mountain in the world, discovered in the course of his survey, was named Mount Everest in his honor.

Outstanding Engineering Achievements:

Everest's vast survey of the Indian subcontinent yielded the longest arc of meridian (a section of a great circle passing through the earth's poles) that had ever been measured; it was 21 degrees in length from the southern cape of India to the Himalayas. The establishment of the arc provided a precise yardstick for estimating the size of the earth and gave future trigonometrical studies an accurate basis for their own geodetic measurements. The Everest theodolite, a telescope-like instrument for measuring vertical and horizontal triangles, was introduced by Everest during the course of the survey.

In 1854 the geologist J.H. Pratt used Everest's measurements and his own observations of pendulum deflection in the Himalayas to calculate that the density of the earth in mountainous areas is less than had been expected. Later geologists confirmed Pratt's findings and supported them with the theory of isostasy, which holds that the weight of the earth's crust is uniform in all places, with less density in mountainous regions and greater density in compressed areas such as the ocean floor. ■

Further Reading:

Dictionary of National Biography, s.v. "Everest."

Toni Hagen et al., *Mount Everest: Formation, Population, and Exploration of the Everest Region.* London, 1963.

J. H. Pratt, *On the Attraction of the Himalaya Mountains and of Elevated Regions Beyond Upon a Plumb-Line in India.* 1855.

CANVASS WHITE
b. Sept. 8, 1790, Whitestown, New York
d. 1834, St. Augustine, Florida
American Civil Engineer and Surveyor

Life and Times:

After studying mathematics, science and surveying at an academy, White became in 1816 an assistant to Benjamin Wright [q.v.], chief engineer of New York's Erie Canal. He was later one of the project's leading engineers, working on the canal until 1824.

Because little was known in the U.S. about canal construction when the Erie Canal was begun, New York's Gov. DeWitt Clinton sent White to England to obtain the most advanced instruments and information available. White was in England in 1817–18 and returned with the latest surveying devices plus drawings of the most important structures on English canals.

After working on the Erie Canal, White served as chief engineer of the Union Canal and the Lehigh Canal in Pennsylvania and of the Delaware and Raritan Canal in New Jersey. He also did a study of the future water needs of New York City and suggested the best sources of water for that metropolis.

Outstanding Engineering Achievement:

White made a number of significant contributions to the construction of the Erie Canal. In 1818, he discovered a new type of lime rock near the route of the canal in Madison County. After numerous experiments he converted it into a cement, equal in quality to the imported cement then being used and less costly to the state. The cement was eventually used in all the face work of the canal's locks and arches. White received a patent for his discovery in 1820.

In 1819–20, White surveyed possible routes for the canal between the Seneca and Genesee rivers. He was resident engineer for construction

Canvass White, a leading canal engineer in the mid-Atlantic states.

of the canal in the vicinity of Utica in 1820. In 1821, White and two other engineers advised that a proposed route from Schenectady connecting with the Hudson River at Albany was impracticable and instead located the line by way of Cohoes and Troy. In 1822, he laid out the Glens Falls feeder and planned and directed the building of the lock and dam between Troy and Waterford. ■

Further Reading:

J. S. McNown, "Canals in America," *Scientific American*, July 1976.

Charles Stuart, *Lives and Works of Civil and Military Engineers of America.* New York, 1871.

ERNST ALBAN

b. Feb. 7, 1791, Neubrandenburg, Germany
d. June 13, 1856, Rostock, Mecklenburg,
Germany
German Surgeon and Engineer

Life and Times:

So little was known of engineering in Mecklenburg that it was difficult for Ernst Alban to obtain—or to persuade his father to allow him—

a technical education. Nevertheless, Alban was responsible for introducing English and American high-pressure steam engine technology to this part of Germany and for raising it to new heights.

Taking up residence at Rostock University, Alban became famous as a surgeon over the next decade, while he pursued his passion for engineering. He built his first steam engine from a kettle and two syringes. In time there followed a tube boiler capable of attaining pressures in the 50 to 80 atmosphere range. When Alban published his results, the first response was from an English company which was formed just to acquire and patent his invention. Alban left for England in 1825, and was delighted to find not only interest in his invention but offers of money as well. After a two-year stay, he returned to Mecklenburg to gather his thoughts and study the technical and scientific materials he had acquired.

Alban continued to design high-pressure steam engines, carrying on from where the American Oliver Evans [q.v.] left off. In 1830 he established a machine works, first producing agricultural machines and then equipment to make paper and linen thread. In Guestrow he established a foundry that built the engines, primarily 30 horsepower, for a textile firm in Plau. His own Plau Works followed in 1840. After completing a masterly book on the high pressure steam engine, Alban journeyed to Russia in 1848 with a plan to build an even larger steam engine works. But, wearied from his stay in St. Petersburg, he turned down an attractive offer from the Russian government and returned home in 1850. The next year he began to suffer apoplectic fits, which recurred with increasing frequency until his death.

Outstanding Engineering Achievements:

Alban built both small and large steam engines in his machinery works. The smaller ones—less than 10 hp (7 kw)—had furnaces with two layers of tubes, the upper ones being larger and partially filled. The water entered the lower tubes first, then the upper ones, with the furnace flue gases passing counter to the water flow in each layer. In larger furnaces, the tubes were arranged in multiple alternating layers much like those in the nonradiative part of a modern furnace boiler. In both cases, the design was excellent for conductive heat transfer, but less suited to radiative heat transfer. Alban did not rely on relief valves, but designed his boilers to survive the rupture of a boiler tube.

Alban designed engines with oscillating cylinders, in which the entire piston and rod were pivoted on the steam inlet to follow the crank. His engines usually had two pistons, which were kept separate from the boilers for safety. An 1828 engine with two single-acting opposed pistons resembled Richard Trevithick's [q.v.] plunger-pole engine, except that the pistons were horizontal.

Alban rarely used a condenser. Instead, he found alternative uses for the spent steam, such as heating buildings, though he acknowledged the increased efficiency of low-pressure condensers and used them in larger engines where cooling water was abundant. He anticipated the use of superheated steam, but did not consider it to be practical in his own time. His engines were notable for attention to minute detail in construction, although they were kept simple to operate and maintain. ■

Further Reading:

Ernst Alban, *The High Pressure Steam Engine Investigated,* trans. by William Pole, C.E. London, 1848.

Conrad Matschoss, "Dr. Ernst Alban," *Geschichte der Dampfmaschine.* (1901).

PETER COOPER

b. Feb. 12, 1791, New York, New York
d. April 4, 1883, New York, New York
American Inventor and Industrialist

Life and Times:

In the first half of the nineteenth century, fledgling American industries faced stiff competition from England, with its superior techniques and skilled labor force. But U.S. industrial expansion, after reaching its take-off point in the 1860s, fostered the growth of monopolies and the accumulation of unprecedented fortunes. Although Peter Cooper's long life spanned both these periods, his ideas were shaped by the first. His struggles against British imports made Cooper a staunch opponent of free trade. His contributions to the development of transportation, industry and communication helped shape American economic development. Nevertheless, in 1876 this millionaire philanthropist ran for President on a third-party ticket, decrying the growing concentration of economic power and the formation of "an aristocracy of wealth."

Peter Cooper, engineer, millionaire philanthropist, founder of an engineering school, and politician.

Cooper was the fifth of nine children of a hat manufacturer and brewer. Like other American heroes, he worked from earliest childhood and at 17 became an apprentice with a coach-making firm. After selling the first of his inventions, a machine for mortising coach hubs, Cooper went into business on his own; he began manufacturing shearing machines, for a time ran a grocery store, and in 1827 bought a glue factory for $2,000. Cooper's innovations made his business prosper.

Cooper next became part of the flurry of activity surrounding the plans for the Baltimore and Ohio Railroad. He was forced to buy out his partners in this venture, a foundry for track rail, and eventually found himself undersold by British imports. To add to his woes, the B & O was nearing early bankruptcy, for imported British locomotives could not handle its winding tracks. In the fall of 1829 Cooper began building the famous "Tom Thumb." Although this locomotive lost its race with a stagecoach—a belt to the furnace blower broke—it restored faith in the B & O and proved the value of Jonathan Knight's [q.v.] anti-derailing wheel design.

Cooper bought and built further iron foundries and rolling mills, becoming one of the leading iron manufacturers in the country. He had long known the family of Abram S. Hewitt; in these years his family and Hewitt formed close alliances, among them the firm of Cooper and Hewitt, which took over control of Cooper's enterprises. In the 1850s Cooper also served as president of the North American Telegraph Company; his perseverance assured the success of Cyrus Field's scheme for laying a transatlantic telegraph cable.

With his election as alderman in 1840, Cooper became involved in New York City's civic affairs. Despite his undoubted humanitarianism, he remained associated with the corrupt Tammany machine until the 1850s. In 1853 Cooper founded the Cooper Union for the Advancement of Science and Art in order to provide New Yorkers with a free education in science, engineering and art. In his later years he devoted much time and money to this institution, which still thrives. In 1876 Cooper campaigned for the presidency on the Greenback party ticket, receiving almost 100,000 votes.

Outstanding Engineering Achievements:

For his glue factory Cooper developed a double boiler which allowed him to make most of the glue and table gelatins in the U.S. He also introduced an inferior but cheaper isinglass using domestic fish bladders instead of the byproducts of caviar-making.

Cooper was enamored of the endless chain or belt principle. He used it for a four-horsepower, mile-long tow route on New York's East River; for removing sand from a large Baltimore property, using an endless chain of railroad cars on a moving double track; and for carrying coal downhill to one of his forges, by means of a three-mile system of buckets hanging from a bar. If time had permitted, the "Tom Thumb" would have been built with an endless chain instead of an ordinary shacklebar crank; the locomotive's brass engine was otherwise unremarkable.

In his ironworks Cooper helped pioneer the use of anthracite or hard coal. He also developed a cylindrical machine for puddling iron, an arduous process of stirring out impurities that previously had to be performed by hand.

In addition to his mechanical innovations, Cooper did important work as a civil engineer. For the construction of Cooper Union he used wrought iron beams in combination with masonry to produce a spacious but fire-resistant building. His system of construction was soon adopted for the expansion of Washington's Capitol Building and the construction of other federal buildings. Cooper was also responsible for securing New York City's water supply by creating Croton Lake and building an aqueduct to the

Cooper's locomotive Tom Thumb, *hauled a car carrying 36 people at a maximum speed of 18 miles per hour.*

city, where the lake's waters were directed to the Yorkville reservoir in what is now Central Park. ■

Further Reading:

Edward L. Mack, *Peter Cooper: Citizen of New York.* New York, 1949.

National Cyclopedia of American Biography, s.v. "Cooper."

Allan Nevins, *Abram S. Hewitt: With Some Account of Peter Cooper.* New York, 1935.

John Celivergos Zachos, Peter Cooper and Abram S. Hewitt, *Autobiography of Peter Cooper.* Boston, n.d.

SAMUEL FINLEY BREESE MORSE
b. April 27, 1791, Charlestown, Massachusetts
d. April 2, 1872, New York, New York
American Inventor

Life and Times:

Samuel Morse has become a folk hero of American technology, an artist with little mechanical training whose development of the telegraph revolutionized communications in the U.S. and Europe. The son of a Calvinist clergyman and prominent geographer, Morse received his formal education at Phillips Academy and Yale College. He was noted as being an indifferent student who painted portraits and displayed an avid (though extracurricular) interest in the infant science of electricity.

After graduating from Yale in 1810, Morse travelled to England, where he studied the historical style of painting with Washington Allston. He returned to the U.S. five years later and began painting portraits, including among his

Samuel Finley Breese Morse, inventor of the telegraph and the Morse Code.

Version of Morse's telegraph receiver in which a mark on paper is made whenever the circuit is closed.

patrons such notables as the Marquis de Lafayette and William Cullen Bryant. He also founded and headed the National Academy of Design, before becoming professor of painting and sculpture at New York University. A man of deeply-held conservative views, Morse briefly entered politics as a member of the Native American Party, which worked against the influence of Catholics and recent immigrants. In 1827 he launched the *New York Journal of Commerce* as part of a campaign against licentiousness in the theater. Morse also became a prominent defender of slavery as the Civil War approached, working to preserve the status quo as president of the Society for the Diffusion of Political Knowledge.

Morse became interested in telegraphy in 1832, when he learned in a casual conversation about experiments with electromagnetic telegraphs being conducted in Paris. Within three years, he succeeded in constructing a successful model telegraph, and began devoting most of his time to perfecting the instrument. In 1838 he developed the Morse code, a system of dots and dashes for transmitting messages.

Morse received financial support for his experiments from Dr. Leonard Gale of New York University and from Joseph Henry [q.v.], secretary of the Smithsonian Institute, whose pioneer work in transmitting electrical impulses over long distances laid the groundwork for Morse's invention. He established a partnership with Alfred Vail, who redesigned the telegraph and helped bring it to the attention of Congress. In 1843 the partners secured a federal grant of $30,000 for construction of a 38-mile experimental telegraph line between Baltimore and Washington. Instantaneous communication caused a public sensation, and by 1846 telegraph lines extended north from Washington to Portland, Maine and West to Louisville, Kentucky and Milwaukee, Wisconsin. By 1848, every state east of the Mississippi except Florida was linked by the telegraph network.

Morse was awarded patent rights to the telegraph in 1854, after the Supreme Court disallowed claims to the invention by Vail and rival inventors. The decision made Morse wealthy, and he became a philanthropist in his later years, helping Vassar College and giving abundantly to Yale College, theological institutions and to charities for struggling artists. Morse's original telegraph can be found today in the National Museum of History and Technology in Washington, D.C.

Outstanding Engineering Achievement:

Morse's basic design for the telegraph made use of the quantity magnet developed by Joseph

Henry [q.v.], an iron stud surrounded by multiple coils of coarse wire activated by a single battery. When the circuit was completed by an operator at the other end of the line, the magnetized stud could be used to perform a variety of functions: sound a bell, produce a click or move a pen across a piece of paper. Morse finally settled on the click, which sounded when a flexible piece of metal was attracted onto the electromagnet upon completion of the circuit. Messages could be transmitted through the now-familiar dots and dashes of the Morse code. Morse also developed the relay, a device which increased the distance over which transmission was possible by amplifying the current from a single copper wire through a thick coil composed of thousands of turns of wire. Relays installed at intervals on telegraph lines permitted messages to be sent over any distance.

Morse also worked on other inventions, including a flexible piston pump and a marble-cutting machine. An acquaintance of the French photographic pioneer Louis Daguerre, he introduced the daguerreotype process to the U.S. and became one of its first American practitioners. ■

Further Reading:

P. Dunsheath, *A History of Electrical Engineering*. London, 1962.

E. A. Marland, *Early Electrical Communication*. London, 1964.

Carleton Mabee, *The American Leonardo: A Life of Samuel Morse*. New York, 1943.

MICHAEL FARADAY
b. Sept. 22, 1791, Newington, Surrey, England
d. Aug. 25, 1867, Hampton Court, Middlesex, England
British Physicist

Life and Times:

By the early nineteenth century the study of electricity had produced two sources of electrical power: the Leyden jar, an electrostatic storage device, and the voltaic pile, a chemical battery invented by Alessandro Volta [q.v.] in 1800. The discovery that electricity can be converted into magnetism, first made by Hans Christian Oersted [q.v.] in 1820, was soon followed by William Sturgeon's [q.v.] invention of the electromagnet. Michael Faraday, in a brilliant series of experi-

Michael Faraday, the physicist whose research in electricity produced the generator and the electric motor.

ments between 1821 and 1831, revolutionized electrical research with the discovery of electromagnetic induction and the subsequent development of the first electrical generator, or dynamo. He defined the laws of electrolytic chemistry and, in his last papers, foreshadowed the electromagnetic field theory of James Clerk Maxwell [q.v.]. Although no practical applications were found for his discoveries for a half century, Faraday can fairly be said to have formulated the principles on which modern electrical technology is based. This achievement is the more remarkable when considered in light of his complete ignorance of mathematics; Faraday was the last great physicist of whom this was true.

The son of a blacksmith, Faraday had little formal education but became an avid reader of scientific literature while serving as an apprentice in a bookbindery. In 1812 he attended a series of popular science lectures given by the chemist Humphry Davy [q.v.], who later hired him as a laboratory assistant.   Under Davy's guidance, Faraday began his scientific work in the chemistry of oils and gases at the Royal Institution in London. In 1818 he developed high-grade alloys of rust-resistant steel, incorporating platinum, rhodium, and silver. During the next six years he produced an extremely clear glass with a high refractive index and discovered the solvent benzene. He was elected to the Royal Society in 1824 and became director of the Royal Institution's laboratory in 1825. The *Dictionary of National Biography* notes that Faraday singlehandedly preserved the Royal Institution from bankruptcy through the proceeds from his extremely popular scientific lectures.

Oersted's discovery in 1820 that a magnetic field encircles an electrified wire prompted Faraday to conduct his own investigation into "electromagnetic rotation" in 1821. His experimental apparatus, in which wire immersed in mercury pivoted about a bar magnet when current was applied, was the first device to convert electricity into mechanical energy, the forerunner of the electric motor.

In 1831 the American scientist Joseph Henry [q.v.] discovered that the positive and negative poles of an electromagnet can be switched by reversing the direction of current. This result inspired Faraday to resume his electromagnetic research. Convinced that Oersted's discovery was equally true in reverse—that magnetism could be converted into electricity, since electricity could be converted into magnetism—he set up an experiment in which an electromagnet was bound with two separate wire windings, one connected to a battery and one to a galvanometer. At the instant that current was applied to one winding, and again when the current was shut off, the galvanometer showed the presence of a current in the other wire. Faraday had demonstrated the existence of electromagnetic induction—the creation of an electric current in an unattached conductor by a nearby changing magnetic field—and had incidentally invented the transformer. He also found that a changing magnetic field could be produced by mechanically moving a permanent magnet into or out of a coil of wire. This is the principle of an electric generator, or dynamo. Joseph Henry, whose work paralleled Faraday's in many respects, had developed a dynamo one year earlier, but had failed to publish his results. Faraday is thus usually credited with the invention.

In 1832 Faraday formulated his laws of electrolysis (the analysis of substances in a solution by the action of an electrical current). These laws explained the relationship of the amount of current to the mass of the substance liberated. By 1838 he had developed a coherent overall theory of electricity, not widely accepted at the time, based on the concept of electromagnetic "lines of force," a visualization of force as lines

in space corresponding to the pattern formed by iron filings around a magnet.

The exhausted Faraday suffered a nervous breakdown in 1839 and abstained from research for the next three years, occupying himself with traveling and writing. He gradually returned to his earlier studies of gases and solvents, then embarked on a further attempt to demonstrate the unity of forces, in which he proved that polarized light is deflected by a strong magnetic field. This experiment, coupled with his "lines of force" concept, laid the groundwork for Maxwell's electromagnetic field theory, which in turn led to the work of Hendrik Lorentz, Baron Hermann Ludwig Ferdinand von Helmholtz, and eventually Albert Einstein. Faraday himself lacked the mathematical knowledge to formulate such a field theory.

By the mid-1850s Faraday had withdrawn from all scientific work. He continued to teach and lecture until 1861, after which he retired to a house provided by Queen Victoria.

Outstanding Achievements:

Faraday's most important innovations related to engineering were the prototype electric motor, the transformer and the dynamo. His electric motor, powered by a voltaic pile, consisted of a vessel of mercury through which a current was passed. A pivoted bar magnet fixed in the mercury rotated around an electrified wire extending down into the mercury from a bridge above the vessels. In another version, a pivoted wire circled a fixed bar magnet. As long as current was applied, rotatory motion of the pivoted wire and magnet continued. Like Henry's electric motor, developed ten years later, this device was purely experimental. Widespread use of efficient direct-current motors was still more than half a century away.

Faraday's dynamo in one form was a copper disk on a spindle set to rotate between the poles of a bar magnet. As long as the disk rotated, cutting the magnetic lines of force, a current was generated in a circuit connecting the outer rim and the center of the disk.

Faraday's chemical and electrochemical research also had important technological results. His work with steel alloys and glass formulas helped put development of these products on a scientific footing and pointed the way to the regular use of scientific methods by industry. His laws of electrolysis have been helpful in the electrotyping and electrochemical industries. The unit of capacitance, the farad, is named for him. ■

Further Reading:

Dictionary of National Biography, s.v. "Faraday."
Dictionary of Scientific Biography, s.v. "Faraday."
L. Pearce William, *Michael Faraday*. New York, 1965.

ASA WHITNEY

b. Dec. 1, 1791, Townsend, Massachusetts
d. June 4, 1874, Philadelphia, Pennsylvania
American Industrialist and Engineer

Life and Times:

Asa Whitney was the first of the U.S. railroad magnates, an entrepreneur who made his fortune in the rail construction boom that swept the Northeast in the 1840s and 1850s. The son of a blacksmith, he had an extensive if informal mechanical education in his father's shop and as an apprentice wheelwright in New York and New Hampshire. By 1830 he had become co-owner of a cotton machinery plant near Brownesville, N.Y. The same year Whitney was appointed assistant engineer, or master machinist of the Mohawk and Hudson Railroad; among other duties, he was responsible for supervising erection of machinery and construction of the company's railway cars. Within three years he rose to become superintendent of the line.

As an expert in overland transportation, Whitney was named New York State canal commissioner in 1839. He realized, however, that the future lay with rail transport, and kept up his contracts with railroad men. In 1842 he joined with a Philadelphia locomotive designer, Matthias W. Baldwin, to open a railroad machinery construction shop. Six years later Whitney and his three sons established Asa Whitney & Sons, which quickly became the country's largest manufacturer of railroad car wheels. Whitney went on to become president of the Reading Railroad shortly before his retirement in 1861. He bequeathed $50,000 to the University of Pennsylvania for establishment of a chair of dynamic energy.

Outstanding Engineering Achievements:

Whitney was responsible for patenting a substantial proportion of the machinery used during the country's first great railroad boom. He is most famous for three patents on which he based the success of Asa Whitney & Sons: a cast iron railroad car wheel with a corrugated center web; a new method of manufacturing the wheel; and an improved process for annealing the cast iron to make it less brittle. Whitney also patented a locomotive steam engine in 1840. ∎

Further Reading:

American Society of Civil Engineers, *A Biographical Dictionary of Civil Engineers*.

JAMES BEAUMONT NEILSON

b. June 22, 1792, Shettleston, Scotland
d. Jan. 18, 1865, Queenshill, Scotland
Scottish Mechanical Engineer

Life and Times:

During the eighteenth century a series of innovations by Henry Cort [q.v.], the Darby family [q.v.] and others helped to make the British iron industry the strongest in Europe. However, the construction of increasingly large blast furnaces in Britain created a new technical problem: even with the help of blowers, blast air was not raising the temperature in the furnaces to the level required for smelting. The hot blast process developed by James Beaumont Neilson did more than solve this problem. By sharply reducing manufacturing costs, it helped maintain Britain's commercial advantage despite the tariffs imposed by other countries to protect their less efficient iron industries. More importantly, iron was soon competitive in price with wood, and its use in tools and machinery began to grow exponentially.

The son of an engine-wright at a coal works near Glasgow, Neilson had little formal education; at fourteen he was working in the colliery, and several years later he was apprenticed to his elder brother John, an engineman. Neilson was a skilled mechanic and at 22 became an engine-wright. When the colliery where he worked shut down, he moved to Glasgow and secured a job as foreman in the city's recently established gasworks. In five years Neilson was appointed manager and chief engineer; his connection with the gasworks lasted 30 years.

The gift for invention which Neilson had already begun to display was nurtured by constant study. Once in Glasgow he took courses at the Andersonian University. He also encouraged workers at the gasworks to follow his example and was instrumental in establishing a vocational school. As a result of Neilson's growing reputation, the owner of an ironworks asked him in 1824 to investigate means of improving the efficiency of blast furnaces. It was this investigation which led Neilson to develop the hot blast process.

Neilson inspected a particularly inefficient furnace whose blower was half a mile distant. In the course of his studies, he had learned that heating expanded the volume of a gas and thus increased the work done by it. Neilson concluded that heating the blast near the furnace end would overcome the effects of distance. Preliminary tests on a smith's fire proved his hunch correct, although the physics of the day hardly offered an adequate explanation.

At first no ironmaker in Scotland would allow Neilson to install hot blast equipment at a foundry, for his process ran counter to accepted wisdom. It had long been noted that iron produced in winter was of higher quality than that produced in summer. Hence it seemed logical to conclude that cold blast was superior to hot; some foundry owners had even installed refrigeration equipment. But Neilson was finally able to test his theories at the Clyde ironworks, with favorable results.

In 1828 Neilson went into partnership with the inventor Charles Macintosh [q.v.] to patent the process, which Neilson further improved over the next five years. By 1835 hot blast equipment had been installed in all Scottish ironworks, and until 1842 the partners repeatedly went to court to sue unlicensed users. Nevertheless, Neilson was wealthy by the time he retired in 1847, and in the following year he was elected a Fellow of the Royal Society in recognition of his achievements.

Outstanding Engineering Achievements:

Neilson began his field tests at Clyde by applying heat directly to the *tuyère*, the pipe carrying the blast to the furnace. The red-hot *tuyère* raised the air temperature to 80°F (27°C), but much higher temperatures were needed. The next step was to introduce the cold air into a square heating chamber made of wrought iron and set in brick. A grate below heated the air to 200°F (93°C) as it passed through the chamber and into the *tuyère*. Cast iron proved more durable, and dome-shaped chambers completely enclosed in brick allowed the air temperature to reach 280°F (138°C). By heating the pipe leading

to the chamber and passing the blast through the chamber in arched tubes, temperatures of 600°F (315°C) were obtained.

Furnaces using Neilson's final design produced three times more iron than conventional furnaces using the same amount of fuel. A hot blast did twice as much work as the same amount of cold blast. Hot blast furnaces could use raw coal, even anthracite, instead of the more expensive coke, and previously unusable deposits of black band ironstone now began to be smelted.

Neilson was also responsible for various improvements in the manufacture of gas, including the use of clay retorts and the purification of gas with iron sulfate. To regulate the gas at the point of use, Neilson designed the fish- or swallowtail burner, which soon found general acceptance. ■

Further Reading:

Maurice Daumas, *Histoire Générale des Techniques*, Vol. III. Paris, 1968.
Dictionary of National Biography, s.v. "Neilson."
Singer et al., *A History of Technology*, Vol. III.

CHARLES BABBAGE
b. Dec. 26, 1791, London, England
d. Oct. 18, 1871, London, England
British Inventor

Life and Times:

Before the advent of modern electronics, men of various cultures constructed calculating machines with limited but by no means negligible capabilities. An experienced user of the abacus, developed 5,000 years ago in the Middle East, can make surprisingly rapid and complex calculations. The French scientist and philosopher Blaise Pascal [q.v.] was the first European to devise a calculating machine capable of addition and subtraction. The German mathematician Gottfried Wilhelm von Leibniz later developed a machine that could also multiply and divide, though not always correctly. It was the British inventor Charles Babbage, however, who brought the preelectronic calculating machine to its peak performance, in both the accuracy and the number of operations it could undertake.

The son of a banker, Babbage began his studies at Cambridge University in 1810. In-

Charles Babbage, developer of a pre-electronic computer, using the punched-car system of data processing.

tensely interested in mathematics, he was initially disappointed to discover that he knew more than his tutor. Yet he soon began to flourish among like-minded students, including George Peacock and John Herschel, son of the great astronomer. Babbage, Peacock and Herschel all shared the conviction that the pursuit of pure science had declined in England since the era of Newton; in 1814, the year of Babbage's graduation, they founded the Analytical Society of Cambridge with the aim of creating a more favorable atmosphere for scientific research. Though Babbage's future interests had not yet solidified, he published work on the calculus of functions and drafted notes to the Royal Society on the relation between notation and mechanism, developing ideas that anticipated his life's work. In 1816 the Royal Society elected Babbage to membership.

Babbage's mature work began in his attempt to correct the notoriously faulty logarithmic and astronomical tables then in use, which repeatedly constrained advances in astronomy. It was in the course of this work that he first conceived of a machine which would both calculate and print out logarithms. By 1822, he had constructed the first model of a "difference engine," which when fully developed would be capable of adding, subtracting, multiplying and dividing more quickly and accurately than the earlier machines of Pascal and Leibniz.

Babbage's early version of the difference engine, like all of his later, more complex designs, was never completed in his lifetime. It ran up against the fundamental constraints of the existing technology, achieving with wheels and levers what a century later would be accomplished with electronic equipment. Nevertheless, Babbage's initial concept attracted attention and government support, which together with his own private resources enabled him to devote several decades to successive, ever more complex models. He also traveled widely in Europe, keeping abreast of the latest innovations in science, mathematics and technology. He admired the strong support for scientific work in France and summarized his findings in *Reflections on the Decline of Science in England, and Some of its Causes,* published in 1830, in which he returned to the themes which inspired the founding of the Analytical Society fifteen years earlier.

In 1834 Babbage finally brought to near-completion the first model of his 1822 design of the difference engine. His calculator could compute logarithmic tables from 1 to 100,000. As he was to do repeatedly, however, Babbage abruptly scrapped his original plan and sought funds to build an entirely new model.

The government refused his request, but his work attracted attention from other quarters, notably from the daughter of Lord Byron, whose description of some early models of the difference engine helped preserve them for posterity. Babbage ultimately replaced the difference engine with the "analytical engine," which was capable of extended computations based on results arrived at from the machine's initial instructions. He also borrowed from Joseph-Marie Jacquard [q.v.] the idea of feeding information into his machine by means of punched cards. To the end of his life, Babbage sought to elaborate and perfect his brilliant but never completed computer.

Babbage made pioneering contributions not only to the modern field of data processing, but also to what is now called "operations research." While traveling in England and Europe he analyzed the functioning of railroads and other new technologies, embodying the results of his study in *Economy of Machines and Manufactures* (1834). Several years later the British postal service used Babbage's operations research methods to replace its cumbersome and costly system of rates based on distance with the much simpler uniform rate system used by modern post offices.

In addition to his engineering work, Babbage

remained interested throughout his life in the general advancement of science. In 1834 he founded the Statistical Society to promote the social uses of statistical methods. Despite the honor shown him by the Royal Society, he became increasingly estranged from the group, which he blamed in part for the decline of scientific research in England. The Royal Society, in his view, was "a collection of men who elect each other to office and then dine together at the expense of the society to praise each other over wine and to give each other medals." Babbage submitted a sweeping reform proposal to the Society, which was ignored. In 1831 he joined with several friends to found the British Association for the Advancement of Science, designed to encourage research and the exchange of scientific information. In this respect he was successful; the British Association, though never as prestigious as the Royal Society, was far more accessible to scientists and became a forum for some of the most important scientific controversies of the nineteenth century.

Outstanding Engineering Achievement:

Babbage's outstanding achievement was never completed in his lifetime. The unfinished 1834 model of the difference engine, today preserved in the Science Museum in London, was the closest he came to a working model. The 1822 design upon which it is based consisted of 96 wheels and 24 axes, later modified to 18 wheels and 3 axes. The initial model and the later realization consisted of toothed wheels mounted on shafts, with each shaft used for a digit in the desired operation. When each shaft was primed for the appropriate digit, the simple turn of a

Part of Babbage's analytical engine, intended to perform arithmetical operations in accordance with instructions and data on punched cards.

crank activated a series of levers and cams which punched out the answer. This initial plan was expanded in the 1834 model to a 20-place capacity, which considerably increased the machine's complexity. The final plan for the analytical engine, when completed, would have required two tons of brass, steel and pewter clockwork made to gauged standards, something never accomplished up to that time. The later models made use of punch cards for programming information and for information storage on a scale which rivalled those of early computers.

Babbage's work on calculators led him to promote the industrial production of standardized precision parts. Another spinoff of his work with gears was his invention of the first working speedometer. Interested from his student days in statistics, he worked out the first reliable actuarial tables for an insurance company. In 1847 Babbage invented an ophthalmoscope, a device permitting study of the eye's retina. ■

Further Reading:

Dictionary of Scientific Biography, s.v. "Babbage."

Philip and Emily Morrison, eds., *Charles Babbage and his Calculating Engines*. New York, 1961.

Maboth Mosley, *Irascible Genius: A Life of Charles Babbage, Inventor*. London, 1964.

GOLDSWORTHY GURNEY
b. Feb. 14, 1793, Treator, Cornwall, England
d. Feb. 28, 1875, Reeds, Cornwall, England
British Mechanical Inventor

Life and Times:

As steam power spread through industry during the early nineteenth century, inventors attempted to harness the steam engine to transportation. The best-known efforts in this direction—because successful—were George Stephenson's [q.v.] locomotive and John Fitch's [q.v.] steamship. One interesting failure in the development of steam transport was Goldsworthy Gurney's steam carriage.

Gurney studied medicine and became a practicing medical doctor, but he spent much of his time learning chemistry and mechanical engineering. He moved to London in 1820 and gave a series of lectures on chemical science at the Surrey Institution.

Goldsworthy Gurney whose road steam carriages ran in regular service for three months.

In 1823 Gurney began efforts to build a mechanically-driven vehicle to operate on common roads. He built an ammonia engine, probably the first ever made, and used it to power a small locomotive. His subsequent engines were more conventional, employing steam derived from heated water. In 1827 Gurney built a steam carriage that he drove in and around London for almost two years.

Gurney's most important journey came in July 1829, when he drove a steam carriage from London to Bath and back, achieving a speed of 15 miles (24 km) an hour. It was the first long trip at a sustained speed by any locomotive on road or rail. The trip was marred at one point by an attack on the vehicle by a group of hostlers, horse dealers, drivers and others who felt their livelihood to be imperiled by the steam carriage.

During 1831 one of Gurney's steam carriages ran between Gloucester and Cheltenham for three months. The nine-mile (14 km) trip was made in 45 to 55 minutes. In 396 trips, the vehicle carried 3,000 passengers without a serious accident.

Although the service was faster than that provided by horse-drawn vehicles at half the fare, common road steam carriages did not survive for long. They used too much fuel and damaged the roads. During the 1830s, proprietors of horse-drawn stage coaches induced Parliament to impose heavy tolls on the steam carriages. More importantly, they were unable to compete with the railroads.

Gurney's vehicles—which carried from 15 to 20 passengers—were impressive engineering achievements for an era in which there was no inexpensive steel, artificial abrasives, standardized screws, cutting tools or mineral oil for lubrication. Only when these materials—plus gasoline, reinforced concrete, rubber, and assembly-line production—were developed did mechanically-powered common road vehicles become feasible.

Outstanding Engineering Achievement:

The typical Gurney steam carriage weighed 1½ to 2½ tons—about the weight of modern American automobiles—had wheels 4 feet (122 cm) in diameter with iron tires almost 4 inches (10 cm) broad, and operated under steam pressures of up to 70 pounds (32 kg).

One notable feature of the carriage was its water tube boiler. In the cylindrical boiler prevalent at the time, the warmer water at the bottom of the cylinder near the furnace flowed upward while the colder water at the cylinder's top flowed down. The two currents interfered with each other, impeding circulation, preventing the establishment of a uniform temperature throughout the boiler, and thereby inducing boiler explosions. Gurney's water tube boiler reduced the chance of explosion. It consisted of water-filled U-tubes turned 90 degrees and connected at their ends by vertical cylinders. At the top of each cylinder was the steam chamber. Upon the application of heat to one leg of the tube, a circulation was set up that eliminated the possibility of interference between up and down currents.

Gurney's steam carriage successfully completed the 200-mile London to Bath round trip at 15 miles per hour.

The carriage also included a braking system consisting of iron shoes lowered to skid the vehicle to a halt and a long rod that served as a steering device. The boiler was fired by coke to prevent smoke. ■

Further Reading:

Robert H. Thurston, *A History of the Growth of the Steam Engine*. New York, 1903.

CHARLES BLACKER VIGNOLES
b. May 31, 1793, Woodbrook, Ireland
d. Nov. 17, 1875, Hythe, England
British Civil Engineer

Life and Times:

Railway mania began in England and spread around the world in the second quarter of the nineteenth century. As soon as the success of the Liverpool and Manchester Railway, from its opening in 1830, had demonstrated the practicality of steam-powered transportation, railroad engineers were in demand, worldwide. The first requirement was a track that could take the weight of a train, meticulously graded, without sudden inclines or sharp turns, and with whatever bridges and tunnels were necessary. Charles Blacker Vignoles was one of the early civil engineers who built railroads in many countries, living a remarkably colorful life while achieving recognition in his own profession.

Vignoles was the descendent of a noble Huguenot family which had left Languedoc and settled in Ireland a century before Charles was born. As a baby, Charles was taken to Guadeloupe where his father, a British Army officer, was captured by the French and died. Within a short time, Charles' mother also died. The orphan was immediately commissioned as an ensign in the British Army and placed on half pay until the age of 20. He kept his commission for forty years, by which time it was the oldest in the army.

His first years of active service took Vignoles to Canada and France. He also went to Venezuela to aid the colonial revolt against Spain. After a stint as a state surveyor for South Carolina, he returned to England and started work for the civil engineer John Rennie Jr. In 1825 a bill came before Parliament to allow construction of a railroad between Liverpool and Manchester.

Rennie's rival, George Stephenson, the appointed engineer, was called to present his opinion. With his thick Tyneside dialect and ill-formed sentences, he was virtually incomprehensible and the bill was withdrawn. The next year, Vignoles was called to the hearings on a new bill. With his military bearing he so impressed Parliament that the bill was passed and Vignoles was appointed engineer—under Stephenson, but still employed by Rennie. The situation was difficult, and Vignoles resigned before the line was operational. Independently of Stephenson, Vignoles later built a branch line of the Liverpool and Manchester.

In 1832, Vignoles built the first railroad in Ireland, connecting Dublin and Kingston. Three years later he became chief engineer of the Sheffield, Ashton and Manchester Railway, in which capacity he began a three-mile long tunnel under the Pennines. Vignoles invested in this project and persuaded his friends to do so too. In 1838 he found himself unable to meet his financial commitments; rather than risk his friends' holdings, he resigned, losing 10,000 pounds. The tunnel and railroad were completed by others.

Undaunted, Vignoles continued building railroads, including another in Ireland, several in England, one in Switzerland (the first in that country), and one in Spanish Basque territory. He surveyed a route in Brazil, built an iron bridge over the river Trent, constructed a suspension bridge at Kiev (see below), and worked on the Warsaw-Terespol line which opened in 1865.

Professional recognition came in 1841, when Vignoles was appointed as the first professor of civil engineering at University College in the University of London. He was made a Fellow of the Royal Society and also of the Royal Astronomical Society. In 1869 he was elected presi-

The suspension bridge built by Bignoles across the Dnepr River at Kiev.

dent of the Institute of Civil Engineers. Two of Vignoles' sons became engineers; a third, a clergyman, wrote a biography of his father.

Outstanding Engineering Achievements:

Between 1848 and 1855, Vignoles was engaged in the construction of the Nicholas suspension bridge across the Dnepr river at Kiev. The site for the bridge had already been chosen without regard to the river bed or banks, preventing Vignoles from selecting the best location. There were other unexpected difficulties; local steel mills refused to make the 4 miles (6 km) of iron chain that the bridge required, and the links had to be brought overland from the port of Odessa. Local contractors were unable to handle the project; the ones who could were Jews, banned from Kiev. Vignoles had to obtain permission from the Tsar to allow them to enter the city.

Across the half mile (.8 km) of river, Vignoles constructed five masonry towers, each supporting the chains for what looked like a series of four suspension bridges. Between one bank and its nearest tower was a swivel bridge that allowed tall-masted ships to pass through. The roadway, a substantial construction of trussed iron girders and wood, was 35 feet (11 m) wide, with a 9-foot (3 m) footpath cantilevered out on each side. Like so much of Kiev, the bridge did not survive World War II.

In addition to his construction work, Vignoles introduced a number of improvements in railway equipment. Among these was a locomotive with a special gear wheel that ran on a third track; the device provided improved traction and could be used for pulling a train up a steep hill. In 1832 he experimented with iron wagons, which had previously been thought too heavy and unwieldy for railway use. They were found suitable, particularly for carrying coal. In 1837 Vignoles designed a rail with a very broad base allowing it to be laid with a small supporting "chair," or even no chair at all. The rail was widely used in Victorian times outside England; since World War II its use has prevailed in England as well. ■

Further Reading:

Frank Ferneyhough, *The History of Railways in Britain*. Osprey, Reading, 1975.

Jack Simmons, *The Railway in England and Wales 1830–1914*. London, 1978.

Olinthus Vignoles, *Life of Charles Blacker Vignoles*. London, 1889.

BARTHOLOME THIMONNIER
b. 1793, L'Arbesle, Rhone, France
d. Aug. 5, 1857, Amplepuis, France
French Tailor and Inventor

Life and Times:

The development and successful marketing of the sewing machine in the mid-nineteenth century had enormous economic consequences. It made possible the mechanization of the garment industry and the availability of cheap, ready-made clothing. One of the first mass-marketed home appliances, it led to new sales techniques and freed many women from the drudgery of hand sewing. The first successful sewing machines were designed by the Americans Elias Howe and Isaac M. Singer. Even earlier, however, the French tailor Bartholome Thimonnier had invented a sewing machine which he could not market in his own country. The failure of the first sewing machine illustrates the obstacles to the mechanization of artisan production in France and a more general resistance to innovation which handicapped French industry.

Son of a Lyons textile worker who himself had attempted to construct a sewing machine, Thimonnier grew up in central France prior to the great artisan revolts of the 1830s in the silk and textile industries. He became a tailor when the hook needle was still the dominant tool of the trade. Supporting himself on his meager earnings, he spent most of the decade after 1821 at work on a mechanical sewing machine. Though he had little formal education and no training in mechanics, by 1829 he had developed a simple working model. In 1830 Thimonnier obtained a patent for his device and began a long effort to market it.

A mining inspector named Beaunier, having heard of the machine, sought out Thimonnier in St-Etienne and persuaded him to relocate to Paris, where a small firm, Germain, Petit et Cie., outfitted its shop with 80 of his machines. The workers of the shop, however, seeing their livelihood threatened, stormed the factory and destroyed every machine. The company was reluctant to try the experiment again, and ended its association with Thimonnier in 1832. Returning to work as a tailor, Thimonnier nonetheless continued his campaign to interest French commerce and industry in his machine. He toured France in 1834, carrying the machine from town to town while giving demonstrations along the way, but with no significant response. He continued to improve the machine, however, and by 1845 it was capable of 200 stitches per minute.

Thimonnier's sewing machine with its single thread pulled up by a crochet hook.

At this point Jean-Marie Magnin, an engineer, took an interest in Thimonnier's work. In a joint venture the two began production of the machines in southern France. With further improvements, Thimonnier obtained a renewed patent in 1848 for a machine capable of 300 stitches per minute. While his earlier models were made of wood, the new one was made of iron. The February 1848 revolution, however, bankrupted the venture. Thimonnier departed for England, where he ceded his patent to a Manchester firm. He attempted to have his invention displayed at the great world exhibition in London in 1851, but the machine arrived late. While visitors from all over the world saw Howe's and Singer's machines on display, a turning point which made their respective business fortunes, Thimonnier remained virtually unknown. As a consolation, he did receive a prize from the Paris world exposition of 1855, which wrongly described his machine as the prototype for all sewing machines in existence. But Thimonnier was still, after 25 years, unable to earn any significant income from his machine, and he died in obscurity.

Outstanding Engineering Achievement:

In contrast to the later, more sophisticated machines of Howe and Singer, Thimonnier's sewing machine merely mechanized the process previously done by hand. The machine was operated by a hand-crank, which moved a crochet-style needle with a barbed loop on the point instead of an eye. The needle passed through the fabric that was moved by hand beneath it, bringing up a loop of thread on the barbed end. Each loop returned through the previously made loop, forming a chain of thread on the upper surface of the fabric. This differed from the so-called lock stitch produced by later sewing machines, which operated with two threads, one on each side of the fabric. Since Thimonnier's machine was hand-fed, the seam it produced was often crooked and uneven, a problem solved only in the machine patented in 1851 by Isaac M. Singer. ∎

Further Reading:

Maurice Daumas, ed., *Histoire Générale des Techniques,* Vol. III. Paris, 1969.

MATTHIAS WILLIAM BALDWIN
b. Nov. 10, 1795, Elizabethtown, New Jersey
d. Sept. 7, 1866, Philadelphia, Pennsylvania
American Inventor and Locomotive Manufacturer

Life and Times:

During the 1820s British experiments with railway transportation were followed with great interest in America. The first British locomotive was shipped to the United States in 1829. But imported locomotives often proved unfit for American tracks, which had sharp curves and steep grades. American inventors, beginning with Oliver Evans [q.v.], were soon designing their own locomotive engines. By 1837 the United States, with 1,450 miles (2300 km) of railway track, had a more extensive rail network than Great Britain, and 80 percent of the 350 locomotives used were of domestic manufacture. Most of these were produced in the locomotive works of Matthias Baldwin.

Baldwin's father, a carriage maker, died when his son was four years old. Baldwin was apprenticed to a jewelry shop in Philadelphia and followed the jeweler's trade until he was 30. He then became partners with David Mason, a

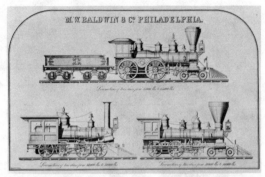

Some of the locomotives built by Baldwin's works: top, 35–65,000 lb class; bottom left, 48–70,000 lb; bottom right, 50–70,000 lb.

Matthias William Baldwin and his first full-size locomotive, Old Ironsides.

machinist, and set up a manufacturing business. Beginning with bookbinders' and engravers' tools, the partners were soon making hydraulic presses and calico printers' rolls. In 1827 Baldwin built a six-horsepower stationary steam engine to power their calico printing machinery. When the shop began receiving orders from other factories for steam engines, the unadventurous Mason withdrew from the business.

One of Baldwin's orders was from Franklin Peale, who wanted a model locomotive for his popular Philadelphia museum. Working from sketchy descriptions, Baldwin was able to construct a miniature locomotive that could haul two small cars with four delighted passengers around a circular track. The success of the miniature locomotive led to a request for a full-sized one from the Philadelphia, Germantown, and Norristown Railroad Company. Fortunately, Baldwin was able to inspect first-hand an English locomotive recently bought by the Camden and Amboy Railroad Company. Baldwin's engine, "Old Ironsides," began hauling passenger cars in 1832.

As demand rose, Baldwin devoted himself exclusively to the construction of locomotives. By 1837 his company was building 40 a year. The financial crisis of that year dealt Baldwin a severe blow. He was forced to lay off some of his 300 workers, and five years passed before he fully recovered. Nevertheless, the Baldwin Locomotive Works in Philadelphia built 1,000 en-

gines by 1861 and an additional 500 during the Civil War years; the company long remained the world's largest producer of locomotives.

Outstanding Engineering Achievements:

"Old Ironsides" weighed eight tons fully loaded and could haul 30 tons on a level road; the engine's maximum speed was 30 miles (48 km) an hour. The engine had four wheels. The two driving wheels, 4½ feet (1.3 meters) in diameter, were located in back, under the engine. The two front wheels were nine inches (23 cm) smaller in diameter. The engine delivered its power by a crank drive. The two cylinders were attached horizontally outside the smoke box in line with the center of the cranks. The cylinders had a bore of 9½ inches (24 cm) in diameter; the piston stroke was 18 inches (46 cm).

"Old Ironsides" was a hybrid of wood and metal. The frame was wooden, as were the spokes and wheels. The wheel rims, however, were of wrought iron. The boiler contained thirty copper tubes. Construction of the locomotive took six months, largely because skilled mechanics and proper tools were lacking. To bore the cylinders, Baldwin had to embed a chisel in a block of wood and turn it by hand. Small wonder that the first trips of "Old Ironsides" were beset with problems. Even so, it stayed in service for 20 years.

One of Baldwin's most important innovations was an improved design for joints in the steam tubes. Steam joints in British locomotives, made of canvas and red lead, leaked severely under high pressure. Baldwin carefully ground his steam joints; they fit so tightly that the engines could safely generate 120 pounds of steam per square inch (827 kPa), double the normal British pressure. The form that Baldwin gave his boilers, a high dome over the fire box, became standard in America.

Baldwin was quick to adopt the flexible truck, or "bogie," for the front wheels of his engines, a device that was essential for running around sharp curves. But he clung conservatively to a six-wheel design long after his competitors had started building eight-wheeled locomotives with four driving wheels. ■

Further Reading:

Dictionary of American Biography, s.v. "Baldwin."

Kranzberg and Pursell, *Technology in Western Civilization*, Vol. I. New York, 1967.

Robert H. Thurston, *A History of the Growth of the Steam Engine*. New York, 1903.

A founder of thermodynamics, Nicolas Leonard Sadi Carnot made major discoveries on the relationship between heat and mechanical energy.

NICOLAS-LÉONARD-SADI CARNOT
b. June 1, 1796, Paris, France
d. Aug. 24, 1832, Paris, France
French Mechanical Engineer and Physicist

Life and Times:

As the steam engine became important in the industrial economies of Britain and other countries, the efforts of engineers turned to increasing the machine's thermal efficiency. The British engineers who invented and made most of the early improvements in the steam engine worked largely by trial and error, possessing little theoretical knowledge of physics. In spite of major improvements in tool design and machine construction, growth of efficiency in the high-pressure engine was slow in the early nineteenth century. James Watt's [q.v.] double-acting steam engine, for instance, operated at only about five per cent thermal efficiency. Efforts to improve this level of performance helped originate the branch of physics called thermodynamics.

Sadi Carnot, a founder of the study of thermodynamics, came from a distinguished family. His father, Lazare Carnot [q.v.], was a military engineer and minister of the interior under Napoleon I. Sadi attended the École Polytechnique, and served as a military engineer after his studies. Carnot's only publication during his lifetime, *Reflections On the Motive Force of Fire* (1824), was the first systematic theory of heat engines. Through an investigation of the opera-

tion of the steam engine, Carnot sought to determine the limits of the motive power, or work, that an engine could produce from a given amount of heat.

Carnot's book had no influence on the improvement of the steam engine in the early nineteenth century. The appallingly low efficiencies obtained with these engines resulted largely from difficulties in machine construction, and Carnot's theoretical insights were inapplicable to these problems. Moreover, the book's mathematical and scientific concepts were expressed in an abstract language that was beyond the grasp of most early nineteenth century engineers. Initially neglected, the book was not revived until after Carnot's untimely death at the age of 36 in a cholera epidemic. Yet his work is important as a first attempt to apply theoretical knowledge to an understanding of the steam engine's capabilities and operation. Carnot's death was a great loss to science.

Outstanding Engineering Achievement:

In studying the relation between heat and motive power, Carnot sought to discover the maximum thermal efficiency of a heat engine operating between two heat reservoirs. Carnot determined that this depended only upon the temperatures of the heat source and the heat sink. (In the steam engine, the temperature of the heat source is measured as steam flows from the boiler to the cylinder, exerting pressure on the piston; the temperature of the heat sink is determined while the condenser cools the steam, allowing the piston to return.) Carnot tested this principle by carrying out a thought experiment with an ideal engine which could also work in reverse. For example, if a certain amount of work is produced as heat passes from its highest to its lowest temperature (an ideal heat engine), then the same amount of work would be required to raise the heat from its lowest to its highest temperature (an ideal heat pump). Carnot agreed that if maximum efficiency were dependent on factors other than the two temperatures, then one could, in theory, connect a less efficient heat pump to a more efficient engine, both of which were operating between the same two temperatures and utilizing the same amounts of heat. But then the heat engine would be not only driving the heat pump, but also producing excess work, representing its excess efficiency. This is a perpetual motion machine, which Carnot (and his contemporaries) regarded as impossible. Hence, ideal thermal efficiency must depend only on operating temperatures. This is an important consequence of the second law of thermodynamics. (Although Carnot is thus justly regarded as the founder of the second law, it was not until the 1850s that the law was stated in its full form by Rudolph Clausius and William Thomson.) ■

Further Reading:

Dictionary of Scientific Biography, s.v. "Carnot."

Milton Kerber, "Sadi Carnot and the Steam Engineers," *Isis.* Vol. LI (1960).

E. Mendoza, ed., *Reflections on the Motive Power of Fire by Sadi Carnot.* New York, 1960.

ANTOINE GALY-CAZALAT
b. *July 6, 1796, Saint-Girons, France*
d. *Dec. 8, 1869, Paris, France*
French Mechanical Engineer

Life and Times:

The first half of the nineteenth century saw the development of increasingly powerful steam engines and their application to specialized uses. With the use of higher steam pressures, the construction and safety features of the first generation of steam engines became obsolete. In particular, the capacity to control the pressure in

a boiler was critical if engine operators were to be protected from disastrous explosions. Antoine Galy-Cazalat was one of the engineers who contributed to solving this problem, although he did not restrict himself to the field of steam power.

Galy-Cazalat graduated from the Ecole Polytechnique in 1816. For ten years he taught mathematics and physics at the secondary school level, working in turn at Perpignan, Nancy and Versailles. Tiring of his teaching duties, Galy-Cazalat changed careers; he moved to Paris, where he became an engineer. In 1848 he became caught up in politics, winning election to the new Constituent Assembly. He voted with the moderate democrats in opposition to the socialist schemes of Louis Blanc. When radical workers barricaded the streets and took up arms, Galy-Cazalat attempted to mediate. He was taken hostage by the insurgents during the "Bloody June Days," but escaped injury. Defeated in the 1849 elections, he returned to private life and devoted himself to the study of industrial processes.

Outstanding Engineering Achievements:

The need to monitor the vapor pressure in a steam engine was recognized before Galy-Cazalat. However, with the advent of high-pressure engines, manometers became cumbrous and hard to read; constructed of crystal, they easily shattered, making them impractical for use in locomotives or steamships. Galy-Cazalat developed a sturdy and easily read manometer that remained in use for several decades, until the metallic manometer rendered all previous designs obsolete.

Galy-Cazalat investigated the application of steam to various forms of transportation. In 1837 he wrote a theoretical and practical guide to steamships. He was better known in his day for constructing a steam-powered wagon in 1830; intended for use on ordinary roads, it found little acceptance.

In 1855 Galy-Cazalat described a procedure for making steel similar to that patented by Henry Bessemer four months later. He also developed a process for obtaining gas for lighting. ■

Further Reading:

Maurice Daumas, ed., *Histoire Générale des Techniques,* Vol. III. Paris, 1968.

Grand Larousse Encyclopédie, ss. vv. "Galy-Cazalat" and "Acier."

ADHEMAR JEAN CLAUDE BARRE DE SAINT-VENANT

b. Aug. 23, 1797, Fortoiseau, France
d. Jan. 6, 1886, Saint-Ouen, France
French Civil Engineer

Life and Times:

From the mid-eighteenth century the institution charged with the construction of bridges, roads and canals in France was the Corps des Ponts et Chaussées. More than a few of the organization's engineers contributed to the theory of mechanics as a result of the problems they faced in the field. Adhémar Jean Claude Barré de Saint-Venant was in the forefront of this group. Even so, France was among the last of the European countries to recognize his accomplishments. The reason was political: Saint-Venant was once rash enough openly to express his opposition to Napoleon.

Saint-Venant's father, an agronomist, died while his son was still young. His mother sent him to Bruges to pursue a classical education; but the boy's real love was mathematics, and at age sixteen he entered the Ecole Polytechnique. In 1814 the event occurred which would make him an outcast. When the students at the Polytechnique were mobilized to defend the capital, Saint-Venant refused to fight for the "usurper" Napoleon. For this act he was expelled from school and until 1823 relegated to a minor post in the gunpowder service. He was then allowed to enter the Ecole des Ponts et Chaussées, although none of his classmates would speak with him.

On his first field assignment, the construction of a bridge over the Creuse river at Guéret, Saint-Venant began to consider the role of shear in the deformation of bodies. His theories matured over the next years, during which he worked on canals at Arles, in Nièvre and in the Ardennes. In 1834 Saint-Venant published several papers on general mechanics and the dynamics of fluids. They attracted the attention of Gaspard Gustave de Coriolis, professor of applied mechanics at the Ecole des Ponts et Chaussées, who asked Saint-Venant to serve as his assistant. Saint-Venant worked with his patron from 1837 to 1842, lecturing on the new concepts of shearing stress and shearing strain.

While Saint-Venant's theoretical accomplishments won some recognition, his technical capability was soon unjustly questioned. He had begun work with the Paris paving service in 1839; but the innovations he introduced drew the fire of the municipal authorities, who dismissed him in 1843. Although promoted to chief engineer in that year and enrolled in the Legion of Honor in 1847, Saint-Venant was not assigned (or did not seek) further work as a civil engineer. Instead he continued to write about mechanics.

Following the Revolution of 1848, Saint-Venant was retired from the Corps. In protest, he applied for and was awarded the chair of agricultural engineering at the new Institute of Agricultural Engineering in Versailles. In the two years before the Institute closed its doors, Saint-Venant published memoirs on erosion control, pond drainage and the shape of ploughshares.

Saint-Venant sought no further employment, but devoted himself to his wife and six children in the time he could spare from writing. His internationally acclaimed research finally earned him admission to the Academy of Sciences at age 71. Even then he did not slow the pace of his work. On his deathbed he reviewed the proofsheets for the last of his several hundred publications.

Outstanding Engineering Achievements:

The innovations for which Saint-Venant was dismissed in Paris soon became standard municipal practices for a generation. Wherever possible, he reduced the slope of steep roadways after careful study of the house foundations adjoining the street. He then laid granite borders along the sidewalks, with recessed areas for gutters and iron reinforcement at carriage-entrances. One of his less controversial suggestions was to plant trees along the principal streets.

While surveying the Nièvre department in 1826 and 1828, Saint-Venant concluded that the Sologne river area would benefit if the waters of the Sauldre river were diverted towards it. He submitted a proposal to that effect; construction of a canal finally began in 1851 along the route he had suggested. Saint-Venant himself was an innovative canal builder. Faced with extremely broken and watery terrain in the Ardennes, he used sheets of treated canvas as floating caissons for positioning concrete correctly.

Saint-Venant also made important contributions in the areas of mechanics of solid bodies, elasticity, torsion and bending. He always kept in view the ultimate practical benefits that would accrue from theoretical advances, and chose his problems and approaches accordingly. This outlook is apparent in his 1855 solution to the general problem of equilibrium of an elastic prism of any base. The solution is mixed rather than theoretically pure, but perfectly useful. It was soon adopted into the curriculum of engineering schools and is still known throughout Europe as "Saint-Venant's problem." ■

Further Reading:

Joseph Bertrand, *Eloges Academiques*. Paris, 1902.
M. J. Boussinesq and M. Flamant, "Notice sur la Vie et les Travaux de M. de Saint-Venant," *Annales des Ponts et Chaussées*. Vol. XII (1886).
Dictionnaire de Biographie Française, s.v. "Barre de Saint-Venant."
Stephen Timoshenko, *History of the Strength of Materials*. New York, 1953.

ANDREW TALCOTT
b. April 20, 1797, Glastonbury, Connecticut
d. April 22, 1883, Richmond, Virginia
American Civil Engineer and Astronomer

Life and Times:

As the United States spread westward, the accurate determination of boundaries became increasingly necessary to prevent border disputes. Until Andrew Talcott's time, terrestrial latitude was estimated by determining the altitude or distance from the zenith of a single star. This method left a wide margin of error that made it unsatisfactory for fixing anything but approximate borders. In 1732 the Danish astronomer Peder Horrebow had described a method of determining latitude by comparing the altitudes of two stars; but at that time the instrumentation was not very accurate and, more important as far as the method was concerned, not enough star positions were tabulated to provide many desirable pairs. The technique of paired measurement was forgotten until Talcott, working independently, developed his own method and instruments a century later.

Talcott graduated from the U.S. Military Academy and joined the Army Corps of Engineers in 1818. He helped plan and construct various fortifications from the East Coast to the Missouri and Yellowstone rivers, rising to the rank of captain by 1830. From 1828 to 1835 Talcott served as astronomer in the team surveying the boundary between Ohio and the Territory of Michigan, though he was also involved in building Fort Calhoun at Hampton Roads, Va. and supervising improvements on the Hudson River.

It was apparently along the Hudson that Tal-cott became acquainted with the instrument that became his zenith telescope. He worked out his method for determining latitude through the measurement of paired stars between 1834 and 1838, when he published a description of it in the *Journal of the Franklin Institute*. The Corps of Engineers immediately adopted the method, which was used (after modification of the zenith telescope) in the U.S. Coast Survey of 1847.

Talcott resigned his Army commission in 1836 to take up practice as a civil engineer. During the remainder of his career he worked as astronomer in the team surveying the northern boundary of Iowa and as chief engineer for several railroads and for the State of Virginia. In 1867 he was arrested on suspicion of having been a Confederate spy and detained until released by Gen. John E. Dix. After a trip abroad Talcott spent the rest of his life in Richmond, Va. and Baltimore.

Outstanding Engineering Achievement:

Talcott's method involved selecting two stars with about the same right ascension and the same distance, one north and one south, from the zenith of the place with the latitude to be determined. The altitude measurement was taken on the star at the time that it crossed the meridian—the line running north to south through the zenith. The telescope was then rotated 180 degrees to take the position of the second star in the field relative to the first. With a good eye and steady hands a surveyor could in principle determine latitude to the nearest angular second, corresponding to about 30 meters or 100 feet. ■

Further Reading:

Dictionary of American Biography, s.v. "Talcott."
W. L. Marshall, *Notes on Talcott's Method of Determining Terrestrial Latitudes, including Horrebow's Claim Thereto*. Richmond, 1919.

THOMAS DRUMMOND
b. Oct. 10, 1797, Edinburgh, Scotland
d. April 15, 1840, Dublin, Ireland
British Civil Engineer

Life and Times:

Drummond entered the University of Edinburgh at age 13 and subsequently studied mathematics and chemistry at the Royal Institution. In 1820 he began working on an ordnance survey headed by Col. Thomas Frederick Colby. While participating in the survey's work in southwestern England during 1823, Drummond found himself hampered for want of a light that would permit observations at long distances and in bad weather. Over the next two years, he devised the Drummond light, or limelight, and the heliostat, or solar reflector, to alleviate this problem (see below).

Entering upon a political career in the 1830s, Drummond became private secretary to the chancellor of the exchequer in 1833. Undersecretary in the Irish administration from 1835 to 40, he was in reality the *de facto* governor of Ireland.

Outstanding Engineering Achievements:

The Drummond light featured an ignited lime ball placed at the focus of a parabolic reflector. Ignition was produced by running a stream of oxygen through an alcohol flame. The glare produced by the Drummond light was remarkable for both its intensity and whiteness. When the ordnance survey moved to Ireland in 1825, both the Drummond light and the heliostat, comprised of a mirror connected with two telescopes, were successfully employed.

During the next several years, Drummond improved his namesake invention for use in lighthouses, most of which had previously employed Argand burners at the focus of a parabolic reflector. His major change entailed substituting oxygen and hydrogen for oxygen and alcohol as the igniting agent, a modification that intensified the light given off by the apparatus. He effected this alteration by employing the oxyhydrogen blowtorch invented by Robert Hare [q.v.]. Drummond reported that his modified illuminating device gave off a light 264 times brighter than that of the Argand burner. The use of Drummond's invention in lighthouses marked a significant advance in navigational safety.

The Drummond light was also employed in the theater to cast a sharp beam on the performers, whence the term "limelight" in common parlance. ■

Further Reading:

Eduard Farber, ed., *Great Chemists*. New York, 1961.

R. Barry O'Brien, *Thomas Drummond*. London, 1889.

JOSEPH HENRY
b. Dec. 17, 1797, Albany, New York
d. May 13, 1878, Washington, D.C.
American Scientist and Inventor

Life and Times:

Joseph Henry contributed to the development of engineering in two roles—that of scientist and that of administrator. As a scientist, he helped advance and systematize the study of electricity, before his time largely a popular curiosity, and developed some of the first practical applications of electromagnetism. As administrator, he served as first secretary of the newly-formed Smithsonian Institution and became the ancestor of the foundation heads and research coordinators who preside over the modern scientific establishment.

The son of a day laborer, Henry had little formal education as a youth. His father died when he was nine, and he grew up strongly influenced by the intense Calvinism of his mother. His first career interest was acting, but he became attracted to science after a chance reading of a popular volume on natural philosophy. Eager to broaden his education, he enrolled in 1819 in the Albany Academy, a private high school. Henry supported himself in various ways

First secretary of the Smithsonian Institution, Joseph Henry independently invented an electric motor and the relay.

while studying, serving for a time as tutor for the van Rensselaers, a wealthy New York State landholding family. In 1825 he gained appointment as engineer in a party surveying a highway route between West Point and Lake Erie. Henry might have become a topographical engineer, but decided one year later to accept a teaching position at the Albany Academy. He remained at the Academy until 1832, when he was named professor of natural history at the College of New Jersey (later Princeton University).

Henry's early experiments in electricity dealt with the electromagnet, invented by William Sturgeon [q.v.] in 1823. Sturgeon's instrument was fairly weak, capable of lifting a weight of only nine lb (4 kg). By winding the iron core tightly with insulated wire (see below), Henry was able to produce a much stronger magnetic field that lifted correspondingly greater weights. After further improvements he eventually constructed an electromagnet which could lift over a ton with the current of a normal battery. Though Henry did not exploit it, this was the first application of electricity with industrial potential.

Lifting heavy weights was not the only practical use of electromagnetism which Henry originated. By 1831 he had developed a small electromagnet that could be activated over more than a mile of wire and made to ring a bell. This was the basic apparatus of the telegraph. In 1835 he invented the electric relay (see below), a means of transmitting electrical impulses over long distances. Thus the most important technical problems of telegraphy were solved. Again, however, Henry refused to patent his invention or pursue its obvious commerical possibilities, allowing credit for the telegraph to go to Samuel Morse [q.v.] and Charles Wheatstone.

In 1831 Henry invented yet another electromagnetic device with even greater possibilities—the electric motor (see below). Powered by a single battery, Henry's motor produced reciprocating motion at the rate of 75 oscillations per minute. Henry himself regarded his invention as "a philosophical toy," and, as usual, made no attempt to put it to use.

The electric motor, of course, needed a source of electricity to run. For Henry's contemporaries, the only such source was the clumsy and stationary battery. But another of Henry's discoveries—electromagnetic induction—pointed towards an alternative means of generating electricity. Henry's other work with electromagnets involved creating a magnetic field from the application of electric current. In 1830 he succeeded in producing electricity from a moving magnetic field; a coil of wire passed across an activated electromagnet, he found, registered the presence of electric current on a galvanometer. This was the first experiment indicating that electricity can be generated by mechanical movement—the basis of electrical generation. Henry neglected to publish his finding immediately. Credit for the discovery therefore went to the British physicist Michael Faraday [q.v.], who carried out and published a similar experiment one year later.

Despite his extreme modesty, Henry's work in electricity soon made him one of the most famous scientists in America. In 1837 he made a celebrated tour of Britain and France, meeting Faraday, Wheatstone and other prominent contemporaries. In 1846, when the Smithsonian Institution was founded by the bequest of a British scientist named James Smithson, the federal government asked Henry to become its first secretary. The appointment virtually ended Henry's innovative work, but brought him an entirely new administrative career. His name was given to the unit of inductance, the henry.

Outstanding Engineering Achievements:

Henry first improved the electromagnet, which formed the basis of his subsequent work in electricity, by winding the iron core with silk-insulated wire. William Sturgeon's original electromagnet had been wound with uninsulated wire; in order to prevent the device from short-circuiting, the wire coils had to be spaced so that they did not touch. Use of insulated wire allowed Henry to wind the coils tightly and at right angles to the magnetic field, vastly increasing the electromagnet's power. Henry later discovered that even greater strength could be obtained by winding the core with several separate coils of wire attached to a single battery. This was the so-called quantity magnet, the basic constituent of the telegraph.

Henry also made use of electromagnets in developing the electric relay for transmission of current over long distances. Henry's relay, which differed from the one invented by Samuel Morse, consisted of a small electromagnet which, when activated by current from a battery, lifted a small iron key. This closed a second circuit supplied with current from another battery, activating yet another electromagnet, and so on indefinitely.

The electric motor invented by Henry was a fairly simple device consisting of an electromagnet balanced on a pivot. Beneath both ends of the electromagnet were vertically fixed per-

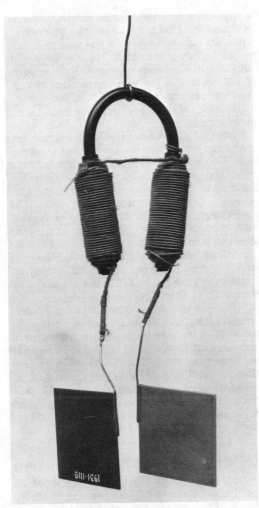

The electric motor invented by Henry.

manent magnets, each with the same pole facing up. When current was turned on, the electromagnet was attracted to one of the permanent magnets and repelled from the other. Reversing the current produced a reverse spin. ∎

Further Reading:

Dictionary of Scientific Biography, s.v. "Henry."

Bernard Jaffe, *Men of Science in America.* New York, 1944.

Kranzberg and Pursell, *Technology in Western Civilization*, Vol. I.

MARIE JOSEPH DENIS FARCOT
b. Nov. 16, 1798, Paris, France
d. Aug. 30, 1875, Saint-Ouen, France
French Mechanical Engineer, Industrialist

Life and Times:

The mechanization of industry in France hardly began until the nineteenth century. Before then, investment in machinery had been hampered by government policies as well as the conservatism of the propertied classes. Maintaining standing armies and providing for the court at Versailles drained the royal treasury, and strict regulations inhibited the formation of private joint-stock companies. In any case, wealthy members of the middle class preferred buying land and titles to risking their money in speculative investments. As a result, as late as 1810 fewer than 200 steam engines were being used in French mills, mines, and factories. Although Joseph Farcot did not establish his machine works until 1823, he was not too late to power the French industrial revolution.

Farcot's father, a self-made man, ran a textile factory in Paris at the time of the Revolution. He took an active part in politics from 1789, but by 1792 had come under suspicion for his moderate views. He was arrested in 1793 and his mill and warehouses were sacked. His son Joseph thus experienced poverty in childhood while the father slowly recouped his fortunes. When the elder Farcot died in 1815, Joseph found himself head of the family.

Farcot had an aptitude for mechanics. Apprenticed at an early age to a maker of precision instruments, by 1820 he was working as a fitter at the Périer factory at Chaillot, the largest manufacturer of steam engines in France. In 1823, aged 25, Farcot founded his own machine works in Paris, where he began to produce presses, mills, pumps and steam engines. By 1830, some 50 steam engines a year were being built in France, and the Maison Farcot was capturing an increasing share of the market.

Although the economy was expanding, Farcot's success was due in large part to a series of machines he invented after 1829 (see below). In 1845 Farcot made his son a partner in the enterprise, which continued to grow; it was forced to relocate to Saint-Ouen four years later. At the Paris world's fair of 1855, the Maison Farcot was awarded a medal for the high quality of its entire product line. Farcot retired in 1869, leaving the company in the capable hands of his son.

Outstanding Engineering Achievements:

Farcot's most important invention, patented in 1836, was the first practical system allowing controlled variation of steam pressure in an engine. A cam located in the port through which steam was admitted to the cylinder could be rotated on its axis to widen or narrow the aperture. The cam was operated either manually, using a throttle, or automatically by means of a balance wheel; in either case the speed of the engine could be kept constant under variable work conditions. A similar mechanism was developed ten years later by the American George Henry Corliss.

Farcot's other inventions included a pump producing a continuous stream of water, the first steam-operated kneading machine, an oil press that automatically maintained a steady rate of work, and an improved planing machine. ■

Further Reading:

Maurice Daumas, *Histoire Générale des Techniques,* Vol. III. Paris, 1968.
Dictionnaire de Biographie Française, s.v. "Farcot."
Grand Larousse Encyclopédie, ss.vv. "Farcot" and "Détente."

BENOIT PAUL EMILE CLAPEYRON
b. Feb. 26, 1799, Paris, France
d. Jan. 28, 1864, Paris, France
French Civil Engineer, Mathematician

Life and Times:

During the first decades of the nineteenth century, France lagged behind England in the design, construction, and use of steam engines. England also saw the first major developments in a new application of the steam engine—the railroad. After the successful opening of the Liverpool-Manchester rail line in 1830, railroad fever swept France. The first freight line opened between Alais and Beaucaire in 1833; four years later passenger service was inaugurated between Paris and St. Germain. The railroad network that would soon be the pride of France was being born. Guiding every stage of the birth—from promotion and fund-raising to surveying, construction of track and bridges, and engine design—was Benoît Paul Emile Clapeyron.

Clapeyron was born into a prosperous Parisian family. He entered the Ecole Polytechnique in 1816 and the Ecole des Mines two years later. Upon graduation Clapeyron was sent to Russia by the French government. His mission was to help train the recently organized Russian corps of engineers. For ten years he worked on construction projects and taught pure and applied mathematics at the School of Public Works in St. Petersburg.

Returning to France in 1830, Clapeyron immediately began to promote railway construction. He conceived the idea of a line between Paris and the nearby town of St. Germain. Funding was finally obtained in 1835, and Clapeyron undertook the actual construction. The Englishman Robert Stephenson, son of the railroad pioneer George Stephenson [q.v.], was asked to furnish locomotives that could negotiate a long continuous grade on the Versailles stretch of the line. When he refused, Clapeyron himself drew up the plans for the engines; they were built by Sharp and Roberts.

Starting in 1837 Clapeyron planned and supervised construction of railways and iron bridges in the north of the country; in 1852 he was called in as consultant for the southern lines. From 1844 on Clapeyron taught the course on steam engines at the Ecole des Ponts et Chaussées, an advanced civil engineering academy. He was elected to the Academy of Sciences in 1858 and participated in the activities of that body until his death six years later.

Outstanding Engineering Achievement:

Clapeyron's most important contribution to the design of steam engines came in 1842. He reasoned that if steam pressure from the boiler were cut off during the piston stroke, the expansion of the steam already present in the cylinder would be enough to move the piston completely downward. What was needed was a modification of the slide valve that alternately opened and closed the ports leading to the boiler and condenser. Clapeyron simply widened the surfaces of the valve covering those ports. Together with an adjustment to the eccentric that controlled the slide valve, this minor change greatly improved the engine's performance. The locomotives that had previously pulled eight cars up the Versailles grade could now pull twelve.

While drawing up plans for a large iron bridge at Asnières, Clapeyron improvised a method for calculating the forces acting on continuous beams. This is the origin of the classical "theorem of three moments."

In 1834 Clapeyron published an exposition of

Sadi Carnot's [q.v.] *Réfléxions sur la Puissance Motrice du Feu.* In that paper, which had been largely ignored since its publication ten years before, Carnot explored the working capacity and efficiency of various heat engines. Clapeyron translated Carnot's argument into the language of calculus and represented the Carnot cycle analytically in a pressure-volume graph, essentially the Watt indicator diagram. In time this work became the basis of the second law of thermodynamics. ∎

Further Reading:

Grand Larousse Encyclopédie, ss. vv. "Clapeyron" and "Détente."

Milton Kerker, "Sadi Carnot and the Steam Engine Engineers," *Isis.* Vol. LI (1960).

Glossary of Technical Terms

achromatic lens—ideally, a lens that focuses all the wavelengths of white light at the same point, thus avoiding colored fringes; approximated by combining two different types of glass

amalgamation—the combining of a metal with mercury; used in extracting precious metals from their ores

aqueduct—a conduit built to carry water along a downhill gradient

architrave—the part of an entablature resting directly upon a column; the various parts around a door or window

Archimedean screw—a hollow spiral tube rotating on an axis and used to raise water; also known as a cochlea

armature—coils of wire that carry current in the magnetic field of an electric motor or generator; either the armature or the magnet will rotate

armillary sphere—an astronomical instrument composed of rings designed to show the positions and movements of celestial objects

astrolabe—a circular instrument used before invention of the sextant to determine the positions of celestial objects

azimuth—the arc of the horizon between the observer's meridian, usually the north point, and a vertical circle through the object

balance spring—a coiled spring whose regular oscillations may be used as the control in the escapement of a mechanical clock

ballista—a large crossbow used by ancient and medieval armies as a field weapon or siege engine

ballistics—the study of projectiles in flight

basilica—an oblong building design used in ancient Rome and adopted frequently in early Christian church architecture

bastions—sharply angled towers that replaced round ones during the Renaissance

boiler—a device consisting of a firebox and water tubes designed to produce steam for use in steam engines

caisson—a watertight chamber used in underwater construction work, also as a foundation for bridge piers

camber—a curving or arching from the center of an object to its sides, often applied to road surfaces

carding—making the fibers of cleaned cotton or wool parallel; analogous to combing one's hair

catapult—one of a variety of missile-hurling siege engines used in antiquity and the middle ages

chronometer—a highly accurate timepiece

civil engineering—the branch of engineering devoted to the construction of public works (such as roads, bridges, and canals) and other structures

clepsydra—a water clock; a device measuring time by the passage of water from a tank

cofferdam—a watertight chamber with no bottom, used to expose part of a riverbed in underwater construction work

coke—fuel obtained by heating coal without combustion until the volatile matter is distilled off

contrate wheel—a gear wheel in which the teeth are at right angles to the plane of the wheel

crankshaft—a device for converting vertical into rotary motion, consisting of an axle attached at right angles to a rotating or oscillating arm (the crank)

cruciform—in the shape of a cross

cupellation—a process for separating precious metals from lead and other impurities through exposure to a hot blast in a porous container (the cupel)

dynamics—the study of motion and the forces that produce it

entablature—part of a wall supported on columns

escapement—the mechanism in clockwork that regulates the release of power from the mainspring or weight, thus governming the movement of the gear train turning the hands

flash locks—single gates placed at intervals along a canal gradient in order to move boats by releasing a sudden rush of water

fusee—a mechanism for transmitting a constant force from the power source to the gear train in spring-driven clocks and watches

gnomon—the vertical part of a sundial that indicates time by the length or position of its shadow

grist-mill—a device for grinding grain, often consisting of impinging circular stones

gimbals mounting—a framework consisting of concentric circles mounted at right angles to one another in such a way as to maintain an object within the innermost circle in an upright position; also known as the Cardan suspension

hydraulics—the mechanics of fluid flow; includes hydrostatics and hydrodynamics

isochronism—the property of recurring at regular intervals, as of the motion of a pendulum

jacks—figures used to mark the passage of time in early clocks by appearing on a platform, sounding a gong or drum, or pointing along an indicator

mastaba tombs—rectangular stone masses with sloping sides and flat tops, used in the construction of early Egyptian pyramids

mechanics—the study of physical forces and their action on bodies (includes statistics and dynamics)

meridian circle—a great circle of the celestial sphere passing through the poles and zenith at a given place; also, an astronomical telescope mounted in the plane of this circle

metallurgy—the science of the structure and properties of metals, and the technology of producing and working them

nave—the main hall of a cruciform church, ending in the choir and intersecting with the transept

noria—a large waterwheel equipped with buckets along the rim, formerly used to raise water in Middle Eastern countries

obelisk—a four-sided, tapering pillar erected as a monument in ancient Egypt

optics—the study of light and its properties, often with a view to practical application in the manufacture of lenses

orrery—a movable model of the solar system showing the relative positions and motion of the planets

pendulum—a weight suspended from a fixed point and allowed to oscillate in one plane, often used to regulate clocks and other machinery

pier—a bridge support resting on the ground or river bottom

pinion—a gear attached to the end of a shaft and meshing with a larger wheel or other toothed device

platen—a horizontal plate holding a page of type in hand-operated printing presses

pneumatics—the study of gases and their properties

polder—a tract of reclaimed land originally covered by water

pound lock—two closely-spaced gates forming an enclosure along a canal gradient, used to move boats by changing the level of water within the enclosure

puddling—a process developed by Henry Cort for the manufacture of wrought iron, in which unrefined pig iron is heated to a molten state and stirred with a rod to separate out impurities

pylon—in ancient Egyptian architecture, a large gateway in the shape of a truncated pyramid

quanat—a slightly sloping tunnel used in the Middle East to supply water from an underground source

quadrant—a navigational instrument with a graduated 90° arc, used to measure altitudes

retort—a container or chamber in which a substance is heated

reverberatory furnace—a blast furnace developed for the smelting and refining of metals, in which the material being heated is kept from direct contact with the fuel

rocking beam—a horizontal beam used in early steam engines to transmit the vertical motion of the piston rod to the device (pump or wheel) being moved

roving—a slightly twisted string of cotton or wool, ready to be spun into yarn

saqiya—a Middle Eastern water-raising device consisting of a horizontal axle fitted with cogwheels turned by an animal, by means of which a series of buckets is dipped into the water source

shaduf—a Middle Eastern water-raising device consisting of a weighted lever with a bucket at one end

shuttle—part of a loom which inserts the woof (or crosswise) threads between the warp (or lengthwise) threads

sliver—an untwisted rope of carded cotton or wool prepared for spinning

solenoid—a coil of wire that acts as a magnet when carrying a direct current

spandrel—a section of stonework or masonry bordering an arch

stackfreed—a mechanism for maintaining constant motive force in spring-driven clocks and watches, analogous to the fusee

statics—the study of forces on bodies in equilibrium, often applied to determining the strength and resistance of structural materials

steelyard—a balance consisting of a lever whose shorter arm supports the object being weighed by means of a counter-weight moved along a scale on the longer arm

sump—a pool from which liquid waste is drained

theodolite—a surveying instrument consisting in its modern form of a telescope moving on vertical and horizontal axes and equipped with scales on which angles can be read

tortoise—an ancient siege engine consisting usually of a wheel-mounted canopy used to protect soldiers attacking a wall

transept—the part of a cruciform church that crosses the nave at right angles

trebuchet—a huge medieval siege engine consisting of a lever with a counterweight at one end and a sling at the other for hurling rocks

triangulation—a surveying technique in which an area is mapped by dividing it into a series of adjoining triangles

truss—a rigid framework of wooden or metal beams designed to support a bridge or other structure

voussoir—a wedge-shaped piece of stone or masonry placed with similar pieces to form an arch

warp—yarn strung lengthwise on a loom, forming a framework through which the woof is placed

woof—yarn threaded crosswise in a loom through the warp; also known as the weft

Chronology of Important Engineering Events from Ancient Times to 1850

c. 3000 B.C.	The Step Pyramid of Sakkara, the oldest surviving Egyptian pyramid, is built for the Pharaoh Zoser by Imhotep.
c. 1500 B.C.	Sericulture and silk manufacture originate in China.
	Common use of iron for tools and weapons begins in Syria and Palestine.
c. 1250 B.C.	The priest-architect Bekhnechons gives the temple of Amon at Luxor, the greatest building project of Egypt's New Kingdom, its final form.
c. 700 B.C.	Chinese engineers begin constructing reservoirs along the Yellow River for irrigation purposes.
c. 600 B.C.	The first stone bridge is constructed in Rome.
c. 570 B.C.	The Temple of Hera at Samos, one of the largest buildings of the Greek world, is built by Theodorus.
c. 550 B.C.	The first Temple of Artemis at Ephesus, the largest Greek building of its time, is built by Chersiphron and Metagenes of Cnossos.
c. 530 B.C.	Eupalinos constructs the first known water tunnel through Mount Castro on Samos, beginning the excavation at both ends of the mountain and finishing in the center.
512 B.C.	Mandrokles of Samos constructs the first pontoon bridge over the Bosporus as part of a military campaign conducted by Persia's Darius I.
c. 490 B.C.	Hippodamos of Miletos lays out the Athenian port of Piraeus, the first known instance of city planning.
c. 480 B.C.	Artachaies of Persia builds the first known transport canal across the Athos peninsula in Greece as part of a military campaign conducted by King Xerxes.
c. 460 B.C.	Kallikrates constructs the Long Walls between Athens and Piraeus.
c. 440 B.C.	The Parthenon is built in Athens by Iktinos.
c. 350 B.C.	Common use of iron in tools and weapons begins in China.
c. 340 B.C.	The second Temple of Artemis at Ephesus is built by Deinokrates following the destruction of the first temple by arson.

c. 330 B.C.	Deinokrates supervises the planning and building of Alexandria as Egypt's new capital and chief port.
c. 312 B.C.	The censor Appius Claudius Crassus supervises construction of the Appian Way, the first paved Roman road, and the Aqua Appia, the first Roman aqueduct.
c. 300 B.C.	Sostratos builds the Pharos (lighthouse) of Alexandria.
c. 280 B.C.	Khares of Lindos completes work on the Colossus of Rhodes.
c. 220 B.C.	Engineers of the Ch'in Empire, the first unified Chinese state, begin work on the Great Wall of China.
	The Magic Transport Canal, the first transport canal in China, is built in present-day Kwangsi Province.
c. 210 B.C.	Chinese engineers build the first bridge across the Yellow River, a pontoon structure.
145 B.C.	The praetor Quintus Marcius Rex supervises construction of the Aqua Marcia, the first high-level Roman aqueduct.
105 B.C.	Heron establishes the first academy of technology in Alexandria.
c. 100 B.C.	The draw loom originates in China.
c. 50 B.C.	Andronikos of Kyrrhos constructs the Tower of Winds in Athens.
c. 25 B.C.	Marcus Vitruvius Pollio writes *De Architectura,* a comprehensive treatise on Roman architecture.
24 B.C.	Marcus Vipsanius Agrippa supervises construction of the Pantheon in Rome.
18 B.C.	Marcus Vipsanius Agrippa supervises construction of the multi-level Pont du Gard, an aqueduct in southern Gaul.
c. 100 A.D.	Gaius Julius Lacer builds the Roman bridge at Alcantra, Spain.
	The Chinese instrument-maker Chang Heng designs the first mechanical armillary sphere, with rings turned automatically by a water-powered system.
c. 200 A.D.	The wheelbarrow originates in China.
c. 260 A.D.	The water-powered trip hammer comes into use in China.
537 A.D.	Anthemios of Tralles and Isidoros of Miletos complete construction of the Hagia Sophia (Church of the Divine Wisdom) in Constantinople.
c. 600 A.D.	Chinese engineers construct the first (or Sui) Grand Canal, connecting the capital of Ch'ang-an with the southern port of Hangchow.
	The first printed documents appear in China.
	Japanese Prince Shotoku Taishi builds the Horyu-ji Temple, the best example of early Buddhist architecture in Japan and one of the world's oldest surviving wooden buildings.
725	The Buddhist monk I-Hsing and the Chinese instrument-maker Liang Ling-tsan construct the world's first mechanical clock, a water-powered device with an escapement regulating the movements of the parts.
750	The Chinese Emperor Hsüan Tsung establishes the Hanlin Academy to encourage scholarship in science.
752	The Daibutsu (Great Buddha) of Nara, one of the world's largest statues, is dedicated in Japan.
c. 860	The Indian engineer Suyya completes a comprehensive flood-control and irrigation project along the Jhellum River in Kashmir.

976	The Chinese instrument-maker Chang Ssu-Hsün designs a mechanical clock that for the first time uses a chain drive to transmit motion from the power source to the mechanism.
c. 1060	Pound locks are introduced in China during the reconstruction of the Ling Ch'ü Canal.
1090	The Chinese official Su Sung and the instrument-maker Han Kung-lien construct the largest and most accurate mechanical clock in the line of water-powered timepieces.
1144	The abbey church of St. Denis-en-France, the first example of true Gothic architecture in France, is completed.
1151	Chinese troops make the first recorded use of explosives (delivered by rocket) in warfare.
1174	William of Sens supervises reconstruction of the choir of Canterbury Cathedral, bringing Gothic architectural style to England.
1176	Peter of Colechurch begins construction of the first stone bridge across the Thames River at London.
1180	Windmills with vertical sails are first used in Europe.
c. 1200	Al-Hanafi designs water-powered mills at Homs in central Syria.
1252	The Japanese architect Ono Goroemon casts the Daibutsu (Great Buddha) of Kamakura.
1293	Chinese and Mongol engineers complete construction of the modern (or Yuan) Grand Canal, connecting the capital city of Peking with the southern port of Hangchow.
1317	Pierre de Chelles completes work on Notre Dame Cathedral in Paris.
c. 1330	The first weight-driven mechanical clocks appear in Europe, built by Richard of Wallingford, Jacopo and Giovanni de' Dondi and others.
	Water-powered sawmills come into common use in Europe.
1368	Engineers of the newly-established Ming dynasty begin large-scale restoration of the Great Wall of China.
1397	The former Japanese ruler Ashikaga Yoshimutsu constructs the Kinkaku (Golden Pavilion) near Kyoto, showing the beginnings of Zen influence in architecture.
c. 1400	The first European canal with pound locks is built in Belgium.
1403	The German physician Konrad Kyeser writes *Bellifortis,* an illustrated treatise on military technology.
1420	Filippo Brunelleschi begins constructing the dome of the Duomo (Cathedral of Santa Maria del Fiore) in Florence.
1455	Johannes Gutenberg's printing shop produces the 42-line Mainz Bible.
c. 1485	Leonardo da Vinci introduces the outward-swinging miter gate in canals built near Milan.
1495	The first dry dock for loading and unloading of goods is built in Portsmouth, England.
1502	The instrument-maker Peter Henlein constructs the first watches known as "Nuremberg eggs."
1521	Silk manufacturing is introduced in France.
c. 1550	Girolamo Cardano popularizes the "Cardan suspension," a gimbals mounting widely used in compasses and gyroscopes, in Europe.

1556	Georgius Agricola's *De re metallica,* a treatise on mining and metallurgy, is published posthumously.
1585	Federigo Giambelli constructs the first time bomb for use against Spanish forces besieging Antwerp.
1596	The first water closet is invented in England.
1609	Galileo begins constructing a series of telescopes, with which he observes the rotation of the sun and other phenomena supporting the Copernican heliocentric theory.
1612	Jan Adriaasz Leeghwater completes drainage of the Beemstermeer, the largest project of its kind in Holland (17,000 acres).
1613	Hugh Myddleton constructs the New River, England's longest artificial waterway to date, as part of London's water supply.
1653	Cornelius Vermuyden finishes draining the Great Level of the English Fens, one of the largest drainage projects in history (302,000 acres).
1654	Otto von Guericke, mayor of Magdeburg, first demonstrates the existence of a vacuum.
1656	Christiaan Huygens begins work on the design of a pendulum-driven clock.
1658	Robert Hooke develops the balance spring to power watches (though priority of invention is disputed by Christian Huygens).
1662	Charles II charters the Royal Society, England's first organization devoted to experimental science.
1663	Edward Somerset, Marquis of Worcester, constructs and demonstrates a steam-operated water pump.
1668	Isaac Newton constructs the first reflecting telescope.
1671	Louis XIV establishes the *Corps du Genie,* the military engineering branch of the French army.
1681	Work is completed on the Languedoc Canal, the largest engineering project of its kind in Europe.
1698	Thomas Savery patents his "miner's friend," the first practical steam pump.
1709	Abraham Darby I begins smelting iron in a coke-fired blast furnace.
1712	Thomas Newcomen and John Calley construct the first atmospheric steam engine at Dudley Castle in Worcestershire.
1716	The French government establishes the *Corps de Ponts et Chaussées,* an agency responsible for all state-supported civil engineering projects.
	Hubert Gautier's *Traité des Ponts,* the first book devoted entirely to bridges, is published in Paris.
c. 1720	Christopher Polhem begins to manufacture uniform clock gears in Sweden, an early step in the mass production of standardized parts.
1733	John Kay patents the flying shuttle for the hand loom, greatly increasing the rate of weaving.
1735	The British instrument-maker John Harrison develops the first practical marine chronometer.
1738	Daniel Bernoulli's *Hydrodynamica,* the first systematic treatment of fluid pressure and velocity, is published.
1740	Lewis Paul and John Wyatt open England's first spinning factory in London.

1742	The instrument-maker Benjamin Huntsman develops the crucible process for manufacturing steel, improving the metal's quality and sharply reducing its cost.
1745	The Dutch physicist Petrus van Musschenbroek discovers the Leyden jar, a means of storing static electrical charge.
1746	John Roebuck begins manufacture of sulfuric acid on an industrial scale.
1747	Louis XV of France establishes the *Ecole des Ponts et Chaussées,* the world's first civil engineering school.
1753	The final volume of Bernard Forest de Belidor's *Architecture hydraulique,* a four-volume compendium of hydraulic engineering techniques, is published in Paris.
1759	John Smeaton completes construction of the Eddystone Lighthouse.
1762	James Brindley completes construction of the Bridgewater Canal, beginning a canal boom in Britain.
1769	James Watt patents his first steam engine, a single-acting model with a separate condenser.
1770	The spinning jenny and water frame, the first successful spinning machines, are patented by James Hargreaves and Richard Arkwright.
	Jesse Ramsden invents the first screw-cutting lathe, permitting the mass production of standardized screws.
1771	The Society of Engineers (also called the Smeatonian Club), Britain's first professional engineering association, is formed in London.
1774	John Wilkinson invents the first accurate boring mill for the manufacture of steam engine cylinders.
	Jean-Rodolphe Perronet completes construction of the Pont de Neuilly, the most daring use of elliptical arches in bridge design.
1775	James Watt and Matthew Boulton form a partnership for the manufacture of steam engines.
	David Bushnell designs the first man-carrying submarine.
1776	John Wilkinson installs a steam engine to power machinery at his foundry in Shropshire, the first factory use of the steam engine.
1779	Samuel Crompton develops the spinning mule, a machine combining features of the spinning jenny and water frame.
	Abraham Darby III constructs the world's first cast iron bridge over the Severn River near Coalbrookdale.
1781	Jonathan Carter Hornblower patents the first two-cylinder compound steam engine.
1782	James Watt patents a double-acting steam engine, the first model powered by the force of expanding steam.
1783	Claude Jouffroy d'Abbans sails a steamboat upstream for the first time on the Saône River.
	Joseph-Michel and Jacques-Etienne Montgolfier construct the first passenger-carrying hot air balloon.
1784	Henry Cort patents the puddling furnace for the production of wrought iron.
	Joseph Bramah designs his patent lock, which remains unpicked for 67 years.
	The British civil engineer John Rennie completes the Albion Flour Mills in London, the first building made entirely of cast iron.

1785	Edmund Cartwright patents the first power loom for the weaving of cotton.
1787	Nicholas Leblanc develops a chemical method for the manufacture of sodium bicarbonate.
1788	The first passenger-carrying steamboat, built by John Fitch, sails on the Delaware River.
1791	The American inventor Nathan Read patents the first multi-tubular boiler.
1793	Eli Whitney develops his version of the cotton gin, the most sophisticated and least expensive model available.
1794	Work ends on the Canal du Centre (Charolais Canal), completing the first inland water route between the English Channel and the Mediterranean.
1798	Aloys Senefelder invents the lithography process.
1799	Johann Albert Eytelwein establishes the Bauakademie in Berlin, the first university-level German engineering school.
c. 1800	Richard Trevithick in Britain and Oliver Evans in the U.S. begin constructing high-pressure steam engines.
1800	Alessandro Volta constructs the first wet battery, a column of zinc and copper discs.
1801	Philippe Lebon stages his widely-publicized exhibition of gas lighting at the Hotel Seignelay in Paris.
	Joseph Marie Jacquard demonstrates the first fully automatic and workable draw loom for the weaving of silk.
1803	The French inventor Thomas-Charles-Auguste Dallery constructs the first steamboat driven by screw propellers.
1804	Richard Trevithick constructs the first steam locomotive for use on a railroad.
1805	William Jessop completes the Thames River dock, the first self-contained loading and storage facility in England.
1806	The Phillips and Lee cotton mill near Manchester installs a gas lighting system developed by William Murdock, the first factory use of gas illumination.
1807	Robert Fulton's *Clermont,* the first commercially successful passenger steamboat, makes its maiden voyage on the Hudson River.
1808	Marc Isambard Brunel begins manufacturing pulley blocks for ships in a Portsmouth factory equipped with machines built by Henry Maudslay; it is one of the first instances of mass production by machine tools.
1809	George Cayley constructs the first fixed-wing glider.
1811	Friedrich Koenig constructs the first steam-powered flatbed printing press.
1814	Samuel Clegg completes the first central gasworks, which lights a district of London, the beginning of large-scale gas illumination.
1818	Britain's Institution of Civil Engineers is established, at first including both civil and mechanical engineers among its members.
1819	U.S.S. *Savannah* becomes the first steamship to cross the Atlantic, traveling from New York to Liverpool in 31 days.
1820	The Danish physicist Hans Christian Oersted observes that an electric current deflects a magnetized needle, first establishing the connection between electricity and magnetism. André-Marie Ampère elaborates this finding into a description of the magnetic field surrounding a current-carrying wire.

1823	William Sturgeon creates the first electromagnet by winding a current-bearing wire around a piece of soft iron.
1825	Work is completed on the Erie Canal, the longest canal in the Western Hemisphere.
1829	George Stephenson's locomotive the "Rocket" wins the Rainhill Locomotive Trials and goes into service on the Liverpool and Manchester Railway, hauling passengers at a maximum speed of 30 miles (48 km) per hour. In the U.S., Peter Cooper builds the locomotive "Tom Thumb" for use on the Baltimore and Ohio Railroad.
1830	The French tailor Bartholome Thimonnier patents the first sewing machine.
1831	Michael Faraday invents the dynamo, a generator that converts mechanical motion into an electric current.
1834	Charles Babbage begins work on his "analytical engine," a computer capable of carrying out complex mathematical functions by mechanical means.
1835	Samuel F.B. Morse constructs a model telegraph, the prototype of the first economically successful telegraph system.
1837	Louis Daguerre develops the first practical and commercially successful photographic process.
	The *Great Western*, built by Isambard Kingdom Brunel with engines by Joshua Field, becomes the first steamship to cross the Atlantic primarily under its own power.
1842	The first tunnel under the Thames River is completed by Marc Isambard Brunel and his son, Isambard Kingdom Brunel.
1847	Britain's Institution of Mechanical Engineers is established, with George Stephenson as its first president.
1848	Augustus Applegath builds the first rotary printing press, used by *The Times* of London.
	John Stringfellow constructs and flies a small steam-driven model airplane, the first powered heavier-than-air device.

Bibliography of Works on Engineering

History

The history of technology, like other branches of history, is a rapidly growing field whose scholars are hard pressed even to follow the literature in their own specialties. This bibliography is intended for the general reader and attempts to strike a balance between classics of engineering history, many of them older works, and more recent publications. Only books judged essential to a broad understanding of the field are included here; more specialized books and articles can be found in the "Further Reading" lists which follow each biographical entry. The bibliography is divided according to the chronological sections of the text.

General Works

Burke, James, *Connections*. Boston, 1978.
   A popular history of Western technology which, as the title implies, outlines unexpected relationships in the development of various types of engineering.

Daumas, Maurice, ed., *Histoire générale des techniques*. Three volumes. Paris, 1962–68. (English edition: *A History of Technology and Invention,* trans. by Eileen B. Hennessy. New York, 1979).
   The French counterpart to Singer's *History of Technology* (see below). As might be expected, it gives greater emphasis to Continental European developments, but provides a reliable general survey of Western engineering history. All three volumes (The Origins of Technological Civilization, The First Stages of Mechanization, and The Expansion of Mechanization) are relevant to this book.

Dictionary of Scientific Biography. Sixteen volumes. New York, 1970–81. This authoritative, recently-completed reference work deals only with individuals known for contributions to one of the theoretical sciences; but many of the entrants also did important work in engineering.

Finch, James Kip, *Engineering and Western Civilization*. New York, 1951.
Idem. *The Story of Engineering*. New York, 1960.
   Widely respected surveys of engineering history, especially useful in civil engineering, by the former dean of the Columbia University School of Engineering.

FitzSimons, Neal, ed., *Engineering Classics of James Kip Finch*. Kensington, Md., 1978.
   Reprints of 33 articles written by Finch for *Consulting Engineer* between 1959 and 1968. The articles range in time from ancient Egypt to modern America and include Finch's famous series on the writings of Bernard Forest de Belidor.

Giedion, Sigfried, *Mechanization Takes Command*. New York, 1948.
   Though somewhat outdated, this survey contains many provocative observations on the development of machine technology.

Kranzberg, Melvin, and Pursell, Carroll W., eds., *Technology in Western Civilization*. Two volumes. New York, 1967.
   An authoritative collection of essays with contributions from such leading scholars as Bertrand Gille and James Kip Finch. Volume One extends from Antiquity through 1900.

Mumford, Lewis, *The Myth of the Machine*. Two volumes. New York, 1934.
   A study of man's relationship to technology covering most of recorded history. Especially valuable for insights on how machines influenced ways of thought.

Pacey, Arnold, *The Maze of Ingenuity: Ideas and Idealism in the Development of Technology*. New York, 1975.
   An imaginative discussion of problems in the history of technology, emphasizing the medieval and early modern periods, by the author of the Introduction to this volume.

Sarton, George, *An Introduction to the History of Science*. Three volumes. Baltimore, 1927–47.

Essays on scientists and technologists from Antiquity through the Middle Ages, with emphasis on the latter period.

Singer, Charles, et al., *A History of Technology*. Seven volumes. Oxford, England, 1954–79.

The most extensive, and probably the most consulted survey of the history of technology. Though general in scope, the series focuses on technology in the West. There is no separate section on the Far East, and treatment of Islamic engineering is sketchy. Relevant to the time period covered in this book are the first four volumes: From Early Times to the Fall of Ancient Empires; The Mediterranean Civilisations and the Middle Ages; From the Renaissance to the Industrial Revolution; and The Industrial Revolution.

Smith, Norman, *Man and Water*. London, 1976. Idem. *A History of Dams*. London, 1971.

Smith is a specialist in irrigation, water supply and water-power. Both books contain good chapters on the Middle Ages, the Industrial Revolution and modern times.

Usher, Abbott Payson, *A History of Mechanical Inventions*. Boston, 1959.

A technical study that focuses on machines of the Industrial Revolution but emphasizes the importance of their many antecedents as far back as the Middle Ages.

Williams, Trevor I., *A Biographical Dictionary of Scientists*. Second edition. New York, 1974.

Includes many engineers as well as scientists, but entries are shorter than those of the *Dictionary of Scientific Biography*.

Ancient Engineering

Casson, Lionel, *Ships and Seamanship in the Ancient World*. Princeton, 1971.

A well-written book which makes much of the limited evidence in its field.

Childe, V. Gordon, *Man Makes Himself*. London, 1936.

Written by a respected archeologist for the lay public, this book surveys the development of civilization to the end of the Egyptian-Mesopotamian period, with emphasis on technology. The author's Marxist orientation is explicit.

Drachmann, Aage Gerhard, *The Mechanical Technology of Greek and Roman Antiquity: a Study of Literary Sources*. Madison, Wisc., 1963.

The standard work in its field.

Fakhry, Ahmed, *The Pyramids*. Chicago, 1961. Another standard work of careful scholarship.

Forbes, Robert J., *Studies in Ancient Technology*. Nine volumes. Leiden, Netherlands, 1955–64.

Covers many areas of ancient engineering, such as water supply, road-building and power, in many cultures.

Hall, Marie Boas, ed., *The Pneumatics of Hero of Alexandria*. New York, 1971.

A recent edition of the standard English translation of Hero's informative work, written about 70 A.D.

Hodges, Henry, *Technology in the Ancient World*. New York, 1970.

Provides a useful summary of the state of technology, including engineering, at various times and places in the ancient world.

Smith, Cyril Stanley, "Materials and the Development of Civilization and Science," in *Science,* Vol. CXLVIII (May 14, 1965), pp. 908–917.

A classic statement of the importance of the aesthetic appreciation of the structural materials as a spur to investigating and developing new building techniques in the prehistoric and early historic periods. Smith is the foremost historian of materials science and engineering.

Smith, Norman, "Roman Hydraulic Technology," in *Scientific American* (May 1978), pp. 154–161.

A concise examination of all aspects of Roman water supply systems.

Sprague de Camp, Lyon, *The Ancient Engineers*. New York, 1964.

A popular history of engineering from the beginning of civilization through the Renaissance. Often detailed and usually accurate.

Medieval and Islamic Engineering

Colvin, H.M., ed., *The History of the King's Works*. Two volumes. London, 1963.

Useful for information on medieval English public works, especially the great royal castles erected in Wales and elsewhere.

Gimpel, Jean, *The Medieval Machine: the Industrial Revolution of the Middle Ages*. New York, 1977.

An influential statement of the thesis that medieval Europe experienced a rapid expansion of machine technology that rivalled the Industrial Revolution of the modern era in importance and established many attitudes that helped bring about the Machine Age.

Hall, Bert S., and West, Delno C., eds., *On Pre-Modern Technology and Science*. Malibu, Calif., 1976.

A volume of essays in honor of Lynn White, Jr. (see below), containing valuable contributions on the history of both medieval and Renaissance technology.

Hill, Donald R., ed., *The Book of Knowledge of Ingenious Mechanical Devices*. Dordrecht, Netherlands, 1974.

Idem. *The Book of Ingenious Devices*. Dordrecht, Netherlands, 1979.

Idem. "Medieval Arabic Mechanical Technology," in *Proceedings of the First International Symposium for the History of Arabic Science*. Aleppo, Syria, 1976.

Idem. *Arabic Water-Clocks*. Aleppo, Syria, 1981.

Hill, who has contributed the essay on Medieval and Islamic engineering in this volume, is a leading authority on Islamic mechanical technology. His annotated translations of the writings of al-Jazari and the Banū Mūsābin Shākir have helped make these authors accessible and their work appreciated among Western scholars.

Nasr, Sayyid Hossein, *Islamic Science—an Illustrated Study*. London, 1976.

Includes chapters on technology and excellent illustrations.

Schiøler, Thorkild, *Roman and Islamic Water-Lifting Wheels*. Odense, Denmark, 1973.

A scholarly and thorough treatment of the subject.

Watt, W. Montgomery, *The Influence of Islam on Medieval Europe*. Edinburgh, Scotland, 1972.

Includes information on the diffusion of technology in Spain, Italy and other meeting points of the two cultures.

White, Lynn, Jr., *Medieval Technology and Social Change*. New York, 1966.

Idem. *Machina ex Deo: Essays in the Dynamism of Western Culture*. Cambridge, Mass., 1968.

Along with Gimpel, White is the leading exponent of the view that the Middle Ages in Europe were a time of fundamental mechanical innovation that saw the rise of attitudes favorable to industrialism.

Wiedemann, E., *Aufsätze zur Arabischen Wissenschaftsgeschichte*. Two volumes. Hildesheim, Germany, 1970.

A collection of papers that Wiedemann contributed to the Erlangen Society in the early part of this century. It is important as the only major non-Arabic source for the study of Islamic science and technology.

Engineering in the Far East

Chŏn, Sang-un, *Science and Technology in Korea: Traditional Instruments and Techniques*. Cambridge, Mass., 1974.

A survey of scientific culture among the most technically proficient of China's neighbors.

Nakayama, Shigeru, *A History of Japanese Astronomy: Chinese Background and Western Impact*. Cambridge, Mass., 1969.

A useful survey of a field which gave many Japanese instrument-makers their first chance to observe Western techniques and devices.

Needham, Joseph, et al., *Science and Civilisation in China*. Five volumes, in progress. Cambridge, England, 1953–.

Needham, Joseph, "China and the Invention of the Pound-Lock," in *Newcomen Society Transactions*. Vol. XXXVI (1963–64), pp. 85–107.

Idem. *The Development of Iron and Steel Technology in China*. London, 1964.

Idem. "Chinese Priorities in Cast Iron Metallurgy," in *Technology and Culture*, Vol. V., Pt. 3 (1964), p. 398.

Idem. *Clerks and Craftsmen in China and the West*. Cambridge, England, 1970.

Joseph Needham is by far the foremost figure in the study of traditional Chinese science and technology. His massive Science and Civilisation in China project, still under way, is more extensive than any comparable regional survey. Sections so far published deal with civil, nautical, hydraulic, chemical and mechanical engineering as well as mathematics, astronomy and other branches of theoretical work. All periods are covered from ancient times through the nineteenth century, and comprehensive bibliographies cover the full range of literature. Needham is also the author of specialized studies on Chinese innovations in canal-building, metallurgy and other fields.

Perrin, Noel, *Giving Up the Gun: Japan's Reversion to the Sword, 1543–1879*. Boston, 1979.

An interesting study of a unique instance of disarmament and technological regression: the banning of firearms in Japan by the Tokugawa shoguns. Provides information on early Japanese gunsmiths who learned their trade before the ban went into effect.

Sivin, Nathan, ed., *Science and Technology in East Asia*. New York, 1977.

A useful collection of articles gathered by the editor of *Chinese Science*.

Sugimoto, Masayoshi, and Swain, David L., *Science and Culture in Traditional Japan, A.D. 600–1854*. Cambridge, Mass., 1978.

A survey of scientific culture in Japan, tracing successive waves of foreign influence and Japanese assimilation and counter-influence.

The Renaissance and Early Modern Periods

Cipolla, Carlo M., *Guns and Sails in the Early Phases of European Expansion, 1400–1700*. London, 1965.
Idem. *Clocks and Culture, 1300–1700*. London, 1967.
Studies of major technologies in which Renaissance engineers did some of their most innovative work.

Dijksterhuis, Eduard Jan, *Simon Stevin: Science in the Netherlands around 1600*. The Hague, Netherlands, 1970.
A study of Dutch scientific culture in the early modern period through one of its representative figures, whose achievements covered fields as diverse as physics and land reclamation.

Drake, Stillman, and Drabkin, I.E., eds., *Mechanics in Sixteenth Century Italy*. Madison, Wisc., 1969.
Selections from the writings of noted engineers of the Italian Renaissance, including Guido Ubaldo and Galileo.

Eisenstein, Elizabeth, *The Printing Press as an Agent of Change*. Two volumes. New York, 1978.
The most recent and extensive work on the social impact of printing, with valuable comments on the media studies of Marshall McLuhan.

Gille, Bertrand, *Engineers of the Renaissance*. Cambridge, Mass., 1966.
A survey of the period by a leading authority on medieval and Renaissance technology.

Harris, L.E., *The Two Netherlanders*. Leiden, Netherlands, 1961.
A study of Dutch contributions to engineering in the persons of the drainage expert Humphrey Bradley and the technologist Cornelis Drebbel.

Keller, Alex G., *A Theatre of Machines*. London, 1964.
A well-known study of the voluminous machine book literature that appeared during the Renaissance, by the author of the essay on Renaissance engineering in this volume.

Parsons, William Barclay, *Engineers and Engineering in the Renaissance*. Baltimore, 1939.
A classic survey of Renaissance engineering by a versatile scholar.

Prager, Frank D., and Scaglia, Giustina,

Brunelleschi: Studies of his Technology and Inventions. Cambridge, Mass., 1970.
Idem. *Mariano Taccola and his Book De ingeneis*. Cambridge, Mass., 1972.
Notable works on individuals who exerted great influence, Taccola through his writings and Brunelleschi through his buildings.

Richeson, Allie Wilson, *English Land Measuring to 1880: Instruments and Practices*. Cambridge, Mass., 1966.
A history of surveying that concentrates on the Renaissance and early modern period; developments outside England are also discussed.

Smith, Cyril Stanley, and Gnudi, Martha Teach, eds., *The Pirotechnia of Vannoccio Biringuccio*. New York, 1942.
An annotated edition of the first printed work to deal with the entire field of metallurgy.

Van Veen, Johan, *Dredge, Drain, Reclaim: the Art of a Nation*. The Hague, Netherlands, 1948.
A brief but enthusiastic history of Dutch land reclamation projects over the centuries.

The Industrial Revolution

Ashton, Thomas Southcliffe, *The Industrial Revolution, 1760–1830*. New York, 1957.
Idem. *An Economic History of England: the Eighteenth Century*. London, 1955.
General economic and technological histories of the period by an expert on the growth of British heavy industry.

Cardwell, D.S.L., *Steam Power in the Eighteenth Century: a Case Study in the Application of Science*. London, 1963.
Underlines the key role of the steam engine in the Industrial Revolution and (like Musson and Robinson, below) describes how its development resulted from the interaction of scientific theory and engineering practice.

Clow, Archibald and Nan, *The Chemical Revolution: a Contribution to Social Technology*. London, 1952.
Describes how the chemical industry developed in the eighteenth and nineteenth centuries from the demands of textile manufacture and other areas of production.

Henderson, W.O., *Britain and Industrial Europe, 1750–1870*. Second edition. Leicester, England, 1965.
A useful account of the spread of industrial technology from England to Continental Europe.

Hills, Richard L., *Power in the Industrial Revolution*. Manchester, England, 1970.

Describes the gradual transition from water to steam power in Britain's textile industry, contradicting the popular impression that Watt's steam engine immediately conquered the industrial landscape.

Landes, David S., *The Unbound Prometheus: Technological Change and Industrial Development in Western Europe from 1750 to the Present.* Cambridge, England, 1969.

A survey of eighteenth and nineteenth century technology which, like Burke's *Connections* but on a more scholarly level, points out relationships in the development of various aspects of engineering. Also useful for its description of the diffusion of industrial technology.

Musson, A.E., and Robinson, Eric, *Science and Technology in the Industrial Revolution.* Toronto, 1969.

A detailed study of the relationship between experimental science and engineering practice in seventeenth and eighteenth century Britain, refuting the long-accepted view that engineers of the early Industrial Revolution operated in total ignorance of scientific theory.

Nef, John U., *The Rise of the British Coal Industry.* Two volumes. London, 1932.

Idem. *Industry and Government in France and England, 1540–1640.* Ithaca, N.Y., 1957.

Idem. *The Conquest of the Material World: Essays on the Coming of Industrialism.* New York, 1967.

Works by a scholar who played a major part in revising the notion that the Industrial Revolution sprang full-blown from the factories of eighteenth-century Britain. These books analyze developments in the early modern period that prefigured and formed the basis of Britain's technological dynamism.

Toynbee, Arnold, *Lectures on the Industrial Revolution of the Eighteenth Century in England.* London, 1902.

Based on a series of lectures delivered at Oxford in the 1880s, this study focuses on the role of the textile industry in Britain's economic development and helped popularize the term "Industrial Revolution" as it is now commonly understood.

Woodbury, Robert S., *History of the Gear-Cutting Machine.* Cambridge, Mass., 1958.

Idem. *History of the Grinding Machine.* Cambridge, Mass., 1959.

Idem. *History of the Lathe to 1850.* Cambridge, Mass., 1961.

Idem. *History of the Milling Machine.* Cambridge, Mass., 1960.

A series of monographs that discusses the development of the "American System" of mass production of interchangeable parts, refuting the popular impression that Eli Whitney was responsible for its origin.

List of Illustrations

Index